The **U**niversity of **C**hicago **S**chool **M**athematics **P**roject

ALGEBRA

Teacher's Edition

VOLUME 1 · CHAPTERS 1–6

Authors
Susan A. Brown
R. James Breunlin
Mary Helen Wiltjer
Katherine M. Degner
Susan K. Eddins
Michael Todd Edwards
Neva A. Metcalf
Natalie Jakucyn
Zalman Usiskin

Director of Evaluation
Denisse R. Thompson

Wright Group

The **McGraw·Hill** Companies

Authors

3rd EDITION AUTHORS

Susan A. Brown, *Mathematics Department Chair*
York High School, Elmhurst, IL

R. James Breunlin, *Mathematics Department Chair*
Schaumburg High School, Schaumburg, IL

Mary Helen Wiltjer, *Mathematics Teacher*
Oak Park and River Forest High School, Oak Park, IL

Katherine M. Degner, *Mathematics Teacher*
Williamsburg Comm. High School, Williamsburg, IA

Susan K. Eddins, *Mathematics Teacher (retired)*
IL Mathematics & Science Academy, Aurora, IL

Michael Todd Edwards, *Assistant Professor of Mathematics Education*
Miami University, Ohio, Oxford, OH

Neva A. Metcalf, *Mathematics Teacher*
Evanston Township High School, Evanston, IL

Natalie Jakucyn, *Mathematics Teacher*
Glenbrook South High School, Glenview, IL

Zalman Usiskin, *Professor of Education*
The University of Chicago

AUTHORS OF EARLIER EDITIONS

John W. McConnell, *Instructional Supervisor of Mathematics*
Glenbrook South High School, Glenview, IL

Sharon Senk, *Professor of Mathematics*
Michigan State University, East Lansing, MI

Ted Widerski, *Mathematics Teacher*
Waterloo High School, Waterloo, WI

Cathy Hynes Feldman, *Mathematics Teacher*
The University of Chicago Laboratory Schools

James Flanders, UCSMP

Margaret Hackworth, *Mathematics Supervisor*
Pinellas County Schools, Largo, FL

Daniel Hirschhorn, UCSMP

Lydia Polonsky, UCSMP

Leroy Sachs, *Mathematics Teacher (retired)*
Clayton High School, Clayton, MO

Ernest Woodward, *Professor of Mathematics*
Austin Peay State University, Clarksville, TN

www.WrightGroup.com

Send all inquiries to:
Wright Group/McGraw-Hill
P.O. Box 812960
Chicago, IL 60681

ISBN 978-0-07-611011-7
MHID 0-07-611011-7

1 2 3 4 5 6 7 8 9 VHP 13 12 11 10 09 08 07

The *McGraw·Hill* Companies

UCSMP EVALUATION, EDITORIAL, AND PRODUCTION

Director of Evaluation
Denisse R. Thompson, *Professor of Mathematics Education*
University of South Florida, Tampa, FL

Evaluation Assistants
Gladys Mitchell, Zhuo Zheng

Editorial Staff
Catherine Ballway, Grant Owens, Asaf Hadari

Evaluation Consultant
Sharon L. Senk, *Professor of Mathematics*
Michigan State University, East Lansing, MI

Executive Managing Editor
Clare Froemel

Manuscript Production Coordinator
Benjamin R. Balskus

Since the first two editions of *Algebra* were published, millions of students and thousands of teachers have used the materials. Prior to the publication of this third edition, the materials were again revised, and the following teachers and schools participated in evaluations of the trial version during 2005–2006:

Shannon Johnson, *Junction City Middle School*
Junction City, KS

Julie Pellman, *Hyman Brand Hebrew Academy*
Overland Park, KS

Dan Kramer, *Highlands High School-Ft. Thomas*
Fort Thomas, KY

Craig Davelis, Megan Mehilos, Sue Nolte, Lynette TeVault, *York High School*
Elmhurst, IL

Jan Boudreau, *Rosemont Middle School*
La Crescenta, CA

Tammy Anderson, *Ashland High School*
Ashland, OR

Dennis Massoglia, *Washington Middle School*
Calumet, MI

Erica Cheung, *Stone Scholastic Academy*
Chicago, IL

The following schools participated in field studies in 1992–1993, 1987–1988, or 1986–1987 as part of the first edition or the second edition research.

Rancho San Joaquin Middle School
Lakeside Middle School
Irvine High School
Irvine, CA

D.W. Griffith Jr. High School
Los Angeles, CA

Mendocino High School
Mendocino, CA

Chaffey High School
Ontario, CA

Eagleview Middle School
Colorado Springs, CO

Lincoln Junior High School
Lesher Junior High School
Blevins Junior High School
Fort Collins, CO

Bacon Academy
Colchester, CT

Rogers Park Jr. High School
Danbury, CT

Clearwater High School
Clearwater, FL

Safety Harbor Middle School
Safety Harbor, FL

Aptakisic Junior High School
Buffalo Grove, IL

Austin Academy
Bogan High School
Disney Magnet School
Hyde Park Career Academy
Von Steuben Metropolitan Science Center
Washington High School
Chicago, IL

Morton East High School
Cicero, IL

O'Neill Middle School
Downers Grove, IL

Elk Grove High School
Elk Grove Village, IL

Glenbrook South High School
John H. Springman School
Glenview, IL

Mendota High School
Mendota, IL

Carl Sandburg Jr. High School
Winston Park Jr. High School
Palatine, IL

Grant Middle School
Springfield, IL

McClure Junior High School
Western Springs, IL

Hubble Middle School
Wheaton, IL

Central Junior High School
Lawrence, KS

Old Rochester High School
Mattapoisett, MA

Fruitport High School
Fruitport, MI

Sauk Rapids-Rice Schools
Sauk Rapids, MN

Parkway West Middle School
Chesterfield, MO

Taylor Middle School
Van Buren Middle School
Albuquerque, NM

Crest Hills Middle School
Shroder Paideia Middle School
Walnut Hills High School
Cincinnati, OH

Lake Oswego Sr. High School
Lake Oswego, OR

Springfield High School
Springfield, PA

R.C. Edwards Jr. High School
Central, SC

Easley Junior High School
Easley, SC

Liberty Middle School
Liberty, SC

Northeast High School
Clarksville, TN

Hanks High School
El Paso, TX

Robinson Middle School
Maple Dale Middle School
Fox Point, WI

Glen Hills Middle School
Glendale, WI

UCSMP The University of Chicago School Mathematics Project

The University of Chicago School Mathematics Project (UCSMP) is a long-term project designed to improve school mathematics in grades pre-K through 12. UCSMP began in 1983 with a 6-year grant from the Amoco Foundation. Additional funding has come from the National Science Foundation, the Ford Motor Company, the Carnegie Corporation of New York, the Stuart Foundation, the General Electric Foundation, GTE, Citicorp/Citibank, the Exxon Educational Foundation, the Illinois Board of Higher Education, the Chicago Public Schools, from royalties, and from publishers of UCSMP materials.

From 1983 to 1987, the director of UCSMP was Paul Sally, Professor of Mathematics. Since 1987, the director has been Zalman Usiskin, Professor of Education.

UCSMP *Algebra*

The text *Algebra* has been developed by the Secondary Component of the project, and constitutes the core of the third year in a seven-year middle and high school mathematics curriculum. The names of the seven texts around which these years are built are:

- *Pre-Transition Mathematics*
- *Transition Mathematics*
- *Algebra*
- *Geometry*
- *Advanced Algebra*
- *Functions, Statistics, and Trigonometry*
- *Precalculus and Discrete Mathematics*

Why A Third Edition?

Since the second edition, there has been a general increase in the performance of students coming into middle school due, we believe, to a combination of increased expectations and the availability of improved curricular materials for the elementary grades. These materials are more ambitious and take advantage of the knowledge students bring to the classroom.

In addition, increased expectations for the performance of all students in both middle schools and high schools and the increased levels of testing that have gone along with those expectations, are requiring a broad-based, reality-oriented, and easy-to-comprehend approach to mathematics. UCSMP third edition is being written to better accommodate these factors.

The writing of the third edition of UCSMP was also motivated by the recent advances in technology both inside and outside the classroom, coupled with the widespread availability of computers with internet access at school and at home.

Another factor for the continued existence of UCSMP is the increase in the number of students taking a full course in algebra before the ninth grade. These students will have four years of mathematics beyond algebra before calculus and other college-level mathematics. UCSMP is the only secondary curriculum to make such a sequence available.

Thousands of schools have used the first and second editions and have noted success in student achievement and in teaching practices. Research from these schools shows that the UCSMP materials really work. Many of these schools have made suggestions for additional improvements in future editions of the UCSMP materials. We have attempted to utilize all of these ideas in the development of the third edition.

UCSMP *Algebra*–Third Edition

The content and questions of this book integrate geometry, probability, and statistics together with algebra. Pure and applied mathematics are also integrated throughout. The earlier editions of *Algebra* introduced many features that have been retained in this edition. There is a **wider scope**, including significant amounts of geometry and statistics, and some combinatorics and probability. These topics are not isolated as separate units of study or enrichment. A **real-world orientation** has guided both the selection of content and its applications. Applications are essential because being able to do mathematics is of little use to an individual unless he or she can apply that content. We require **reading mathematics** because students must read to understand mathematics in later courses and learn to read technical matter in the world at large. The use of **new and powerful technology** is integrated throughout. *Graphing calculator* use is assumed while *spreadsheets* and *computer algebra systems* are used periodically throughout the materials to develop patterns and practice skills.

Four dimensions of understanding are emphasized: skill in carrying out various algorithms; developing and using mathematics properties and relationships; applying mathematics in realistic situations; and representing or picturing mathematical concepts. We call this the SPUR approach: **S**kills, **P**roperties, **U**ses, and **R**epresentations.

The **book organization** is designed to maximize the acquisition of both skills and concepts. Ideas introduced in a lesson, as well as ideas from prior chapters, are reinforced through Review questions in the succeeding lessons. This daily review feature allows students several nights to learn and practice important new concepts and skills and increase retention of old ones. Then, at the end of each chapter, a carefully focused Self-Test and a Chapter Review are used to solidify performance of skills and concepts from the chapter so that they may be applied later with confidence. The Self-Test and Chapter Review, which are keyed to objectives in all the dimensions of understanding, aid student self-assessment.

Those familiar with the earlier editions will note a rather significant reorganization of the content in the third edition, particularly a restructuring of the beginning of the course so that some ideas are introduced one or two months earlier than before. We were encouraged to do this because a high percentage of *Algebra* students enter this course with a better mathematical background than could have been expected when we wrote the earlier editions. There are also a number of instructional features new to this edition, including the following: **Activities** are more extensive and have been incorporated within lessons to enable students to take a more active approach to learning and developing concepts. There are **Guided Examples** that provide partially completed solutions to encourage active learning. **Quiz Yourself** stopping-point questions ask students to periodically check their understanding. There are many more questions requiring **writing** because writing helps students clarify their own thinking. Also, writing is an important aspect of communicating mathematical ideas to others.

Comments about these materials are welcomed. Please address them to:

UCSMP
The University of Chicago
6030 S. Ellis Avenue
Chicago, IL 60637
ucsmp@uchicago.edu
773-702-1130

▷ Contents

VOLUME 1

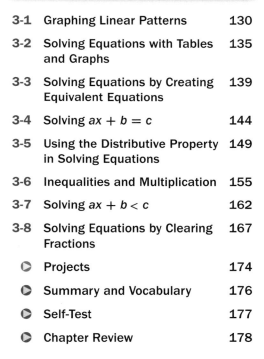

 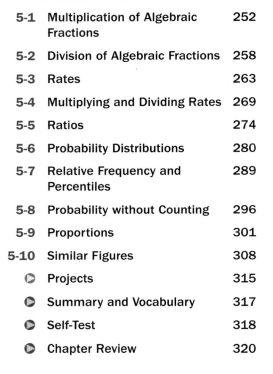

VOLUME 2

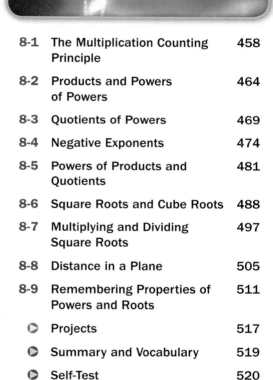

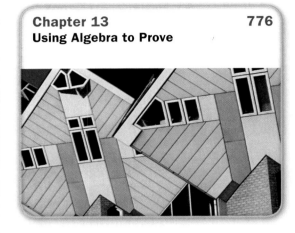

UCSMP Program Overview

The development and testing of the first edition of the University of Chicago School Mathematics Project (UCSMP) materials for K–12 students began in 1983, when UCSMP started, and continued through 1996. Second editions were developed from 1992 to 2003. This book is part of the third edition of the series which, with publishing partner the Wright Group/McGraw-Hill, covers pre-kindergarten through 12th grade. A field trial version of *Algebra* was used in over 20 classrooms during the 2005–2006 school year so that student results could guide revisions made for this published version. UCSMP is unique in the amount of research that has been conducted on its materials over its lifetime.

The UCSMP program emphasizes the following features and benefits.

Key Program Features	Advantages	Benefits
ENRICHED CONTENT Wider scope of mathematical content than traditional programs including more statistics and transformational geometry.	A bridge between algebraic functions and geometric representation	Upgrades student achievement providing continual opportunities for problem solving
PROBLEM-SOLVING Continual emphasis on problem solving with real-world application	Up-to-date curriculum which develops connections to other disciplines	Students are better prepared for jobs in computer related/technology-based industries
TECHNOLOGY All teachers and students in all courses will be expected to have access to graphing calculators, both in class and for assignments	Up-to-date use of calculators and computers	Real-world experiences and greater understanding of technology
FOUR DIMENSIONS OF UNDERSTANDING The SPUR Approach: Skills, Properties, Uses, Representations	A unique four-dimensional approach to understanding.	Maximizes student performance and fosters independent learning

Guided Instruction and Active Learning

Easy-to-follow, partially completed Guided Examples model skills and problem solving, and assist students as they become independent learners. Activities engage students to discover ideas within the lesson. Projects and open-ended activities provide an opportunity to do research or to draw or build models (often collaboratively).

New and Powerful Technology

The use of technology – including graphing calculators at all grade levels, dynamic geometry systems, spreadsheets, the internet, and other computer applications – is an essential component of the third edition of the UCSMP Program. Computer algebra system (CAS) technology is recommended in this and other courses and required beginning with *Advanced Algebra*.

Real-life Applications

A major UCSMP feature is that real-life applications are used to introduce and develop concepts in lessons. These real-world applications have been brought up to date for the third edition and new applications have been added.

Mastery and Review for Improved Student Performance

Continuous opportunities for review help students master concepts. Review Questions within lesson Question Sets allow students to learn over time. Students are encouraged to assess their own understanding with an End-of-Chapter Self-Test correlated to objectives. They can then target specific areas for practice and remediation in the SPUR Chapter Review, which is organized by objective.

UCSMP Program Goals

Three general problems in mathematics education in the United States lead to three major goals of the UCSMP secondary mathematics curricula. UCSMP believes all students can accomplish these three goals.

General Problems	UCSMP Goals
GENERAL PROBLEM 1 Students do not learn enough mathematics by the time they leave school.	**GOAL 1** The curriculum seeks to upgrade student achievement. Years of research on the materials confirm improved student performance.
GENERAL PROBLEM 2 The school mathematics curriculum has not kept up with changes in mathematics and the ways in which mathematics is used.	**GOAL 2** The curriculum must be up to date, including today's calculator and computer technology; inclusion of statistical ideas; more discrete mathematics so students are prepared for jobs in computer related industries; and applications must permeate the materials.
GENERAL PROBLEM 3 Too many students have been sorted out of the mathematics needed for employment and further schooling.	**GOAL 3** Increase the number of students who take mathematics beyond algebra and geometry. Moreover, with the proper materials, algebra should be the general course of study for all or most eighth grade students.

Multi-dimensional Approach to Understanding

SKILLS	Skills understanding means knowing a way to obtain a solution.
PROPERTIES	Properties understanding means knowing properties which you can apply. (Identify or justify the steps in obtaining answer.)
USES	Uses understanding means knowing situations in which you could apply the solving of this equation. (Set up or interpret a solution.)
REPRESENTATIONS	Representations understanding means having a representation of the solving process or a graphical way of interpreting the solution.

Understanding the SPUR Approach

UCSMP includes the unique opportunity for students to develop the mathematical skills and concepts vital in their everyday life. The SPUR approach provides students with four dimensions of understanding so that they are able to approach and solve problems in different ways.

"Understanding" is an easy goal to have, for who can be against it? Yet understanding means different things to different people. In UCSMP texts an approach to the development of mathematical power is taken that we call the SPUR approach. The SPUR approach involves four different aspects, or dimensions, of understanding.

SKILLS For many people, understanding mathematics means simply knowing how to get an answer to a problem with no help from any outside source. But in classrooms, when we speak of understanding how to use a calculator or a computer, we mean using the technology to do something for us. In UCSMP texts, these are both aspects of the same kind of understanding, the understanding of algorithms (procedures) for getting answers. This is the S of SPUR, the Skills dimension, and it ranges from the rote memorization of basic facts to the development of new algorithms for solving problems. These include doing things "in your head," with paper and pencil, or with technology.

PROPERTIES During the 1960s, understanding why became at least as important as understanding how. Mathematicians often view this kind of understanding as the ultimate goal. For instance, mathematics courses for prospective elementary school teachers assume these college students can do arithmetic and instead teach the properties and principles behind that arithmetic. This is the P of SPUR, the Properties dimension, and it ranges from the rote identification of properties to the discovery of new proofs.

USES To the person who applies mathematics, neither knowing how to get an answer nor knowing the mathematical reasons behind the process is as important as being able to use the answer. For example, a person does not possess full understanding of linear equations until that person can apply them appropriately in real situations. This dimension ranges from the rote application of ideas (for instance, when you encounter a direct-variation situation, form a proportion) to the discovery of new applications or models for mathematical ideas.

REPRESENTATIONS To some people, even having all three dimensions of understanding given above does not comprise full understanding. They require that students represent a concept and deal with the concept in that representation in some way. Ability to use concrete materials and models, or graphs and other pictorial representations demonstrates this dimension of understanding. This is the R of SPUR, the Representations dimension, and it ranges from the rote manipulation of objects to the invention of new representations of concepts.

Hardcover Student Edition

> Provides in-depth instruction on integrated mathematical concepts, with statistics presented at all grade levels.

> Extensive End-of-Chapter review materials check comprehension and mastery. These include the Summary, Vocabulary list, a Self-Test correlated to objectives for self-assessment, and a comprehensive SPUR Review, which allows students to select problems from specific objectives for targeted practice.

> Exciting lesson features are shown below.

Big Idea
NEW! A "Big Idea" highlights the key concept(s) of each lesson.

Vocabulary
New terms are listed at the beginning of each lesson.

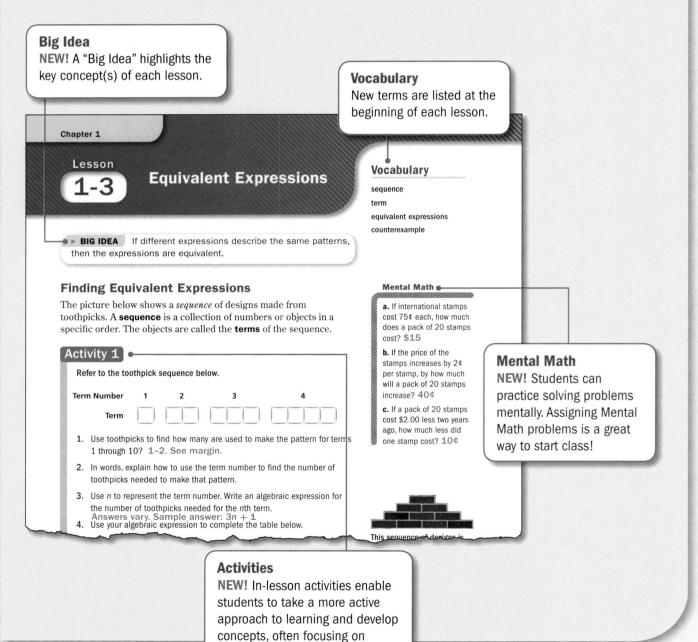

Chapter 1

Lesson
1-3   **Equivalent Expressions**

Vocabulary

sequence
term
equivalent expressions
counterexample

▶ **BIG IDEA**   If different expressions describe the same patterns, then the expressions are equivalent.

Finding Equivalent Expressions

The picture below shows a *sequence* of designs made from toothpicks. A **sequence** is a collection of numbers or objects in a specific order. The objects are called the **terms** of the sequence.

Mental Math

a. If international stamps cost 75¢ each, how much does a pack of 20 stamps cost? $15

b. If the price of the stamps increases by 2¢ per stamp, by how much will a pack of 20 stamps increase? 40¢

c. If a pack of 20 stamps cost $2.00 less two years ago, how much less did one stamp cost? 10¢

Mental Math
NEW! Students can practice solving problems mentally. Assigning Mental Math problems is a great way to start class!

Activity 1

Refer to the toothpick sequence below.

Term Number   1   2   3   4

Term

1. Use toothpicks to find how many are used to make the pattern for terms 1 through 10? 1–2. See margin.

2. In words, explain how to use the term number to find the number of toothpicks needed to make that pattern.

3. Use n to represent the term number. Write an algebraic expression for the number of toothpicks needed for the nth term.
   Answers vary. Sample answer: $3n + 1$

4. Use your algebraic expression to complete the table below.

This sequence of designs is

Activities
NEW! In-lesson activities enable students to take a more active approach to learning and develop concepts, often focusing on manipulatives and technology.

GUIDED

Example 1

At the start of the school year, a school's library had a total of 3,600 individual magazines that it had collected over time. Each month 22 new magazines are added to the collection.

a. Complete the table to show the number of magazines in the library each month.

b. Define a variable and write an algebraic expression for the number of magazines.

Solution

a.

Months Since Start of School Year	Calculation	Pattern	Magazines in Library
0	?	3,600 + 22(0)	3,600
1	?	?	?
2	3,600 + 22 + 22	?	3,644
3	?	3,600 + 22(?)	?

> **Guided Examples**
> **NEW!** Guided examples provide partially completed solutions to encourage independent practice. Independent problems provide an additional opportunity for students to practice skills.

works for a few numbers and fails for all others. For example, suppose you are not sure whether $2w$ and w^2 have the same meaning.

STOP See Quiz Yourself 1 at the right.

The Quiz Yourself shows that $2w$ and w^2 are not equal for all values of w. When you evaluate an expression for several values of the variable, a table of values helps to organize your work.

> ▶ **QUIZ YOURSELF 1**
> a. Show that $2w$ and w^2 have the same value when $w = 2$.
> b. Show that $2w$ and w^2 have different values when $w = 5$.

GUIDED

Example 1

Compare Alf's and Beth's expressions for several instances by filling in the tables below.

Alf	
n	$(n + 1) + 3 + (n + 1)$
1	?
2	?
3	?
10	?

Beth	
n	$5 + 2n$
1	?
2	?
3	?
10	?

> **Quiz Yourself**
> **NEW!** Students are instructed to stop for a periodic check of their understanding.

A rich variety of problems are presented in the Question Sets. Each set begins with the **Covering the Ideas** questions that demonstrate the student's knowledge of the overall concepts of the lesson. The **Applying the Mathematics** questions go beyond lesson examples with an emphasis on real-world problem-solving. The **Review** questions relate either to previous lessons in the course or to content from earlier courses. The **Exploration** questions ask students to explore ideas related to the lesson, and frequently have many possible answers.

Teacher's Edition

The wrap-around format and design of the teacher's edition presents each lesson using a four-step method:

❶ Warm-Up
❷ Teaching
❸ Assignment
❹ Wrap-Up

Lesson 1-3

Activity 2

Now consider a different toothpick sequence. The picture at the right shows the number of toothpicks required to construct a sequence of rectangles. The first and second terms are shown. Each rectangle is one toothpick wider and one toothpick taller than the previous rectangle.

1. How many toothpicks are needed for the 1st term? 6 toothpicks
2. How many toothpicks are needed for the 2nd term? 10 toothpicks
3. Draw the 3rd term in the sequence. How many toothpicks are needed?
4. In words, describe a method to find the number of toothpicks it takes to make the nth term.
5. Write an algebraic expression to find the number of toothpicks it takes to make the nth term.
   Answers vary. Sample answer: $4n + 2$
6. Fill in the table below.

Term Number	Calculation	Number of Toothpicks	
4	?	?	$4(4) + 2$; 18
5	?	?	$4(5) + 2$; 22
6	?	?	$4(6) + 2$; 26
13	?	?	$4(13) + 2$; 54
58	?	?	$4(58) + 2$; 234

3. 14 toothpicks;

4. Answers vary. Sample answer: Two sides have n toothpicks, while the other two have $n + 1$ toothpicks.

In the activities, you looked at sequences of toothpicks and the number of toothpicks needed to make them. For each sequence, you used the term number n to determine the number of toothpicks needed for the nth term. You and your classmates may have found that there can be more than one expression to describe the nth term.

Consider the sequence of dots at the right. Students were asked to describe the number of dots needed to make the nth term.

Alf explained that in each term he saw 2 columns of dots and 3 dots between the columns. He wrote the following.

left column   middle   right column
$(n + 1)$ +   3   + $(n + 1)$

Beth saw a row of 5 dots at the bottom and 2 columns above the row. She wrote the following.

bottom row   two columns
5   + $2n$

Equivalent Expressions   21

---

❶ Use the **Warm-Up** as questions for students to work on as you begin the class.

---

1   Warm-Up

Draw or project the toothpick diagram below along with the question, "How many toothpicks are needed to make this design?" Ask students to explain how they arrived at their answers.

Accommodating the Learner ⬤

...may find it difficult to start ...le in Activity 1 because it ...number 11. It might be ...s extend the table so the ...column begins with the ...ows each whole number... ...st that st... ...ber of to... ...ey also... ...term.

Additional Answers

1. 4 toothpicks; 7 toothpicks; 10 toothpicks; 13 toothpicks; 16 toothpicks; 19 toothpicks; 22 toothpicks; 25 toothpicks; 28 toothpicks; 31 toothpicks
2. Answers vary. Sample answer: The nth ...sign has... 1 vertical toothpick... and...

1-3

❶   Warm-Up

Draw or project the toothpick diagram below along with the question, "How many toothpicks are needed to make this design?" Ask students to explain how they arrived at their answers.

60; students' explanations will vary.

❷   Teaching

Notes on the Lesson

You should do **Activities 1 and 2** before discussing this lesson. Neither activity requires toothpicks.

Notes on the Activity

Activity 1 Have students work in pairs. While discussing this activity, it is very important not to give students a particular way of counting the toothpicks in the first design. Here are some possible ways that students might think about the counting.

Method 1: Count the top (n toothpicks), count the bottom (n), count the sides ($n + 1$), so that the expression is $n + n + (n + 1)$. Keep the parentheses so that the counting is evident.

Method 2: Count 4 for the first term in the sequence and add 3 for each additional square shown in the other terms. Since there is one less additional square than the term number in the sequence, the expression is $4 + 3(n - 1)$.

Method 3: Count 1 for the left end and 3 more to make each square. The expression is $1 + 3n$.

Students may want to know the right answer. Any expression equivalent to $3n + 1$ is fine. You can see which methods ...asking for all the ...It may come as ...t you are asking ...t out to them that ...ect.

...e)

Lesson 1-3   21

---

2   Teaching

Notes on the Lesson

You should do **Activities 1 and 2** before discussing this lesson. Neither activity requires toothpicks.

Notes on the Activity

Activity 1 Have students work in pairs. While discussing... is very important not... a particular way of coun... toothpicks in the first d... are some possible ways... might think about the c...

Method 1: Count the to... count the bottom (n), count the sides ($n + 1$), so that the expression is $n + n + (n + 1)$. Keep the parentheses so that the counting is evident.

...**Method 2:** Count 4 for the first term in the...

---

❷ **Teaching** provides notes and procedures for activities included in each lesson. These embedded activities help students to understand the lesson as they read.

1-3

3 Assignment

Recommended Assignment
- Questions 1–19
- Questions 20 and 21 (extra credit)
- Reading Lesson 1-4
- Covering the Ideas 1-4

Notes on the Questions
Question 3 We are careful to say that the expressions "seem to be equivalent." Without some rule, we do not know whether the expressions would generate the same values

Chapter 1

3. Two diffe
values be
seem to l
have the

x
10
9
8
7
6
5

Accommodating the Learner ⬇

Some students may find it difficult to start filling in the table in Activity 1 because it starts with term number 11. It might be helpful if students extend the table so the Term Number column begins with the number 1 and shows each whole number up to 15. Suggest that students not only record the number of toothpicks for each term but that they also write down how they calculated each term.

1-3

4 Wrap-Up

Ongoing Assessment
On a piece of paper, have students write two algebraic expressions that they know to be either equivalent or not equivalent. Instruct them to exchange their papers with other students. Students should determine whether the two expressions they receive are equivalent or not. If they believe the expressions are not equivalent, they should provide a counterexample. When all students have made a determination, they should check th_____ ___ ___ with their partners

Chapter

13. Give
    a. *x*
    13a
14. a. E
    b. Eva
    c. Find
       value
In 15–17, fill
15. $(-25)(-$
16. $3^3 + 3^3$
17. $(8 \cdot$
18. Raul
    all of
    to pu
    total

Teaching and Assessment Resources
- ❯ Lesson masters (one- and two-page practice and review blackline masters)
- ❯ Teaching aids
- ❯ Chapter, cumulative, comprehensive, and performance-based tests
- ❯ Chapter quizzes
- ❯ Assessment forms

UCSMP has many opportunities for assessment.

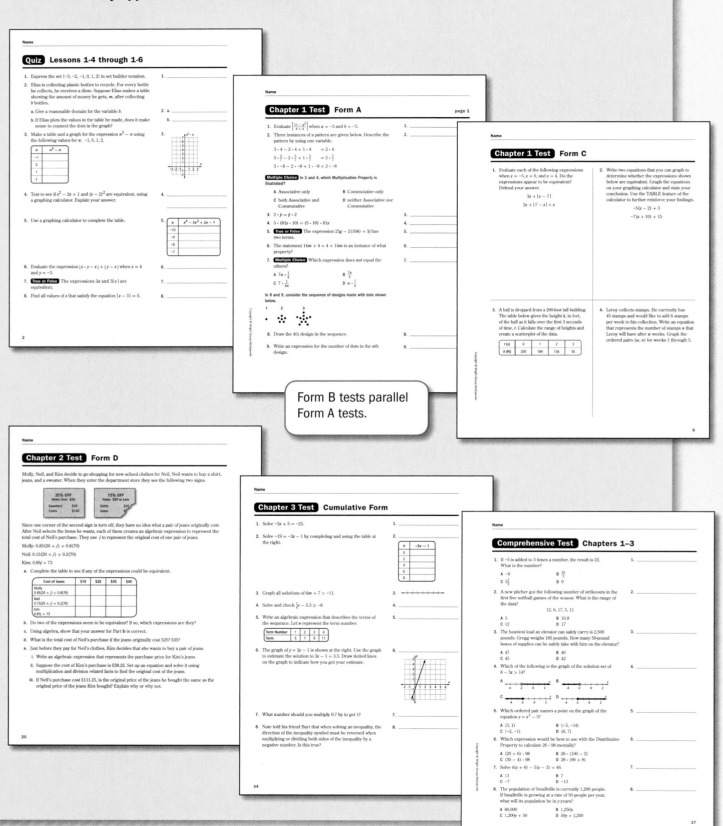

Form B tests parallel Form A tests.

This program includes many features that address the needs of special student populations including the following.

Extension

Have students consider the following problem. Juanita's portfolio is currently worth 1.2 million dollars but is losing value at a rate of $100,000 per year. Let y be the value of Juanita's portfolio in x years. Ask students to write an equation representing this situation. Students should then graph the equation, labeling both the x- and y-intercepts. Ask students to explain what the x- and y-intercepts mean in the context of the problem. Have them identify the slope and explain its meaning.

Accommodating the Learner

You should divide the assignment for students who are having difficulty with writing inequalities in algebraic form. First, they should study the following list of common words and phrases used in inequalities: at most ($\leq$), at least ($\geq$), no more than ($\leq$), more than ($>$), less than ($<$), between ($a < x < b$); and secondly, they should study the note-taking tips.

ENGLISH LEARNERS
Vocabulary Development

Students now have definitions for fractions, complex fractions, algebraic fractions, and reciprocals. Ask students if any of the categories can overlap. For example, can two complex fractions be reciprocals? Can a fraction be complex and algebraic? Ask them to give examples to support their claims.

The Accommodating the Learner and Extensions features in the Teacher's Edition provide alternative suggestions for those learners who could benefit from more challenging activities.

The Accommodating the Learner feature in the Teacher's Edition provides alternative suggestions for those learners who could benefit from more basic activities.

The English Learner/Vocabulary Development notes in the Teacher's Edition give teachers hints about how to help English learners and those with weak vocabulary skills access the mathematics concepts.

The Activities and Guided Example items result in active learning by the students rather than just listening and writing notes while the teacher lectures. Many types of students will benefit by doing the Activities and Guided Examples in class either individually, in pairs, or in small groups. Students will retain more if they are active participants in the material. Although these items may take longer to complete the first few times they are done, the time will be well spent.

Having students answer the Quiz Yourself questions during class actively engages them. The Quiz Yourself questions could be done in conjunction with handheld "clicker" devices or on student slates so that the teacher can quickly assess the overall class understanding of the concept before moving on.

In effective UCSMP classrooms, one sees smaller amounts of lecture, recitation, and individual seatwork than in comparison classes, and more discussions in small groups or with the whole class, more individual or group work with calculators, computers, or other physical materials, and opportunities for students to do extended projects outside of class.

We asked teachers who have used the UCSMP program successfully to share their strategies. You may wish to see how their ideas work in your classroom. They suggest that you:

> Encourage active learning inside and outside of the classroom by utilizing the Guided Examples, Activities, and Quiz Yourself stop points found throughout this book.

> Some teachers use Guided Examples when teaching the lesson to the class. Others asked students to work through Guided Examples at home.

> When reading a lesson at home or in class, students should stop and complete each Quiz Yourself problem. Many teachers review the students' work to make sure they have read the lesson.

> Activities can be completed in small groups or as a whole class. Activities help students discover new concepts together.

> Have students read each lesson and do all the questions before class. Then discuss the lesson and engage in various activities during the next period.

> Preview the next day's lesson, highlighting key points students may need to know to read the lesson and answer the questions.

> Supplement the Student Edition with additional manipulative activities and assign Lesson Masters for homework or in-class group or individual work.

> Assign a warm-up activity. This could come from the Teacher's Edition or consist of all or part of the Lesson Master from the previous lesson. Go over the homework and have students correct their homework assignments. Occasionally the questions can be discussed in small groups.

> Ask students to write out steps taken to answer homework questions they have missed. About once a week, give a quiz, asking students to copy the steps from their notebooks.

> Have students complete Additional Examples from the Teacher's Edition. Students soon learn how to find the parallel Example in the textbook and compare it to the new example.

continued

> Use cooperative reading strategies in the classroom. The class reads a lesson and then in small groups each student identifies a key idea from the lesson and explains it to the group.

> Ask students to read aloud occasionally. Point out that the red headers in each lesson identify the main ideas of the lesson.

> Go over the Covering the Ideas orally in class after the students have read the lesson.

> Display answers on an overhead projector or computer at the beginning of the class to review homework questions. Have students grade their own papers. Groups of students can then discuss questions that were missed and explain answers to each other.

An Articulated Curriculum Across All Grades

The UCSMP program is flexible, allowing schools to offer the appropriate mathematics to students, regardless of their grade level. Students can enter the UCSMP program at any grade but are advantaged by having had the previous UCSMP courses. The chart below shows how *Everyday Mathematics* and the new and third edition texts of the UCSMP program can be used together.

Grade	Top 10-20% of Students	Next 50% of Students	Next 20% of Students	Remainder Students
5	EM 6 or Pre-Transition Mathematics			
6	Transition Mathematics	EM 6 or Pre-transition Mathematics		
7	Algebra	Transition Mathematics	Pre-Transition Mathematics	
8	Geometry	Algebra	Transition Mathematics	Pre-Transition Mathematics
9	Advanced Algebra	Geometry	Algebra	Transition Mathematics
10	Functions, Statistics, and Trigonometry	Advanced Algebra	Geometry	Algebra
11	Precalculus and Discrete Mathematics	Functions, Statistics, and Trigonometry	Advanced Algebra	Geometry
12	Calculus (Not available through UCSMP)	Precalculus and Discrete Mathematics	Functions, Statistics, and Trigonometry	Advanced Algebra

The UCSMP curriculum has been carefully refined through years of field testing and feedback from users. Teachers throughout the country have discovered that UCSMP materials provide a way for more of their students to be successful, learning more mathematics than traditional curricula offer.

First Edition Studies

The first draft of *Algebra* was written and piloted during the 1985–1986 school year. A formative evaluation was conducted during the 1986–1987 school year. Extensive revisions were made after each year. A large summative evaluation was conducted during the 1987–1988 school year, with students in 40 pairs of matched classes in 9 states participating in the study. Overall, on a standardized measure of traditional algebra concepts, no significant differences in achievement were found. However, on two additional tests constructed to assess knowledge of algebra content not found on the standardized test, including representations and applications, UCSMP students outperformed the comparison students.

Second Edition Studies

To prepare for the second edition of *Algebra*, teachers using the text were invited to evaluate each lesson and provide feedback on other aspects of the course. Users' comments, gathered over the years by UCSMP and the publisher, were also considered. Some second edition authors were experienced teachers of *Algebra*. All of this information factored into the changes made in the second edition.

During the 1992–1993 school year, a field-study was conducted of a draft of the Second Edition, with 19 matched pairs of classes in 11 schools throughout the country; some comparison classes used the First Edition of *Algebra* and others used a non-UCSMP comparison text. On a standardized achievement measure given at the end of the year assessing traditional algebra skills, the Second Edition students performed as well as the comparison class students. On a second measure designed to assess knowledge of additional algebra content, including translation from verbal to symbolic forms, linear relationships with two variables, quadratic equations and relationships, geometric relationships, and some basic statistics, UCSMP students outperformed their non-UCSMP comparison peers.

Questionnaire responses indicated that UCSMP students were more likely to recognize that it is helpful to read the textbook in order to understand mathematics. Also, a calculator is helpful in learning mathematics.

UCSMP teachers indicated that students had an opportunity to learn content in the course, such as statistics, that would not previously have been included in an algebra course. In addition, teachers valued the daily applications to the real world and commented that topics were at a higher quality level than those in other texts. Both teachers and students found the text to be interesting and fun. Calculator technology was perceived as broadening the amount of mathematics students could learn.

Third Edition Formative Study

During the 2005–2006 school year, a study was conducted of the field trial version of the third edition of *Algebra*. Six schools were selected based on a number of criteria, including the availability of comparison classes as well as for geographic and demographic diversity in the sample. For detailed analysis, classes within a school were matched at the beginning of the school year on the basis of two pretests of students' knowledge of mathematics – the *Iowa Algebra Aptitude Test* and a test containing many released items from the National Assessment of Educational Progress (NAEP).

At the end of the year, students completed three posttests to measure their progress over the year: the *Terra Nova Algebra Test*, a test using many released items from the NAEP, and a constructed-response test. Calculators were permitted only on the constructed response test. Twenty-seven of the items on the pretest had also been administered on the posttest in order to assess growth. Preliminary analysis suggests no significant overall differences in achievement, although UCSMP students perform better than their non-UCSMP peers on applications of algebra.

UCSMP teachers provided detailed comments about lessons in each chapter they taught. They remarked on the benefits of activities and the use of computer algebra systems (CAS). Those comments guided the authors as they made revisions prior to publication in the spring of 2007.

Summary

In these studies, we have repeatedly found that UCSMP *Algebra* students meet traditional expectations for computational facility with traditional algebra content as successfully as their non-UCSMP peers on standardized measures even though UCSMP students are more likely to use calculators regularly, and often use more powerful calculators. At the same time, UCSMP *Algebra* students learn a considerable amount of geometry. These results hold when UCSMP *Algebra* is used in eighth-grade classes and in high school classes.

The scope of the Third Edition of UCSMP *Algebra* reaches well beyond that of traditional algebra books. Mathematical topics are integrated throughout the text. Concepts and skills are taught with a variety of approaches. New technologies are used to develop concepts and perform skills.

Integrated Mathematical Concepts and Skills

> Introduces skills, properties, and representations through real-world applications
> Statistics and probability integrated throughout

Multiple Approaches to Expressions, Equations, and Functions

> Presents topics tabularly, graphically, and symbolically
> Introduces linear, exponential, quadratic, and polynomial functions
> Visualizes algebraic concepts physically and geometrically

Shows Students Why They Need Algebra

> Applies algebraic expressions to describe patterns
> Shows how algebra can explain properties of arithmetic and geometry
> Introduces functions as objects that help describe change
> Gives practice in the use of algebra to deduce results

Use of new technologies

> Graphing calculators assumed for home use
> Computer algebra system (CAS) technology used to develop patterns and practice skills

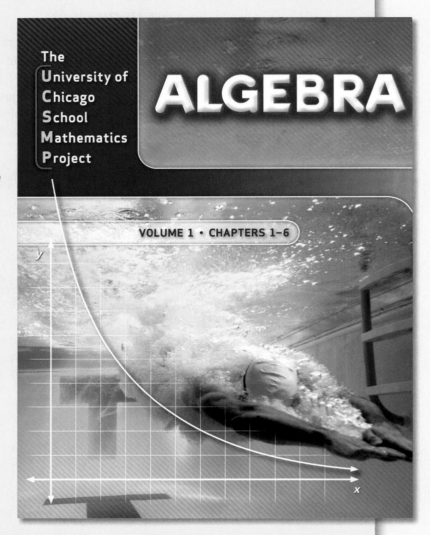

The
University of
Chicago
School
Mathematics
Project

ALGEBRA

VOLUME 1 • CHAPTERS 1–6

Welcome to *Algebra!* We hope you enjoy this book; it was written for you.

Why is Algebra Important?

In almost every country of the world, students learn algebra. But you seldom see algebra when you go into a store, or when you read a newspaper, or when you watch a television show. So why is algebra so important? It is because algebra is the language of generalization. It is used to describe how quantities relate to each other and helps to solve countless numbers of problems.

For those reasons, with a knowledge of algebra:

○ You become eligible for more jobs or training programs that will help you get a job.

○ You are able to take courses that would help you determine your career path.

○ You are able to understand many ideas discussed in business, science, psychology, politics, and in many other areas.

○ You are more likely to make wise decisions about money and other personal matters.

Learning From This Book

We want you to be able to understand the mathematics around you, in newspapers and magazines, on television, in a job, and in school.

To accomplish this goal, you should try to learn from the reading in each lesson as well as from your teacher and your classmates. The authors, who are all experienced teachers, offer the following advice.

1. You can watch basketball hundreds of times on television. Still, to learn how to play basketball, you must have a ball in your hand and practice dribbling, shooting, and passing. Mathematics is no different. You cannot learn much mathematics just by watching other people do it. You must participate in mathematics. Some teachers have a slogan that has served their classes well in the past:

Mathematics is not a spectator sport.

2. You are expected to read each lesson. Here are some ways to improve your reading comprehension:

○ Read slowly, paying attention to each word and symbol.

○ Look up the meaning of any word you do not understand.

○ Work examples yourself as you follow the steps in the text.

○ Reread sections that are unclear to you.

○ Discuss difficult ideas with a fellow student or your teacher.

1

3. Writing can help you understand mathematics, too. So you will sometimes be asked to explain your solution to a problem or to justify an answer. Writing good explanations takes practice. You can look at the solutions to the examples in each lesson as a guide for your own writing.

4. If you cannot answer a question immediately, don't give up! Read the lesson again. Read the question again. Look for examples. If you can, get away from the question and come back to it a little later. Ask questions in class and talk to others when you do not understand something. School is designed so that you do not have to learn everything by yourself. Here is another slogan that many teachers have used:

None of us is as smart as all of us.

What Tools Do You Need for this Book?

You need to have some tools to do any mathematics. The most basic tools are paper, pencil, and erasers. For this book, you will also need the following equipment:

- ◗ a **ruler** with both centimeter and inch markings,

- ◗ a **protractor,**

- ◗ **graph paper,** and

- ◗ a **graphing calculator**

At times in this book, there are activities involving a *computer algebra system* (CAS). Your teacher may want you to have a calculator that has CAS capability, or such calculators may be available in your classroom or school.

Getting Off to a Good Start

One way to get off to a good start is to spend some time getting acquainted with your textbook. The questions that follow are part of an activity designed to help you become familiar with *Algebra*.

We hope you join the millions of students who have enjoyed this book. We wish you much success.

Questions

COVERING THE IDEAS

1. Why is algebra important? See margin.

2. List four things, besides paper and pencil, you will need for your work in *Algebra*.
ruler, protractor, graph paper, and graphing calculator

3. Explain what is meant by the statement "Mathematics is not a spectator sport."
To be good at mathematics, you must do mathematics.

4. Of the five things listed that you can do to improve reading comprehension, list the three you think are most helpful to you. See margin.

5. Where can you look for a model to help you in writing an explanation to justify your answer to a question? in the solution to an Example in the lesson

In 6 and 7, refer to the Table of Contents beginning on page vi.

6. Algebra involves finding the slope of a line. In which chapter would you find the definition of slope? Chapter 6

7. What lesson would you learn how to first use a graphing calculator? Lesson 1-5

In 8–15, refer to other parts of the book.

8. Look at several lessons. Where can you find the answers to the Quiz Yourself questions? Where can you find the answers to the Guided Examples? at the end of the lesson; in the Selected Answers section at the back of the book

9. Suppose you have just finished doing Activity 2 in Lesson 2-6. How can you check your answers? Ask my teacher for the answers.

10. What are the four categories of Questions at the end of each lesson? Covering the Ideas, Applying the Mathematics, Review, and Exploration

11. Suppose you have just finished the Questions in Lesson 1-7. On what page can you find answers to check your work? For which Questions are answers given? p. S2; answers to odd-numbered questions in Covering the Ideas, Applying the Mathematics, and Review

12. Refer to a Self-Test at the end of a chapter. When you finish the test, what is it recommended that you do? See margin.

13. What kinds of questions are in the Chapter Review at the end of each chapter? Skills, Properties, Uses, and Representations

14. Where is the Glossary and what does it contain? It begins on page S26; it has definitions of words and phrases introduced in the book.

15. Locate the Index.

   a. According to the Index, where can you find information about the Carlsbad Caverns? pp. 42 and 45

   b. In what state are the Caverns located? New Mexico

12. Check my work with the solutions given in the back of the book. Make a list of the problems I missed. Write down what I need to study most. Use what I write to help me study and review the chapter.

Chapter
1 Using Algebra to Describe

Chapter Overview	Local Standards	Pacing (in days)		
		Average	Advanced	Block
1-1 Evaluating Expressions **A** Evaluate numerical and algebraic expressions. **F** Apply the Algebraic Definitions of Subtraction and Division. **G** Identify and apply the associative, commutative, and transitive properties.		1	1	0.5
1-2 Describing Patterns **B** Use variables to describe patterns in instances or tables. **G** Identify and apply the associative, commutative, and transitive properties. **H** Create expressions to model real-world situations.		1	1	0.5
1-3 Equivalent Expressions **B** Use variables to describe patterns in instances or tables. **C** Determine if two expressions seem equivalent by substituting values or making a table.		1	0.5	0.75
QUIZ 1		0.5	0.5	0.25
1-4 Picturing Expressions **J** Create a scatterplot from a table or expression. **K** Graph ordered pairs from expressions. **L** Use graphs to determine whether expressions seem to be equivalent.		1	0.5	0.5
1-5 Using a Graphing Calculator **K** Graph ordered pairs from expressions. **L** Use graphs to determine whether expressions seem to be equivalent. **M** Use graphs to find values, create tables, and select appropriate windows.		1	1	0.5
1-6 Absolute Value and Distance **D** Evaluate expressions involving absolute value. **L** Use graphs to determine whether expressions seem to be equivalent.		1	1	0.75
QUIZ 2		0.5	0.5	0.25
1-7 Data and Spread **E** Calculate the range and mean absolute deviation. **I** Calculate and interpret the spread of a distribution using mean absolute deviation.		1	1	0.5
Self-Test		1	1	0.5
Chapter Review		2	2	1
Test		1	1	0.5
TOTAL		12	11	6.5

Differentiated Options Universal Access

	Accommodating the Learner	Vocabulary Development	Ongoing Assessment	Materials
1-1	pp. 8, 9		written, p. 12	scientific or graphing calculator
1-2	pp. 15, 16	p. 14	written, p. 19	scientific or graphing calculator
1-3	pp. 21, 23		group, p. 26	
1-4	pp. 28, 29		written, p. 32	graph paper
1-5	pp. 34–36		written, p. 41	graphing calculator, graph paper
1-6	pp. 44, 45		written, p. 46	graphing calculator
1-7	pp. 49–51	p. 48	oral, p. 54	paper clips, scientific or graphing calculator, spreadsheet software, graph paper, centimeter ruler

Objectives

Skills	Lessons	Self-Test Questions	Chapter Review Questions
A Evaluate numerical and algebraic expressions.	1-1	5	1–10
B Use variables to describe patterns in instances or tables.	1-2, 1-3	1, 6	11–13
C Determine if two expressions seem equivalent by substituting values or making a table.	1-3	5, 7	14–16
D Evaluate expressions involving absolute value.	1-6	9	17–21
E Calculate the range and mean absolute deviation.	1-7	12	22–25

Properties	Lessons	Self-Test Questions	Chapter Review Questions
F Apply the Algebraic Definitions of Subtraction and Division.	1-1	3	26–31
G Identify and apply the associative, commutative, and transitive properties.	1-1, 1-2	2	32–35

Uses	Lessons	Self-Test Questions	Chapter Review Questions
H Create expressions to model real-world situations.	1-2	4	36, 37
I Calculate and interpret the spread of a distribution using mean absolute deviation.	1-7	11–13	38

Representations	Lessons	Self-Test Questions	Chapter Review Questions
J Create a scatterplot from a table or expression.	1-4	6	39, 40
K Graph ordered pairs from expressions.	1-4, 1-5	9	41, 42
L Use graphs to determine whether expressions seem to be equivalent.	1-4, 1-5, 1-6	8	43–45
M Use graphs to find values, create tables, and select appropriate windows.	1-5	10, 14	46–48

Resource Masters Chapter 1

Resource Master 1, Graph Paper (page 2), can be used with Lessons 1-4 and 1-6. **Resource Master 2, Four-Quadrant Graph Paper** (page 3), can be used with Lessons 1-4 through 1-7.

Resource Master 8 Lesson 1-1

Warm-Up

1. What is the value of $100 - 99 - 98$?

2. What is the value of sixty divided by two times three?

3. What is the value of $8x$ when x is 5?

Additional Examples

1. a. If $b = 2$, find $-4b^3$.
   b. If $b = 2$, calculate $(-4b)^3$.

2. Use a calculator to evaluate $\left(\frac{a + \sqrt{10}}{b^3 + a - 1.5}\right)^2$ when $a = 7$ and $b = 2$.

3. Find the volume of a rectangular solid using the formula $V = \ell wh$. Let $\ell = 4$ centimeters, $w = 6$ centimeters, and $h = 7$ centimeters.

Order of Operations

1. Perform operations within parentheses or other grouping symbols.

2. Within grouping symbols, or if there are no grouping symbols:
   a. Evaluate all powers from left to right.
   b. Next multiply and divide from left to right.
   c. Then add and subtract from left to right.

Resource Master for Lesson 1-1

Resource Master 9 Lesson 1-2

Warm-Up

Every lamb has 4 legs. Every chicken has 2 legs.

1. How many legs do 5 lambs and 20 chickens have?

2. How many legs do 100 lambs and 27 chickens have?

3. How many legs do L lambs and C chickens have?

Using Tables to Look at Patterns

Number of Weeks (w)	Calculations	Pattern	Money Saved
0	25	$25 + 15 \cdot 0$	$25
1	25 + 15	$25 + 15 \cdot 1$	$40
2	25 + 15 + 15	$25 + 15 \cdot 2$	$55
3	25 + 15 + 15 + 15	$25 + 15 \cdot 3$	$70
4	25 + 15 + 15 + 15 + 15	$25 + 15 \cdot 4$	$85
5	25 + 15 + 15 + 15 + 15 + 15	$25 + 15 \cdot 5$	$100
6	25 + 15 + 15 + 15 + 15 + 15 + 15	$25 + 15 \cdot 6$	$115

Resource Master for Lesson 1-2

Resource Master 10 Lesson 1-2

Additional Example

1. Paula borrowed $200 from her grandfather today. She intends to pay back the money at a rate of $10 each week.
   a. Complete a table to show how much Paula still owes her grandfather at the end of each week.

Weeks	Calculation	Pattern	Amount Owed
0		$200 - 10(0)$	200
1			
2	$200 - 10 - 10$		
3			170

   b. Define a variable and write an algebraic expression for the amount of money Paula still owes her grandfather at the end of each week.

Question 23

Sun	Mon	Tue	Wed	Thu	Fri	Sat
				1	2	3
4	5	6	7			
11	12	13	14			
18	19	20	21			
25	26	27	28	29	30	31

Resource Master for Lesson 1-2

Resource Master 11 Lesson 1-2

Additional Example

2. A group consisting of 4 adults and 7 children is planning to go to an amusement park. They checked the park's Web site to find the cost of several rides.

Ride	Adult Ticket	Child Ticket
Water Flume	$2.00	$1.00
Bumper Cars	$1.50	$1.00
Roller Coaster	$2.50	$2.00
Ferris Wheel	$3.00	$2.50

   a. Complete the table to show the group's cost for each ride.

Ride	Group's Cost
Water Flume	$4 \cdot 2 + 7 \cdot 1$
Bumper Cars	
Roller Coaster	$4 \cdot 2.50 + 7 \cdot 2$
Ferris Wheel	

   b. How much does each activity cost the group?
   c. Let a = the adult ticket price and c = the child ticket price for any one activity. Write an algebraic expression for the group's total cost for this activity.

Resource Master for Lesson 1-2

Resource Master 12 Lesson 1-3

Warm-Up

How many toothpicks are needed to make this design? Explain how you arrived at your answer.

Additional Examples

1. Dontrell and Melissa both looked at a sequence of designs made up of dots. Dontrell describes the pattern with the expression $2n - 5$ while Melissa describes it with the expression $(n - 3) + (n - 2)$, where n is the term number in the sequence. Compare their expressions for several instances by filling in the table below. What can you conclude?

Term Number	Dontrell	Melissa
n	$2n - 5$	$(n - 3) + (n - 2)$
1		
2		
3		
10		
20		
35		

2. Suppose Gabriel and Jill both wrote expressions to describe the same pattern. Gabriel wrote $q + 3$ and Jill wrote $4 - 2 + q$. Are the expressions equivalent?

Resource Master for Lesson 1-3

Resource Master 13 Lesson 1-4

Warm-Up

1. Graph the points $(2, 5)$, $(0, -6)$, $(-11, -4)$, and $(-9, 7)$ on the same coordinate graph. Connect the points in order. What figure is formed?

2. One of the vertices of the square is on one of the axes. Which vertex?

3. Is this vertex *above, below, to the right,* or *to the left* of the origin?

Additional Example

In 1870, the steamboats *Robert E. Lee* and *Natchez* raced from New Orleans to St. Louis, a distance of approximately 1,218 miles. The *Robert E. Lee's* average speed was approximately 20 miles per hour. Fill in the table of values to calculate the *Robert E. Lee's* approximate distance from St. Louis each hour after leaving New Orleans.

Hours of Racing	Calculation and Pattern	Remaining Distance (mi)
0		
1		
2		
3		
h		

Write an expression to represent its remaining distance after each hour, and then plot the points on a graph.

Resource Master for Lesson 1-4

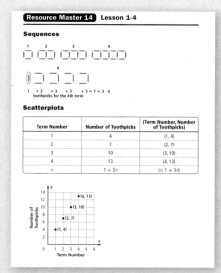

Resource Master for Lesson 1-4

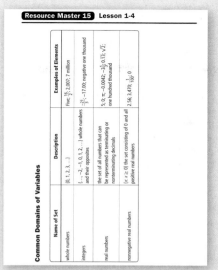

Resource Master for Lesson 1-4

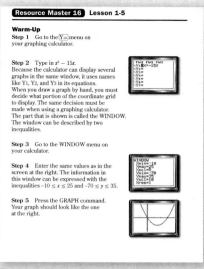

Resource Master for Lesson 1-5

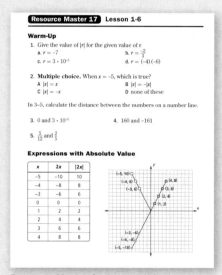

Resource Master for Lesson 1-6

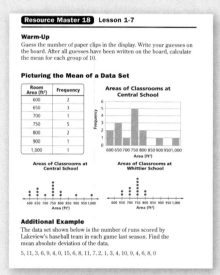

Resource Master for Lesson 1-7

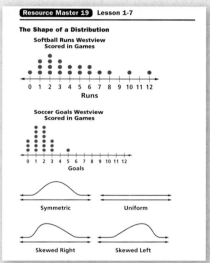

Resource Master for Lesson 1-7

Pacing

Each lesson in this chapter is designed to be covered in one day. At the end of the chapter, you should plan to spend 1 day to review the Self-Test, 1 to 2 days for the Chapter Review, and 1 day for a test. You may wish to spend a day on projects and possibly a day is needed for quizzes. This chapter should therefore take 10 to 13 days. We strongly advise you not spend more than 14 days on this chapter; there is ample opportunity to review ideas in later chapters.

Chapter 1 Projects

At the end of each chapter, you will find projects related to the chapter. At this time you might want to have students look over the projects on pages 55 and 56. You might want to have students tentatively select a project on which to work. Then, as students read and progress through the chapter, they can finalize their project choices.

Sometimes students might work alone; at other times, you might let them collaborate with classmates for a presentation and discussion. We recommend that you allow for diversity and encourage students to use their imaginations when presenting their projects. As students work on projects throughout the year, they should see the many uses of mathematics in the real world.

Chapter

1

Using Algebra to Describe

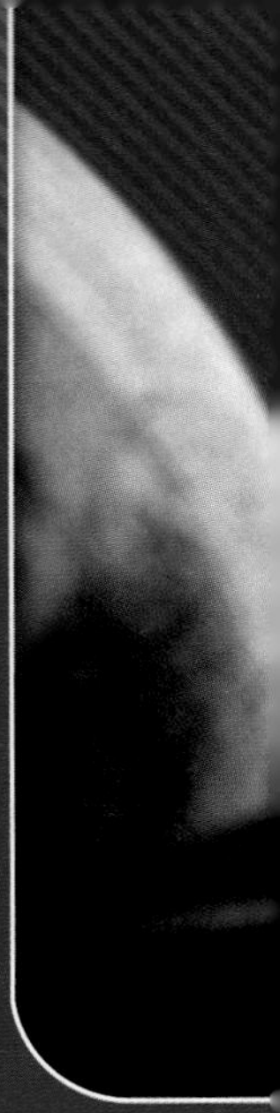

▶ Contents

A picture is worth a thousand words.
In mathematics, pictures and symbols are used to summarize mathematical concepts that normally require many words to describe, as shown below.

For many years you have multiplied fractions. You know that $\frac{5}{8} \cdot \frac{3}{4} = \frac{15}{32}$. Here is the general rule for multiplying fractions.

> To multiply two fractions, multiply their numerators to get the numerator of the product, and then multiply their demoninators to get the denominator of the product.

Wow! This rule is quite a mouthful. It is 26 words long. Here is the same rule in the language of algebra.

$$\frac{a}{b} \cdot \frac{c}{d} = \frac{ac}{bd}, \; b \neq 0, d \neq 0$$

4

Chapter 1 Overview

You might tell students that each chapter of this book begins with a pair of pages that are called the "chapter opener." On these pages is a list of the titles of the lessons of the chapter and a short lead-in to the chapter. In some books, this material is not part of any content to be learned, but in this book the chapter openers often lead directly into the first lesson of the chapter.

In this chapter opener, variables are used to describe the rule for multiplying fractions. We expect that students have seen and used variables in previous mathematics courses.

The rule for multiplying fractions is given as well as an *instance* of the rule, namely that $\frac{5}{8} \cdot \frac{3}{4} = \frac{15}{32}$. You might ask what the values of a, b, c, and d are in this instance. ($a = 5$, $b = 8$, $c = 3$, and $d = 4$)

The description in algebra is much shorter than the description in words, just like showing the photograph above is "shorter" than trying to describe it in words. The algebraic description also shows the arithmetic of fractions. *Algebraic descriptions can make it easier to understand relationships among numbers and quantities.*

In the algebraic description, *a*, *b*, *c*, and *d* are *variables*. Except for the fact that *b* and *d* cannot equal zero (you cannot divide by 0), these variables can stand for any numbers. They could be whole numbers, fractions, decimals, or percents. They could be positive or negative.

The algebraic description works for any situation in which you need to multiply fractions. Algebra is a powerful language that is used throughout the world. This is why almost all students are required to learn some algebra.

In this book you will see how algebra can be used to describe patterns, to explain why numbers act as they do, to solve problems, and to discover and prove relationships between quantities. This first chapter describes patterns with algebra and illustrates them with graphs.

5

You might also ask what the product of a pair of fractions is when $a = 100$, $b = 200$, $c = 300$, and $d = 400$. Students may give the answer $\frac{3}{8}$ or $\frac{30,000}{80,000}$, depending on whether they put the product in lowest terms or not. You can also make up noninteger values of *a, b, c,* and *d* and ask students to give the product. For example, what is the product of $\frac{\frac{3}{8}}{15}$ and $\frac{12}{0.25}$? $\left(\frac{6}{5} \text{ or } 1\frac{1}{5} \text{ or } 1.2\right)$

With these questions, you can begin the year by noting that you expect that students will often get different answers to a question, and by stressing that one of the major themes of algebra is trying to determine whether two or more answers are equivalent.

Lesson 1-1

Lesson 1-1

Evaluating Expressions

Vocabulary

variable

algebraic expression

evaluating the expression

GOAL

Evaluate expressions and recall some of the properties associated with evaluating expressions.

SPUR Objectives

(The SPUR objectives for all of Chapter 1 are found in the Chapter Review on pages 60–63.)

A Evaluate numerical and algebraic expressions.

F Apply the Algebraic Definitions of Subtraction and Division.

G Identify and apply the associative, commutative, and transitive properties.

Materials/Resources

· Lesson Master 1-1A or 1-1B
· Resource Master 8
· Scientific or graphing calculator

HOMEWORK

Suggestions for Assignment

• Questions 1–29
• Question 30 (extra credit)
• Reading Lesson 1-2
• Covering the Ideas 1-2

Local Standards

1 Warm-Up

You might write or project the following so that students can answer these questions as they enter the classroom.

1. What is the value of 100 − 99 − 98? −97

2. What is the value of sixty divided by two times three? 90

3. What is the value of $8x$ when x is 5? 40

(continued on next page)

▶ **BIG IDEA** The order of operations is used to evaluate expressions with variables and expressions with numbers.

Algebraic Expressions

Adults are roughly twice as tall as they were when they were 3 years old, as shown in the photograph at the right. This suggests a simple rule of thumb for predicting the adult height of a 3-year-old child: multiply his or her current height by 2. In the language of algebra, if c represents the height of a 3-year-old child, then $2 \cdot c$, or $2c$ for short, is the child's predicted height as an adult. The letter c is a *variable* and $2c$ is an *algebraic expression*. A **variable** is a letter or other symbol that can be replaced by any number (or other object) from a set. When numbers and variables are combined using the operations of arithmetic, the result is called an **algebraic expression.** Some examples of algebraic expressions are $7y$, $5x - 9$, and $\frac{4n^3p + 16}{z}$. Finding the numerical value of an expression is called **evaluating the expression.** To evaluate an algebraic expression, substitute numbers for its variables. The order of operations for algebraic expressions is the same as in numerical expressions.

Order of Operations in Evaluating Expressions

1. Perform operations within parentheses or other grouping symbols.
2. Within grouping symbols, or if there are no grouping symbols:
   a. Evaluate all powers from left to right.
   b. Next multiply and divide from left to right.
   c. Then add and subtract from left to right.

Activity

Suppose a and b are whole numbers with $a + b = 100$. What is the largest possible value of $a + ab - b$? 2,501

Mental Math

a. For how long did a gym class play softball if they played from 10:45 A.M. to 11:35 A.M.? 50 min

b. For how long did a cross country team run if they ran from 11:10 A.M. to 1:40 P.M.? 2 hr 30 min

c. If a 1 hour, 45 minutes long gym class starts at 11:30 A.M., at what time does it end? 1:15 P.M.

The father is approximately 2 times the height of his daughter.

Background

Order of operations. The need to have unambiguous values of algebraic expressions is motivation enough to have widely agreed-upon rules for the order of operations. Calculators and computers make having rules even more important because they do not take context into account when an algebraic expression is entered. The order of operations stated here is virtually universal and is used in many computer languages.

Algebraic expressions. Remind students that the product of two variables x and y is usually denoted by xy, $x \cdot y$, $x(y)$, or $(x)(y)$, but not by $x \times y$, because the symbol for multiplication can be confused with the variable x. This is the case even when none of the variables being multiplied are x. Be sure that students realize any numbers, not just whole numbers, can replace variables.

Example 1

a. If $a = 5$, find $3a^2$.

b. If $a = 5$, calculate $(3a)^2$.

Solution

a. Substitute 5 for a. There are no grouping symbols, so the power is the first operation to perform. Then multiply.

$3 \cdot 5^2 = 3 \cdot 25 = 75$

b. Substitute 5 for a. Perform the operation within the parentheses first. Then square the product.

$(3 \cdot 5)^2 = 15^2 = 225$

Subtraction and Division Expressions

Subtracting a number yields the same result as adding the opposite of that number. For example, substitute 12 for x in the following equation.

$$35 - 4x = 35 - 4 \cdot 12 \quad \text{Substitute 12 for } x.$$
$$= 35 - 48 \quad \text{Multiply first.}$$
$$= 35 + -48 \quad \text{Rewrite using addition.}$$
$$\quad -48 \text{ is the opposite of 48.}$$
$$= -13 \quad \text{Add.}$$

For some people, rewriting $35 - 48$, as $35 + -48$ makes the computation easier.

When subtracting a negative number, rewriting the expression is helpful.

$$-30 - -6 = -30 + 6 \quad \text{6 is the opposite of } -6.$$
$$= -24$$

The relationship between addition and subtraction is true for all real numbers. It is known as the *algebraic definition of subtraction*.

Algebraic Definition of Subtraction

For all real numbers a and b, $a - b = a + -b$.

There is a similar relationship between multiplication and division. Dividing a number by b is the same as multiplying by the reciprocal of b, or $\frac{1}{b}$. For example, $32 \div 5 = 32 \cdot \frac{1}{5} = 6.4$.

Algebraic Definition of Division

For all real numbers a and b with $b \neq 0$, $a \div b = a \cdot \frac{1}{b}$.

Evaluating Expressions 7

Algebraic definitions of subtraction and division. There are two basic definitions of subtraction and division. The first definitions are from *related facts*. For subtraction, $a - b = c$ if and only if $c + b = a$. In words, $a - b$ is the number c, which when added to b yields a; $9 - 5 = 4$ because $4 + 5 = 9$. For division, $a \div b = c$ if and only if $c \cdot b = a$. In words, $a \div b$ is the number c, which when multiplied by b yields a; $\frac{1}{2} \div 3 = \frac{1}{6}$ because $\frac{1}{6} \cdot 3 = \frac{1}{2}$.

The second basic definitions of subtraction and division are those given in this lesson. They do not require the introduction of a third number c for their statements. In the algebraic definition of subtraction, $9 - 5 = 9 + -5 = 4$. In the algebraic definition of division, $\frac{1}{2} \div 3 = \frac{1}{2} \cdot \frac{1}{3} = \frac{1}{6}$.

The process represented in this definition is sometimes referred to as "invert and multiply."

Each of these Warm-Up questions underscores the need to have agreed-upon *conventions* or *rules* governing how expressions are evaluated.

1. If a person does the right subtraction first, then the result is $100 - 1$, or 99. If a person does the left subtraction first, the result is $1 - 98$, or -97. The rules for order of operations indicate that the left subtraction is to be done first. If you want to do the right subtraction first, you can show that with parentheses: $100 - (99 - 98)$.

2. The English language is ambiguous. There is no way to know from the English language whether you should divide or multiply first. So a student who is confused by this question is right to be confused! Mathematically, "sixty divided by two times three" can be written on one line as $60 \div 2 \cdot 3$. The rules for order of operations say to proceed from left to right, so the division would be done first and the value of the expression is 90.

3. A student who answers "85" is not necessarily wrong, but in this context $8x$ means 8 times x unless otherwise indicated.

2 Teaching

Notes on the Lesson

Evaluating algebraic expressions will be review for many students and should be easy for those seeing algebraic expressions for the first time.

Example 1a points out that powers take precedence over multiplication. For multiplication to be done first, you need to have parentheses, as in **Example 1b**.

Additional Examples

Example 1 a. If $b = 2$, find $-4b^3$. $\quad -32$

b. If $b = 2$, calculate $(-4b)^3$.

-512

Notes on the Lesson

Subtraction and division. The algebraic definitions of subtraction and division are often used to calculate the answers to subtraction and division problems. For subtraction, you "change the sign of the second number and add"; for division, you "take the reciprocal of the second number and multiply."

1-1

Note-Taking Tip

This lesson contains the first of many new vocabulary words, definitions, and properties found in this book. Have students keep a notebook to copy these items for later study and use. Provide students with some tips on how to organize their notebooks. Check their notebooks periodically.

Notes on the Lesson

Emphasize to your students that **Quiz Yourself** (QY) and **Guided Examples** are meant to help them as they read through the lesson. They should always do these questions honestly and check their answers with those given after the lesson (for the QYs) and in the back of the book (for the Guided Examples).

Evaluating with technology. A troublesome weakness of most scientific or graphing calculators when dealing with algebraic expressions is that the expressions have to be entered on one line. Parentheses will be needed unless there is only a single quantity in the denominator. Step 3 in **Guided Example 2** shows a complicated example of this, for not only is there a fraction, but also a power. The power requires a second use of parentheses.

Remember that there are several symbols for division. The operation $a \div b$ can also be written as $\frac{a}{b}$ or a/b. In all cases, b (the denominator or the divisor) cannot be zero. For example:

$$5 \div 12 = \frac{5}{12} = 5/12 = 5 \cdot \frac{1}{12}$$

$$24 \div 6 = \frac{24}{6} = 24/6 = 24 \cdot \frac{1}{6}$$

$$\frac{1}{4} \div 3 = \frac{\frac{1}{4}}{3} = (1/4)/3 = \frac{1}{4} \cdot \frac{1}{3}$$

STOP See Quiz Yourself at the right.

Quiz Yourself (QY) questions are designed to help you follow the reading. You should try to answer each Quiz Yourself question before reading on. The answer to the Quiz Yourself is found at the end of the lesson.

Evaluating with Technology

Scientific and graphing calculators use the algebraic order of operations. However, they can differ in the keys they use for squares, exponents, and square roots. Some possible key sequences are shown below. The order of entry is similar to the order you use to write the symbols by hand.

Key	Example
squaring key	For 5^2 enter 5 $\boxed{x^2}$ to get 25.
exponent key	For 5^3 enter 5 $\boxed{\wedge}$ 3 to get 125.
square root key	For $\sqrt{1{,}156}$ enter $\boxed{\sqrt{}}$ 1156 to get 34.

With most calculators, you must input fractions on one line. Therefore, you must include grouping symbols to show calculations within fractions. For example, to evaluate $\frac{24}{8-2}$, you must enter $24/(8-2)$ to get the correct answer 4. If you enter $24/8 - 2$, the calculator will follow the order of operations doing the division $24 \div 8$ first and then calculating $3 - 2$ to get 1 for the answer.

> **GUIDED**
>
> ### Example 2
> *A Guided Example is an example in which some, but not all, of the work is shown. You should try to complete the example before reading on. Answers to Guided Examples are in the Selected Answers section at the back of the book.*
>
> Use a calculator to evaluate $\left(\frac{6.8 - w}{n + w}\right)^3$ when $n = 21$ and $w = 0.5$.

8   Using Algebra to Describe

► **QUIZ YOURSELF**

Complete the pattern as shown in the three examples above and at the left.

$$a \div b = \frac{a}{b}$$
$$= \frac{?}{}$$
$$= \frac{?}{}$$

Accommodating the Learner ⬆

Ask students to evaluate y^4 when $y = -2$ using their calculators. Some students will obtain the answer 16, and others will get the answer −16. Explain to them that when they evaluate an expression such as y^4 when y is a negative number, they must place the value of y in parentheses on their calculators before raising it to a power. Ask students to decide if parentheses are needed when the value of the variable is positive. Students should be asked to support their answer, no, with examples.

Solution

Step 1 Write the expression. $\left(\dfrac{?}{?}\right)^3 \dfrac{6.8 - w}{n + w}$

Step 2 Substitute given values for the variables. $\left(\dfrac{6.8 - ?}{? + ?}\right)^3$ 0.5; 21; 0.5

Step 3 Enter into a calculator. Here is a start.

$((6.8 - \underline{\ ?\ })/\underline{\ ?\ }$ 0.5; (21 + 0.5))^3

Step 4 Round the result to the nearest thousandth. 0.025

In Example 2 above, notice that w appears in the expression two times. If the same variable appears more than once in an expression, the same number must be substituted for it every time the variable appears.

Evaluating Expressions in Formulas

Sometimes you will need to evaluate an expression as part of working with a formula. For example, the formula $V = \ell wh$ is used to find the volume V of a rectangular solid with length ℓ, width w, and height h as shown in Example 3 below.

Example 3

Find the volume of the box shown at the right.

Solution Substitute the given dimensions for ℓ, w, and h in the expression. Let $\ell = 2$ in., $w = 3$ in., and $h = 5$ in., and evaluate the expression $\ell \cdot w \cdot h$.

Volume $= \ell \cdot w \cdot h = 2 \cdot 3 \cdot 5 = 6 \cdot 5 = 30$

So, the volume is 30 in³.

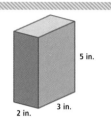

5 in.

2 in. 3 in.

Three Important Properties

In Example 3, we followed the order of operations and multiplied $2 \cdot 3 \cdot 5$ from left to right. However, you could first multiply 3 and 5 and then multiply the product by 2 to get the same answer, 30. This illustrates that $(\ell \cdot w) \cdot h = \ell \cdot (w \cdot h)$. This important general property, true for all real numbers, is called the *Associative Property of Multiplication*. Notice that the product of numbers a and b can be written as ab, $a \cdot b$, $a(b)$, or (ab). The product is usually not written as $a \times b$ in algebra because x is such a common letter for a variable.

Associative Property of Multiplication

For any real numbers a, b, and c, $(ab)c = a(bc)$.

Evaluating Expressions 9

Additional Examples

Example 2 Use a calculator to evaluate $\left(\dfrac{a + \sqrt{10}}{b^3 + a - 1.5}\right)^2$ when $a = 7$ and $b = 2$.

Step 1 Write the expression. $\left(\dfrac{?}{?}\right)^2$

$\left(\dfrac{a + \sqrt{10}}{b^3 + a - 1.5}\right)^2$

Step 2 Substitute given values for the variables. $\left(\dfrac{? + \sqrt{10}}{? + ? - 1.5}\right)^2$ 7; 2³; 7

Step 3 Enter into the calculator using proper notation. Here is a start.

$\left((\underline{\ ?\ } + \sqrt{10})/(\underline{\ ?\ } + ? - 1.5)\right)\text{^2}$

$\left((7 + \sqrt{10})/(2\text{^3} + 7 - 1.5)\right)$

Step 4 Round the result to the nearest thousandth. 0.567

Example 3 Find the volume of a rectangular solid using the formula $V = \ell wh$. Let $\ell = 4$ centimeters, $w = 6$ centimeters, and $h = 7$ centimeters. 168 cm²

Accommodating the Learner

Ask students to evaluate the expression $\sqrt{\dfrac{x}{y}}$ when $x = 24$ and $y = 6$. Emphasize that the expression in the square root symbol must be in parentheses when they use a calculator.

Next ask students to evaluate $\sqrt{\dfrac{x + y}{y}}$ when $x = 16$ and $y = 2$. Emphasize that two sets of parentheses are needed because there are two grouping symbols. One set encloses the entire expression shown under the square root symbol, and one set encloses just the numerator. $\sqrt{\dfrac{x}{y}} = \sqrt{\dfrac{24}{6}} = \sqrt{4} = 2$

$\sqrt{\dfrac{x + y}{y}} = \sqrt{\dfrac{18}{2}} = \sqrt{9} = 3$

1-1

3 Assignment

Recommended Assignment
- Questions 1–29
- Question 30 (extra credit)
- Reading Lesson 1-2
- Covering the Ideas 1-2

Notes on the Questions
You might want to go over the questions one at a time, in order, having students in the class work at their seats or in pairs to do them.

Question 1 The incorrect answer 132 indicates that students subtracted before multiplying.

Question 2 The incorrect answer 5 indicates that students multiplied before dividing. Emphasize that multiplications *and* divisions are done from left to right and have the same priority. The incorrect answer 46 means that students have incorrectly subtracted the negative.

Questions 3 and 4 In this context, students will usually (correctly) obtain different values for these two expressions. Point out that the two expressions are visually similar but their values are different. Later in the course, a common error is to view the expressions $(a + b)^2$ and $a^2 + b^2$ as being equivalent.

A similar property is true for addition. You can regroup numbers being added without affecting the sum. For example, the sum $(67 + 98) + 2$ is easier to calculate in your head if the numbers being calculated are regrouped.

$$(67 + 98) + 2 = 67 + (98 + 2)$$
$$= 67 + 100$$
$$= 167$$

This is an example of the *Associative Property of Addition*.

> **Associative Property of Addition**
>
> For any real numbers a, b, and c, $(a + b) + c = a + (b + c)$.

Another property of algebra, called the *Transitive Property of Equality*, has been used throughout this lesson in evaluating expressions. It allows us to look at calculations like $20 - 46 = 20 + {-46}$ and $20 + {-46} = -26$, and deduce that $20 - 46 = -26$.

> **Transitive Property of Equality**
>
> For any real numbers a, b, and c, if $a = b$ and $b = c$, then $a = c$.

Questions

COVERING THE IDEAS

These questions cover the content of the lesson. If you cannot answer a Covering the Ideas question, you should go back to the reading for help in obtaining an answer.

In 1–6, evaluate the expression using the order of operations.

1. $36 - 3 \cdot 4$ **24**
2. $36 \div 3 \cdot 4 - (-2)$ **50**
3. $(4 + 5)^2$ **81**
4. $4^2 + 5^2$ **41**
5. $10 - 70 - 5^{(2+1)} + 4(20)$ **-105**
6. $-16 + 3(4 - 5) \div \frac{9-3}{17-13}$ **-18**

In 7 and 8, use the order of operations to evaluate the expression for the given values of x.

7. $2(4x - 5) + 2$
   a. $x = 5$ **32**
   b. $x = -1$ **-16**
8. $2^x - (1 + x)$
   a. $x = 1$ **0**
   b. $x = 3$ **4**

Extension

Have students exemplify the Associative Properties of Addition and Multiplication and the Transitive Property of Equality using only fractions, and then again using only decimals. Students should then simplify both sides of the equation for each property. This activity will help students recognize the validity of each of the properties.

1-1A Lesson Master

Questions on SPUR Objectives
See pages 60–63 for objectives.*

VOCABULARY

In 1–4, match the name of the algebraic definition or property with its representation using variables where a, b, c are real numbers.

1. Algebraic Definition of Subtraction ___ B
2. Algebraic Definition of Division ___ D
3. Associative Property of Multiplication ___ A
4. Associative Property of Addition ___ C

A $(ab)c = a(bc)$ B $a - b = a + {-b}$
C $(a + b) + c = a + (b + c)$ D $a \div b = a \cdot \frac{1}{b}$ if $b \neq 0$

SKILLS Objective A

In 5 and 6, state the first operation performed and evaluate each expression.

5. $\sqrt{(3 + 6)}$ **addition, 3**
6. $(14 \cdot 4 + 7)^2$ **multiplication, 3,969**

In 7 and 8, evaluate the algebraic expression for the given value of the variable.

7. $5a^4$ for $a = -6$ **6,480**
8. $\left(\frac{x+y}{x-y}\right)^2$ for $x = 9$ and $y = 5$ **12.25**

PROPERTIES Objectives F, G

In 9 and 10, rewrite the expression using addition instead of subtraction.

9. $3 - 7$ **3 + -7**
10. $(7 - 5) \cdot 4$ **(7 + -5) · 4**

In 11 and 12, rewrite the expression using multiplication instead of division.

11. $4 \div 11$ **$4 \cdot \frac{1}{11}$**
12. $(8 + 5) \div 8$ **$(8 + 5) \cdot \frac{1}{8}$**

13. If $x + 58 = y + 15$ and $y + 15 = w$, what conclusion can be made based on the Transitive Property of Equality?   **x + 58 = w**

*See the Student Edition for SPUR objectives.

100   Algebra

9. Evaluate each expression when $t = 10$.
   a. $5t^2$ 500
   b. $(5t)^2$ 2,500

10. Evaluate $(-1 + r)^3$ when $r = \frac{1}{3}$. Write your answer as a fraction. $-\frac{8}{27}$

11. Evaluate $\frac{a + 2b}{5}$ when $a = 11.6$ and $b = 9.2$. 6

In 12–14, use the Associative Properties of Addition and Multiplication to classify each statement as true or false. Then check your answer by doing the arithmetic.

12. $5 \cdot (2 \cdot 7) = (5 \cdot 2) \cdot 7$

13. $-2 \cdot \left(\frac{1}{2} + 6\right) = \left(-2 + \frac{1}{2}\right) \cdot 6$ false, $-13 \neq -9$

14. $13.5 + (-2 + 3 + -4) = (13.5 + -2 + 3) + -4$

APPLYING THE MATHEMATICS

These questions extend the content of the lesson. You should study the examples and explanations if you cannot answer the question. For some questions, you can check your answers with the ones in the back of this book.

15. Joshua found that $\frac{63}{225} = \frac{7}{25}$. Sabrina realized that $\frac{7}{25} = \frac{28}{100}$.
   a. What can be deduced from Joshua's and Sabrina's results using the Transitive Property of Equality?
      $\frac{63}{225} = \frac{28}{100}$
   b. $\frac{28}{100} = 28\%$. Is it true that $\frac{63}{225} = 28\%$? Explain your answer. yes, by the Transitive Property of Equality

In 16 and 17, which expression is *not* equal to the others?

16. $27 - 3$ $-27 + 3$ $27 + -3$ $-3 + 27$ $-27 + 3$

17. $-9 \div 4$ $-9 \cdot \frac{1}{4}$ $\frac{1}{-9} \cdot 4$ $\frac{-9}{4}$ $\frac{1}{-9} \cdot 4$

18. When an object is shot from the ground into the air, the formula $h = -16t^2 + vt$ gives the height h in feet of the object t seconds later, where v is the velocity of the object in feet per second when it first leaves the ground. If a toy rocket is launched with a velocity of 80 feet per second, find its height 2 seconds later. 96 ft

19. Use the rule $\frac{a}{b} \cdot \frac{c}{d} = \frac{ac}{bd}$ to multiply the fractions $\frac{-2}{11}$ and $\frac{-3}{5}$. Write your answer as a single fraction. $\frac{6}{55}$

20. Elias and Marissa are the same height. Samuel and Elias are equally tall.
   a. What conclusion can be made based on the Transitive Property of Equality? Samuel and Marissa are the same height.
   b. Write another real-world situation that uses the same property.

In 1926, Robert H. Goddard launched the first liquid-fueled rocket and laid the foundation for a technology that would eventually take humans to the moon.
Source: NASA

12. true, by the Associative Property of Multiplication;
    $5 \cdot (14) = 70$,
    $5 \cdot (14) = 70$ and
    $(10) \cdot 7 = 70$

14. true, by the Associative Property of Addition;
    $13.5 + (-3) = 10.5$ and
    $(14.5) + -4 = 10.5$

20b. Answers vary. Sample answer: Dida and Buffon punt the ball equally far. Buffon punts the ball exactly as far as Kahn. Therefore, Dida punts the ball as far as Kahn.

Evaluating Expressions   **11**

Notes on the Questions

Question 6 This question has several potential trouble spots. First, the student must see the fraction bar as representing two sets of implicit parentheses—one enclosing the numerator; another enclosing the denominator. Students must then follow the order of operations. Additionally, students must take into account rules for performing operations with negative numbers.

Questions 12–14 The purpose of these questions is to show that the Associative Properties of Addition and Multiplication really work when using numbers and not just variables.

Questions 21–29 These questions review arithmetic skills. You can use them as an indicator of how much arithmetic work your students may need as they progress through this book.

Question 25 You might wish to preview the Distributive Property (first mentioned in Lesson 2-1) by noting that one way to calculate $19 \cdot 32.50$ is as $20 \cdot 32.50 - 1 \cdot 32.50$. Since $2 \cdot 32.50 = 65$, then $20 \cdot 32.50 = 650$; so the entire calculation can be done in one's head: $650 - 32.50 = 617.50$.

Question 30 The answer 1,331 can be found without trial and error using algebra the student has not yet learned. Start with the facts that $c = a - 5$ and $b = 100 - a - c - d$. To find the greatest value of $ab - cd$, letting $d = 1$ is a natural choice since it will minimize the value of cd. Then by substitution, $b = 100 - a - (a - 5) - 1$, or $b = 104 - 2a$. So the expression $ab - cd$ becomes $a(104 - 2a) - (a - 5)(1)$, or $-2a^2 + 103a + 5$. This function can either be graphed or differentiated to find the value of a that leads to the maximum function value. The exact result, $a = 25.75$, is not an integer, so the value of a is then rounded up to 26. Therefore, $a = 26$, $b = 52$, $c = 21$, and $d = 1$. Many students will simply use trial and error to find the values of a, b, c, and d that give a maximum value for $ab - cd$.

1-1

4 Wrap-Up

Ongoing Assessment

Ask students to write two examples of an algebraic expression that contains two variables. They should then write the values of the variables for each expression. Have students exchange their papers with other students and evaluate both algebraic expressions on the paper they receive, using the given values for the variables.

Project Update

If you have not had students look over the projects on pages 55 and 56, you might want to do so now. Project 2, Estimating Square Roots, and Project 3, Formula 1, on page 55, relate to the content of this lesson.

REVIEW

Every lesson contains review questions to practice ideas you have studied earlier.

In 21–23, compute in your head. (Previous Course)

21. $-4 \cdot \$1.25$ $-\$5$ 22. $1{,}000 \cdot 11.4$ $11{,}400$ 23. $3\frac{1}{2} \cdot 20$ 70

24. Put these numbers in order from least to greatest.
(Previous Course) $-7, -\frac{2}{7}, -\frac{1}{6}, 2, \pi, 5.3, 5.39, 12$

12   5.3   2 $-\frac{2}{7}$ -7 5.39 $-\frac{1}{6}$ π

25. Nikki's Bike Shop gives customers a free helmet with the purchase of any new bike from the store. Last week, 19 new bikes were purchased from Nikki's Bike Shop. If the cost of each helmet was $32.50, what was the total cost of all the helmets that the store gave away last week? (Previous Course) $617.50

In 26–29, compute without a calculator. (Previous Course)

26. $5 + -9 - 22$ -26

27. $4 + 11 - -7$ 22

28. $\frac{3}{4} + \frac{2}{3} - \frac{1}{6}$ $\frac{5}{4}$

29. $-3.52 - 11.4 + 30$
15.08

EXPLORATION

These questions ask you to explore topics related to the lesson. Sometimes you will need to use references found in a library or on the Internet.

30. Suppose a, b, c, and d are different positive integers whose sum is 100, and $a - c = 5$. What is the greatest possible value of $ab - cd$? 1,331; if $a = 26$, $b = 52$, $c = 21$, and $d = 1$

Wearing a bicycle helmet while riding helps reduce injuries by up to 88%.

Source: Bicycle Helmet Safety Institute

QUIZ YOURSELF ANSWER

$a/b,\ a \cdot \frac{1}{b}$

Lesson 1-2

Describing Patterns

Vocabulary

pattern

instance

define a variable

term

factor

▶ **BIG IDEA** Patterns in tables are often described by expressions with variables.

Using Tables to Look at Patterns

Ian wants to save money to buy a new bike. He already has $25, and he decides he can save $15 each week. If the bike costs $220, will Ian have saved enough to buy the bike after 12 weeks?

To answer this question it may help to look at a table.

Mental Math

a. During a 25%-off sale, what is the cost of a pair of shoes that normally costs $80? $60

b. How much do you save on that pair of shoes? $20

Number of Weeks (w)	Calculation	Pattern	Money Saved
0	25	25 + 15 • 0	$25
1	25 + 15	25 + 15 • 1	$40
2	25 + 15 + 15	25 + 15 • 2	$55
3	25 + 15 + 15 + 15	25 + 15 • 3	$70
4	25 + 15 + 15 + 15 + 15	25 + 15 • 4	$85
5	25 + 15 + 15 + 15 + 15 + 15	25 + 15 • 5	$100
6	25 + 15 + 15 + 15 + 15 + 15 + 15	25 + 15 • 6	$115

The table shows the amount Ian has saved after 0, 1, 2, 3, 4, 5, and 6 weeks. The key to the table is the *pattern* column. In that column, the repeated adding of 15 is rewritten as multiplication. A **pattern** is a general idea for which there are many **instances.** The last row of the table shows one instance, stating that after 6 weeks, Ian has saved $25 + 15 • 6$, or $115. The pattern lets you write an algebraic expression to describe the amount of money Ian has after *any* number of weeks. If the variable w is used to represent the number of weeks that have passed, an expression that describes the pattern is $25 + 15 • w$, as shown in the table on page 14.

Background

Two types of patterns in tables are shown in this lesson. In the first type, the rows of the table are in a sequence, and the student is finding a formula for the nth term. In the second type, the values of variables change, and the student has to see which numbers change and which do not.

Explicit versus recursive formulas for nth terms of sequences. There are two ways to describe terms in a sequence. One way is to have an expression for the nth term. In the case of the first table of this lesson, the wth

term is $25 + 15w$. This is called an **explicit expression** or **explicit formula** for the wth term. The second way is to indicate the first term (or first few terms) and how each succeeding term follows. In the case of the first table of this lesson, the first term is 25 and each succeeding term is 15 greater. (In later courses, this rule is described as $t_0 = 25$ and $t_n = t_{n-1} + 15$. This is called a **recursive rule** or **recursive formula** for the sequence.)

Lesson 1-2

GOAL

See a pattern in a table well enough to describe it with variables.

SPUR Objectives

B Use variables to describe patterns in instances or tables.

G Identify and apply the associative, commutative, and transitive properties.

H Create expressions to model real-world situations.

Materials/Resources

· Lesson Master 1-2A or 1-2B
· Resource Masters 9–11
· Scientific or graphing calculator

HOMEWORK

Suggestions for Assignment

• Questions 1–22
• Question 23 (extra credit)
• Reading Lesson 1-3
• Covering the Ideas 1-3

Local Standards

---

1 Warm-Up

Present the following problems.

Every lamb has 4 legs. Every chicken has 2 legs.

1. How many legs do 5 lambs and 20 chickens have?
2. How many legs do 100 lambs and 27 chickens have?
3. How many legs do L lambs and C chickens have?

(continued on next page)

14   Chapter 1

It is important to show the arithmetic that leads to the answers to Questions 1 and 2. The answer to Queston 1 is $5 \cdot 4 + 20 \cdot 2$, or 60 legs. The answer to Question 2 is $100 \cdot 4 + 27 \cdot 2$, or 454 legs. The answer to Question 3 is $L \cdot 4 + C \cdot 2$, or $4L + 2C$. Point out that when a number is multiplied by a variable, we usually place the number at the left. We can justify this switching of the order because of the Commutative Property of Multiplication.

2   Teaching

Notes on the Lesson

Using tables to look at patterns. You could begin your discussion with the question that opens the lesson. Ask students to cover the table on page 13 with a piece of paper. Instruct them to unveil the table one row at a time, making certain that they understand how each value was found before unveiling the next row. When the entire table has been revealed, have students focus their attention on the 1st and 3rd columns. Here we see 0, 1, 2, 3, 4, 5, and 6 in the 1st column, and $25 + 15 \cdot 0$, $25 + 15 \cdot 1$, $25 + 15 \cdot 2$, and so on in the 3rd column. Stress that the number at the end of each arithmetic expression in the 3rd column is the same as the number in the 1st column. Emphasize that this is the key to the pattern. If w represents the number of weeks, then $25 + 15 \cdot w$ defines the pattern.

Defining a variable. We indicate in this lesson that the word "let" is used to define a variable. For instance, we might define a variable s as follows: Let $s =$ the speed of the car (in miles per hour). We could also use the words "suppose" or "if" or "when" in place of "let."

You might wish to have students copy **Guided Example 1** into their notebooks and complete it.

Number of Weeks	Calculation	Pattern	Money Saved
w	$25 + \underbrace{15 + 15 + ... + 15}_{w\ \text{addends}}$	$25 + 15 \cdot w$	$25 + 15w$

The expression $25 + 15w$ can be used to find out how much money Ian will have after 12 weeks. Replace w with 12 and evaluate $25 + 15 \cdot 12$. In 12 weeks, Ian will have $25 + 15(12)$, or $205. Since the bike costs $220, he will not have enough money after 12 weeks.

STOP **See Quiz Yourself at the right.**

Notice that an important step is to define the variable used in the algebraic expression. To **define a variable** means to describe the quantity the variable represents. This is an important step. Defining a variable is often signaled by the word *let,* as in "Let $x = \ldots$".

▶ **QUIZ YOURSELF**

Assuming the pattern continues, will Ian have enough money after 14 weeks? How much money will he have saved up?

GUIDED

Example 1

At the start of the school year, a school's library had a total of 3,600 individual magazines that it had collected over time. Each month 22 new magazines are added to the collection.

a. Complete the table to show the number of magazines in the library each month.

b. Define a variable and write an algebraic expression for the number of magazines.

Solution

a.

Months Since Start of School Year	Calculation	Pattern	Magazines in Library
0	?	$3,600 + 22(0)$	3,600
1	?	?	?
2	$3,600 + 22 + 22$	?	3,644
3	?	$3,600 + 22(\,?\,)$	?

3,600

3,600 + 22; 3,600 + 22(1); 3,622

3,600 + 22(2)

3,600 + 22 + 22 + 22; 3; 3,666

b. Let $m = \underline{\ ?\ }$.

The number of magazines after m months is $\underline{\ ?\ }$. $3,600 + 22m$

Part b. Let $m =$ the number of months since the beginning of the school year.

ENGLISH LEARNERS

Vocabulary Development

It may be necessary to point out several instances of a pattern when introducing these terms. Rather than highlighting only one instance, $25 + 15 \cdot 6$, of Ian's saving pattern, be sure to highlight several of them in the table. Ask students to describe how each successive instance in the table is related to the previous one.

Patterns Having Two or More Variables

Some patterns have two or more variables and can also be represented by tables and expressions.

Example 2

A family consisting of 2 adults and 3 children was planning a vacation. They looked in a tour book to find the cost of some activities.

a. Complete the table to show the family's cost for each activity.

Activity	Adult Ticket	Child Ticket	Family's Cost
Movie	$15.00	$8.00	$2 \cdot 15 + 3 \cdot 8$
Ferryboat	$22.00	$10.00	?
Water Park	$10.00	$4.50	?

b. How much does each activity cost the family?

c. Let a = the adult ticket price for an activity and let c = the child ticket price. Write an algebraic expression for the family's total cost for this activity.

Approximately 73 million people visited North American water parks during the summer 2004 season.

Source: World Waterpark Association

Solution

a. Multiply the cost of an adult ticket by the number of adults (2), and the cost of a child ticket by the number of children (3).

Activity	Adult Ticket	Child Ticket	Family's Cost
Movie	$15.00	$8.00	$2 \cdot 15 + 3 \cdot 8$
Ferryboat	$22.00	$10.00	$2 \cdot 22 + 3 \cdot 10$
Water Park	$10.00	$4.50	$2 \cdot 10 + 3 \cdot 4.50$

b. Movie: $2 \cdot 15 + 3 \cdot 8 = 30 + 24 = \$54$
Ferryboat: $2 \cdot 22 + 3 \cdot 10 = 44 + 30 = \$74$
Water Park: $2 \cdot 10 + 3 \cdot 4.50 = 20 + 13.50 = \$33.50$

c. The total cost is $2 \cdot a + 3 \cdot c$, or $2a + 3c$.

The Commutative Properties of Addition and Multiplication

Numbers or expressions that are added are called **terms.** Numbers or expressions that are multiplied are called **factors.** In the expression $2a + 3c$ of Example 2, there are two terms: $2a$ and $3c$. 2 and a are factors of $2a$, and 3 and c are factors of $3c$.

Describing Patterns   **15**

Additional Example

Example 1 Paula borrowed $200 from her grandfather today. She intends to pay back the money at a rate of $10 each week.

a. Complete the table to show how much Paula still owes her grandfather at the end of each week.

Weeks Since Borrowing the Money	Calculation
0	?
1	?
2	$200 - 10 - 10$
3	?

$200; 200 - 10; 200 - 10 - 10 - 10$

Pattern	Amount Paula Still Owes Her Grandfather
$200 - 10(0)$	200
? $200 - 10(1)$	? 190
? $200 - 10(2)$	? 180
? $200 - 10(3)$	170

b. Define a variable and write an algebraic expression for the amount of money Paula still owes her grandfather at the end of each week. **Let w = the number of weeks since borrowing the money; $200 - 10w$.**

Notes on the Lesson

Patterns having two or more variables.
As in Example 1, the idea in Example 2 is to do the arithmetic. Point out to students that the total cost is never given in the table as a single number. This is because we are concerned with the *pattern of computation* that leads to the total cost. That pattern is quite easy: multiply the number of adults by the adult ticket price; then multiply the number of children by the child ticket price; and finally, add these two costs together.

Accommodating the Learner ⬆

As an extension of Example 2, have students consider the following scenario.

Just before the family's trip is to begin, two of the children's grandparents decide to meet the family at their vacation destination. The grandparents qualify for a discounted price at the movie ($10 each), on the ferryboat ($14 each), and at the water park ($7 each).

Have students repeat Parts b and c of Example 2 for this new scenario.

b. Movie: $2 \cdot 10 + 2 \cdot 15 + 3 \cdot 8 = 20 + 30 + 24 = \$74$; Ferryboat: $2 \cdot 14 + 2 \cdot 22 + 3 \cdot 10 = 28 + 44 + 30 = \$102$; Water Park: $2 \cdot 7 + 2 \cdot 10 + 3 \cdot 4.50 = 14 + 20 + 13.50 = \$47.50$

c. Letting g = the grandparent ticket price, the total cost is $2 \cdot g + 2 \cdot a + 3 \cdot c$.

1-2

Additional Example

Example 2 A group consisting of 4 adults and 7 children is planning to go to an amusement park. They checked the park's Web site to find the cost of several rides.

Ride	Adult Ticket	Child Ticket
Water Flume	$2.00	$1.00
Bumper Cars	$1.50	$1.00
Roller Coaster	$2.50	$2.00
Ferris Wheel	$3.00	$2.50

a. Complete the table to show the group's cost for each ride.

Ride	Group's Cost
Water Flume	$4 \cdot 2 + 7 \cdot 1$
Bumper Cars	$? \; 4 \cdot 1.50 + 7 \cdot 1$
Roller Coaster	$4 \cdot 2.50 + 7 \cdot 2$
Ferris Wheel	$? \; 4 \cdot 3 + 7 \cdot 2.50$

b. How much does each activity cost the group? Water Flume: $15; Bumper Cars: $13; Roller Coaster: $24; Ferris Wheel: $29.50

c. Let a = the adult ticket price and c = the child ticket price for any one activity. Write an algebraic expression for the group's total cost for this activity. $4a + 7c$

Notes on the Lesson

The term term. In some books, a term is a number or expression that is added *or subtracted.* Which characterization of *term* you use does not affect the number of terms in an expression, but it does affect the naming of the term. If a *term* is a number or expression that is added, then $a + b - c$ has three terms, a, b, and $-c$. If a *term* is a number or expression that is added or subtracted, then $a + b - c$ has three terms, a, b, and c. In this book, we have chosen to think of terms as added. This is the characterization most often used in later mathematics.

The expression $2a + 3c$ stands for "twice the cost of an adult ticket added to three times the cost of a child ticket." The order of operations indicates to do both multiplications before adding. But you can switch the terms being added because the total cost is the same whether you buy adult tickets first or child tickets first. The expression $3c + 2a$ gives the same values as $2a + 3c$.

It is also the case that you can switch the order of the factors. $2 \cdot a$ gives the same values as $a \cdot 2$. These examples are examples of the *commutative properties,* The word *commutative* comes from the French word *commutatif,* which means "switchable."

> **Commutative Property of Addition**
>
> For all real numbers a and b, $a + b = b + a$.

> **Commutative Property of Multiplication**
>
> For all real numbers a and b, $a \cdot b = b \cdot a$.

Examples of the commutative properties can also be numerical. They are true for all real numbers. For example, when $a = 72$ and $b = 10$, $72 \cdot 10 = 10 \cdot 72$.

Questions

COVERING THE IDEAS

In 1–4, give two instances of each pattern.
1–4. Answers vary. Sample answers are shown.

1. $y - y = 0$
$7 - 7 = 0$ and $2 - 2 = 0$

2. $x + x = 2x$ $\;\; 2 + 2 = 2(2)$ and $3 + 3 = 2(3)$

3. $x \cdot x = x^2$
$5 \cdot 5 = 5^2$ and $6 \cdot 6 = 6^2$

4. $\frac{x}{y} = x \cdot \frac{1}{y}$ $\;\; \frac{3}{4} = 3 \cdot \frac{1}{4}$ and $\frac{9}{4} = 9 \cdot \frac{1}{4}$

In 5 and 6, describe the given pattern using one variable.

5. $(3 + 9) - 2 = 1 + 9$
$(3 + 4) - 2 = 1 + 4$
$(3 + 90) - 2 = 1 + 90$
$(3 + x) - 2 = 1 + x$

6. $15 + 2 \cdot 15 = 3 \cdot 15$
$\frac{1}{3} + 2 \cdot \frac{1}{3} = 3 \cdot \frac{1}{3}$
$47.1 + 2 \cdot 47.1 = 3 \cdot 47.1$
$a + 2 \cdot a = 3 \cdot a$

7. Pearl is starting a lawn mowing business. She plans to spend $1,200 on advertising during the first few weeks that she is in business. Each week she spends $45 to place an ad in a newspaper. 7a. $1,155; $1,110; $1,065

  a. Give the amount of money she will have left to spend on advertising after 1, 2, and 3 weeks of advertising.

  b. Write an algebraic expression for the amount she will have left to spend after w weeks of advertising. $1,200 - 45w$ dollars

Accommodating the Learner

As an alternative to Example 2, have students consider the following scenario.

A family consisting of 1 adult and 1 child is planning an activity for next Saturday. The table at the right lists the activities they are considering.

a. Complete the table to show the family's cost for each activity.

Activity	Adult Ticket	Child Ticket	Family's Cost
Art Museum	$10.00	$7.00	$1 \cdot 10 + 1 \cdot 7$
Aquarium	$5.50	$3.50	$? \; 1 \cdot 5.50 + 1 \cdot 3.50$
Concert	$60.00	$45.00	$1 \cdot 60.50 + 1 \cdot 45.00$
Baseball Game	$37.00	$37.00	$? \; 1 \cdot 37 + 1 \cdot 37$

b. How much does each activity cost the group? Art Museum: $17; Aquarium: $9; Concert: $105.50; Baseball Game: $74

c. Let a = the adult ticket price and c = the child ticket price for each activity. Write an algebraic expression for the family's total cost for this activity. $a + c$

8. A group consisting of 1 adult and 5 children went to a special Kid's Day baseball game that offered special prices for children. Some prices are shown in the table below.

JACKSON FIELD
Home of the Barracudas

Item	Adult Price	Child Price	Group's Cost	
Ticket	$17.00	$10.00	?	$67.00
Hot Dog	$5.00	$3.50	?	$22.50
Drink	$3.00	$2.00	?	$13.00

   a. Fill in the group's cost for each item.

   b. Write an algebraic expression that would describe the group's cost for *any* item in terms of the adult price P and the child price p. **$P + 5p$**

9. **Multiple Choice** Which expression below has three terms? **C**

   A $4ab + 25$ **B** pqr **C** $2n + 6y + 15$ **D** $3x$

APPLYING THE MATHEMATICS

10. The following describes a pattern. A number is multiplied by 12, the product is divided by 2, and then 3 is subtracted from the result.

   a. Give three instances of the pattern.

   b. Write an algebraic expression to describe the pattern if the original number is n. $\frac{12 \cdot n}{2} - 3$

11. Istu is 5 years older than his sister Christine.

   a. Copy the table at the right and fill in Christine's age.

   b. Let $i =$ Istu's age. Write an expression for Christine's age.

   c. Flor is 3 years older than Christine. Use your answer to Part b to write an expression for Flor's age. **$(i - 5) + 3$ or $i - 2$**

12. Use the following information. When m is positive and n is greater than m, there exists a right triangle with side lengths given by the expressions $n^2 - m^2$, $2nm$, and $n^2 + m^2$, as shown in the diagram at the right.

   a. Let $n = 2$ and $m = 1$. Find the lengths of the three sides of the right triangle. **3, 4, 5**

   b. Let $n = 3$ and $m = 2$. Find the lengths of the three sides of the right triangle. **5, 12, 13**

10a. Answers vary. Sample answers:
$\frac{12 \cdot -4}{2} - 3$;
$\frac{12 \cdot -0.34}{2} - 3$;
$\frac{12 \cdot 2}{2} - 3$

11b. $i - 5$

Istu's Age	Christine's Age	
9	?	4
16	?	11
25	?	20
89	?	84

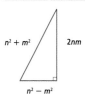

Describing Patterns   **17**

Notes on the Lesson
Comparing associative and commutative properties. Students often confuse the associative and commutative properties because they both involve switching. We have purposely separated them in Lessons 1-1 and 1-2 so that students will see the associative properties as switching order of operations, while the commutative properties involve switching the order of addends (in addition) or factors (in multiplication).

The Commutative Properties of Addition and Multiplication. The simple expression $2a + 3c$, the answer to **Example 2b,** involves both addition and multiplication. You might ask students for all the ways that this expression could be rewritten using only the commutative properties of these operations. There are 7 other ways:

$2 \cdot a + c \cdot 3$ $a \cdot 2 + c \cdot 3$
$a \cdot 2 + 3 \cdot c$ $c \cdot 3 + a \cdot 2$
$c \cdot 3 + 2 \cdot a$ $3 \cdot c + a \cdot 2$
$3 \cdot c + 2 \cdot a$

Note-Taking Tip
Suggest that students create a set of index cards for the properties in this lesson and the previous one. They should write the property name on one side and the algebraic statement on the other side. Students can use these cards for study purposes by looking at one side and stating the contents of the other side before flipping the card around to check their accuracy.

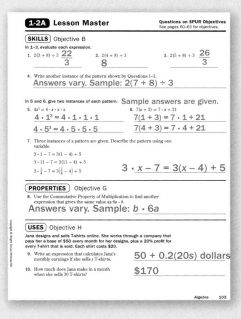

1-2

3 Assignment

Recommended Assignment
- Questions 1–22
- Question 23 (extra credit)
- Reading Lesson 1-3
- Covering the Ideas 1-3

Notes on the Questions

Questions 1–6 These are basic questions to help students know what is meant by an algebraic description of a pattern.

Question 2 You might wish to ask students what is another way of writing $x + x$. ($2x$) Then give patterns for $x + x = 2x$.

Question 7 This question is like Example 1.

Question 8 This question is like Example 2.

Question 13 Here is a challenging extension of this question: Ask students to give an expression for the maximum number of pieces that you could make with n straight cuts of a pizza? (The cuts do *not* have to go through the center.) Help students see that the pattern for the number of pieces is 2, 4, 7, 11, 16, 21, ..., and that the nth term of this pattern is $\frac{1}{2}n(n + 1) + 1$.

Question 18 Students may not know that the planet Neptune, like Jupiter, Saturn, and Uranus, is gaseous, so it does not have a solid surface like Earth. Point out that this fact makes any value for its dimensions only an estimate.

Question 23 This calendar pattern, though obvious once it is seen, surprises many students and should be discussed.

---

13. A pizza is cut into pieces by making each cut pass through the center.

1 cut	2 cuts	3 cuts

a. Describe the number of pieces made for 1, 2, 3, 4, and 5 cuts.

b. Use two variables to describe the pattern.

14. a. Evaluate each expression.

$\frac{2}{3} \cdot \frac{3}{2}$ 1 $\frac{23}{11} \cdot \frac{11}{23}$ 1 $\frac{-7}{5} \cdot \frac{5}{-7}$ 1 $\frac{0.03}{6} \cdot \frac{6}{0.03}$ 1

b. Describe the pattern. $\frac{a}{b} \cdot \frac{b}{a} = 1$

c. Do you think the pattern is true for all numbers? Why or why not? No, it is not true if either number is 0.

15. Suppose $x = 58$ and $y = 31$.

a. Evaluate $xy - yx$. 0

b. Suppose the values of x and y are changed. Will the answer to Part a change? Why or why not?
No; $xy = yx$ by the Commutative Property of Multiplication.

REVIEW

In 16–17, evaluate when $x = 2$, $y = 8$, and $z = 4$. (Lesson 1-1)

16. $x^3 + \frac{y}{z}$ 10

17. $y + z + \frac{x + z}{x} - z(z - 1)^4$ –309

18. The planet Neptune is approximately a sphere with radius (r) of 25,000 kilometers. Use the formula $V = \frac{4}{3}\pi r^3$ to estimate the volume V of Neptune in scientific notation. (Lesson 1-1, Previous Course) $6.54 \cdot 10^{13}$ km³

19. Evaluate each of the following without a calculator. (Previous Course)

a. $3 \cdot -5$ –15

b. $-70 \cdot -6$ 420

20. Round π to the nearest thousandth. (Previous Course) 3.142

21. Often, 20% of a restaurant bill is left for a tip. If a bill is $34.76, what would be a 20% tip rounded to the nearest dollar? (Previous Course) $7

22. *Skill Sequence* Find the sum. (Previous course)

a. $\frac{3}{5} + \frac{4}{5}$ $\frac{7}{5}$

b. $\frac{3}{5} + \frac{4}{15}$ $\frac{13}{15}$

c. $\frac{3}{5} + \frac{4}{17}$ $\frac{71}{85}$

18   Using Algebra to Describe

13a. For 1 cut there are 2 pieces; for 2 there are 4; for 3 there are 6; for 4 there are 8; and for 5 there are 10.

13b. Let c be the number of cuts and p be the number of pieces. Then, $p = 2c$.

EXPLORATION

23. A monthly calendar contains many patterns.

Sun	Mon	Tue	Wed	Thu	Fri	Sat
☀️ July ☀️						
				1	2	3
4	5	6	7	8	9	10
11	12	13	14	15	16	17
18	19	20	21	22	23	24
25	26	27	28	29	30	31

a. Consider a 3×3 square such as the one drawn on the calendar. Copy the square and insert the nine dates. Then add the numbers along the diagonals. What is the relationship between the sums? Try this again with a different 3×3 square. Does it always seem to work?

b. In a 3×3 square portion of the calendar, if the middle date is expressed as N, then the date above would be $N - 7$ because it is 7 days earlier. Copy the chart at the right and fill in the other blanks.

$$\begin{array}{ccc} N-8 & & N-6 \\ \hline ? & N-7 & ? \\ N-1 \quad ? & N & ? \quad N+1 \\ N+6 \quad ? & ? & ? \quad N+8 \\ \hline & N+7 & \end{array}$$

c. Show how your result from Part a can be used to explain your conclusion in Part a. $(N - 8) + N + (N + 8) = 3 \cdot N$ and $(N - 6) + N + (N + 6) = 3 \cdot N$, so the two diagonals have equal sums.

23a. The sums of the two diagonals are both equal to 48. Yes, the sums of the two diagonals will always be equal.

QUIZ YOURSELF ANSWER

yes; $235

Describing Patterns   **19**

4 Wrap-Up

Ongoing Assessment

Ask students to write a paragraph describing the difference between a *pattern* and an *instance* of a pattern. In this paragraph they should include at least one example of a pattern and one example of an instance of the pattern. Have several students share their work with the class.

Project Update

Project 4, Figurate Numbers, on page 56 relates to the content of this lesson.

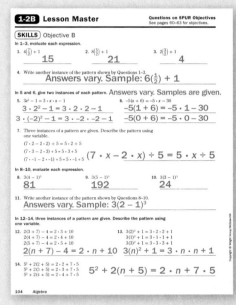

Lesson 1-3

GOAL

Recognize that equivalent expressions give the same values for all values of the variables in them, and tables can suggest when expressions are equivalent while one counterexample can show that they are not.

SPUR Objectives

B Use variables to describe patterns in instances or tables.

C Determine if two expressions seem equivalent by substituting values or making a table.

Materials/Resources

· Lesson Master 1-3A or 1-3B
· Resource Master 12
· Quiz 1
· toothpicks (50 per pair)

HOMEWORK

Suggestions for Assignment
• Questions 1–19
• Questions 20 and 21 (extra credit)
• Reading Lesson 1-4
• Covering the Ideas 1-4

Local Standards

Lesson 1-3 — Equivalent Expressions

Vocabulary

sequence
term
equivalent expressions
counterexample

▶ **BIG IDEA** If different expressions describe the same patterns, then the expressions are equivalent.

Finding Equivalent Expressions

The picture below shows a *sequence* of designs made from toothpicks. A **sequence** is a collection of numbers or objects in a specific order. The objects are called the **terms** of the sequence.

Activity 1

Refer to the toothpick sequence below.

Term Number	1	2	3	4
Term				

1. Use toothpicks to find how many are used to make the pattern for terms 1 through 10? **1–2. See margin.**

2. In words, explain how to use the term number to find the number of toothpicks needed to make that pattern.

3. Use n to represent the term number. Write an algebraic expression for the number of toothpicks needed for the nth term.
   Answers vary. Sample answer: $3n + 1$

4. Use your algebraic expression to complete the table below.

Term Number	Calculation	Number of Toothpicks	
11	?	?	$3(11) + 1; 34$
12	?	?	$3(12) + 1; 37$
15	?	?	$3(15) + 1; 46$
100	?	?	$3(100) + 1; 301$

5. Compare your expression with others in your class. Are the expressions the same or different? Write down all the expressions that you think are correct. Answers vary. Sample answer: $(n + 1) + n + n$, $2n + 1 + n$, and $3n + 1$ are all equal.

Mental Math

a. If international stamps cost 75¢ each, how much does a pack of 20 stamps cost? **$15**

b. If the price of the stamps increases by 2¢ per stamp, by how much will a pack of 20 stamps increase? **40¢**

c. If a pack of 20 stamps cost $2.00 less two years ago, how much less did one stamp cost? **10¢**

This sequence of designs is made from bricks.

Additional Answers

1. 4 toothpicks; 7 toothpicks; 10 toothpicks; 13 toothpicks; 16 toothpicks; 19 toothpicks; 22 toothpicks; 25 toothpicks; 28 toothpicks; 31 toothpicks

2. Answers vary. Sample answer: Multiply the term number by 3 and add 1.

Background

Two expressions are *equivalent* when they yield the same result for any values of the variables in them. Chapters 1 and 2 deal with determining when two expressions are equivalent. The idea that you cannot tell whether expressions are equivalent from looking at a table is untrue. With linear expressions like those in this lesson's examples, if the tables agree in two places, the expressions are equivalent because the graphs of linear functions are lines, and exactly one line runs through two different points. Still, we ask students to fill in many rows of a table to show equivalent expressions. Why? Because we want students to understand the meaning of equivalence, and that understanding comes from seeing the values of expressions for many values of the variables.

Later in this course, we want students to be able to routinely check whether expressions such as $(x + 1)(x + 2)$ and $x^2 + 2$ are equivalent (they are not) by substituting values for the variables in them.

Activity 2

Now consider a different toothpick sequence. The picture at the right shows the number of toothpicks required to construct a sequence of rectangles. The first and second terms are shown. Each rectangle is one toothpick wider and one toothpick taller than the previous rectangle.

1. How many toothpicks are needed for the 1st term? **6 toothpicks**

2. How many toothpicks are needed for the 2nd term? **10 toothpicks**

3. Build the 3rd term in the sequence. How many toothpicks are needed?

4. In words, describe a method to find the number of toothpicks it takes to make the *n*th term.

5. Write an algebraic expression to find the number of toothpicks it takes to make the *n*th term.
Answers vary. Sample answer: $4n + 2$

6. Fill in the table below.

Term Number	Calculation	Number of Toothpicks
4	?	?
5	?	?
6	?	?
13	?	?
58	?	?

3. 14 toothpicks;

4. Answers vary. Sample answer: Two sides have *n* toothpicks, while the other two have $n + 1$ toothpicks.

$4(4) + 2; 18$
$4(5) + 2; 22$
$4(6) + 2; 26$
$4(13) + 2; 54$
$4(58) + 2; 234$

In the activities, you looked at sequences of toothpicks and the number of toothpicks needed to make them. For each sequence, you used the term number *n* to determine the number of toothpicks needed for the *n*th term. You and your classmates may have found that there can be more than one expression to describe the *n*th term.

Consider the sequence of dots at the right. Students were asked to describe the number of dots needed to make the *n*th term.

Alf explained that in each term he saw 2 columns of dots and 3 dots between the columns. He wrote the following.

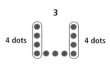

left column		middle		right column
$(n + 1)$	+	3	+	$(n + 1)$

Beth saw a row of 5 dots at the bottom and 2 columns above the row. She wrote the following.

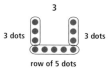

bottom row		two columns
5	+	$2n$

Accommodating the Learner ⬇

Some students may find it difficult to start filling in the table in Activity 1 because it starts with term number 11. It might be helpful if students extend the table so the Term Number column begins with the number 1 and shows each whole number up to 15. Suggest that students not only record the number of toothpicks for each term but that they also write down how they calculated each term.

1 Warm-Up

Draw or project the toothpick diagram below along with the question, "How many toothpicks are needed to make this design?" Ask students to explain how they arrived at their answers.

60; students' explanations will vary.

2 Teaching

Notes on the Lesson

You should do **Activities 1 and 2** before discussing this lesson. Neither activity requires toothpicks.

Notes on the Activity

Activity 1 Have students work in pairs. While discussing this activity, it is very important not to give students a particular way of counting the toothpicks in the first design. Here are some possible ways that students might think about the counting.

Method 1: Count the top (*n* toothpicks), count the bottom (*n*), count the sides $(n + 1)$, so that the expression is $n + n + (n + 1)$. Keep the parentheses so that the counting is evident.

Method 2: Count 4 for the first term in the sequence and add 3 for each additional square shown in the other terms. Since there is one less additional square than the term number in the sequence, the expression is $4 + 3(n - 1)$.

Method 3: Count 1 for the left end and 3 more to make each square. The expression is $1 + 3n$.

Students may want to know the right answer. Any expression equivalent to $3n + 1$ is fine. You can see which methods your students used by asking for all the answers to Question 2. It may come as a surprise to them that you are asking for their answers. Point out to them that many answers are correct.

(continued on next page)

Activity 2 Check to see if students are beginning to understand the idea of generalizing a pattern with an nth term. Make certain they understand that the expression for the nth term is used to generate the terms of the sequence. As in Activity 1, point out that there is more than one way to count the number of toothpicks. Here are some possibilities.

Method 1: Count each of the four sides: $n + (n + 1) + n + (n + 1)$

Method 2: Determine the length and width, and double: $2(n + (n + 1))$

Method 3: Notice that the result is always one more toothpick added to the top and bottom of the rectangle: $4n + 1 + 1$

Notes on the Lesson

Alf's and Beth's formulas. Have students draw the 11th design in the sequence so that they can see the 27 dots. Then have them count the dots in the two ways that Alf and Beth counted them.

Additional Example

Example 1 Dontrell and Melissa both looked at a sequence of designs made up of dots. Dontrell describes the pattern with the expression $2n - 5$ while Melissa describes it with the expression $(n - 3) + (n - 2)$, where n is the term number in the sequence. Compare their expressions for several instances by filling in the tables below. What can you conclude?

Dontrell		Melissa	
n	$2n - 5$	n	$(n - 3) + (n - 2)$
1	? –3	1	? –3
2	? –1	2	? –1
3	? 1	3	? 1
10	? 15	10	? 15
20	? 35	20	? 35
35	? 65	35	? 65

Because the values in the second columns of the tables are the same, the expressions $2n - 5$ and $(n - 3) + (n - 2)$ appear to be equivalent.

Are both Alf and Beth correct? One way to tell is by substituting a value for n and testing whether the two expressions equal the same value. For instance, let $n = 11$.

Alf's expression: $(n + 1) + 3 + (n + 1) = (11 + 1) + 3 + (11 + 1)$
$$= 12 + 3 + 12$$
$$= 27$$

Beth's expression: $5 + 2n = 5 + 2(11)$
$$= 5 + 22$$
$$= 27$$

However, it is risky to test only one instance. Sometimes a pattern works for a few numbers and fails for all others. For example, suppose you are not sure whether $2w$ and w^2 have the same meaning.

STOP See Quiz Yourself 1 at the right.

The Quiz Yourself shows that $2w$ and w^2 are not equal for all values of w. When you evaluate an expression for several values of the variable, a table of values helps to organize your work.

▶ **QUIZ YOURSELF 1**

a. Show that $2w$ and w^2 have the same value when $w = 2$.

b. Show that $2w$ and w^2 have different values when $w = 5$.

GUIDED

Example 1
Compare Alf's and Beth's expressions for several instances by filling in the tables below.

Alf		
n	$(n + 1) + 3 + (n + 1)$	
1	?	7
2	?	9
3	?	11
10	?	25
20	?	45
35	?	75

Beth		
n	$5 + 2n$	
1	?	7
2	?	9
3	?	11
10	?	25
20	?	45
35	?	75

Solution Comparing the second columns of the two tables, you should have found that when the expressions $(n + 1) + 3 + (n + 1)$ and $5 + 2n$ are evaluated for these values of n, the same result is obtained. Therefore, $(n + 1) + 3 + (n + 1)$ and $5 + 2n$ appear to be *equivalent*.

Equivalent expressions are expressions that have the same value for *every* number that can be substituted for the variable(s). If two expressions produce different results when evaluated for the same number, then the expressions are not equivalent.

22   Using Algebra to Describe

Example 2

Suppose Azami and Haley both wrote expressions to describe the same pattern. Azami wrote $k - 8 + 5$ and Haley wrote $k - 13$. Are the expressions equivalent?

Solution Pick a number to substitute for k. Let $k = 10$.

Azami's expression: $k - 8 + 5 = 10 - 8 + 5 = 7$

Haley's expression: $k - 13 = 10 - 13 = -3$

When $k = 10$ the expressions have different values, so the expressions are not equivalent.

To show that $k - 8 + 5$ and $k - 13$ are not always equal, you only need to show one instance in which the expressions have different values. The situation in which $k = 10$ is a *counterexample*. A **counterexample** is an instance which shows that a general statement is not always true. It is not true that for all values of k, $k - 8 + 5 = k - 13$.

 See Quiz Yourself 2 at the right.

Questions

COVERING THE IDEAS

1. Consider the sequence created with square tiles shown below.

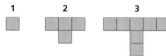

a. Evaluate the expression $3n - 2$ for various values of n to show that it describes the number of squares in the nth term for the 1st, 2nd, and 3rd terms.

b. Use the expression to find the number of tiles in the 100th term.

2. Consider the sequence of dots below.

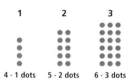

4 · 1 dots   5 · 2 dots   6 · 3 dots

a. Draw the 4th and 5th terms. For each, write the multiplication expression for the number of dots. See margin.

b. In words, describe how to find the number of dots in the nth term if you know the term number.

c. Write an expression for the number of dots in the nth term.

> **QUIZ YOURSELF 2**
>
> Which two of these expressions seem to be equivalent? How do you know?
>
> $(n + 3)^2$
>
> $n^2 + 9$
>
> $n^2 + 6n + 9$

1a. For $n = 1$, $3n - 2 = 1$; for $n = 2$, $3n - 2 = 4$; and for $n = 3$, $3n - 2 = 7$.

1b. 298 tiles

2b. Multiply the term number by three more than the term number.

2c. $(n + 3) \cdot n$

Equivalent Expressions   23

Notes on the Lesson

Example 2. Since Azami's and Haley's expressions are not equivalent, it is natural to ask if there is any value of k for which the expressions have the same value. This leads to solving the equation $k - 8 + 5 = k - 13$. Since the left side of this equation equals $k - 3$ and the right side equals $k - 13$, students should see that there is no value of k for which the two expressions have the same value.

Additional Example

Example 2 Suppose Gabriel and Jill both wrote expressions to describe the same pattern. Gabriel wrote $q + 3$ and Jill wrote $4 - 2 + q$. Are the expressions equivalent? No. Let $q = 5$. Gabriel's expression: $q + 3 = 5 + 3 = 8$; Jill's expression: $4 - 2 + q = 4 - 2 + 5 = 7$; when $q = 5$, the expressions have different values, so the expressions are not equivalent.

Accommodating the Learner

Write the algebraic expressions $(x + 4) - (3x + 5)$ and $x + (4 - 3x) + 5$ on the board. Ask students to decide whether the expressions are equivalent. If they determine that the expressions are not equivalent, ask students to provide a counterexample. After completing this discussion, ask students to move the parentheses in the second expression so the first expression and their rewritten expression are equivalent. Have students discuss why the placement of the parentheses is important.

Additional Answers

2a.

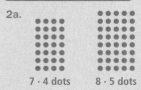

7 · 4 dots   8 · 5 dots

No; $(0 + 4) - (3 \cdot 0 + 5) \neq 0 + (4 - 3 \cdot 0) + 5$; $(x + 4) - (3x + 5) = x + 4 - (3x + 5)$

1-3

Recommended Assignment

- Questions 1–19
- Questions 20 and 21 (extra credit)
- Reading Lesson 1-4
- Covering the Ideas 1-4

Notes on the Questions

Question 3 We are careful to say that the expressions "seem to be equivalent." Without some rule, we do not know whether the expressions would generate the same values for other values of x. For example, if expression 1 was $3x - 17$ and expression 2 was $|3x| - 17$, then these expressions would generate the same values for the values of x shown in the tables, but they do not give the same values if x is negative.

Question 4 This is the same design as in Activity 1.

3. Two different expressions were used to generate each table of values below. Use the tables to decide whether the expressions seem to be equivalent. Explain how you know. Since the tables have the same values, the expressions seem to be equivalent.

x	3x − 17	
10	?	13
9	?	10
8	?	7
7	?	4
6	?	1
5	?	−2

x	x − 6 − (11 − 2x)	
10	?	13
9	?	10
8	?	7
7	?	4
6	?	1
5	?	−2

4a. For $n = 1$, $n + n + (n + 1) = 4$; for $n = 2$, $n + n + (n + 1) = 7$; and for $n = 3$, $n + n + (n + 1) = 10$, as the sequence shows.

4. Consider the sequence of toothpicks shown at the right. A student describes the number of toothpicks required to make the nth pattern in the following way: I split the toothpicks up into three kinds: (1) top toothpicks; (2) bottom toothpicks; and (3) vertical toothpicks.

	1	2	3	n
	1 on top 1 on bottom 2 vertical	2 on top 2 on bottom 3 vertical	3 on top 3 on bottom 4 vertical	n on top n on bottom n + 1 vertical

In the nth figure, there were n toothpicks on top, n on the bottom, and $n + 1$ vertical ones. So, in the nth figure, there are $n + n + (n + 1)$ toothpicks.

a. Substitute for n to verify that the expression $n + n + (n + 1)$ describes the number of toothpicks needed for the first three terms.

b. Use the expression to find the number of toothpicks in the 100th term. For $n = 100$, $n + n + (n + 1) = 301$.

In 5–7, two expressions are given.

a. Using a table, evaluate each expression for four different values of the variable.

b. Based on your results, do the two expressions appear to be equivalent?

5. $25 + (x - 5)(x + 5)$ and x^2 b. Yes, they appear equivalent.

6. $\frac{8n - 4}{4}$ and $8n - 1$ b. No, they are different.

7. $x^2 - 4x - 3$ and $(x - 3)(x + 1)$ b. No, they are different.

5a. Answers vary. Sample answer:

x	25 + (x − 5)(x + 5)	x²
0	0	0
2	4	4
3	9	9
−1	1	1

6a. Answers vary. Sample answer:

n	8n − 4 4	8n − 1
−1	−3	−9
0	−1	−1
2	3	15
1	1	7

7a. Answers vary. Sample answer:

x	x² − 4x − 3	(x − 3) (x + 1)
0	−3	−3
2	−7	−3
3	−6	0
−1	2	0

24   Using Algebra to Describe

APPLYING THE MATHEMATICS

Notes on the Questions
Question 8 Allow any expressions that are equivalent to the given answers for Parts a–c.

8. Tile patterns are often used in bathroom flooring. Consider this sequence created with green and yellow hexagonal tiles.

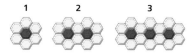

    1   2   3

  a. Write an expression describing the number of green hexagonal tiles in the nth term of the sequence. n

  b. Write an expression describing the number of yellow hexagonal tiles in the nth term of the sequence. $4n + 2$

  c. Use your answers from Parts a and b to write an expression describing the total number of hexagonal tiles in the nth term of the sequence. $n + (4n + 2)$

  d. How many hexagonal tiles are in the 100th term? 502 tiles

9. Give a counterexample to show that the equation $(a - 5) + b = a - (5 + b)$ is not true for all real numbers a and b.

9. Answers vary. Sample answer: Let $a = 0$ and $b = 1$. Then $(a - 5) + b = -4$ and $a - (5 + b) = -6$.

10. An airplane manufacturer sells small planes that have seats arranged so there is a center aisle. In the each row, there are 3 seats on the left side of the aisle and 2 seats on the right side of the aisle. If there are r rows of seats, find two different expressions for the total number of seats in a plane.
Answers vary. Sample answer: $2r + 3r$ and $5r$

REVIEW

11. Describe the general pattern using one variable. **(Lesson 1-2)**

$$8^2 - 8 = 8(8 - 1) \quad x^2 - x = x(x - 1)$$
$$30^2 - 30 = 30(30 - 1)$$
$$6.5^2 - 6.5 = 6.5(6.5 - 1)$$

12. Each morning, Crystal buys a cup of coffee for $2.25. She uses a table to record her total coffee expenditures. **(Lesson 1-2)**
Day 4: $2.25 + $2.25 + $2.25 + $2.25; $9.00

Day	Calculation	Cost
1	$2.25	$2.25
2	$2.25 + $2.25	$4.50
3	$2.25 + $2.25 + $2.25	$6.75
4	?	?
5	?	?

Day 5: $2.25 + $2.25 + $2.25 + $2.25 + $2.25; $11.25

  a. Complete the table. 12b. $821.25 ($823.50 in a leap year)

  b. After one year how much will Crystal have spent on coffee?

  c. After d days, how much will Crystal have spent on coffee?
    $2.25d$ dollars

Newer airplanes have seats that are made with a lightweight carbon fiber-reinforced frame that helps reduce weight and fuel costs.
Source: www.boeing.com

Equivalent Expressions   **25**

1-3

4 Wrap-Up

Ongoing Assessment

On a piece of paper, have students write two algebraic expressions that they know to be either equivalent or not equivalent. Instruct them to exchange their papers with other students. Students should determine whether the two expressions they receive are equivalent or not. If they believe the expressions are not equivalent, they should provide a counterexample. They should check their answers with their partners.

Project Update

Project 5, Encoding and Decoding Using Formulas, on page 56 relates to the content of this lesson.

13. Give two instances of each pattern. (**Lesson 1-2**)
    a. $x^2 \cdot x = x^3$ b. $3g - g - g = g$ c. $n(3 + 8) = 3n + 8n$
    13a–c. See margin.
14. a. Evaluate $\frac{1}{10}x^2$ when $x = 200$. 4,000
    b. Evaluate $\left(\frac{1}{10}x\right)^2$ when $x = 200$. 400
    c. Find a value of x so that the value of $\frac{1}{10}x^2$ is the same as the value of $\left(\frac{1}{10}x\right)^2$. (**Lesson 1-1**) $x = 0$

In **15–17**, fill in the blank with =, <, or >. (**Lesson 1-1**)

15. $(-25)(-16)$ __?__ $-25 + -16$ >
16. $3^3 + 3^3$ __?__ 3^6 <
17. $(8 \cdot 6) \cdot 3 + 1$ __?__ $8 \cdot (6 \cdot 3) + 1$ =

18. Raul's Video Store has certain DVDs on sale for $9.95, but all others are priced at $14.95. Suppose a customer wishes to purchase 7 DVDs, 2 of which are on sale. What is the total cost? (**Lesson 1-1**) $94.65

19. In 2006, the city of Los Angeles charged a sales tax of 8.25%. If you bought a pair of jeans in Los Angeles that cost $35 before tax, what was the total cost after tax? (**Previous Course**) $37.89

EXPLORATION

20. In this sequence of dots, two rows are added to each term to get the next term.

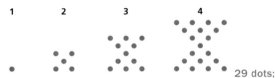

1   2   3   4

29 dots;

a. Find the number of dots in the 5th and 6th terms. 41 dots
b. Find the number of dots in the 20th term. 419 dots
c. Try to find an expression for the number of dots in the nth term. $n^2 + n - 1$

21. Two terms in a sequence of squares are shown.
    a. Draw the 3rd and 4th terms.
    b. Give the number of toothpicks in the 1st, 2nd, 3rd, 4th, and 5th term. 21a–c. See margin.
    c. In words, describe a method to find the number of toothpicks it takes to make the nth term.
    d. Write an algebraic expression to find the number of toothpicks in the nth term.
    Answers vary. Sample answer: $2(n + 1)n$

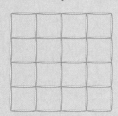

1   2

26   Using Algebra to Describe

A DVD has about 26 times the storage capacity of a CD.

Source: about.com

QUIZ YOURSELF ANSWERS

1a. When $w = 2$, $2w = 2 \cdot 2 = 4$ and $w^2 = 2^2 = 32 \cdot 2 = 4$.

1b. When $w = 5$, $2w = 2 \cdot 5 = 10$ and $w^2 = 5^2 = 5 \cdot 5 = 25$.

2. $(n + 3)^2$ and $n^2 + 6n + 9$ are equivalent. $(n + 3)^2$ and $n^2 + 9$ are not equivalent since $(1 + 3)^2 = 4^2 = 16$, $1^2 + 9 = 1 + 9 = 10$. $n^2 + 9$ and $n^2 + 6n + 9$ are not equivalent since $1^2 + 9 = 10$, $1^2 + 6 \cdot 1 + 9 = 1 + 6 + 9 = 16$. Thus, we know that $(n + 3)^2$ and $n^2 + 6n + 9$ are equivalent.

Additional Answers

13a. Answers vary. Sample answer: $2^2 \cdot 2 = 2^3$ and $(-1)^2 \cdot (-1) = (-1)^3$

13b. Answers vary. Sample answer: $3(-1) - (-1) - (-1) = -1$ and $3(0) - 0 - 0 = 0$

13c. Answers vary. Sample answer: $3(3 + 8) = 3(3) + 8(3)$ and $45(3 + 8) = 3(45) + 8(45)$

21a.   3   4

21b. 4 toothpicks; 12 toothpicks; 24 toothpicks; 40 toothpicks; 60 toothpicks

21c. Answers vary. Sample answer: Each design has n toothpicks in each column and each row, and has $n + 1$ columns and rows.

Lesson
1-4 Picturing Expressions

Vocabulary

scatterplot

domain of the variable

▶ **BIG IDEA** Graphing the ordered pairs (value of variable, value of expression) helps you understand the relationship between these values.

Activity 1 in Lesson 1-3 discussed this toothpick sequence.

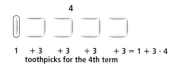

Suppose a student looks at each instance as one vertical toothpick on the left and 3 more toothpicks being added for each additional square.

4

$1 + 3 + 3 + 3 + 3 = 1 + 3 \cdot 4$
toothpicks for the 4th term

Then the student might write the expression $1 + 3n$ to describe the sequence.

Scatterplots

The table shows values for the term number n and for $1 + 3n$, the number of toothpicks in the nth term. Each row can be written as an ordered pair. These pairs can then be graphed on the coordinate plane.

Term Number	Number of Toothpicks	(Term Number, Number of Toothpicks)
1	4	(1, 4)
2	7	(2, 7)
3	10	(3, 10)
4	13	(4, 13)
n	$1 + 3n$	$(n, 1 + 3n)$

Every point in the plane of the graph can be identified with *coordinates*. A graph like this, in which individual points are plotted, is called a **scatterplot**, as shown on the next page.

Picturing Expressions **27**

Mental Math

a. If cantaloupes cost $2.98 each, estimate how much 5 cantaloupes cost. **$15**

b. If you paid for the 5 cantaloupes with $15, how much change would you expect? **10¢**

GOAL

Graph ordered pairs to see visual patterns in sequences.

SPUR Objectives

J Create a scatterplot from a table or expression.

K Graph ordered pairs from expressions.

L Use graphs to determine whether expressions seem to be equivalent.

Materials/Resources

· Lesson Master 1-4A or 1-4B
· Resource Masters 1, 2, and 13–15
· Graph paper

HOMEWORK

Suggestions for Assignment

• Questions 1–21
• Question 22 (extra credit)
• Reading Lesson 1-5
• Covering the Ideas 1-5

Local Standards

1 Warm-Up

1. Graph the points (2, 5), (0, –6), (–11, –4), and (–9, 7) on the same coordinate graph. Connect the points in order. What figure is formed? **a square**

2. One of the vertices of the square is on one of the axes. Which vertex? **(0, –6)**

3. Is this vertex *above, below, to the right,* or *to the left* of the origin? **below; An incorrect answer may indicate that students switched the order of the coordinates of each ordered pair.**

Background

The title of this lesson, *Picturing Expressions,* was carefully chosen. Because the word "function" has not yet been introduced, we did not want to say we are graphing functions. But that indeed is what is being graphed. The "expression" is a description of the value of the function.

We assume that students are familiar with graphing ordered pairs in all four quadrants.

When a point is graphed in rectangular coordinates, the mathematician Leibniz in the 1690s called the first coordinate the *abscissa*; the second coordinate he called the *ordinate*. These names are still in use today, though we do not use them here.

In the world, "scatterplot" (one word) and "scatter plot" (two words) are used with about the same frequency. The key idea is that a scatterplot consists of individual points that are not connected.

Synonyms for the term "domain of the variable" are "replacement set," "domain of definition," and occasionally "universe."

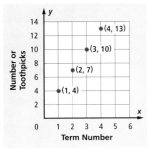

1-4

2 | Teaching

Notes on the Lesson

Scatterplots. Emphasize that parentheses are needed to identify an ordered pair. An ordered pair (f, s) consists of two *components.* When these components are real numbers that are graphed, we call them *coordinates of the point (f, s).* Some scatterplots, such as frequencies of scores on a test, do not have algebraic formulas describing them. But others, such as the one on the first page of the lesson, can be described with algebraic expressions.

Connected graphs. When a variable stands for something that is a measure (such as length, time, area, or weight), we pick the set of real numbers or the set of positive real numbers as the domain. These graphs will almost always either be completely connected or have many connected parts. But when the domain of a variable is the set of integers or some subset of the integers, then the graph will be a scatterplot.

If the points on the graph had been connected with a line, then the numbers between 1, 2, 3, and 4 would be allowed for *n,* and therefore the numbers for $1 + 3n$ between 4, 7, 10, and 13. But this is not possible in the toothpick sequence because *n* represents the term number. There is a third term and a fourth term, but for $n = 3.5$ there is no toothpick term. In this situation, *n* must be a positive integer. All the values that may be meaningfully substituted for a variable make up the **domain of the variable.** For the toothpick sequence on page 27, the domain is the set of positive integers {1, 2, 3, 4, ...}.

Connected Graphs

When writing expressions for real-world problems, you often must decide what domain makes sense for a situation.

Example 1

Suppose Rebecca drives to her grandmother's house, which is 500 miles away. Her average speed is 65 miles per hour. Fill in the table of values to calculate her remaining distance after each hour. Write an expression to represent her remaining distance, and then plot the points on a graph.

Hours of Driving	Remaining Distance (mi)
0	
1	
2	
3	
h	

California drivers consume about 11% of the fuel used in the United States.

Source: U.S. Department of Transportation

Solution Let *h* represent the number of hours spent driving.

Hours of Driving	Calculation and Pattern	Remaining Distance (mi)
0	500	500
1	500 − 65	435
2	500 − 65 − 65 = 500 − 65(2)	370
3	500 − 65 − 65 − 65 = 500 − 65(3)	305
h	500 − 65 − ... − 65 = 500 − 65h (h terms)	500 − 65h

So after *h* hours, Rebecca is 500 − 65*h* miles away from her grandmother's house. The graph is shown on the next page.

28   Using Algebra to Describe

Accommodating the Learner ⊕

Consider offering several real-world examples of situations that can be described by each set of numbers given on page 29. For example, the set of whole numbers can describe anything countable, like the number of eagles sighted at a wildlife preserve; the integers can describe the scores at a golf tournament; the real numbers can describe any situation dealing with elapsed time; and the rational numbers can describe the change in the value of a company's stock. You might also ask students to suggest their own examples.

Connecting the points is appropriate because time and distance are both measures and do not need to be integers. Rebecca could drive for a half hour or an hour and fifteen minutes. Substituting these numbers into the expression $500 - 65h$ will result in a distance that is not a whole number. The points (0.5, 467.5) and (1.25, 418.75) are plotted here. By connecting the points on the graph, you are showing that all nonnegative real numbers make sense in this situation. Therefore, the domain of h is the set of nonnegative real numbers.

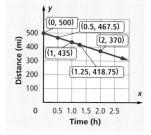

Common Domains of Variables

The following domains are frequently used in arithmetic and algebra.

Name of Set	Description	Examples of Elements
whole numbers	$\{0, 1, 2, 3, \ldots\}$	Five; $\frac{16}{2}$; 2,007; 7 million
integers	$\{\ldots, -2, -1, 0, 1, 2, \ldots\}$ whole numbers and their opposites	$\frac{-21}{3}$, -17.00, negative one thousand
real numbers	the set of all numbers that can be represented as terminating or nonterminating decimals	$5, 0, \pi, -0.0042, -3\frac{1}{3}, 0.\overline{13}, \sqrt{2},$ one hundred thousand
nonnegative real numbers	$\{x\colon x \geq 0\}$ the set consisting of 0 and all positive real numbers	$2.56; 3,470; \frac{1}{100}; 0$

In the above table, the sets of whole numbers and integers are described with a *roster*, or list of elements. Set-builder notation is used to describe the set of nonnegative real numbers. In $\{x\colon x \geq 0\}$, the symbol "$:$" is read "such that." It is followed by an expression that describes the set. The set $\{x\colon x \geq 0\}$ is read "the set of numbers x such that x is greater than or equal to 0." Some people write $\{x\mid x \geq 0\}$, using a single vertical bar to mean "such that."

1a.

n	$n(n + 2)$
1	3
2	8
3	15
4	24
5	35

Questions

COVERING THE IDEAS

1. Each term in the following sequence is a rectangular array of squares. The nth term has n rows and $n + 2$ columns and therefore $n(n + 2)$ squares.

1   2   3

a. Make a table of values for $n(n + 2)$ using $n = 1, 2, 3, 4,$ and 5.
b. Make a scatterplot to graph the values from Part a.

1b.

Example 1 In 1870, the steamboats *Robert E. Lee* and *Natchez* raced from New Orleans to St. Louis, a distance of approximately 1,218 miles. The *Robert E. Lee*'s average speed was approximately 20 miles per hour. Fill in the table of values to calculate the *Robert E. Lee*'s approximate distance from St. Louis each hour after leaving New Orleans.

Hours of Racing	Calculation and Pattern	Remaining Distance (mi)
0	1,218	1,218
1	$1{,}218 - 20$	1,198
2	$1{,}218 - 20 - 20$	1,178
3	$1{,}218 - 20 - 20 - 20$	1,158
h	$1{,}218 - 20 - \ldots - 20$ (h terms of 20)	$1{,}218 - 20h$

Write an expression to represent its remaining distance after each hour, and then plot the points on a graph. After h hours, the *Robert E. Lee* is $1{,}218 - 20h$ miles away from the finish line.

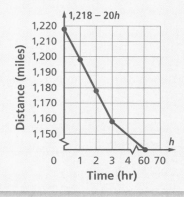

Note-Taking Tips

The various number sets (whole numbers, integers, real numbers, and the nonnegative real numbers) can be confusing for many students, especially for English language learners. Suggest that students write each of the set names on one side of an index card and a description of the set on the other. These cards can then be used as study aids.

Accommodating the Learner ⬆

The lesson says that both the set of whole numbers and the set of integers can be described with a roster. Ask students to think of two other infinite sets of numbers that can be described with a roster. Have them write the roster for each of these sets of numbers on a piece of paper and then write a sentence or two that explicitly describes each set. Stress that their descriptions of each set should be clear enough so that another student who reads it will be able to write the roster of numbers.

Extension

Organize the class in groups of 3 students. Ask each group to create a word problem for which the solution is a set of ordered pairs that can be used to create a connected graph. Then ask each group to create a word problem whose solution is a set of ordered pairs that when graphed should *not* be connected. Instruct the students to create graphs that model each of their problems. The graphs should be properly labeled and should be clearly drawn.

1-4

3 Assignment

Recommended Assignment
- Questions 1–21
- Question 22 (extra credit)
- Reading Lesson 1-5
- Covering the Ideas 1-5

Notes on the Questions

Question 1b Students may be surprised that the plotted points do not lie on a line. They lie on the right side of a parabola with vertex at (0, 0). Graphing the equation $y = x(x + 2)$ on a graphing calculator can quickly show this fact.

Question 2 You might ask students to describe a sequence of toothpick designs that could lead to these points.

Question 4 If the values are graphed for all positive integer values of n, then the points all lie on one of two lines, $y = x$ and $y = -x$. This is because when n is even, $n(-1)^n = n$; and when n is odd, $n(-1)^n = -n$.

---

2. The graph below shows the number of toothpicks used to make each term in a sequence.

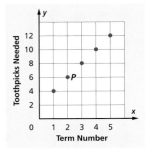

a. Give the coordinates of P. (2, 6)

b. Describe the situation that corresponds to P, giving the term number and number of toothpicks needed.

c. Explain why the domain of n is the set of positive integers.
The term number is only meaningful for positive integers.

2b. P corresponds to term number 2, which requires 6 toothpicks.

3. Make a table and scatterplot for $4n - 5$ using the following numbers for n: –3, –2, 0, 2, and 3. **See margin.**

4. Make a table and graph for values of the expression $n \cdot (-1)^n$ when $n = 1, 2, 3, 4,$ and 5. **See margin.**

In 5–7, values of a variable x and an expression are graphed. The coordinates of each point are integers.

5. Fill in the table based on the graph.

x	Value of Expression
–3	? 4
0	? –2
2	? –6
?–1	0
?–4	6
? 1	–4

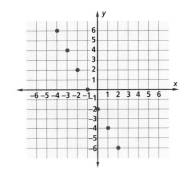

6. Use the graph at the right.
   a. What is the value of the expression when x is 2? –4
   b. What value(s) of x makes the value of the expression equal to 2? 5

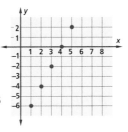

30   Using Algebra to Describe

Additional Answers

3.

n	$4n - 5$
–3	–17
–2	–13
0	–5
2	3
3	7

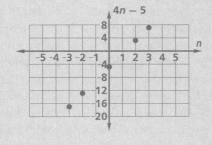

---

7. **a.** If $x = 5$, what is the value of the expression graphed below? **5**
   b. What value(s) of x makes the value of the expression equal to 5?

   3 and 5

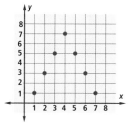

8. Express the set $\{x: x$ is an integer and $x \geq 20\}$ in roster form.
   {20, 21, 22, 23, …}
9. Express the set $\{-9, -10, -11, …\}$ in set-builder notation.

   Answers vary. Sample answer: $\{x: x$ is an integer and $x < -8\}$

APPLYING THE MATHEMATICS

In 10 and 11, consider these two situations.

a. A landscaper sells black dirt for $20 per cubic yard, plus a $40 delivery fee. Let $x =$ number of cubic yards ordered.

b. Arrangements for special dinners can be made at a restaurant. There is a $40 rental fee for a special room, plus the $20 per person cost for the food. Let $x =$ number of people at the dinner.

10. For which situation does it make sense to have $x = 2\frac{1}{2}$? In that situation, find the cost when $x = 2\frac{1}{2}$. **a.; $90**

11. Match each graph below with the situation it represents.

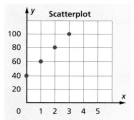 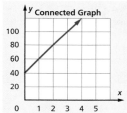

Scatterplot corresponds to b.; Connected graph corresponds to a.

In 12–14, choose the most reasonable domain for the variable.

a. set of whole numbers   **b.** set of real numbers
c. set of integers   **d.** set of positive real numbers

12. $n =$ the number of people at a restaurant on Friday night **a**

13. $t =$ time it takes to do your homework **d**

14. $E =$ elevation of a place in the United States **b**

Topsoil is sold in 40-pound bags or in bulk measured in cubic yards.

1-4

Notes on the Questions

Question 9 Set-builder notation may seem strange here because the set is given. Set-builder notation identifies the variable that takes on the values of that set.

Question 16 For a counterexample, students should supply a value of x and a value of n. These values do not have to be different. Any value of x other than 1, together with any value of n, will supply a counterexample.

Question 20 You might wish to ask students to explain why the answers to Parts a and c are the same. (The product of two numbers is the same as the product of their opposites.)

Question 21 The answer is given by the expression $\frac{2}{13} \cdot \frac{3}{7} \cdot 273$. Since multiplication is associative, either multiplication can be done first. Most students will probably follow the wording of the question and first do the multiplication at the right. But if the multiplication at the left is done first, the expression becomes $\frac{6}{91} \cdot 273$, and since $273 \div 91 = 3$, the answer 18 appears quite quickly.

Question 22 The numbers 1, 3, 6, 10, … from this pattern of dots are the triangular numbers. Triangular numbers appear in many kinds of situations. The nth triangular number is the sum of the whole numbers from 1 to n; it is the number of segments needed to connect n points on the plane; it is the number of handshakes if n people are each to shake hands with one another.

4.

n	$n \cdot (-1)^n$
1	−1
2	2
3	−3
4	4
5	−5

$n(-1)^n$

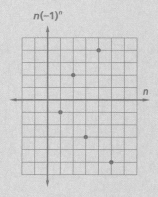

1-4

4 Wrap-Up

Ongoing Assessment

Ask students to write a definition of *domain* on a piece of paper. Then ask them to provide one situation where the domain is continuous (connected) and one situation where the domain is discontinuous (discrete).

REVIEW

15. Complete the table of values for each expression. Use the table to conclude whether the expressions seem to be equivalent. Explain your reasoning. **(Lesson 1-3)**

n	$2(n - 3)$
-5	? -16
-3	? -12
1	? -4
2	? -2
5	? 4

n	$2n - 3$
-5	? -13
-3	? -9
1	? -1
2	? 1
5	? 7

15. The expressions are not equivalent, since for given values of n, the expressions give different values.

16. Find a counterexample to show that the equation $(n + 10) \cdot x = n + 10 \cdot x$ is not true for all real numbers n and x. **(Lesson 1-3)**
Answers vary. Sample answer: $n = 1, x = 0$

In 17 and 18, an equation describing a pattern is given.
a. Give three instances of the pattern. **(Lesson 1-2)**
b. Do you think the equation is true for all real numbers? Explain your reasoning. **(Lesson 1-3)** 17–18. See margin.

17. $t - 2t + 3t = 2t$

18. $9 - (2x - 4) = -2x + 13$

19. Using the formula $V = \ell wh$, find the volume of the figure at the right. **(Lesson 1-1)** 150.28 cm^3

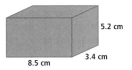

5.2 cm
3.4 cm
8.5 cm

20. Evaluate the expression $a^2 + b^2 + 2ab$ for the following values of a and b. **(Lesson 1-1)**
a. $a = 2, b = 3$ 25
b. $a = -2, b = 3$ 1
c. $a = -2, b = -3$ 25

21. Suppose there are 273 students in a school. Of these, $\frac{3}{7}$ play on an athletic team, and of those that are on an athletic team, $\frac{2}{13}$ play on the soccer team. How many students play on the soccer team? **(Previous Course)** 18 students

EXPLORATION

22. Here is a pattern of dots.
22a. Answers vary. Sample answer: $\frac{1}{2} \cdot n(n + 1)$

1   2   3   4

a. Find an expression for the nth term in the pattern.
b. Make a scatterplot. See margin.

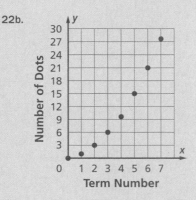

In 2004–2005, there were a total of 670,691 high school soccer players, including both boys and girls.

Source: The National Federation of State High School Associations

Additional Answers

17a. For $t = 0, t - 2t + 3t = 0$ and $2t = 0$; for $t = 1, t - 2t + 3t = 2$ and $2t = 2$; and for $t = -2, t - 2t + 3t = -4$ and $2t = -4$.

17b. The pattern holds for all real numbers, since the expressions are equivalent.

18a. For $x = 0, 9 - (2x - 4) = 13$ and $-2x + 13 = 13$; for $x = 2, 9 - (2x - 4) = 9$ and $-2x + 13 = 9$; and for $x = -3, 9 - (2x - 4) = 19$ and $-2x + 13 = 19$.

18b. The pattern holds for all real numbers, since the expressions are equivalent.

22b.

Lesson 1-5

Using a Graphing Calculator

▶ **BIG IDEA** By letting $y =$ the value of an expression with variable x, a graphing calculator or computer can automatically generate a graph of the relationship between x and y.

Graphing with Technology

An algebraic expression such as $x^2 - 15x$ shows calculations that are performed on a variable. In Lesson 1-4, you evaluated expressions by substituting variables with numbers taken from tables. In much the same way, graphing calculators find values and graph the points they describe. These machines were first introduced in 1985 and are popular today because they perform repeated calculations quickly and allow a person to focus on the mathematical relationships shown by graphs and tables.

Vocabulary

window
Xmin
Xmax
Ymin
Ymax
Xscl
Yscl
standard window

Mental Math

Evaluate
$3n + (5 - n) - 2n$ when:
a. $n = 3.5$
b. $n = 0.5$
c. $n = -2.5$
d. $n = 1,000.5$

Activity 1

To graph values of an expression on a graphing calculator, a second variable y is used. It represents the value of the expression that is calculated for each x-value.

Step 1 Go to the $\boxed{Y=}$ menu on your graphing calculator.

Step 2 Type in $x^2 - 15x$.

Since the calculator can display several graphs on the same window, it uses names like Y_1, Y_2, and Y_3 in its equations.

When you draw a graph by hand, you must decide what portion of the coordinate grid to display. The same decision must be made when using a graphing calculator. The part that is shown is called the **window.** The window can be described by two inequalities.

Step 3 Go to the WINDOW menu on your calculator.

Step 4 Enter the same values as in the screen at the right. The information in this window can be expressed with the inequalities $-10 \leq x \leq 25$ and $-70 \leq y \leq 35$.

(continued on next page)

Using a Graphing Calculator   **33**

Background

Graphing calculators. Today's graphing calculators do far more than just graph. They have powerful features that enable them to be useful devices in helping students learn algebra. For this reason, in this book we assume that students have continual access to graphing calculators not only in school but at home. Many schools treat these and other calculators as they do textbooks; they issue them to students at the beginning of the school year and pick them up at the end.

Technically, we do not graph expressions. We graph relationships between two variables. Sometimes we say that we are graphing an equation, by which we mean that we are graphing ordered pairs that satisfy the equation. When we say that we are "graphing an expression," we mean that we are graphing ordered pairs of the form (value of variable, value of expression). For instance, when we are graphing $2x + 5$, we are graphing the ordered pairs (x, y) where $y = 2x + 5$.

Lesson 1-5

GOAL

Discuss the settings of the window and the use of the table feature on a graphing calculator.

SPUR Objectives

K Graph ordered pairs from expressions.

L Use graphs to determine whether expressions seem to be equivalent.

M Use graphs to find values, create tables, and select appropriate windows.

Materials/Resources

· Lesson Master 1-5A or 1-5B
· Resource Masters 2 and 16
· Graphing calculator
· Graph paper

HOMEWORK

Suggestions for Assignment

• Questions 1–26
• Questions 27 and 28 (extra credit)
• Reading Lesson 1-6
• Covering the Ideas 1-6

Local Standards

1   Warm-Up

Use Steps 1-5 of Activity 1 as the Warm-Up. Have students work in groups of 2 or 3. The goal is for students to learn what keys on their calculators they need to press in order to access the place where equations are entered, to set the ranges of the axes of the graphing window, and to have an equation graphed.

1-5

2 Teaching

Notes on the Lesson

This lesson is essentially a set of activities to be done by students. Before beginning, you should try to determine how much experience your students have had with graphing calculators. If there are some very knowledgeable students, you might want to enlist them to assist their classmates with the activities.

Setting a window. A graph is a picture and the picture must fit inside a frame. With paper-and-pencil graphs, schoolbooks often have put the origin in the center of the graph and then asked students to graph only relationships and ordered pairs that are close to the origin. Many students could leave algebra never having graphed a point with a coordinate less than –15 or greater than 15! Their entire graphing experience would be with the window $-15 \leq x \leq 15, -15 \leq y \leq 15$. Graphing calculators handle a greater variety of relationships and they allow windows that are broader and windows that zoom in. The default window of a graphing calculator, the window that appears if you do nothing to change it, is similar to the usual paper-and-pencil window.

The window is set by identifying the range for each axis, as described above Activity 2 on page 34. The window is described by the two double inequalities $Xmin \leq x \leq Xmax$ and $Ymin \leq y \leq Ymax$. Calculators do not show the coordinates of a point next to the point as is often done on paper-and-pencil graphs. Instead, the location of a cursor on the screen may appear at the bottom of the screen as $x = ..., y = ...$. By moving the cursor (using the up, down, right, and left arrows), the user can find the approximate coordinates of any point.

Step 5 Press the GRAPH command. Your graph should look like the one at the right.

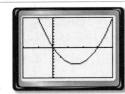

Most graphing calculators use the variables x and y for graphing. If a problem uses other letters for variables, you must replace those letters with x and y. On a calculator, the four numbers that describe the boundaries of the window are each given a name. For the x-coordinates, the minimum edge, or least value displayed, is called **Xmin** or x-min (the left edge of the screen) and the maximum edge, or greatest value, is **Xmax** or x-max (the right edge of the screen). Similarly, **Ymin** (or y-min) and **Ymax** (or y-max) are the least (bottom edge) and greatest (top edge) values for the y-coordinates.

The calculator does not put coordinates by the tick marks on the axes, so you need to look carefully at the window description to understand what numbers are being shown. In the graph above, the tick marks are spaced 5 units apart on the x-axis, and 10 units apart on the y-axis. This scale is described by **Xscl** (x-scale) and **Yscl** (y-scale) on the window settings screen.

Activity 2

Step 1 Go to the $\boxed{Y=}$ menu and enter $-7x^2 + 3x - 4$.

Step 2 Go to the WINDOW menu and enter the settings $-3 \leq x \leq 3$ with x-scale of 1 and $-25 \leq y \leq 0$ with a y-scale of 5.

Step 3 Copy your window screen and sketch the graph your calculator displays.

Activity 3

Step 1 Enter $y = \dfrac{5}{x^2 + 1}$ into the $\boxed{Y=}$ menu. (Type in as $5 \div (x^2 + 1)$.)

Step 2 Go to the ZOOM menu. Press STANDARD.

Step 3 Copy your graph down on a sheet of paper.

Step 4 Describe the window by completing the inequalities below.
$-10 \underline{\ ?\ } \leq x \leq \underline{\ ?\ } 10$ and $-10 \underline{\ ?\ } \leq y \leq \underline{\ ?\ } 10$
x-scale $= \underline{\ ?\ } 1$ y-scale $= \underline{\ ?\ } 1$

Anytime you use the **standard window**, your calculator will display in the above window.

Activity 2, Step 3

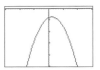

Activity 3, Step 3

Accommodating the Learner

A graphing calculator can be very intimidating to some students, especially when so many new ideas are being presented at once. Do not assume students will be able to figure things out on their own. Things like how to turn it on and off or how to clear the home screen are all new ideas to some students. Take time to go over the basic layout of the calculator. Begin with the keyboard zones. Show students the part of the keyboard that works like a typical scientific calculator. Then point out the advanced function keys, and finally the graphing keys. Provide students with a preview of the menu structure, stopping momentarily to show them how some of the functions work. For example, show them how to cube a number using the MATH command followed by selecting the cubic function found in the MATH menu that appears. When you begin the activities in the lesson, do not assume everyone will be able to keep up. Consider pairing students so that students with experience on a graphing calculator can help students who have no experience.

You may find that when you try to graph an equation, no graph appears. This may mean that your window settings are not appropriate for your equation. Deciding on a good window is an important skill, so learn to think about it each time you graph!

Activity 4

Step 1 Enter $y = 5x(x + 4)(x - 3)$ into the $\boxed{Y=}$ menu. (*Caution:* You may need to enter multiplication symbols that are not shown in the expression.)

Step 2 Use your calculator to match the windows below and graphs of $y = 5x(x + 4)(x - 3)$ at the right.

Window 1
$-6 \leq x \leq 6$ with x-scale of 1
$-100 \leq y \leq 150$ with y-scale of 25

Window 2
$-2.8 \leq x \leq -2.1$ with x-scale of 0.1
$40 \leq y \leq 145$ with y-scale of 10

Window 3 (Standard window)
$-10 \leq x \leq 10$ with x-scale of 1
$-10 \leq y \leq 10$ with y-scale of 1

Window 4
$-30 \leq x \leq 30$ with x-scale of 5
$-500 \leq y \leq 500$ with y-scale of 100

Graph 1
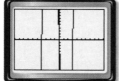

Graph 2
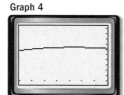

Graph 3

Graph 4

Activity 5

Step 1 The graph at the right shows $y = x^2 - 15x$ graphed on the window $-10 \leq x \leq 20$ and $-100 \leq y \leq 100$. Use the tick marks on the graph to find the coordinates of the points where the curve crosses the x-axis.

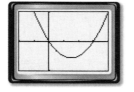

Step 2 Use the TRACE or VALUE commands to verify your answers to Step 1.

Step 3 Substitute those x-values into $x^2 - 15x$ and evaluate.

Step 4 Do your results match the y-coordinates? **yes**

Activity 4, Step 2
Window 1 corresponds with Graph 2.
Window 2 corresponds with Graph 4.
Window 3 corresponds with Graph 1.
Window 4 corresponds with Graph 3.

Activity 5, Step 1
The graph crosses the x-axis at $x = 0$ and $x = 15$.

Notes on the Activities

As you start **Activity 2,** this is a good time to show students how they can have more than one equation entered at a time. You need to show them how to "turn off" one or more of the graphs by placing the cursor on top of the equal sign of the graph(s) they would like to turn off and press ENTER. In this way students can maintain the equations in the calculator for later use without reentering them.

Many students are familiar with the zoom feature when focusing a camera. The ZOOM feature on a graphing calculator is similar. In **Activity 3,** students learn to use the ZOOM feature to change the window. Later, this ability will help in getting better estimates of the points of intersections of graphs. You might point out that when people display statistics to highlight a point they wish to make, they often use different views of the same data. Changing the window and/or the scales stretches or shrinks a graph as well as determines the portion of the graph that will be shown.

Prior to discussing **Activity 4,** tell students that they need to think about the parameters of the window based on the equation before pressing GRAPH. Point out that sometimes the best thing to do is to start in a standard window and proceed to a better window. Tell them that for any given equation there may not be a single best choice for the window, but rather several similar windows that show the graph equally well.

In **Activity 5,** students learn how to find the coordinates of points on a graph using the TRACE or VALUE feature of the calculator. There is another command that students can use to find the value of the x-intercept(s). Use the TRACE command followed by the ZERO command. If students are introduced to this new command, they must also be taught how to set a left boundary and right boundary and how to make a guess. Point out that only one x-intercept can be located between the left and right boundaries.

Accommodating the Learner

Have students enter and graph the equations $Y1 = 2x^2 - 3x + 15$ and $Y2 = 8x + 75$ in a standard window on their graphing calculators. (They may need to explicitly enter $2 * x^2$, $3 * x$, and $8 * x$.) Students are then to decide which of these four windows provides the most detail about the two graphs.

Window 1: Standard window

Window 2: $-4 \leq x \leq 5$ and $-5 \leq y \leq 30$ with x-scale of 1 and y-scale of 5

Window 3: $-6 \leq x \leq 6$ and $-20 \leq y \leq 120$ with x-scale of 1 and y-scale of 20

Window 4: $-10 \leq x \leq 10$ and $-25 \leq y \leq 250$ with x-scale of 2 and y-scale of 25

continued on next page

Notes on the Lesson

Tables from a graphing calculator. If you have a formula for y in terms of x, such as $y = 200 - 12x$, then a graphing calculator can easily create a table of values. You need to input the formula for y, set the first value of x (called `Tb1Start` in some calculators), and set the increment (called `ΔTb1`). Then the calculator will automatically fill in the values of a table with many rows.

You can also create a table from a spreadsheet. But some spreadsheets do not have the capability to create smooth graphs in the coordinate plane.

Notes on the Activities

In Step 8 of **Activity 6,** it is suggested that students scroll down to where $x = 35$ to find the corresponding value of y. Ask students what they would do if they needed to find the value of y when $x = 904$. Students should quickly realize that scrolling down to where $x = 904$ will take quite a bit of time. Ask them if they could use **TABLE SETUP** to get the value of y. Setting `Tb1Start = 900` and `ΔTb1 = 1` will allow them to find the corresponding value of y quickly.

Activity 7 uses two quadratic functions whose graphs have only one point in common. You might ask students to give the coordinates of that point. ((0, 9)) You might also point out that graphing is not the only way students can compare two expressions. With $Y1 = (x - 3)^2$ and $Y2 = (x + 3)^2$ go to **TBLSET** and set `Tb1Start = -5` and `ΔTb1 = 1`. Instruct students to go to **TABLE** where they will find three columns of numbers. The first column shows the x-values chosen in **TBLSET** and the next two columns are the values of Y1 and Y2, respectively, for the given values of x.

Tables from a Graphing Calculator

In Lesson 1-4, you drew graphs from tables you had created. The graphing calculator will also make a table of values for an expression entered in the Y= menu.

Activity 6

Step 1 Enter $y = x^2 - 15x$ into the Y= menu.

Step 2 Go to TABLE SETUP.

Step 3 Start table at −10 and have the table increment or △TABLE equal 1.

Step 4 Go to TABLE. Your screen should match the one at the right.

Step 5 Notice that the first x-value is −10 and that the x-values go up by 1 each step.

Step 6 In TABLE SETUP menu, change table start to 2 and △TABLE to 3. Write down the x- and y-values that appear in the table.

Step 7 Scroll up to where $x = -4$. What is the corresponding y-value? 76

Step 8 Scroll down to where $x = 35$. Give the corresponding y-value. 700

Activity 6, Step 6

Comparing Expressions with Technology

You can also use your graphing calculator to see how the values of the two expressions are similar or different. Be careful in setting the window so you can see the important features of both graphs.

Activity 7

Compare the expressions $(x - 3)^2$ and $(x + 3)^2$ by graphing.

Step 1 Graph $y = (x - 3)^2$ and $y = (x + 3)^2$ in a standard window. Sketch your results. **See margin.**

Step 2 Give the coordinates of the intersection of the graph of $y = (x - 3)^2$ and the x-axis. (3, 0)

Step 3 Give the coordinates of the intersection of the graph of $y = (x + 3)^2$ and the x-axis. (−3, 0)

Since the graphs are different, the two expressions $(x - 3)^2$ and $(x + 3)^2$ are not equivalent.

🛑 **See Quiz Yourself 1 at the right.**

▶ **QUIZ YOURSELF 1**

Use your calculator to determine which equation below is represented by the given graph.

$y = \sqrt{x}$

$y = \sqrt{-x}$

$y = -\sqrt{-x}$

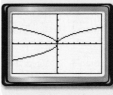

Additional Answers

Activity 7:

Step 1

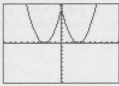

Have students explain the reasons for their choices. Now have the students regraph in the standard window. Instruct students to use the ZOOM command followed by the ZOOMFIT command, which is found in the ZOOM menu. Ask them what they notice. Have students use the WINDOW command. What window did the calculator use? How does this window compare to the window they chose from the list above?

Creating Scatterplots with Technology

A graphing calculator can plot individual points. To do this, enter a table of values into lists. Many calculators use names L1, L2, and L3 for the lists (just as Y1, Y2, and Y3 are used for the graphing of equations).

Activity 8

Step 1 Clear any equations in the Y= menu and turn on the STAT PLOT function.

Step 2 Enter the table below in the STAT lists. Then graph the points.

x	y
2	6
5	−1
−7	−4
3	10

To decide on a window for a scatterplot, look at the values you are graphing. Find the least x-value in the table of values. Your x-minimum in the window should always be *less than* that value. Likewise, find the greatest x-value in the table and set the x-maximum in the window to a *greater* value. Follow the same procedure for the y-minimum and y-maximum in the window.

Step 3 Complete the following using the table above.
Answers vary for second column. Sample answers are given.
−7 least x-value __?__   a lesser x-value for x-min __?__ −10
5 greatest x-value __?__   a greater x-value for x-max __?__ 10
−4 least y-value __?__   a lesser y-value for y-min __?__ −10
10 greatest y-value __?__   a greater y-value for y-max __?__ 15

Step 4 Use your results to graph the points. One possible graph is shown below.

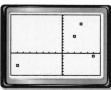

🛑 **See Quiz Yourself 2 at the right.**

▶ **QUIZ YOURSELF 2**

Plot the following table of values using lists and a proper window.

x	y
61	−681
64	−661
58	−661
67	−651
55	−651
70	−661
52	−661
50.5	−681
71.5	−681
70	−705
52	−705
67	−725
55	−725
64	−745
58	−745
61	−765

Notes on the Activity

Activity 8 shows students how to graph using lists. In this activity, students should try to come up with a result like that shown on page 37. It is important for students to know that the PLOTS feature should be *on* when doing scatterplots, and *off* when just graphing equations. Students often forget to turn STAT PLOT off when they are done using it. Later on when they are using their calculator to complete their homework, not only does the equation they are trying to graph appear but the scatterplot also appears. Generally students do not know what is happening because they forgot they had previously turned STAT PLOT on. Now is a good time to impress upon students the need to turn STAT PLOT off immediately after using the feature.

1-5

3 Assignment

Recommended Assignment
- Questions 1–26
- Questions 27 and 28 (extra credit)
- Reading Lesson 1-6
- Covering the Ideas 1-6

Additional Answers

5.

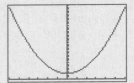

Questions

COVERING THE IDEAS

1. Write the two inequalities that describe the window for the graph at the right.
   __?__ $\leq x \leq$ __?__ and __?__ $\leq y \leq$ __?__ **−7; 6; −10; 20**

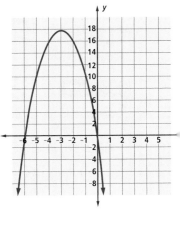

2. a. Write the two inequalities that describe the window below. **−60 ≤ x ≤ 40 and −3 ≤ y ≤ 3.5**

   b. Find the distance between tick marks on the x-axis and on the y-axis. **10 on the x-axis and 0.5 on the y-axis**

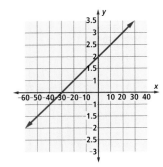

3. The window at the right is described by $-10 \leq x \leq 25$ and $-10 \leq y \leq 10$. Copy the window and label the tick marks with their coordinates.

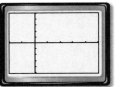   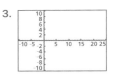

3.

4. Use the graphing calculator screen below to make a table of values for the expression $2x + 1$. List the first five ordered pairs in the table. **(−6, −11), (−4, −7), (−2, −3), (0, 1), (2, 5)**

```
TABLE SETUP
 TblStart=-6
 ΔTbl=2
Indpnt: Auto Ask
Depend: Auto Ask
```

5. Use a graphing calculator to make a table of values and graph for $y = x^2 + 3$ using the window $-6 \leq x \leq 6$ and $0 \leq y \leq 40$. Adjust your table settings so that x increases by 2 for each row in the table. **See margin.**

38   Using Algebra to Describe

6. **a.** Use lists on a calculator to graph the ordered pairs in the table below. 6a, c. See margin.

x	−59	−41	67	13	103	58	31	85	−23	4	121	49	31	−5
y	371	375	383	387	375	379	391	379	379	379	371	387	379	383

b. Use inequalities to show a window that contains all the points.

c. Sketch the graph using your window from Part b.

7. **a.** Graph $y = x^3 - 6x^2 - 9x + 4$ on a graphing calculator in a standard window.

b. Now change the values in the window so the graph looks like the image at the right. Give the values of your window's Xmin, Xmax, Ymin, and Ymax. Xmin: −4, Xmax: 10, Ymin: −80, Ymax: 10

8. **a.** Graph the equation $y = -0.04x^4 + 2.12x^2 - 7.84$ on a graphing calculator's standard window. Sketch the graph on paper.

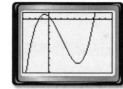

b. Change the y-max value in the window so the graph looks like the letter M, as shown at the right.

c. Change the x-values and the y-values in the window so only the right "bump" of the graph appears, as shown below.

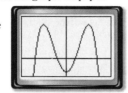

d. Enlarge the window to $-100 \le x \le 100$ with x-scale of 10, and $-500 \le y \le 500$ with y-scale of 100. Copy this graph on your paper.

e. Change to a window of $-3 \le x \le 3$ with x-scale of 0.5 and $-3 \le y \le 3$ with y-scale of 1. Copy this graph on your paper.

APPLYING THE MATHEMATICS

In 9 and 10, an equation is given. 9–10. See margin.
a. Graph the equation in a standard window.
b. Label at least three points on the graph with their coordinates.

9. $y = 3x - 4$ 　　　　　 10. $y = x^2 - 3$

6b. Answers vary.
Sample answer:
$-65 \le x \le 125$ and
$370 \le y \le 395$

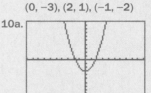

7a.
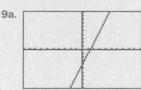

8a.
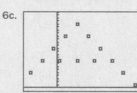

8b. Xmin: −10,
Xmax: 10, Ymin:
−10, Ymax: 25

8c. Xmin: 1, Xmax: 10,
Ymin: −10,
Ymax: 25

8d.
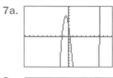

8e.
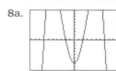

6a.

6c.
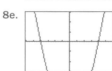

9a.
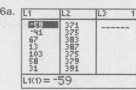

9b. Answers vary. Sample answer:
(0, −3), (2, 1), (−1, −2)

10a.
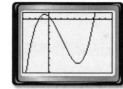

10b. Answers vary. Sample answer:
(0, −4), (2, 2), (−1, −7)

15b. Answers vary. Sample answer:

m	54 + 26m
0	$54
1	$80
2	$106
3	$132
4	$158
5	$184

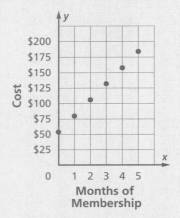

In 11 and 12, first graph the equation using the window $-10 \leq x \leq 10$ and $-10 \leq y \leq 10$. The result will be a line. Then adjust the window so the points where the line crosses both the x- and y-axes are visible. Describe your window with two inequalities.

11. $y = -4x - 32$

12. $y = \frac{1}{2}x - 12$

13. Test to see if $(6x - 14) - (x + 11)$ and $5x + 3$ are equivalent using a graphing calculator. Explain your conclusion.

14. Graph $y = \sqrt{x}$ on a calculator. Use the window $-10 \leq x \leq 10$ and $-10 \leq y \leq 10$.

REVIEW

15. Ayita's Gym charges new members a sign-up fee of $54, which they pay only once. For every month a person is a member, there is a fee of $26. Let $m =$ the number of months of membership. **(Lessons 1-1, 1-4)**

    a. Write an expression for the cost of membership for m months. **54 + 26m dollars**

    b. Make a table of values and plot the graph. **See margin.**

In 16–18, choose the most reasonable domain for the variable. **(Lesson 1-4)**

    a. the set of whole numbers
    b. the set of integers
    c. the set of real numbers
    d. the set of positive real numbers

16. the number of students n in your math class **a**

17. the time t it takes to drive to school **d**

18. the temperature T of a location on Earth **c**

19. An air conditioning unit with a high energy efficient ratio (EER) gives more cooling with less electricity. To find the EER of a unit, divide the BTU (British Thermal Unit) number by the number of watts the unit uses. The higher the EER, the more efficient the air conditioner. **(Lesson 1-1)**

$$EER = \frac{BTU}{\text{number of watts}}$$

    a. Find the EER to the nearest tenth for an air conditioner having 8,500 BTUs and 925 watts. **9.2**

    b. Find the EER to the nearest tenth for an air conditioner having 12,700 BTUs and 1,500 watts. **8.5**

    c. Which of the two air conditioners above is more efficient? Justify your answer. **The air conditioner in Part a is more efficient, since it has a higher EER.**

40   Using Algebra to Describe

11. Answers vary. Sample answer: $-10 \leq x \leq 10$ and $-40 \leq y \leq 10$

12. Answers vary. Sample answer: $-10 \leq y \leq 30$ and $-20 \leq y \leq 10$

13. The expressions are not equivalent since the graphs do not overlap entirely.

Walking for 20–45 minutes four to five times per week at 3 miles per hour is a great way to stay fit.

14.
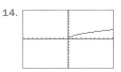

Extension

Have students enter and graph the equations Y1 = $-x^2$ + 7 and Y2 = x + 2 in a standard window on their graphing calculators. Ask students to identify the number of points of intersection. (There are two.) Have students use the **TRACE** command to estimate the coordinates representing the points of intersection, rounding the coordinates to the nearest hundredth. **The points are (−2.79, −0.79) and (1.79, 3.79).**

If necessary, show them how to move the cursor from the graph of Y1 to the graph of Y2 using the up and down arrows. Now introduce the **INTERSECT** command, found in the menu under the **CALC** command. Explain the concept of first curve, second curve, and guess. After you help them find one set of coordinates representing one point of intersection, have students find the other one.

20. Evaluate the expression $\frac{a+b}{3} + 3(a-b)$ for the given values of a and b. **(Lesson 1-1)**

    a. $a = 11, b = 4$ 26   b. $a = 7, b = 2$ 18

In 21–26, compute in your head. (Previous Course)

21. $15 + -19 + 4$ 0   22. $-10,000 - 20,000$ $-30,000$

23. $\frac{-16 + 8}{2}$ -4 24. $-6 - -10 + 3$ 7

25. $-8 - 16 + 5$ -19 26. $\frac{1}{3} + \frac{1}{2} - \frac{1}{5}$ $\frac{19}{30}$

EXPLORATION

27. Explain what the following features do on your graphing calculator.

    a. Zoom In zooms the window in

    b. Zoom Out zooms the window out

    c. ZBox zooms into specified box

28. Graph $y = \frac{19x}{x^2 + 4}$ on your graphing calculator. Experiment with the values of the window until the graph looks like each of the following. Give the values for your window's Xmin, Xmax, Ymin, and Ymax.

    a. a horizontal line Xmin: 50, Xmax: 60, Ymin: −10, Ymax: 10

    b. a diagonal crossing from the lower left corner to the upper right corner of the window

    c. a vertical line 28b. Xmin: −0.5, Xmax: 0.5, Ymin: −2, Ymax: 2

    d. a diagonal crossing from the upper left corner to the lower right corner of the window Xmin: 2.5, Xmax: 3.5, Ymin: 4.1, Ymax: 4.64

28c. Xmin: −3.617021...,
Xmax: 4.89361702...,
Ymin: −0.3225806...,
Ymax: 0

QUIZ YOURSELF ANSWERS

1. Each equation is represented in the graph.

2. The window $45 \leq x \leq 65$, and $-800 \leq y \leq -600$ displays the scatterplot.

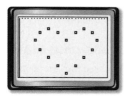

4 Wrap-Up

Ongoing Assessment

Have students enter the equation $Y1 = -3x^2 + 5x - 1$ into their graphing calculators. Instruct them to go to the TABLE SETUP feature and start the table at 0, with the table increment (ΔTbl) set to 1. Ask students to write an explanation of how they can find the values of Y1 when $x = 143$ and when $x = -16.5$ using the table.

Start table at 140 with an increment of 1, scroll down to 143, $Y1 = 60,633$;

Start table at 0 with an increment of 0.5, scroll up to −16.5, $Y1 = -900.3$.

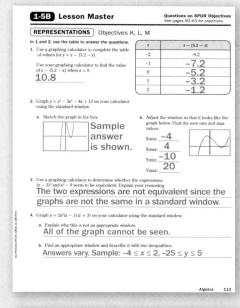

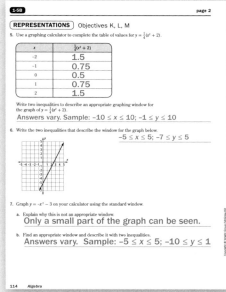

Lesson 1-6

Lesson 1-6
Absolute Value and Distance

GOAL

Recognize the connections between absolute value and distance, and the implications the definition of absolute value has for distinguishing x from $|x|$.

SPUR Objectives

D Evaluate expressions involving absolute value.

L Use graphs to determine whether expressions seem to be equivalent.

Materials/Resources

· Lesson Master 1-6A or 1-6B
· Resource Masters 1, 2, and 17
· Graphing calculator
· Quiz 2

HOMEWORK

Suggestions for Assignment
• Questions 1–21
• Question 22 (extra credit)
• Reading Lesson 1-7
• Covering the Ideas 1-7

Local Standards

Absolute Value and Distance

Vocabulary

absolute value

origin

▶ **BIG IDEA** The absolute value of a number and the distance between two numbers on a number line are closely related.

Cameron and Maria took a vacation to White's City, New Mexico, near the Guadalupe Mountains and the famous Carlsbad Caverns. Being avid hikers, they wanted to go mountain climbing and explore the caves. They found the following information on the Internet.

Mental Math

a. How many words can you type in 10 minutes if you type 52 words per minute? **520**

b. How many words can you type in 20 minutes if you type 52 words per minute? **1,040**

c. How many words can you type in t minutes if you type 52 words per minute? **52t**

Guadalupe Peak is the highest point in Texas.

Source: National Park Service

White's City is at an elevation of 5,740 feet (above sea level). Guadalupe Peak in Guadalupe Mountains National Park, 35 miles away, is at 8,749 feet. The entrance to Carlsbad Caverns National Park is 7 miles away. The entrance to Carlsbad Caverns is at an elevation of 4,400 feet, and the King's Palace Cavern is 900 feet below the entrance.

STOP See Quiz Yourself 1 at the right.

▶ **QUIZ YOURSELF 1**

What is the elevation of King's Palace Cavern?

Measuring Elevations from White's City

Because they were starting from White's City (W), Cameron and Maria wanted to know how much they would be going up and down from 5,740 feet. They subtracted the elevation of White's City from the

---

Background

The algebraic definition of *absolute value* requires students to realize that –x can be a positive number. This is difficult for some students. In this lesson and the next, we attack that difficulty by emphasizing the two relationships between absolute value and distance: (1) the absolute value of a number is its distance on the number line from 0, and (2) the distance between two numbers x and y on the number line is $|x - y|$. Property (1) is the special case of (2) when $y = 0$.

Property (2) is derived from the Comparison Model for Subtraction that students have seen in earlier courses, namely that $x - y$ is the difference between x and y. This difference may be positive or negative, based on whether y is less than or greater than x. So, for example, if y is the actual number of kernels of popcorn in a bag and x is an estimate, the difference $x - y$ will be positive if the estimate is too high and negative if the estimate is too low.

elevation of each destination. The difference is a positive number if they were going up and a negative number if they were going down.

Destination	Elevation (ft)	Difference from White's City (ft)
Guadalupe Peak (*G*)	8,749	$8{,}749 - 5{,}740 = 3{,}009$
Carlsbad Caverns entrance (*C*)	4,400	$4{,}400 - 5{,}740 = -1{,}340$
King's Palace Cavern (*K*)	3,500	$3{,}500 - 5{,}740 = -2{,}240$

These elevations are graphed on the left vertical number line at the right.

The difference from White's City's elevation to the other places is a *deviation* in altitude. A deviation can be positive or negative. The deviations are on the right vertical number line. However, sometimes we just want to know how much difference there is, and not the direction of the deviation. Then we take the *absolute value* of the deviation.

The symbol for absolute value is two vertical lines: | |.

If $x > 0$, then $|x| = x$.

If $x < 0$, then $|x| = -x$.

Since $3{,}009 > 0$, $|3{,}009| = 3{,}009$.

Since $-1{,}340 < 0$, $|-1{,}340| = -(-1{,}340) = 1{,}340$.

Then we say that the *absolute difference* in elevations between White's City and the entrance to Carlsbad Caverns is 1,340 feet.

 See Quiz Yourself 2 at the right.

Absolute Value and Distance

From the right vertical number line drawn above, you can see the geometric interpretation of absolute value.

Absolute Value

The **absolute value** of a number is its distance from 0.

Because the absolute value of a number is a distance, it is never negative. Using the definition of absolute value, $-x$ looks like a negative number. But that is only the definition when x is negative, so $-x$ stands for a positive number. For example, when $x = 830$, $|x| = |830| = 830$ and when $x = -830$, $|x| = |-830| = -(-830) = 830$.

 See Quiz Yourself 3 at the right.

Absolute Value and Distance   43

▶ **QUIZ YOURSELF 2**

a. What is $|-2{,}240|$?

b. What is the absolute difference in the elevations of White's City and the King's Palace Cavern?

▶ **QUIZ YOURSELF 3**

Evaluate each expression.

a. $|3 - 24|$

b. $|3| - |24|$

c. $|-3| - |-24| - |18|$

But suppose we do not care whether the estimate is high or low and just wonder how close the estimate is to the actual number of kernels. Then we use $|x - y|$, because if the difference $x - y$ is negative, then $|x - y|$ changes it to its opposite, a positive number. And if the difference is positive, then $|x - y|$ keeps the difference as it is. And if the guess is right on, then the difference is 0, and $|0| = 0$.

Students have seen absolute value if they have studied from *UCSMP Transition Mathematics*. But they may not have graphed $y = |x|$.

---

1. Give the value of $|r|$ for the given value of r.

a. $r = -7$ 7

b. $r = \frac{-2}{3}$ $\frac{2}{3}$

c. $r = 3 \cdot 10^{-5}$ 0.00003

d. $r = (-4)(-6)$ 24

2. Multiple choice When $x = -5$, which is true? **C**

A $|x| = x$

B $|x| = -|x|$

C $|x| = -x$

D none of these

In 3–5, calculate the distance between the numbers on a number line.

3. 0 and $3 \cdot 10^{-5}$ 0.00003

4. 160 and −161 321

5. $\frac{5}{12}$ and $\frac{2}{5}$ $\frac{1}{60}$

2 Teaching

Notes on the Lesson

White's City, the closest town to Carlsbad Caverns National Park, is 7 miles from the entrance to Carlsbad Caverns. It would seem to have been named after Jim White, who in 1898 became either the first or one of the first people to enter the Carlsbad Caverns. He was then 16 years old. Jim White remained a devotee of the caverns all his life and was a major influence in the caverns becoming a national monument 25 years later. However, in actuality, White's City is named after Charlie White, no relation to Jim, who in 1927 homesteaded the land that later became White's City. There are a number of places to stay in White's City, so it would be natural to measure one's elevation from White's City.

Stress that *deviations* may be positive or negative, but *distances* cannot be negative. Distance is the absolute value of deviation. Or we could say that distance is the absolute value of the difference, which we call *absolute difference*. In the next lesson, this is called *absolute deviation*.

1-6

Notes on the Lesson

Graphing absolute values is perhaps the best way for students to be sure that they graph enough of an expression to know what the entire graph resembles. The graph of $y = |2x|$ looks like a line if only nonnegative values of x are used as the domain; but the entire graph is an angle, as shown by the Activity answer. In general, students will learn in later courses that the graph of $y = |f(x)|$ is identical to the graph of $y = f(x)$ when the graph of $y = f(x)$ is above or on the x-axis, but not otherwise.

If you are using a graphing calculator to distinguish the graphs of $y = 2x$ and $y = |2x|$, you may wish to graph one with a thin line and the other with a thick line. Or, if your calculator has a color feature, graph them in different colors.

Notes on the Activity

Activity The activity presents a good opportunity for students to visualize how two similar absolute-value expressions differ. After students complete the Activity, you might ask them to graph $y = abs(x)$, $y = abs(x + 3)$, and $y = abs(x - 3)$ on their graphing calculators at the same time. Then ask them to describe how the three graphs appear to be related.

The graphs are congruent angles opening up. The graph of $y = abs(x)$ has its vertex at the origin. The graph of $y = abs(x + 3)$ has its vertex at $(-3, 0)$. The graph of $y = abs(x - 3)$ has its vertex at $(3, 0)$.

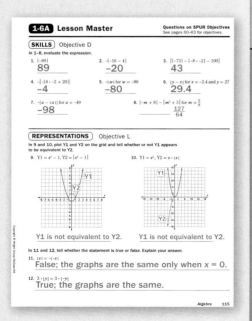

Expressions with Absolute Value

In this chapter you have seen many tables where the values are small, positive integers. However, using only these numbers can give you misleading information. For example, consider the expressions $2x$ and $|2x|$. The table at the right seems to show that $2x$ and $|2x|$ are equivalent. When x is a positive number, both expressions double it. So both $2x$ and $|2x|$ are positive. On the graph below the table, points for $2x$ are shown with open circles (O) and points for $|2x|$ are marked with squares (□). They are the same points.

But this is misleading! No negative numbers were used in the table above. As soon as negative numbers are included, you can see that the expressions $2x$ and $|2x|$ have different values. In fact, for negative numbers the values are opposites. For negative values of x, $2x$ is also negative, so taking the absolute value changes its sign. This can be seen on the graph below by looking to the left of the point $(0, 0)$, called the **origin.** For each negative value of x, the point for $2x$ (marked O) and the point for $|2x|$ (marked □) are on opposite sides of the x-axis.

x	2x	|2x|
0	0	0
1	2	2
2	4	4
3	6	6
4	8	8

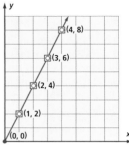

x	2x	|2x|
−5	−10	10
−4	−8	8
−3	−6	6

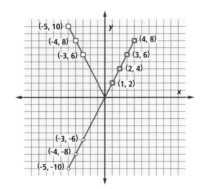

Activity

The graphing calculator or computer symbol for absolute value of a number x is **abs(x)**. In Lesson 1–5, you used technology to compare expressions. Now we use technology to compare $|x + 4|$ and $|x| + 4$.

Enter Y1=abs(x+4) and Y2=abs(x)+4 in your graphing calculator with window $-10 \leq x \leq 10$ and $-10 \leq y \leq 10$. Sketch the graphs in your window. Do the expressions appear to be equivalent?
No, the expressions are different because they do not overlap entirely.
🛑 See Quiz Yourself 4 at the right.

Activity

▶ **QUIZ YOURSELF 4**

Test whether $|x^2 - 6|$ and $-(x^2 - 6)$ are equivalent. Explain your reasoning.

Accommodating the Learner ⬆

On graphing calculators, have students graph Y1 = $|x|$ in the standard viewing window. While Y1 remains graphed, have them graph Y2 = $|x + 2|$. Ask students to describe the difference between the graphs of Y1 and Y2. The graph of Y2 is the graph of Y1 shifted 2 units to the left.

Have them set their calculators so that Y2 is not graphed, and then graph Y3 = $|x - 2|$. Ask students to describe the difference between Y1 and Y3. The graph of Y3 is the graph of Y1 shifted 2 units to the right.

Repeat the process for Y4 = $|x| + 2$ and Y5 = $|x| - 2$. The graph of Y4 is the graph of Y1 shifted 2 units up; the graph of Y5 is the graph of Y1 shifted 2 units down.

Ask students to write an absolute-value equation that is similar to Y1 but whose graph is shifted 3 units to the left. $y = |x + 3|$

Ask students to write an absolute-value equation that is similar to Y1 but whose graph is shifted 4 units down. $y = |x| - 4$

1-6A Lesson Master   Questions on SPUR Objectives
See pages 60–63 for objectives.

SKILLS Objective D

In 1–8, evaluate the expression.

1. $|-89|$ **89**

2. $-|-16 - 4|$ **−20**

3. $||-73| - |-8 \cdot -2| - 100|$ **43**

4. $-|-|8 \cdot -2 + 20||$ **−4**

5. $-|w|$ for $w = -80$ **−80**

6. $|y - x|$ for $x = -2.4$ and $y = 27$ **29.4**

7. $-|a - |a||$ for $a = -49$ **−98**

8. $|-m + 6| - |m^2 + 3|$ for $m = \frac{5}{8}$ **$\frac{127}{64}$**

REPRESENTATIONS Objective L

In 9 and 10, plot Y1 and Y2 on the grid and tell whether or not Y1 appears to be equivalent to Y2.

9. Y1 = $x^2 - 1$, Y2 = $|x^2 - 1|$

Y1 is not equivalent to Y2.

10. Y1 = x^2, Y2 = $x \cdot |x|$

Y1 is not equivalent to Y2.

In 11 and 12, tell whether the statement is true or false. Explain your answer.

11. $|x| = -|-x|$
False; the graphs are the same only when $x = 0$.

12. $3 \cdot |y| = 3 \cdot |-y|$
True; the graphs are the same.

Algebra 115

---

44   Chapter 1

Questions

COVERING THE IDEAS

1. The deepest cavern in Carlsbad Caverns is 1,567 feet below its entrance, making it the deepest cave in the United States.
   a. What is the elevation of that deepest cavern? **2,833 ft**
   b. What is the difference in its elevation from White's City?
   c. What is the absolute difference in its elevation from White's City? **2,907 ft**
   1b. −2,907 ft
2. Suppose you begin the day at an elevation of E feet. After some hiking, you are at an elevation of H feet.
   a. What is the deviation of where you are now from where you began? **$H - E$**
   b. What is the absolute deviation of where you are now from where you began? **$|H - E|$**
   c. When will the answers to Parts a and b be different? **When you are climbing lower, or when $E > H$.**
3. If $x = -40$ and $y = 35$, find each expression.
   a. $|x - y|$ **75**
   b. $|y - x|$ **75**
   c. $|x + y|$ **5**
   d. $|x| + |y|$ **75**

In 4–7, evaluate each expression.

4. $\left|\frac{3}{5}\right| + \left|\frac{3}{-5}\right|$ **$\frac{6}{5}$**

5. $|-1 - (-2)|$ **1**

6. $\text{abs}(2) - \text{abs}(-20)$ **−18**

7. $\frac{\text{abs}(x)}{\text{abs}(-x)}$ when $x = 4.8673$ **1**

8. Graph $y = |x + 5|$.

9. Find a value of t for which $3t$ and $|-3t|$ are not equal. **Answers vary. Sample answer: $t = -3$**

APPLYING THE MATHEMATICS

10. Test whether $|x + 4|$ and $|x| + 4$ are equivalent. **They are not equivalent.**
11. Graph $y = |x - 3| - 5$ on your calculator.
    a. Sketch the graph in a standard window.
    b. Sketch the graph in the window $-20 \le x \le 25$ with an x-scale of 5, and $-6 \le y \le 2$ with a y-scale of 1.
    c. Give Xmin, Xmax, Ymin, and Ymax for a window where only the left side of the angle is visible. **Xmin: −15, Xmax: 0, Ymin: −6, Ymax: 10**

In 12–15, find all values of the variable that satisfy the equation.

12. $|x| = 15$ **−15, 15**
13. $|w - 5| = 0$ **5**
14. $|z| = -8.8$
15. $|A| = |A - 1|$ **$\frac{1}{2}$**

Carlsbad Caverns in New Mexico has more than 100 caves.

Source: National Park Service

8.

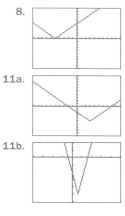

11a.

11b.

14. There are no values of z which satisfy the equation.

Absolute Value and Distance **45**

1-6

4 Wrap-Up

Ongoing Assessment

The Mariana Trench in the Pacific is the deepest part of the world's oceans at 35,839 feet deep. Mount Everest is the tallest mountain in the world with an elevation of 29,141 feet above sea level. If the base of Mount Everest was located at the bottom of the Mariana Trench, approximately how many miles of water would be above the peak of Mount Everest? (Hint: Use the absolute value of the deviation of the heights and divide by 5,280 feet.) **about 1.27 mi**

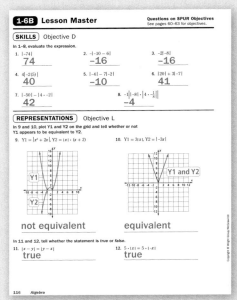

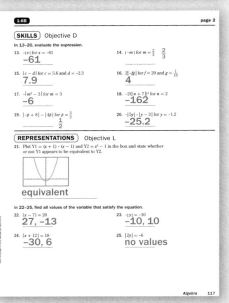

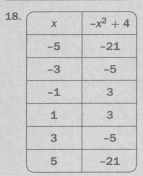

---

16. Use the graph at the right to answer the following questions. (**Lesson 1-4**)

    a. Complete the following table of values.

x	1	2	3	4	5
y	? 2	? 3	? 4	? 3	? 2

    b. What is the value of the expression when x equals 4? **3**

    c. What is the x-value when the value of the expression is 4? **3**

    d. **Multiple Choice** Which of the following equations best describes the graph? **C**

       A $y = |x - 2|$

       B $y = |x - 3| + 4$

       C $y = -1 \cdot |x - 3| + 4$

       D $y = x + 1$

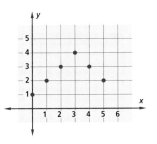

REVIEW

17. a. Graph $y = x^3 - 3x^2 + 3x - 1$ using the standard window.

    b. What are the coordinates of the x-intercept? (**Lesson 1-5**) **(1, 0)**

18. Make a table of values and a graph for $y = -x^2 + 4$ using the window $-5 \le x \le 5$, and $-30 \le y \le 30$. On your table, increase x by 2 for each row. (**Lesson 1-5**) **See margin.**

19. Express the set $\{x: x \text{ is an integer}, 5 \le x \le 10\}$ in roster form. (**Lesson 1-4**) $\{5, 6, 7, 8, 9, 10\}$

20. a. Give a counterexample to show that the following pattern is not true for all real numbers x and y. (**Lesson 1-3**)
    $$x - y = y - x$$

    b. State the result of Part a using the word *commutative*. (**Lesson 1-2**) **Subtraction is not commutative.**

21. Evaluate the following expressions for the given value of x. (**Lesson 1-1**)

    a. $-(-x^2) + x \cdot x \div (-x)$ for $x = 4$ **12**

    b. $\left(\dfrac{2}{1 - (-x)}\right)^{x + 1}$ for $x = 1$ **1**

EXPLORATION

22. Describe all integer values of x that satisfy $|x| < |x + 1|$.
    $\{x : x \ge 0\}$

17a.
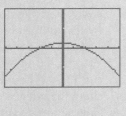

20a. **Answers vary. Sample answer:**
$x = 1$ and $y = 2$;
$1 - 2 = -1$ and
$2 - 1 = 1$

QUIZ YOURSELF ANSWERS

1. 3,500 ft

2. a. 2,240
   b. 2,240 ft

3. a. 21
   b. –21
   c. –39

4. The expressions are not equivalent. For example, when
   $x = 3: |3^2 - 6| =$
   $|9 - 6| = 3$, and
   $-(3^2 - 6) =$
   $-(9 - 6) = -3.$

Additional Answers

18.

x	$-x^2 + 4$
-5	-21
-3	-5
-1	3
1	3
3	-5
5	-21

Lesson
1-7

Lesson 1-7
Data and Spread

▶ **BIG IDEA** Two measures of the spread of a data set are *range* and *mean absolute deviation*.

In this chapter you have investigated number sequences that fit a pattern exactly and are described by an expression. However, many collections of numbers are "messy" and do not have an exact algebraic description. Statistics can help analyze and summarize these kinds of data.

Picturing the Mean of a Data Set

Suppose that a school board has received complaints that classrooms at Central School are small and crowded. To decide if this is the case, data about room size were gathered. Areas of 15 rooms were calculated in square feet, then rounded to the nearest 50 square feet. Here are the areas they found.

750; 700; 800; 750; 650; 800; 750; 750; 650; 750; 600; 900; 650; 600; 1,000

You can represent this data in a frequency table at the right.

Two other ways are in a *dot plot* (below at the left) and a *bar graph* (below at the right).

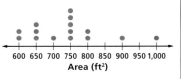

Areas of Classrooms at Central School

Area (ft²)

Areas of Classrooms at Central School

It is customary to use the Greek letter μ (*mu*, pronounced "mew") to stand for the mean. The mean classroom area is shown below.

$$\mu = \frac{2 \cdot 600 + 3 \cdot 650 + 1 \cdot 700 + 5 \cdot 750 + 2 \cdot 800 + 1 \cdot 900 + 1 \cdot 1,000}{15}$$
$$= 740 \text{ ft}^2$$

Vocabulary

range
mean absolute deviation
symmetric
skewed right
skewed left
uniform

Mental Math

a. What is the mean of 2, 3, and 4? 3

b. What is the mean of −2, −3, and −4? −3

c. What is the mean of −1, 0, and 1? 0

d. What is the mean of $x − 1$, x, and $x + 1$? x

Room Area (ft²)	Frequency
600	2
650	3
700	1
750	5
800	2
900	1
1,000	1

Data and Spread **47**

Lesson
1-7

GOAL
Discuss the range and mean absolute deviation of a data set and relate these statistics to ideas seen earlier in the chapter.

SPUR Objectives
E Calculate the range and mean absolute deviation.

I Calculate and interpret the spread of a distribution using mean absolute deviation.

Materials/Resources
· Lesson Master 1-7A or 1-7B
· Resource Masters 2, 18, and 19
· Paper clips
· Scientific or graphing calculator
· Spreadsheet software
· Graph paper
· Centimeter ruler

HOMEWORK
Suggestions for Assignment
• Questions 1–21
• Question 22 (extra credit)
• Reading Lesson 2-1
• Covering the Ideas 2-1

Local Standards

Background

Students have for many years dealt with the mean and median of a data set. These are measures of *central tendency*. They have spent much less time with measures of *spread* (or *dispersion*). After a quick review of plotting data sets, the *range* of a data set is discussed. The rest of the lesson is devoted to a second measure of spread, the *mean absolute deviation*.

The *range of a data set* is different from the *range of a function*. The range of a data set is a single number, calculated by subtraction. The range of a function is a set consisting of all the values taken by the dependent variable.

The mean absolute deviation (abbreviated as m.a.d.) is somewhat like the standard deviation of a data set, but it is easier to calculate and its relatively simple derivation is easy for students to understand. For this reason, the m.a.d. is a measure of spread that the American Statistical Association recommended that students study before encountering the standard deviation.

1-7

1 Warm-Up

Have the class begin with an activity. Display a large collection of paper clips. Have students guess the number of paper clips and write their guesses on the board so they are visible to the class. You may wish to separate these guesses into groups of 10 to simplify calculations. Have students calculate the mean for each group of 10 (and a last group likely to have a fewer number of guesses). If the class size is less than 20, you might wish to consider smaller groups of guesses.

2 Teaching

Notes on the Lesson

Representing the mean of a data set. Picturing data in dot plots and bar graphs is a previously learned skill for UCSMP students; do not spend class time teaching these display methods. However, the introduction of the Greek letter μ (pronounced "mew") to represent the mean is new. We use this letter for two reasons. First, we want to use M and m for the maximum and minimum values, respectively, of a data set. Second, statisticians routinely use μ for the mean and students will see it in their later encounters with statistics.

Students might ask how the expression for the mean classroom area on page 47 was found. (Instead of listing each classroom area individually, those with the same area are grouped together using multiplication rather than showing the repeated addition.)

Range of a data set. Like the mean, the range of a data set can be significantly affected by a single value in the data set, particularly if that value is an *outlier*. For example, if in a small business the owner has a salary of $200,000 while 4 other employees have salaries of $40,000, the owner's salary alone increases the range by $160,000. This increase shows why we call the range a measure of spread.

The school board at Central decided to compare the areas of classrooms at Central with those of Whittier School. Here is the list of classroom areas and a dot plot for Whittier.

750; 750; 750; 700; 800; 750; 700; 750; 800; 650; 700; 650; 750

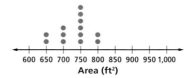

**Areas of Classrooms at
Whittier School**

Area (ft²)

The Range of a Data Set

The mean of the classroom areas for Whittier is about 730 square feet, which is less than the mean of 740 square feet for Central. But notice that the room areas at Central are more spread out than those at Whittier. The data values for Whittier lie in the interval $650 \leq A \leq 800$, where A is the area of a room. For Central, A is in the interval $600 \leq A \leq 1,000$. The **range** r of a collection of data is the difference between the maximum value M and minimum value m, so $r = M - m$. The range of classroom areas for Whittier is $800 - 650$, or 150 square feet.

 See Quiz Yourself 1 at the right.

▶ QUIZ YOURSELF 1

What is the range of classroom areas for Central School?

The Mean Absolute Deviation of a Data Set

The range is a measure of the spread of a data set. Another measure of spread is the average difference between the areas of the rooms and the mean area. This is the **mean absolute deviation** of the data set.

Example

Use the information about the classroom areas at Central School on page 47 to find the mean absolute deviation.

Solution We show how to find the mean absolute deviation for the classroom areas at Central School using spreadsheets or lists, although the same computations can be done by hand or on a calculator without lists. See the table on the next page.

48   Using Algebra to Describe

ENGLISH LEARNERS
Vocabulary Development

This lesson contains an extensive list of new terms. Students should not only write the definition of each term in their notebooks but also include an example for each new idea. For example, when defining the range, the student should include a data set and show how the range of the data is calculated.

Step	Spreadsheet	Graphing Calculator
1. Organize the data.	After naming column A in cell A2, enter the 15 room areas in cells A3 through A17.	Enter the 15 room areas into L1, the first list on your calculator.
2. Calculate the mean.	As shown below, it is 740 square feet. Find the mean from cells B3 through B17.	Keep the mean in mind.
3. Calculate the deviation of each area from the mean.	Enter "=A3−B3" in cell C3. Copy down to C17.	Enter L1−740 in place of L2 at the top of the screen. L2 will contain the deviations.
4. Calculate the mean of the deviations.	In cell C19 use the formula "=average(C3:C17)". The mean of the deviations should be 0 because the positive and negative differences balance.	Leave the LIST screen to calculate mean(L2).
5. Put the absolute value of each deviation in column D.	Enter "=abs(C3)" in cell D3 and copy the formula down the rest of the column.	Return to LIST. Enter abs(L2) for L3.
6. Calculate the mean absolute deviation.	In cell D19 enter "=average (D3:D17)". The mean of the absolute deviations is approximately 78.7.	Leave LIST again. Calculate mean(L3).

◇	A	B	C	D
1	Central School			
2	classroom area	mean area	Deviation (area − mean area)	Absolute Deviation (|area − mean area|)
3	750	740	10	10
4	700	740	-40	40
5	800	740	60	60
6	750	740	10	10
7	650	740	-90	90
8	800	740	60	60
9	750	740	10	10
10	750	740	10	10
11	650	740	-90	90
12	750	740	10	10
13	600	740	-140	140
14	900	740	160	160
15	650	740	-90	90
16	600	740	-140	140
17	1000	740	260	260
18				
19	740		0	78.66667
20				

Notes on the Lesson

The **Example** shows how to calculate the mean absolute deviation using either a spreadsheet or the List function on a graphing calculator; you can use either technology. A spreadsheet on a computer has the advantage of being able to display all the data at once. The List function on a graphing calculator may have the advantage of being available to more students.

Additional Example

Example The data set shown below is the number of runs scored by Lakeview's baseball team in each game last season. Find the mean absolute deviation of the data.

5, 11, 3, 6, 9, 4, 0, 15, 6, 8, 11, 7, 2, 1, 3, 4, 10, 9, 4, 6, 8, 0
3.045, or about 3.05 runs

Accommodating the Learner

Have each student write the number of hours of sleep they had last night (rounded to the nearest quarter of an hour) on a slip of paper. Collect the slips of paper in a box. Organize the class into groups of 3 students. Each group of students should draw 10 slips of paper from the box, record the times, and return the slips to the box. Have the groups organize their data in a table and then find the mean, μ, of the data values. For each data value v, have students find the absolute value of its deviation from the mean, which is represented by $|v - \mu|$, and then find the mean of these absolute values. As a class, have students compare the mean of the absolute deviations that each group found.

1-7

Notes on the Lesson

QY2 is not a simple question, but an activity that will take most students 10–15 minutes. It should be done.

Algorithm for finding the m.a.d. Students need only remember what the letters m, a, and d represent, and then use them in reverse order. First find the Deviations, then their Absolute values, and then the Mean of those absolute values.

Shape of a distribution. Here we identify four shapes: symmetric, skewed left, skewed right, and uniform. Point out that a uniform distribution is always symmetric. However, not all distributions are of one of these shapes, and very few distributions are precisely symmetric. The adjective *skew* has various meanings: "slanted," "asymmetrical," "off of a true value." The last of these is the one we think of when we think of "skew lines"—they are off from one another. Notice that the direction of skewing is the direction of the "tail" of the graph and not the direction where most of the data values lie.

🛑 See Quiz Yourself 2 at the right.

An abbreviation for mean absolute deviation is m.a.d. You should have found that the m.a.d. for Whittier is much smaller than the m.a.d. for Central. The rooms at Central are larger, on average, than those at Whittier. The range of the rooms at Central is also larger than the range of the rooms at Whittier. Do you see what is probably causing the complaints that the classrooms at Central are too small?

> **An Algorithm for Finding the Mean Absolute Deviation**
>
> As its name indicates, the mean absolute deviation is found using the following three steps:
>
> **Step 1** Find the mean, μ, of the data values.
>
> **Step 2** For each data value v, find the absolute value of its deviation from the mean, which is represented by $|v - \mu|$.
>
> **Step 3** Take the mean of the absolute deviations.

The Shape of a Distribution

Here are dot plots of the number of runs scored by Westview's softball team and the number of goals scored by its soccer team.

Softball Runs Westview Scored in Games

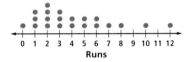

Runs

Soccer Goals Westview Scored in Games

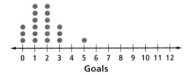

Goals

> **▶ QUIZ YOURSELF 2**
>
> Calculate the mean absolute deviation for the areas of the classrooms at Whittier on page 48.

There was a 67.3% increase in the number of female high school softball players from the 1980–1981 season to the 2000–2001 season.

Source: profastpitch.com

Accommodating the Learner ⬆

The *median* of a numerical list of data is the value in the middle when the numbers are put in order from least to greatest. In the table at the right, three lists of data are given along with their distribution shapes. Have students determine the median of each list. **9; 39; 8** Ask them to suggest reasons why the first list is categorized as skewed right, the second list is skewed left, and the third list is symmetric.

Skewed right	9	7	15	30	5	41	2
Skewed left	40	45	19	11	39	3	50
Symmetric	12	9	1	8	4	15	7

continued on next page

Some shapes of distributions are given special names. When most of the data are centered around one point and the values on the left and right sides are roughly mirror images, the distribution is called **symmetric.** The distribution of goals scored by the soccer team is symmetric. When the upper half of the values extends much farther to the right than the lower half, leaving a tail on the right, the shape is said to be **skewed right.** The softball team's run distribution has this kind of shape because most games are relatively low-scoring, but a few have high scores. Likewise, when the lower half of the data is much farther out, leaving a tail to the left, the shape is said to be **skewed left.** If the distribution has roughly the same height for all values it is called **uniform.**

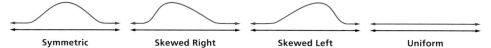

| Symmetric | Skewed Right | Skewed Left | Uniform |

Questions

COVERING THE IDEAS

1. Calculate the mean absolute deviation of the runs scored by Westview's softball team on page 50. about 2.46 runs

2. Calculate the m.a.d. of the goals scored by Westview's soccer team on page 50. about 0.87 goals

3. The table below gives the quiz scores of a group of students. Copy the table and fill in the columns. Then find the mean absolute deviation of the quiz scores. 3.2

Score	Mean	Deviation	Absolute Deviation
21	? 22	? −1	? 1
15	? 22	? −7	? 7
25	? 22	? 3	? 3
22	? 22	? 0	? 0
27	? 22	? 5	? 5

APPLYING THE MATHEMATICS

In 4 and 5, find the mean and mean absolute deviation in your head.

4. 7, 7, 7, 7, 7, 7, 7, 7, 7, 7, 7, 7, 7, 7 mean = 7, m.a.d. = 0

5. 2, 2, 2, 2, 2, 2, 4, 4, 4, 4, 4, 4 mean = 3, m.a.d. = 1

Now have students find the mean of each list and compare the mean to the median. about 15.6, greater than median; about 29.6, less than median; 8, same as median For each list, ask them to suggest reasons why the median is higher, lower, or the same as the mean of the list. Ask students to make conjectures about the relationship between the mean and median in a list whose distribution is skewed right, one that is skewed left, and one that is symmetric.

Answers vary. Sample answer: For a list of data that is categorized as skewed right, the mean is greater than the median; for a list of data that is categorized as skewed left, the mean is less than the median; and for a list of data that is categorized as symmetric, the mean and median are the same.

---

3 Assignment

Recommended Assignment
• Questions 1–21
• Question 22 (extra credit)
• Reading Lesson 2-1
• Covering the Ideas 2-1

Notes on the Questions
Questions 1 and 2 Before any calculations, many students should realize that the answer to Question 2 is less than the answer to Question 1. This is true because, with fewer goals scored in a soccer match, the goals scored in soccer are much closer to the mean, on average, than the runs scored in softball.

Question 5 The reason both the mean and m.a.d. are easy to calculate for this list is that the number of 2s is the same as the number of 4s. If all the deviations are 1 or −1, then the m.a.d. will be 1. What would happen to the m.a.d. if one of the 2s were changed to a 4? The mean would no longer be 3. Would the m.a.d. increase or decrease? (The new mean would be $\frac{38}{12}$; there would be 7 absolute deviations of $\frac{10}{12}$ and 5 of $\frac{14}{12}$, for an m.a.d. of $\frac{140}{144}$, which is a slight decrease from its value before the change.) Without calculations, one can guess that the m.a.d. would decrease because if all the scores changed from 2 to 4, the m.a.d. would decrease to 0.

1-7A Lesson Master Questions on SPUR Objectives
See pages 60–63 for objectives.

SKILLS Objective E

In 1–3, calculate the mean, the mean absolute deviation, and the range for each collection of data.

1. 3, 4, 7, 3, 6, 2, 9, 9, 5, 5, 6
mean: _5.36_
mean absolute deviation: about 1.85
range: _7_

2. −0.3, 0.05, 1, 2.5, 0.2, 0.6
mean: _0.675_
mean absolute deviation: about 0.717
range: _2.8_

3. −25, 64, 49, 4, 625, 400, 9, −81
mean: 130.625
mean absolute deviation: about 190.938
range: 706

USES Objective I

4. Construct a data set of 8 items that has a mean of 5 and mean absolute deviation of 4.
Answers vary. Sample: 1, 1, 1, 1, 9, 9, 9, 9

In 5–8, use the heights, in inches, of a group of students given below.
61, 64, 63, 58, 62, 57, 61, 66, 68, 70

5. What is the mean of the heights of the students? 63 in.

6. What is the mean absolute deviation of the heights of the students? 3.2 in.

7. In another group of students, the mean absolute deviation of the heights is 4.2 inches. In which group are the heights more consistent? Explain.
first group; A mean absolute deviation of 3.2 inches is less than a mean absolute deviation of 4.2 inches.

8. Multiple choice. A dot frequency diagram of the data is shown below. Which term best describes the shape of the graph?
A symmetric   B skewed left
C skewed right   D uniform   D

118 Algebra

Notes on the Questions

Question 10 Students should write a few sentences as their answer to this question.

Question 11 The lengths of terms for the United States presidents include those through Bill Clinton's term, including Grover Cleveland's two terms separately. The years reigned by English rulers begin with William I and continue through the publication of this book.

For 6–9, use the following sketches.

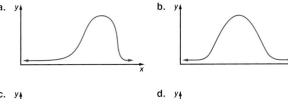

6. Which distribution is symmetric? b and d
7. Which distribution is skewed left? a
8. Which distribution is skewed right? c
9. Which of the distributions most closely describes the scores of all baseball games of one team in a season? c
10. In this lesson, a story is told in which people at Central School complain about the classrooms being too small. Whittier School has a mean classroom size that is lower than Central's, but there are no complaints at Whittier. What seems to be the cause of the complaints at Central?
11. These two data sets give the lengths of terms of Presidents of the United States and the reigns of kings and queens of England. Years served by the first 42 American presidents: 8, 4, 8, 8, 8, 4, 8, 4, 0, 4, 4, 1, 3, 4, 4, 4, 4, 8, 4, 1, 3, 4, 4, 4, 5, 7, 4, 8, 2, 6, 4, 12, 8, 8, 3, 5, 6, 2, 4, 8, 4, 8
Years reigned by 39 English rulers: 21, 13, 35, 19, 35, 10, 17, 56, 35, 20, 50, 22, 13, 9, 39, 22, 0, 24, 38, 6, 5, 44, 22, 24, 25, 3, 13, 6, 12, 13, 33, 59, 10, 7, 63, 9, 25, 1, 15

a. Use a spreadsheet or graphing calculator to calculate the mean, mean absolute deviation, and range of each collection of data.

b. Write a few sentences explaining why the two distributions have such different values for their means, mean absolute deviations, and ranges.

12. a. Construct a data set of 8 items that has a mean absolute deviation of 0.5 and for which $\mu = 8$.

b. What are the M, m, and r for this data set?

12a. Answers vary. Sample answer: 7, 7, 8, 8, 8, 8, 9, 9

12b. Answers vary. Sample answer for our data: $M = 9$, $m = 7$, and $r = 2$

10. Answers vary. Sample answer: The larger spread of room size at Central means they have some very small rooms, which probably sparked the complaints.

11a. For Presidents, the mean is about 5.0 years with a m.a.d. of about 2.1 years and range of 12, while for the English rulers, the mean is about 21.9 years with a m.a.d. of about 12.8 years and range of 63.

11b. Answers vary. Sample answer: Presidents have set term lengths and a limit to the total number of terms, whereas rulers, who may be very old or very young when crowned, typically reign until death.

The first Oval Office was built in 1909 in the center of the south side of the West Wing of the White House.

Source: www.whitehouse.gov

13. Construct a data set of 7 items that has a median of 9 and a mean of 8. **Answers vary. Sample answer: 3, 4, 7, 9, 10, 11, 12**

14. Construct a data set of 12 items that has a mode of 6, and for which $\mu = 9$.

15. The mean absolute deviation can be used to measure consistency. The more consistent data set is the one with the smaller m.a.d. Here are the mean maximum daily temperatures for each month in San Diego and Miami. In which city are the year's high temperatures more consistent? **San Diego**

Month	Miami (°C)	San Diego (°C)
January	24.0	18.8
February	24.7	19.2
March	26.2	19.1
April	28.0	20.2
May	29.6	20.6
June	30.9	22.0
July	31.7	24.6
August	31.7	25.4
September	31.0	25.1
October	29.2	23.7
November	26.9	21.1
December	24.8	18.9

REVIEW

16. Evaluate each expression. (**Lesson 1-6**)
    a. $|3 - |-3 + 9||$ **3**
    b. $|2x - 10|$ when $x = 3.5$ **3**
    c. $-4|x - y|$ when $x = 0.5$ and $y = 3$ **–10**

17. Use the window at the right. The tick marks on the x-axis occur every 20 units. On the y-axis, tick marks occur every 0.25 unit. Find the values of each. (**Lesson 1-5**)

    x-min $\underline{\ ?\ }$ **–120** x-max $\underline{\ ?\ }$ **60**
    y-min $\underline{\ ?\ }$ **–1.5** y-max $\underline{\ ?\ }$ **0.5**

18. On a graphing calculator, graph $y = x^3 - 5x$ using the window $-10 \leq x \leq 10$ and $-10 \leq y \leq 10$. Sketch the graph that results. (**Lesson 1-5**)

19. Make a table and scatterplot for the ordered pair $(n, n^2 - n)$ using the following values of n: $-3, -2, 0, 2,$ and 3. (**Lesson 1-4**)

14. Answers vary.
    Sample answer: 6,
    6, 6, 6, 6, 8, 9, 9, 9,
    12, 13, 18

18.
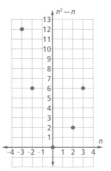

19.

n	$n^2 - n$
–3	12
–2	6
0	0
2	2
3	6

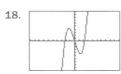

Notes on the Questions
Question 15 Although Miami is warmer, it does not necessarily have an m.a.d. greater than a cooler city. However, in this instance it has a slightly greater m.a.d. than does San Diego.

Data and Spread   **53**

1-7

4 Wrap-Up

Ongoing Assessment

When examining a set of data, an *outlier* is a data value that is not consistent with the rest of the values. Consider the following data.

Day	1	2	3	4	5	6	7	8	9
Rainfall, in./day	0.5	0.4	1	3.4	0.2	1.1	0.1	0.9	0.6

The 3.4 inches of rain that fell on Day 4 would be considered an outlier because it is significantly greater than any of the other data values. Ask students what affect this outlier will have on the mean of the data. Have them calculate the mean of the data with and without the outlier included. Have students explore data in which the outlier(s) is significantly greater than all the other data values and have them explore data in which the outlier(s) is significantly less than all the other data values. What conclusions can they draw from the results of their explorations?

Project Update

Project 1, Examining Pi, on page 56 relates to the content of this lesson.

20. Complete the table of values for each expression. Use the tables to determine whether the expressions appear to be equivalent. Explain your reasoning. (**Lesson 1-3**)

n	(n + 2) + 7 + (n + 2)
−5	? · 1
−3	? · 5
1	? · 13
2	? · 15
5	? · 21

n	3n + 3 − n + 8
−5	? · 1
−3	? · 5
1	? · 13
2	? · 15
5	? · 21

20. They are equivalent, since $(n + 2) + 7 + (n + 2) = 2n + 11 = 3n + 3 − n + 8$.

21. Consider the sequence of triangles. Assume the designs are made with toothpicks. (**Lesson 1-2**)

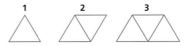

1   2   3

a. Draw a table describing the number of toothpicks needed for the first 5 terms.

b. Write an expression for the number of toothpicks in the nth term. **2n + 1**

c. How many toothpicks will be needed to make the 100th term? **201**

21a.

Term Number	Number of Toothpicks
1	3
2	5
3	7
4	9
5	11

EXPLORATION

22. Choose the data set that would probably have the smaller m.a.d. and explain why.

a. incomes of 10 union members from a factory; incomes of 10 management members from the same factory

b. temperatures in one place on the moon for a month; temperatures in one place on Earth for a month

c. recovery times for 6 people from an appendectomy; recovery times for 6 basketball players from knee operations **See margin.**

22a. The union workers would probably have the smaller m.a.d. There is less variation in the responsibilities of the union workers, and there is probably a greater range in management levels.

22b. The temperatures on Earth would probably have a smaller m.a.d. Earth's temperatures vary much less than the moon's temperatures because the atmosphere helps regulate Earth's temperature.

Two unionized workers inspecting air-bag canisters.

QUIZ YOURSELF ANSWERS

1. $r = 1,000 − 600 = 400 \text{ ft}^2$

2. 39

54   Using Algebra to Describe

Additional Answers

22c. The recovery times from the appendectomy probably have a smaller m.a.d. Appendectomies are routine surgeries and tend to all be about the same. Knee surgeries on basketball players can range from minor to major so there is much more variation here.

Chapter 1 Projects

1 Examining Pi

Look up the first fifty digits of the decimal expansion of π. Calculate the frequency in which each digit 0 through 9 appears. Calculate the mean absolute deviation of these digits. Find two numbers: one whose first fifty digit decimal expansion has a smaller mean absolute deviation and one with a greater mean absolute deviation.

The constant π is used in the formulas to find the circumference and area of a circle.

2 Estimating Square Roots

Al-Karkhi (also known as al-Karaji) was an Arab mathematician who lived during the early 11th century. He found a formula for approximating the square root of a positive integer n. The formula is $\sqrt{n} \approx w + \frac{n + w^2}{2w + 1}$. Before using his formula to find the square root of n, you must first find w, the whole number part of $\sqrt{n}$. Investigate al-Karkhi's method by making a table with different values for n from 1 to 50 and using the formula to estimate $\sqrt{n}$ rounded to the nearest thousandth. Compare the results to what you obtain by finding $\sqrt{n}$ with a calculator. What conclusions can you make concerning al-Karkhi's method?

3 Formula 1

The game of Formula 1 is played in the following way: Two players secretly make up an expression with one variable and write it on a piece of paper. After both players have their formulas, they "race" them in the following way: Substitute the numbers 1 through 10 in the formula and take the sum of all of the results. The player with the higher total wins. Play this game with a friend several times, each time with a new formula. What changes did you make in order to increase your total? (You may want to use a spreadsheet to do the calculations.)

Formula One (F1) also deals with Grand Prix auto racing. The "Formula" in Formula One is a set of rules which all race teams must follow.

Project Rubric

Advanced	Student correctly provides all of the details asked for in the project as well as additional correct independent conclusions.
Proficient	Student correctly provides all of the details asked for in the project.
Partially proficient	Student correctly provides some of the details asked for in the project or provides all details with some inaccuracies.
Not proficient	Student correctly provides few of the details asked for in the project or provides all details with many inaccuracies.
No attempt	Student makes little or no attempt to complete the project.

The projects relate to the content of the lessons of this chapter as follows:

Project	Lesson(s)
1	1-7
2	1-1
3	1-1
4	1-2
5	1-3

1 Examining Pi

Students will need to identify the first fifty digits of the decimal expansion of π before they can calculate the mean absolute deviation of these digits. Suggest to students that they use the Internet or the school library to identify the needed digits. It would enhance the project if they include a table that shows how they calculated the mean absolute deviation. The entries for this table can be found by creating a spreadsheet program or by using a calculator. The most difficult part of this project is finding a number whose first fifty-digit decimal expansion has a smaller mean absolute deviation and one with a greater mean absolute deviation. Engage students in a discussion on what factors might increase or decrease the mean absolute deviation.

2 Estimating Square Roots

Al-Karkhi's method estimates square roots by making equal divisions between square roots of consecutive perfect squares. For example, $\sqrt{27}$ is estimated as $\frac{2}{11}$ of the way between $\sqrt{25}$ and $\sqrt{36}$. Encourage students to look for patterns in the mixed number answers before rounding to the nearest thousandth. You might want to point out that the value of w is the square root of the nearest perfect square less than n. Also, for perfect squares, $n = w^2$, and the fractional part of Al-Karkhi's formula is equal to 0.

3 Formula 1

Ask students to think carefully about the creation of their algebraic expression. Pose the following questions to them. When the numbers 1 through 10 are substituted into your expression, does the value of each result have anything to do with increasing the sum of the terms? What will have the greatest impact on a variable in an effort to increase the value of each result—addition, subtraction, multiplication, division, exponents, or a combination? If you do not want your students to do the calculations by hand and spreadsheet software is not available, consider teaching them how to use the **sum( )** and **seq( )** commands found in the menus of their graphing calculators.

4 Figurate Numbers

As an extension, you might also ask students to find formulas for the nth triangular, square, and pentagonal numbers. nth triangular number: $\frac{n(n+1)}{2}$; nth square number: n^2; nth pentagonal number: $\frac{n(3n-1)}{2}$

5 Encoding and Decoding Using Formulas

Students would benefit from choosing a short word of their own and encoding the word. The students should then decode the word so they practice both the coding and decoding processes. Once they have done this, they should be able to decode their friend's message. A search of the Internet using the search words "frequency analysis" leads to several good Web sites. Suggest to students that they choose an average-size paragraph to complete Part c. Point out that if they choose a paragraph that is very short, they will not have enough data to reach a valid conclusion.

4 Figurate Numbers

Some numbers are called *figurate numbers* because they can easily be represented by geometric figures. Pictured below are the first four triangular numbers, the first four square numbers, and the first four pentagonal numbers.

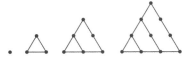

triangular numbers 1, 3, 6, 10

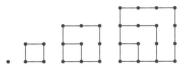

square numbers 1, 4, 9, 16

pentagonal numbers 1, 5, 12, 22

a. Draw a picture of the 5th triangular number, 5th square number, and 5th pentagonal number.

b. Based on the patterns in the number of dots on the side of each figure, find the 10th triangular number, the 10th square number, and the 10th pentagonal number.

c. Make a poster or write a report about figurate numbers for your classroom.

5 Encoding and Decoding Using Formulas

a. Formulas can be used to create codes. Consider the formula $27 - n$. Convert a short sentence to numbers using a = 1, b = 2, and so on. Use the formula to encode it. For example, the word "code" in numbers would be 3, 15, 4, and 5 with c = 3, o = 15, d = 4, and e = 5. Using the formula, we would get the encoded message 24, 12, 23, 22.

b. Have a friend give you their encoded sentence. Explain how you would get the formula to decode their message.

c. One famous method for decoding is called "frequency analysis." This method is based on the fact that some letters in English appear more commonly than others. For example, with our formula, the code for the letter "e" is 22. Because e is the most common letter in written English, the number 22 should be the most common one to appear. Look up the term frequency analysis on the Internet, and find a table describing how commonly each letter is used in English prose. Choose a paragraph from a book, and find the frequencies for the letters "e," "q," and "p" in the paragraph. Does this agree with the table you found? Explain how you would use frequency analysis to decode an encoded message.

This Enigma cypher machine was used to encode wartime messages during World War II.

Notes

_____

_____

_____

_____

_____

_____

_____

_____

Chapter 1 — Summary and Vocabulary

○ Algebra is a powerful language for describing patterns and real-world situations. Its power comes from the use of **variables.** Variables are letters or other symbols that can be replaced by any number from a set, the **domain** of the variable.

○ An **algebraic expression** is a sequence of symbols that contains variables, numbers, and operations. Rules for the **order of operations** ensure that different individuals evaluating the same expressions will get the same values. Scientific and graphing calculators usually follow the same rules of order of operations.

○ Algebraic expressions can describe the nth term in a pattern. Two algebraic expressions are **equivalent** if they have the same value. Graphs and tables can be used to explore whether algebraic expressions are equivalent. For example, tables show that $(x - 1) + 3 + (x - 1)$ and $2x + 1$ each have the same value for any particular value of x. This suggests that the expressions are equivalent. The graphs of $y = (x - 1) + 3 + (x - 1)$ and $y = 2x + 1$ also suggest that the expressions are equivalent. On the other hand, the expression $2x + 3$ produces different values from those of the other two expressions, so it is not equivalent to the others.

○ The **absolute value** of a number is its distance from 0 on a number line. The distance between two numbers on a number line with coordinates x and y is $|x - y|$. Statistics can be useful in describing data that do not fit an exact algebraic pattern. Two measures of spread are the **range** and the **mean absolute deviation (m.a.d.).** The m.a.d. applies the idea of absolute value.

Theorems and Properties

Algebraic Definition of Subtraction (p. 7)
Algebraic Definition of Division (p. 7)
Associative Property of Multiplication (p. 9)
Associative Property of Addition (p. 10)

Transitive Property of Equality (p. 10)
Commutative Property of Addition (p. 16)
Commutative Property of Multiplication (p. 16)

Vocabulary

1-1
variable
algebraic expression
evaluating the expression

1-2
pattern, instance
define a variable
term, factor

1-3
sequence, term
equivalent expressions
counterexample

1-4
scatterplot
domain of a variable

1-5
window
Xmin, Xmax
Ymin, Ymax
Xscl, Yscl
standard window

1-6
absolute value
origin

1-7
range
mean absolute deviation (m.a.d.)
symmetric
skewed right
skewed left
uniform

Self-Test

For the development of mathematical competence, feedback and correction, along with the opportunity for practice, are necessary. The Self-Test provides the opportunity for feedback and correction; the Chapter Review provides additional opportunities for practice. We cannot overemphasize the importance of these end-of-chapter materials. It is at this point that the material "gels" for many students, allowing them to solidify skills and understanding. In general, student performance should improve after these pages are completed.

Assign the Self-Test as a one-night assignment. Worked-out solutions for all questions are in the Selected Answers section of the student book. Encourage students to take the Self-Test honestly, grade themselves, and then be prepared to discuss the test in class.

Advise students to pay special attention to those Chapter Review questions (pages 60–63) that correspond to the questions they missed on the Self-Test.

Additional Answers

1a. $9 \cdot 4 + 9 \cdot 6 = 9 \cdot 10$;
$9 \cdot 4 + 9 \cdot 7 = 9 \cdot 11$;
$9 \cdot 4 + 9 \cdot 8 = 9 \cdot 12$

1b. Generally, for any x,
$9 \cdot 4 + 9 \cdot x = 9 \cdot (x + 4)$.

3. $3x \div 7y = 3x \cdot \frac{1}{7y}$

4. The total cost for the jerseys is the cost of a single jersey times the number of jerseys plus the cost of a single T-shirt times the number of T-shirts, so Total Cost = $179j + 24t$ dollars.

6c. The original design has 10 tiles, and each nth term has an additional $(n - 1) \cdot 7$ tiles, so the nth term has $10 + (n - 1) \cdot 7$, which simplifies to $3 + 7n$.

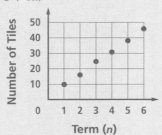

Take this test as you would take a test in class. You will need graph paper. Then use the Selected Answers section in the back of the book to check your work.

1. Consider the following pattern:

$$9 \cdot 4 + 9 \cdot 1 = 9 \cdot 5$$
$$9 \cdot 4 + 9 \cdot 2 = 9 \cdot 6$$
$$9 \cdot 4 + 9 \cdot 3 = 9 \cdot 7$$
$$9 \cdot 4 + 9 \cdot 4 = 9 \cdot 8$$
$$9 \cdot 4 + 9 \cdot 5 = 9 \cdot 9$$

a. Write the next three instances of the pattern. **1a–b. See margin.**

b. Describe the pattern using one variable.

2. Provide an example illustrating the Commutative Property of Multiplication.
Answers vary. Sample answer $3 \cdot 17 = 17 \cdot 3$

3. Rewrite the division problem as a multiplication problem $3x \div 7y$. **See margin.**

4. At a sports store, authentic jerseys cost $179 and customized T-shirts cost $24. Let j = the number of jerseys purchased and let t = the number of T-shirts purchased. Write an expression describing the total cost of all clothing purchased at the sports store. **See margin.**

5. a. Complete the table of values for the provided expressions.

n	$\frac{6n - 12}{3}$		$-4 + 2n$	
−5	?	−14	?	−14
−3	?	−10	?	−10
0	?	−4	?	−4
2	?	0	?	0

b. Do $\frac{6n - 12}{3}$ and $-4 + 2n$ seem to be equivalent expressions? **Yes. For all values on this table, the two expressions are equal.**

6. Consider the sequence of square tile designs shown here.

1 2

3

6a. $10 + 7 + 7 + 7 = 31$ tiles
a. Determine how many tiles would be required to make the next term.

b. Complete the table describing the number of square tiles used for various patterns in the sequence.

n	1	2	3	4	5	6
Number of Tiles	10	17	?	?	?	?

24 31 38 45

c. Write an expression for the number of square tiles in the nth term. **See margin.**

d. Create a scatterplot from the table. **See margin.**

7. Consider the following expressions:

Expression 1: $\frac{m}{2} + \frac{3}{2}$

Expression 2: $\frac{3 + m}{4}$ **7a–b. See margin.**

a. Find a value for m that shows that Expressions 1 and 2 are *not* equivalent.

b. Write an expression that is equivalent to Expression 1.

8. Consider the following expressions.

Expression 1: $\frac{101x + 200}{100}$

Expression 2: $x + 2$

a. What does a standard window seem to suggest about equivalence of the expressions? **8a–b. See margin.**

7a. Answers vary. Sample answer: $m = 0$, since $\frac{m}{2} + \frac{3}{2} = \frac{0}{2} + \frac{3}{2} = 0 + \frac{3}{2} = \frac{3}{2}$, but $\frac{3 + m}{4} = \frac{3 + 0}{4} = \frac{3}{4}$.

7b. Answers vary. Sample answer: By the Distributive Property of Multiplication, we can factor out a $\frac{1}{2}$, and the definition of division gives the expression $\frac{m + 3}{2}$.

8a. They appear to be equivalent.

8b. No. For instance, the value $x = 1$ gives 3.01 for the first expression and 3 for the second.

b. Are the expressions equivalent? Why or why not?

9. An expression is graphed below. Use the graph to answer the following questions.

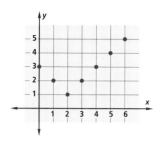

a. What is the value of the expression when $x = 4$? 3

b. Use the graph to complete the following table of values.

x	0	1	2	3	4	5
y	?	?	?	?	?	?

3 2 1 2 3 4

c. **Multiple Choice** Which of the following expressions best describes the values plotted on the graph? B

A $|x + 2|$

B $|x - 2| + 1$

C $|x + 2| - 1$

D $3 - x$

10. Graph $y = x - 15$ using the window $-10 \le x \le 10$ and $-10 \le y \le 10$. The result will be a line. Adjust the window to reveal where the line crosses both the x- and the y-axes. Describe your new viewing window in the space provided. Answers vary.

Xmin: ___?___ –2   Xmax: ___?___ 20

Ymin: ___?___ –20   Ymax: ___?___ 2

In 11–13, use the following information. Over the past week, students in Mr. Cy Metric's class reported paying the following amounts for entrance to a movie. The results are graphed in a dot plot.

$6, $7, $9, $8, $10, $2, $7, $10, $10, $9, $8, $8, $9, $9, $10

11. Identify the shape of the dot plot as symmetric, skewed right, skewed left, or uniform. skewed left

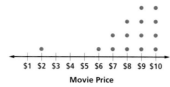

Movie Price

12. Calculate the mean and mean absolute deviation for the data set. Round to the nearest tenth. See margin.

13. Do data have more spread or less spread than a set with a mean of 8.8 and a mean absolute deviation of 2.6? Explain your reasoning. See margin.

14. a. Graph $y = 0.5x^3 + x^2 - 5.5x - 5$ on a graphing calculator. View the graph with the standard window and sketch the results. See margin.

b. Change the values in the window to get the graph to look like the one below. What are the values of your window's Xmin, Xmax, Ymin, and Ymax?

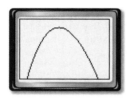

Answers vary. Sample answer:
Xmin = –4, Xmax = –1,
Ymin = 3, Ymax = 8

Additional Answers

13. The m.a.d. is what determines the spread, and because we have a lower m.a.d. in the original data set, there is less spread in the original set.

14a.

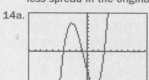

Additional Answers

12. $\mu = \dfrac{6 + 7 + 9 + 8 + 10 + 2 + 7 + 10 + 10 + 9 + 8 + 8 + 9 + 9 + 10}{15}$

$= \dfrac{1(2) + 1(6) + 2(7) + 3(8) + 4(9) + 4(10)}{15}$

≈ 8.1

m.a.d. $= \dfrac{|2 - \mu| + |6 - \mu| + 2|7 - \mu| + 3|8 - \mu| + 4|9 - \mu| + 4|10 - \mu|}{15}$

$= \dfrac{6.1 + 2.1 + 2(1.1) + 3(0.1) + 4(0.9) + 4(1.9)}{15}$

≈ 1.5

Chapter Review

The main objectives for the chapter are organized in the Chapter Review under the four types of understanding this book promotes—Skills, Properties, Uses, and Representations.

Whereas end-of-chapter material may be considered optional in some texts, in *UCSMP Algebra* we have selected these objectives and questions with the expectation that they will be covered. Students should be able to answer these questions with about 85% accuracy after studying the chapter.

You may assign these questions over a single night to help students prepare for a test the next day, or you may assign the questions over a 2-day period. If students work on the questions over two days, then we recommend assigning the *evens* for homework the first night so that students get feedback in class the next day, and then assigning the *odds* the night before the test because the answers are provided to the odd-numbered questions in the Selected Answers at the back of the book.

It is effective to ask students which questions they still do not understand and use the day as a total class discussion of the material that the students find most difficult.

Resources
- Assessment Resources: Chapter 1 Test, Forms A–D

Chapter 1 Chapter Review

SKILLS PROPERTIES USES REPRESENTATIONS

SPUR stands for Skills, Properties, Uses, and Representations. The Chapter Review Questions are grouped according to the SPUR Objectives in this Chapter.

SKILLS Procedures used to get answers

OBJECTIVE A Evaluate numerical and algebraic expressions. (Lesson 1-1)

In 1–4, evaluate the numerical expression.

1. $20 \div 5 \div 5$ 0.8
2. $70 - 4 \cdot (-3) \div 2$ 76
3. $\frac{5 \cdot 0.43^2}{0.43}$ 2.15
4. $\left(\frac{3}{8} + \frac{5}{6}\right) \cdot 4 + \frac{3}{5}$ $\frac{163}{30}$, or about 5.43

In 5–10, evaluate the algebraic expression for the given variable.

5. $4x^2$ for $x = 13$ 676
6. $-6q - q$ when $q = -3.64$ 25.48
7. $\frac{-5x}{2} + \frac{3}{-x}$ if $x = 7$ $-\frac{251}{14}$, or about −17.93
8. $\left(\frac{n}{3}\right)^3$ for $n = 24$ 512
9. $4(p - q)$ when $p = 13\frac{1}{2}$ and $q = 2\frac{3}{5}$ 43.6
10. $y - x \div 4 \cdot (-2)$ when $x = 8$ and $y = -3$ 1

OBJECTIVE B Use variables to describe patterns in instances or tables. (Lessons 1-2, 1-3)

11. Three instances of a pattern are given below. Describe the pattern using one variable. $4x + 3x = 7x$

$$4(2) + 3(2) = 7(2)$$
$$4(-3.1) + 3(-3.1) = 7(-3.1)$$
$$4\left(\frac{2}{5}\right) + 3\left(\frac{2}{5}\right) = 7\left(\frac{2}{5}\right)$$

12. The number of zeros in each term is 2 greater than in the previous term in the table below.

Term Number	1	2	3	4
Term	0	000	00000	0000000

a. How many zeros are in the sixth term? 11 zeros

b. In words, explain how to use the term number to find the number of zeros in the nth term. See margin.

c. Use n to represent the term number. Write an algebraic expression for the number of zeros in the nth term. $2n - 1$

13. Refer to the sequence below.

a. How many dots will be in the seventh term? 25 dots

b. In words, describe a method to find the number of dots in the nth term. See margin.

c. Write an algebraic expression for the number of dots in the nth term. Answers vary. Sample answer: $4n - 3$

OBJECTIVE C Determine if two expressions seem equivalent by substituting values or making a table. (Lesson 1-3)

14. Alyssa and Odell both looked at a pattern. Alyssa thought the nth term could be represented by the expression $3n - 6 + n$, and Odell came up with the expression $-5 + 4n - 1$. Substitute the numbers 3, 5, and 9 in for each expression to determine if they seem to be equivalent. They appear to be equivalent.

Additional Answers

12b. Answers vary. Sample answer: The number of zeros is one less than twice the term number.

13b. Answers vary. Sample answer: There is one central dot and 4 "spokes," each with one less dot than the term number.

15. To convert temperatures from Fahrenheit to Celsius, Kimi used the expression $\frac{5}{9}F - 32$ and Edward used the expression $\frac{5}{9}(F - 32)$. Substitute the numbers 9 and 18 for F in each expression to determine if they seem to be equivalent. They appear not to be equivalent.

16. Fill in each table to determine if $5 + |3n|$ is equivalent to $5 + |-3n|$.

n	$|5 + 3n|$		n	$5 + |-3n|$
-3	?	14	-3	?	14
-2	?	11	-2	?	11
0	?	5	0	?	5
4	?	17	4	?	17
5	?	20	5	?	20

They appear to be equivalent.

OBJECTIVE D Evaluate expressions involving absolute value. (Lesson 1-6)

In 17 and 18, evaluate the numerical expressions.

17. $|(-3)| + |5 - 3|$ 5

18. $|9 \cdot (-2)| + |(-9) \cdot 2|$ 36

In 19–21, evaluate the algebraic expression for the given value of the variable.

19. $|x - 3| \cdot x$ for $x = -2$. -10

20. $|x - |x||$ for $x = -1$ 2

21. $||x| - |2x + 1||$ for $x = -3$ 2

OBJECTIVE E Calculate the range and mean absolute deviation. (Lesson 1-7)

In 22–25, calculate the range and mean absolute deviation of each data set.

22. 12.6, 10.4, 3.8, 7.2, 5.9, 4.1, 1.5, 2.5 $r = 11.1$, m.a.d. = 3.05

23. $\frac{3}{8}, \frac{3}{4}, \frac{5}{2}, \frac{1}{4}, 2\frac{1}{8}$ $r = 2.25$, m.a.d. = 0.89

24. A student's test scores: 87, 94, 90, 73, 84, 83, 97, 72 $r = 25$, m.a.d. = 7

25. The Miami Heat's total points in games played in January 2006: 97, 92, 93, 118, 110, 117, 100, 92, 94, 119, 94, 98, 91, 101, and 118 $r = 28$ points, m.a.d. = about 9.42 points

PROPERTIES Principles behind the mathematics

OBJECTIVE F Apply the Algebraic Definitions of Subtraction and Division. (Lesson 1-1) 26. $x + -y + -z$

In 26 and 27, rewrite each subtraction as an addition. 27. $-8 + -y + -32$

26. $x - y - z$ 27. $-8 - y - 32$

28. **Multiple Choice** Which expression is not equivalent to the others? D

    A $a - b$ **B** $a + -b$ **C** $-b + a$ **D** $b + -a$

29. **True or False** $\frac{x}{7} = \frac{1}{7}x$ true

In 30 and 31, rewrite the division problem as a multiplication problem.

30. $\frac{7d + 2}{4st}$ 31. $6.21 \div 3.14$
    $(7d + 2) \cdot \frac{1}{4st}$ $6.21 \cdot \frac{1}{3.14}$

OBJECTIVE G Identify and apply the associative, commutative, and transitive properties. (Lessons 1-1, 1-2)

32. $(45 + 23) + 77 = 45 + (23 + 77)$ is an example of what property? Associative Property of Addition

33. What property is described by $x \cdot y = y \cdot x$? Commutative Property of Multiplication

34. Wesley was evaluating the expression $(2 - x) + 3$ and used the Associative Property to rewrite it as $2 - (x + 3)$ to make it easier to compute.

    a. Is this correct? no

    b. If so, evaluate the expressions for values of x to show they are equal. If not, find and correct the mistake Wesley made. Answers vary. Sample answer: Wesley should have written $2 + (-x + 3)$.

35. Erin had the expression $x + 2 + 2x + 7$. Jamal had the expression $3x + 9$. Kelly's expression was $x + 9 + 2x$. Erin and Jamal discovered their expressions are equivalent. Erin and Kelly's expressions are also equivalent. What property makes Jamal and Kelly's expressions equivalent? Transitive Property of Equality

Chapter 1 Review

Additional Answers

38a. Store 1: $m = \$44.50$; m.a.d. $= \$4.75$;
Store 2: $m = \$47.50$; m.a.d. $= \$7.50$

38b. Answers vary. Sample answer: On average, the price of a video game is more or less $4.75 away from $44.50 at Store 1 and more or less $7.50 away from $47.50 at Store 2.

38c. Answers vary. Sample answer: Store 1, since the average price and deviation are lower

38d. Store 1, since the m.a.d. is smaller

39b.

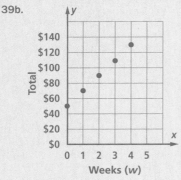

40.

Wind-Chill Index (°F)

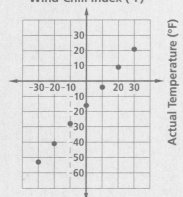

41b.

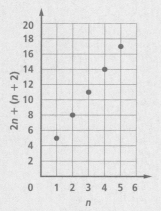

USES Applications of mathematics in real-world situations

OBJECTIVE H Create expressions to model real-world situations. (Lesson 1-2)

36. In a football board game, a person earns 6 points per receiving touchdown and 3 points per passing touchdown. The person will lose a point for interceptions thrown. Let r = the number of receiving touchdowns, let p = the number of passing touchdowns, and let i = the number of interceptions thrown. Write an expression to represent the total points a person playing the football board game has.
$6r + 3p - i$

37. Juan is a wedding photographer. He offers two package deals to his clients. Package A costs $1,225 and Package B costs $1,405. Let a = the number of Package A deals he sells, and let b = the number of Package B deals he sells. Write an expression to represent the total amount Juan makes selling his wedding package deals. **1,225a + 1,405b dollars**

OBJECTIVE I Calculate and interpret the spread of a distribution using mean absolute deviation. (Lesson 1-7)

38. The costs of four video games at two stores are shown in the table below.

Game	Store 1	Store 2
Play Soccer	$35	$40
Adventure Trip	$45	$40
Be a Robot!	$48	$50
Catch the Dragon	$50	$60

38a–d. See margin.

a. Calculate the mean and the mean absolute deviation for the four videogames at each store.

b. What is the meaning of the mean absolute deviations calculated in Part a?

---

c. If you could go to only one store for your video game purchases, which would it be? Explain your reasoning.

d. Which store has less variation in the price of video games? Explain your reasoning.

REPRESENTATIONS Pictures, graphs, or objects that illustrate concepts

OBJECTIVE J Create a scatterplot from a table or expression. (Lesson 1-4)

39. Suppose Ben Inriver begins with $50 in a savings account and adds $20 per week. The table shows the number of weeks that he has saved and the total amount saved.

Week (w)	Total (t)
0	50
1	? 70
2	? 90
3	? 110
4	? 130

a. Complete the table.

b. Plot the five pairs (w, t). **See margin.**

40. The table below shows the wind chill index for various temperatures when there is a 10 mile per hour wind. Plot the data with temperature on the horizontal axis and wind chill on the vertical axis.

Actual Temperature (°F)	Wind Chill Index (°F)
30°	21
20°	9
10°	−4
0°	−16
−10°	−28
−20°	−41
−30°	−53

Source: NOAA's National Weather Service
See margin.

Additional Answers

42a. In the second row, there are 36 seats. In the third, there are 38 seats. In the fourth, there are 40 seats. In the fifth, there are 42 seats. In the sixth, there are 44 seats. In the seventh, there are 46 seats. In the eighth, there are 48 seats.

42b.

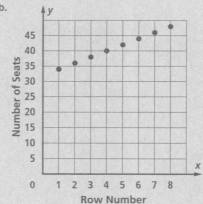

OBJECTIVE K Graph ordered pairs from expressions. (Lessons 1-4, 1-5)

41. Use the table below.

n	$2n + (n + 2)$	
1	5	
2	?	8
3	?	11
4	?	14
5	?	17

a. Complete the table of values.

b. Graph the ordered pairs with n on the x-axis and $2n + (n + 2)$ on the y-axis. **See margin.**

c. From the graph, predict the value of the expression when n is 11. **35**

42a–b. See margin.
42. Suppose the number of seats in the nth row of an auditorium is $32 + 2n$.

a. Evaluate the expression for the rows numbered 2, 3, 4, 5, 6, 7, and 8.

b. Graph the ordered pairs (row number, number of seats) for these values.

OBJECTIVE L Use graphs to determine whether expressions seem to be equivalent. (Lessons 1-4, 1-5, 1-6) 43. They are not equivalent. See margin for graph.

43. Determine if the expressions $x + 2$ and $|x + 2|$ are equivalent by using a graph.
44–45. See margin for graphs.
44. James and Luanda both looked at a pattern. James thought the nth term could be represented by the expression $n - 6 + n$, and Luanda came up with the expression $-6 + 2n$. Graph the data and determine if the expressions seem to be equivalent. **They appear to be equivalent.**

45. Use a graph to determine whether the expressions $(y - 1)^2$ and $y^2 + 1$ seem to be equivalent. **They are not equivalent.**

OBJECTIVE M Use graphs to find values, create tables, and select appropriate windows. (Lesson 1-5)

46. a. Graph $y = x^3 - 3x^2$ on your graphing calculator in the standard window and sketch your result. **46a–b. See margin.**

b. Change your window to match the calculator screen below. Record Xmin, Xmax, Ymin, and Ymax.

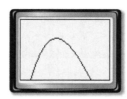

In 47 and 48, use the calculator screen below. Each tick mark represents one unit.

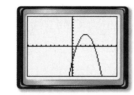

47. Make a table of values for x and y when $x = 0, 2, 3,$ and 6. **See margin.**

48. **Multiple Choice** Which of the following expressions best represents that of the values on the graph? **C**

A $|x - 3| + 4$

B $4(x - 3)$

C $-(x - 3)^2 + 4$

D $(x - 3)^2 + 4$

Assessment

Evaluation The *Assessment Resources* provide four forms of the Chapter 1 Test. Forms A and B present parallel versions of a short-answer format. Form C consists of four to six short-response questions that cover the SPUR objectives from Chapter 1. Form D is a performance assessment that covers a subset of the SPUR objectives for the chapter.

Feedback After students have taken the test for Chapter 1 and you have scored the results, return the tests to students for discussion. Class discussion on the questions that caused trouble for most students can be very effective in identifying and clarifying misunderstandings. You might want to have them note the items they missed and work either in groups or at home to correct them. It is important for students to receive feedback on every chapter test, and we recommend that students see and correct their mistakes before proceeding too far into the next chapter.

Additional Answers

45.

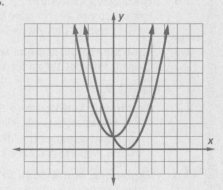

46a.

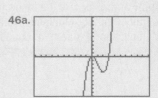

46b. Answers vary. Sample answer:
Xmin = −0.4, Xmax = 0.4,
Ymin = −0.2, Ymax = 0

47.

x	0	2	3	6
y	−5	3	4	−5

Additional Answers

43.

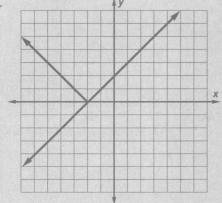

44.

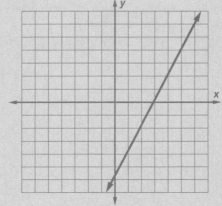

Chapter Overview

	Local Standards	Pacing *(in days)*		
		Average	**Advanced**	**Block**
2-1 The Distributive Property and Removing Parentheses A Use the Distributive Property to expand and combine like terms. F Use and apply the Distributive Property to perform calculations in your head. H Apply the Distributive Property in real-world situations.		1	1	0.5
2-2 The Distributive Property and Adding Like Terms A Use the Distributive Property to expand and combine like terms. H Apply the Distributive Property in real-world situations.		1	1	0.5
2-3 Explaining Number Puzzles G Use algebra to explain how number puzzles work.		1	0.5	0.75
QUIZ 1		0.5	0.5	0.25
2-4 Opposites B Use the Opposite of Opposites Property, the Opposite of a Sum Property, and the Opposite of a Difference Property to simplify expressions. D Apply and recognize the following multiplication properties: Multiplicative Identity Property, Multiplicative Inverse Property, Multiplication Property of Zero, Multiplication Property of Equality, and the Zero Product Property.		1	1	0.5
2-5 Testing Equivalence I Use a spreadsheet or table to test the equivalence of expressions. J Use technology to test for equivalence of expressions.		1	1	0.5
2-6 Equivalent Expressions with Technology J Use technology to test for equivalence of expressions.		1	0.5	0.75
QUIZ 2		0.5	0.5	0.25
2-7 Explaining Addition and Subtraction Related Facts C Use related facts to solve sentences. E Apply and recognize the following properties: Additive Identity Property, Additive Inverse Property, and Addition Property of Equality.		1	1	0.5
2-8 Explaining Multiplication and Division Related Facts C Use related facts to solve sentences. D Apply and recognize the following multiplication properties: Multiplicative Identity Property, Multiplicative Inverse Property, Multiplication Property of Zero, Multiplication Property of Equality, and the Zero Product Property.		1	1	0.5
Self-Test		1	1	0.5
Chapter Review		2	2	1
Test		1	1	0.5
TOTAL		13	12	7

Differentiated Options Universal Access

	Accommodating the Learner	Vocabulary Development	Ongoing Assessment	Materials
2-1	pp. 68, 69		group, p. 71	
2-2	pp. 74, 75		written, p. 78	
2-3	pp. 80, 81		oral, p. 84	
2-4	pp. 87, 88	p. 86	written, p. 90	
2-5	pp. 93, 94		group, p. 97	graphing calculator
2-6	pp. 99, 100	p. 99	written, p. 104	Computer Algebra System (CAS)
2-7	pp. 107, 108		oral, p. 111	
2-8	pp. 114, 115		group, p. 120	

Objectives

Skills		Lessons	Self-Test Questions	Chapter Review Questions
A	Use the Distributive Property to expand and combine like terms.	2-1, 2-2	2, 3, 5, 7	1–12
B	Use the Opposite of Opposites Property, the Opposite of a Sum Property, and the Opposite of a Difference Property to simplify expressions.	2-4	1, 4, 16	13–24
C	Use related facts to solve sentences.	2-7, 2-8	9–11	25–34

Properties		Lessons	Self-Test Questions	Chapter Review Questions
D	Apply and recognize the following multiplication properties: Multiplicative Identity Property, Multiplicative Inverse Property, Multiplication Property of Zero, Multiplication Property of Equality, and the Zero Product Property.	2-4, 2-8	8, 14, 15	35–43
E	Apply and recognize the following properties: Additive Identity Property, Additive Inverse Property, and Addition Property of Equality.	2-7	12, 13	44–50
F	Use and apply the Distributive Property to perform calculations in your head.	2-1	6	51–55

Uses		Lessons	Self-Test Questions	Chapter Review Questions
G	Use algebra to explain how number puzzles work.	2-3	18, 19	56–58
H	Apply the Distributive Property to real-world situations.	2-1, 2-2	17, 22	59–61

Representations		Lessons	Self-Test Questions	Chapter Review Questions
I	Use a spreadsheet or table to test the equivalence of expressions.	2-5	21, 23	62–64
J	Use technology to test for equivalence of expressions.	2-5, 2-6	20	65–68

Resource Masters Chapter 2

Resource Master 1, Graph Paper (page 2), can be used with Lesson 2-3. **Resource Master 2, Four-Quadrant Graph Paper** (page 3), can be used with Lesson 2-5. **Resource Master 6, Fact Triangles** (page 7), can be made with Lessons 2-7 and 2-8.

Resource Master 20 Lesson 2-1

Warm-Up
1. What is an easy way to multiply a number by 21?
2. Apply the idea in Problem 1 to multiply 85 by 21 in your head.
3. What is an easy way to multiply a number by 98?
4. Apply the idea in Problem 3 to find the area of a rectangle that is 98 cm by 52 cm in your head.

Additional Examples
1. Michael has started a pet walking business. He charges x dollars to walk a small pet, y dollars to walk a medium pet, and z dollars to walk a large pet. Each day, he walks a small pet for Ms. Finney, two medium pets for Mr. Jenks, and one large pet for Mr. and Mrs. Rivera. Thus, each day Michael earns $x + 2y + z$ dollars. His clients pay weekly. Since there are 7 days in a week, Michael earns $7(x + 2y + z)$ dollars each week. Use the Distributive Property to give an expression that is equivalent to $7(x + 2y + z)$.
2. Expand $-7(-3 - 2t)$.
3. Expand $3x(2x - 6)$.
$$3x(2x - 6) = 3x \cdot \underline{\qquad} - 3x \cdot \underline{\qquad}$$
$$= \underline{\qquad} - \underline{\qquad}$$
4. Use the Distributive Property to write $\frac{30 + 2x}{10}$ as a sum of two fractions.

Resource Master for Lesson 2-1

Resource Master 21 Lesson 2-2

Warm-Up
Show that *none* of the expressions below are equivalent to $3x + 4y$.
1. $7xy$
2. $7(x + y)$
3. $12xy$
4. $12(x + y)$
5. $3(x + 4)y$

Additional Example
1. Write a simplified expression for the perimeter of quadrilateral *FOUR*.

Resource Master for Lesson 2-2

Resource Master 22 Lesson 2-2

Additional Examples
2. Combine like terms for $(3x^2 - x + 2) + 8(4x - x^2 + 5)$.
First remove parentheses.
$$3x^2 - x + 2 + \underline{\qquad} x - \underline{\qquad} x^2 + \underline{\qquad}$$
Group like terms, changing subtractions to additions.
$$= (\underline{\qquad} x^2 + \underline{\qquad} x^2) + (\underline{\qquad} x + \underline{\qquad} x) + (\underline{\qquad} + \underline{\qquad})$$
Add like terms.
$$= \underline{\qquad} x^2 + \underline{\qquad} x + \underline{\qquad}$$
3. Factor 6 out of the expression $6d + 6e$.
4. Factor $5x^2$ out of the expression $5wx^2 - 10vx^2$.
$$5wx^2 - 10vx^2 = 5x^2(\underline{\qquad} - \underline{\qquad})$$

Accommodating the Learner
Gordon and Chuck are simplifying the following algebraic expression: $4y^2 - 2y + 6 + y^2 + 6y - 2$. Their work is shown.

Gordon
$(4 + 1)y^2 + (-2 + 6)y + (6 + -2)$
$= 5y^2 + 4y + 4$

Chuck
$4y^2 + (-2 + 6)y + (6 + -2)$
$= 4y^2 + 4y + 4$

Which person has completed the problem correctly? Explain what the person making the mistake did incorrectly.

Resource Master for Lesson 2-2

Resource Master 23 Lesson 2-3

Warm-Up
Follow the steps to solve this puzzle.

Step 1 Write your age. _____

Step 2 Add 3. _____

Step 3 Multiply by 5. _____

Step 4 Subtract your age. _____

Step 5 Add 9. _____

Step 6 Divide by 4. _____

Step 7 Subtract 6. _____

The final result should be your age.

Resource Master for Lesson 2-3

Resource Master 24 Lesson 2-3

Additional Example
1. Work the puzzle below with a few numbers. Then use a variable to create an expression to explain why the puzzle works.

Step 1 Begin with a number. _____

Step 2 Add 2. _____

Step 3 Multiply by 3. _____

Step 4 Multiply by 4. _____

Step 5 Subtract 15. _____

Step 6 Add 2. _____

Step 7 Subtract 12 times your original number. _____

Answer = 11

2. Create a number puzzle that begins and ends with the same number.

Step 1 _____ _____

Step 2 _____ _____

Step 3 _____ _____

Step 4 _____ _____

Step 5 _____ _____

Step 6 _____ _____

Step 7 _____ _____

Resource Master for Lesson 2-3

Resource Master 25 Lesson 2-3

Additional Example
3. Create a number puzzle so that the answer is always 1.

Step 1 Begin with n. n

Step 2 Add 4. _____

Step 3 Multiply by 4. $4(n + 4) = $ _____

Step 4 Add $4n$. _____ $= $ _____

Step 5 Divide by 8. _____ $= $ _____

Step 6 Subtract 1. _____ $= $ _____

Step 7 Subtract n. _____ $= $ _____

Question 15

Spectator's Choice	Number of Cards in Small Pile

Resource Master for Lesson 2-3

Resource Master 26 Lesson 2-4

Warm-Up

1. Fill in the following table.

a	b	$-(a+b)$	$-a+-b$	$-a-b$
43	16			
-8	-3			
$\frac{1}{2}$	$\frac{2}{3}$			
0	-51.3			
-77	12			

2. What do you notice about the three expressions $-(a+b)$, $-a+-b$, and $-a-b$?

Additional Examples

1. Simplify $7y - (2y + 11)$.

2. Simplify $(w - 3) - 2(4w + 2)$.

$(w - 3) - 2(4w + 2) = (w + -3) + \underline{\hspace{1cm}}(4w + 2)$

$= w + -3 + \underline{\hspace{1cm}} + \underline{\hspace{1cm}}$

$= \underline{\hspace{1cm}} + \underline{\hspace{1cm}}$

$= \underline{\hspace{1cm}} - \underline{\hspace{1cm}}$

Resource Master for Lesson 2-4

Resource Master 27 Lesson 2-4

Accommodating the Learner

Expression	Opposite of Expression
u	
$-w$	
$u + w$	
$u - w$	
$-u + w$	
$u + -w$	
$-(u + w)$	
$-(u - w)$	

Accommodating the Learner

Describe the error(s) in the following example. Correct the example.

$2(x - 1) - 3(x - 2) = 2(x + -1) + -3(x + -2)$ Definition of Subtraction

$= 2x + -2 + -3x + -2$ Distributive Property

$= -x + -4$ Opposite of a Difference Property

$= -x - 4$ Opposite of a Sum Property

Resource Master for Lesson 2-4

Resource Master 28 Lesson 2-5

Warm-Up

Determine which two of these four expressions are equivalent.

A $x(x + 2) - 2(2 + x)$ B $(2 - x)(x + 2)$

C $x(x - 2) - 2(x - 2)$ D $2(x + 2) - x(2 + x)$

Additional Examples

1. Test whether $3x(x + 2) + 5x$ and $x(3x - 1) + 12x$ are equivalent.

2. A common error that some students make is to think that $7x - x$ is equivalent to 7 for all values of x. Here are three ways to show that these expressions are not equivalent.
   a. Substitute a value for x to show $7x - x$ is not equal to 7.
   b. Graph Y1 $= 7x - x$ and Y2 $= 7$. Are the graphs identical?
   c. Create a table of values for Y1 $= 7x - x$ and Y2 $= 7$.

x	Y1	Y2

Resource Master for Lesson 2-5

Resource Master 29 Lesson 2-5

Additional Examples

3. Are $-x^4$ and $(-x)^4$ equivalent expressions? If so, explain. If not, provide a counterexample.

4. Use properties to show that $5(3a^2 - 2a) + 6(a - 3)$ is equivalent to $2(a - 9) + 3a(5a - 2)$.

Question 6

Consider the expressions $x \cdot x$ and $2x$.
a. Copy and complete the table of values.
b. Give two values of x for which $x \cdot x = 2x$.
c. Give two values of x for which $x \cdot x$ does not equal $2x$.
d. Graph $y = x \cdot x$ and $y = 2x$. Circle the points that correspond to your answer for Part b.

x	$x \cdot x$	$2x$
-3		
-2		
-1		
0		
1		
2		
3		

Resource Master for Lesson 2-5

Resource Master 30 Lesson 2-5

Extension

Fill in the following table. Are the expressions equivalent? Explain.

x	-1	0	1	2
$\frac{x^2 - x - 6}{x - 3}$				
$x + 2$				

Accommodating the Learner

Find the area of the largest rectangle in two ways. First, multiply the length and width of the large rectangle together. Second, add the areas of the two smaller rectangles. Use a number to check the equivalence. Show the two areas are equivalent algebraically.

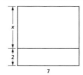

Resource Master for Lesson 2-5

Resource Master 31 Lesson 2-6

Warm-Up

1. Key in $x + x$ and press ENTER. Record the result.
2. Key in $a \cdot a$ and press ENTER. Record the result.
3. Key in $2 * (a - b)$ and press ENTER. Record the result.
4. Key in EXPAND $(2 * (a - b))$ and press ENTER. Record the result.

Additional Example

1. The picture below shows a picture frame surrounding a rectangular photograph. The length of the frame is L and the width of the frame is W. The thickness of the frame is x.

a. Find a formula for the area of the frame by splitting up the frame into 4 rectangles.
b. Split up the frame in another way to find its area.

Resource Master for Lesson 2-6

Resource Master 32 Lesson 2-6

Question 15

Take a piece of paper. Fold it in half. The paper now has a thickness twice that of the original piece of paper. Fold the folded paper in half. The paper now has a thickness four times the original piece of paper.
a. Complete the table.
b. If a piece of paper is folded six times, what is the thickness of the folded paper?
c. Write an expression to describe the thickness of paper for n folds.

0 Folds

1 Fold

2 Folds

Number of Folds	Thickness of Paper
0	1
1	$1 \cdot 2 = 2$
2	$1 \cdot 2 \cdot 2 = 4$
3	
4	

Resource Master for Lesson 2-6

Resource Master 33 Lesson 2-7

Warm-Up

An addition or subtraction fact is given. Give the other three related facts.

1. $47 + 53 = 100$
2. $\frac{1}{3} - \frac{1}{5} = \frac{2}{15}$
3. $-11 + 12 = 1$
4. $x + a = b$
5. $c - x = d$

Additional Examples

1. Solve the equation $y + -3 = 21$
   a. using a fact triangle (the Related Facts Property).
   b. using the Subtraction Property of Equality.

2. Solve the equation $4.7 - a = 5.3$
   a. using a fact triangle.
   b. using properties.

Resource Master for Lesson 2-7

Resource Master 34 Lesson 2-8

Warm-Up

A multiplication or division fact is given. Give the three related facts.

1. $12 \cdot 34 = 408$
2. $\frac{1}{2} \cdot \frac{3}{4} = \frac{3}{8}$
3. $\frac{-78}{-6} = 13$
4. $14x = 7$
5. $\frac{5}{y} = 12$
6. $ax = b; a \neq 0$

Additional Examples

1. Solve $12y = 180$.

2. Solve each equation.
   a. $0q = 0$ b. $0 \cdot 5 = q$ c. $9q = 0$

3. Find the reciprocal of each number.
   a. 1.125   b. $\frac{3}{11}$ c. -17

Accommodating the Learner

Match the numbers in the top row with the numbers in the bottom row. Verify your choice is correct by multiplying the two numbers together.

Number	1.66	0	$-2\frac{7}{8}$	1	0.1	-4	$\frac{1}{4}$
Reciprocal	$\frac{-16}{23}$	$\frac{-1}{4}$	4	$\frac{3}{5}$	0	1	10

Note: Not every number in the top row has a reciprocal in the bottom row.

Resource Master for Lesson 2-8

Pacing

Each lesson in this chapter is designed to be covered in one day. At the end of the chapter, you should plan to spend 1 day to review the Self-Test, 1 to 2 days for the Chapter Review, and 1 day for a test. You may wish to spend a day on projects and possibly a day is needed for quizzes. This chapter should therefore take 11 to 14 days. We strongly advise you not spend more than 15 days on this chapter; there is ample opportunity to review ideas in later chapters.

Chapter 2 Projects

At the end of each chapter, you will find projects related to the chapter. At this time you might want to have students look over the projects on pages 121 and 122. You might want to have students tentatively select a project on which to work. Then, as students read and progress through the chapter, they can finalize their project choices.

Sometimes students might work alone; at other times, you might let them collaborate with classmates for a presentation and discussion. We recommend that you allow for diversity and encourage students to use their imaginations when presenting their projects. As students work on projects throughout the year, they should see the many uses of mathematics in the real world.

Using Algebra to Explain

▷ Contents

Here is a card trick that can be explained using algebra. The trick is typically performed with two people: an illusionist and a spectator. The spectator should not read the directions while the illusionist is performing the trick.

Directions

Step 1 Before the trick begins, shuffle a deck of cards. Look at the card in the ninth position from the top of the deck. Without letting the spectator see, write what the card is on a piece of paper, fold the paper several times, and give it to the spectator. Tell the spectator not to open it.

Chapter 2 Overview

Too many students leave their study of algebra more confused about mathematics than when they started the class. In this chapter, we try to change their perceptions by showing the usefulness of algebra in their everyday lives: shortcuts for computation, number puzzles (pick a number...), and related facts. Along the way, important algebraic properties are used.

The theme of this chapter is given by its title, *Using Algebra to Explain*. In Lesson 2-1, the Distributive Properties of Multiplication over Addition and Subtraction are used to facilitate mental multiplication and multiplication shortcuts.

(continued on next page)

Notes

Step 2 Ask the spectator to choose any number from 10 to 19. Count out that number of cards from the top of the deck. For example, if the spectator chooses 17, count out 17 cards from the top of the deck. Put them in a smaller, new pile faceup next to the deck of cards.

Step 3 Tell the spectator to add the digits of the number they choose. Count out that number of cards from the top of the smaller pile and place them back on top of the original deck. For example, the sum of the digits of 17 is 8. So place 8 cards from the smaller pile back on top of the original deck.

Step 4 Tell the spectator to open the piece of paper. The top card on the smaller deck should match the card written on the piece of paper.

In this chapter, you will use the properties of algebra to explain relationships among numbers, show equivalence, and explain why number tricks, such as this one, work.

65

Lesson 2-2 discusses the use of the Distributive Property to add and subtract like terms in preparation for Lesson 2-3. You may wish to spend an extra day here. Lesson 2-4 discusses another use of the Distributive Property, namely to deal with the opposite of sums and differences. With these skills in hand, we are able to return to the topic of equivalent expressions from Chapter 1. Algebra can explain why expressions are equivalent in a way that tables and graphs cannot. Lesson 2-6 introduces a computer algebra system (CAS) and shows how CAS technology can show whether expressions are or are not equivalent. The last two lessons of the chapter combine properties associated with solving equations and are related to properties students have known since the primary grades; they show how the Addition and Multiplication Properties of Equality help to explain equivalency.

Lesson
2-1

Lesson
2-1

The Distributive Property and Removing Parentheses

GOAL

Use the Distributive Property of Multiplication over Addition and Subtraction to simplify expressions.

SPUR Objectives

(The SPUR Objectives for all of Chapter 2 are found in the Chapter Review on pages 125–127.)

A Use the Distributive Property to expand and combine like terms.

F Use and apply the Distributive Property to perform calculations in your head.

H Apply the Distributive Property in real-world situations.

Materials/Resources

· Lesson Masters 2-1A and 2-1B
· Resource Master 20

HOMEWORK

Suggestions for Assignment

• Questions 1–24
• Question 25 (extra credit)
• Reading Lesson 2-2
• Covering the Ideas 2-2

Local Standards

> ▶ **BIG IDEA** By applying the Distributive Property, you can rewrite the product $a(b + c)$ as the sum $ab + ac$.

Suppose an auditorium has 8 rows of seats with 10 seats to a row. The tickets for the first 3 rows cost more than the tickets for the other 5 rows.

Two ways to count the number of seats in the auditorium illustrate a useful pattern. One way is to treat all the seats alike. Multiply the number of seats in each row, 10, by the total number of rows, $5 + 3$ or 8.

$$10(5 + 3) = 10 \cdot 8 = 80$$

The second way is to count the number of inexpensive seats and premium seats separately, then add the results.

$$10 \cdot 5 + 10 \cdot 3 = 50 + 30 = 80$$

These two ways of counting the number of seats yield the same result.

$$10(5 + 3) = 10 \cdot 5 + 10 \cdot 3$$

This is an example of the basic property that involves both addition and multiplication. It is called the *Distributive Property of Multiplication over Addition* since the multiplication by 10 in $10(5 + 3)$ is "distributed" to both terms in the parentheses.

The Distributive Property of Multiplication over Addition

For all real numbers a, b, and c, $c(a + b) = ca + cb$.

The name of this property is very long, so we just call it the *Distributive Property*. The Distributive Property can be used to rewrite the product $c(a + b)$ as the sum of terms $ca + cb$. This is called expanding the expression. Expanding a product has the effect of removing parentheses.

Inexpensive seats

Premium seats

Stage

Mental Math

a. Order from least to greatest: $\frac{5}{32}, \frac{1}{4}, \frac{1}{8}, \frac{3}{16}$.

b. Order from least to greatest: $-\frac{5}{32}, -\frac{1}{4}, -\frac{1}{8}, -\frac{3}{16}$.

Mental Math

a. $\frac{1}{8}, \frac{5}{32}, \frac{3}{16}, \frac{1}{4}$

b. $-\frac{1}{4}, -\frac{3}{16}, -\frac{5}{32}, -\frac{1}{8}$

---

1 Warm-Up

You might write or project the following so that students can do these questions as they enter the classroom.

1. What is an easy way to multiply a number by 21? **Multiply it by 20, then multiply it by 1, and then add the two products.**

2. Apply the idea in Problem 1 to multiply 85 by 21 in your head. **$85 \cdot 21 = 85 \cdot 20 + 85 \cdot 1 = 1,700 + 85 = 1,785$**

Background

The Distributive Property of Multiplication over Addition (DPMA)—namely that for all real numbers a, b, and c, $c(a + b) = ca + cb$—is the main property that connects these two operations. It states that to multiply a number by a sum, you can distribute the multiplication over the addends.

The Distributive Property has several corollaries. A few are discussed in this chapter.

• The Distributive Property of Multiplication over Subtraction (this lesson)

• Adding Like Terms (Lesson 2-2)

• Opposite of a Sum Property (derivation shown in Lesson 2-4)

• Opposite of a Difference Property (derivation shown in Lesson 2-4)

(continued on next page)

STOP QY1

Example 1

Jason earns money by mowing the lawns of three houses in his neighborhood each week. Since the lawns are of different sizes, he charges the neighbors different prices: *a, b,* and *c.* He mows the second neighbor's lawn twice a week, so each week Jason earns $a + 2b + c$ dollars. The neighbors pay monthly. Assuming 4 weeks per month, Jason earns $4(a + 2b + c)$ dollars each month. Use the Distributive Property to give an expression that is equivalent to $4(a + 2b + c)$.

Solution Distribute 4 over each term. Then simplify.

$$4(a + 2b + c) = 4 \cdot a + 4 \cdot (2b) + 4 \cdot c$$
$$= 4a + 8b + 4c$$

Check The expression $4a + 8b + 4c$ indicates that Jason has mowed the first lawn 4 times, the second lawn 8 times, and the third lawn 4 times during the month.

Recycling grass clippings into lawns lowers soil temperature, reduces water loss, and reduces yard waste going into landfills.

Source: Servicemaster

Explaining a Multiplication Shortcut

Suppose a motel room costs $59 a day, and a person will stay in that room for 8 days. To find the total cost, you can multiply $8 \cdot 60$, and then subtract $8 \cdot 1$. (Calculate as if the price for each of the eight days was $60. Then subtract $1 per day for 8 days.) The Distributive Property explains why this works.

$$8 \cdot 59 = 8(60 - 1) = 8 \cdot 60 - 8 \cdot 1, \text{ or } \$472$$

Here we have distributed the multiplication over a *subtraction.* Since $60 - 1 = 60 + (-1)$, the subtraction can be thought of adding the opposite. Some people like to think of this variant of the Distributive Property as a separate property.

> **The Distributive Property of Multiplication over Subtraction**
>
> For all real numbers *a, b,* and *c,* $c(a - b) = ca - cb$.

Thus, there are two forms of the Distributive Property used to expand expressions. You can use either of these versions to expand a subtraction expression, as shown in Example 2 on page 68.

The Distributive Property and Removing Parentheses **67**

The Distributive Property of Multiplication over Subtraction (DPMS). The advantage of having this property is that the addition property does not need to be used to explain subtraction. Here is a derivation of the DPMS from the DPMA using the Multiplication Property of –1 presented in Lesson 2-4.

$c(a - b) = c(a + -b)$	Algebraic Definition of Subtraction
$= ca + c(-b)$	DPMA
$= ca + c(-1 \cdot b)$	Multiplication Property of –1
$= ca + (-1) \cdot cb$	Associative and Commutative Properties of Multiplication
$= ca + -cb$	Multiplication Property of –1
$= ca - cb$	Algebraic Definition of Subtraction

---

3. What is an easy way to multiply a number by 98? **Multiply the number by 100, then multiply it by 2, and then subtract the second product from the first.**

4. Apply the idea in Problem 3 to find the area of a rectangle that is 98 cm by 52 cm in your head.
$52 \cdot 100 - 52 \cdot 2 = 5{,}200 - 104 = 5{,}096$

2 Teaching

Notes on the Lesson

The Distributive Property of Multiplication over Addition has many variants that look quite different from each other. The key point is that students should understand the form of the basic property and see how the variants fit into that form. For instance, $c(a - b) = c(a + -b)$, so any subtraction can be converted to an addition. Also, $c(a + b) = (a + b)c$, so the multiplier can be on either side. And if c is replaced by $\frac{1}{d}$, then we have the property used to expand a fraction. These are the basic variants discussed in the lesson.

Explaining a multiplication shortcut.
This valuable shortcut should be review for students who have had previous UCSMP courses. Although the example involves the Distributive Property of Multiplication over Subtraction, the same shortcut applies to addition situations.

> ### Additional Example
> **Example 1** Michael has started a pet walking business. He charges x dollars to walk a small pet, y dollars to walk a medium pet, and z dollars to walk a large pet. Each day he walks a small pet for Ms. Finney, two medium pets for Mr. Jenks, and one large pet for Mr. and Mrs. Rivera. Thus each day Michael earns $x + 2y + z$ dollars. His clients pay weekly. Since there are 7 days in a week, Michael earns $7(x + 2y + z)$ dollars each week. Use the Distributive Property to give an expression that is equivalent to $7(x + 2y + z)$.
> **$7x + 14y + 7z$**

2-1

Additional Examples

Example 2 Expand $-7(-3 - 2t)$.

$21 + 14t$

Example 3 Expand $3x(2x - 6)$.

$3x(2x - 6) = 3x \cdot \underline{\quad ? \quad} - 3x \cdot \underline{\quad ? \quad}$
$\qquad\qquad\qquad\qquad\qquad 2x; 6$

$\qquad = \underline{\quad ? \quad} - \underline{\quad ? \quad} \quad 6x^2; 18x$

Notes on the Lesson

Expanding a Fraction. Expanding a fraction is the division variant of the Distributive Property. You might give the following example. Suppose there are 5 salads and 10 cookies to distribute equally among 5 people. How much will each person get? You can use the expression $(5s + 10c) \div 5$, where you could think of s and c as the value of a salad and a cookie, respectively. Each person will get $s + 2c$, that is, one salad and 2 cookies.

Example 2
Expand $-11(5 - 6w)$.

Solution Begin by rewriting the subtraction expression as an addition expression.

$-11(5 - 6w) = -11(5 + (-6w))$

$\qquad\qquad = -11 \cdot 5 + -11 \cdot -6w$

$\qquad\qquad = -55 + 66w$

Check Substitute the same value for w in both the given expression and the expanded expression. We use $w = 3$. Remember to follow the order of operations.

When $w = 3$, $-11(5 - 6w) = -11(5 - 6 \cdot 3) = -11(-13) = 143$.
When $w = 3$, $-55 + 66w = -55 + 66 \cdot 3 = -55 + 198 = 143$.
It checks.

GUIDED

Example 3
Expand $2x(5x - 3)$.

Solution
$\qquad\qquad\qquad\qquad 5x \qquad\qquad 3$

$2x(5x - 3) = 2x \cdot \underline{\;?\;} - 2x \cdot \underline{\;?\;}$ Distributive Property

$\qquad\qquad = \dfrac{?}{10x^2} - \dfrac{?}{6x}$ Multiplication

The Distributive Property also works in the cases where the multiplier is on the right, as in $(a + b)c$, because multiplication is commutative. So, $(a + b)c = c(a + b) = ca + cb$.

Expanding a Fraction

Because every division can be converted to multiplication, the Distributive Property can also be used to rewrite expressions involving division. Suppose the sum $(a + b)$ is to be divided by c.

$\dfrac{a + b}{c} = \dfrac{1}{c}(a + b)$ Dividing by c is the same as multiplying by $\dfrac{1}{c}$.

$\qquad = \dfrac{1}{c} \cdot a + \dfrac{1}{c} \cdot b$ Distributive Property of Multiplication over Addition

$\qquad = \dfrac{a}{c} + \dfrac{b}{c}$ Algebraic definition of division

In this way, a fraction with a sum in its numerator can be rewritten using $\dfrac{a + b}{c} = \dfrac{a}{c} + \dfrac{b}{c}$. This step may allow you to simplify an expression, as shown in Example 4.

68 Using Algebra to Explain

Accommodating the Learner

Ask students to describe how to simplify $3(x - 2) + 5(-3 + 4y)$. $3x + 20y - 21$

Example 4

Use the Distributive Property to write $\frac{36 + 3x}{18}$ as a sum of two fractions.

Solution

$$\frac{36 + 3x}{18} = \frac{36}{18} + \frac{3x}{18} = 2 + \frac{x}{6}$$

Check Let $x = 6$. (Do you see why we chose 6?)

Then $\frac{36 + 3x}{18} = \frac{36 + 3 \cdot 6}{18} = \frac{36 + 18}{18} = \frac{54}{18} = 3$.

Also $2 + \frac{x}{6} = 2 + \frac{6}{6} = 3$. It checks.

 QY2

▶ **QY2**

Multiple Choice For all x, $\frac{20 - 8x}{4}$ equals which of the following?

A $5 - 8x$

B $3x$

C $5 - 2x$

D $3 - 8x$

Note-Taking Tips

Reinforce the usefulness of the Distributive Property by asking students to simplify $-12\left(\frac{1}{3} + \frac{3}{4}\right)$. If students add the fractions and then multiply by 12, they have missed the value of the Distributive Property. Suggest they add this example to their notes on the Distributive Property.

Additional Example

Example 4 Use the Distributive Property to write $\frac{30 + 2x}{10}$ as a sum of two fractions. $3 + \frac{x}{5}$

Questions

COVERING THE IDEAS

1. Use the Distributive Property to find equivalent expressions.
   a. $n(k + w)$ b. $g(d - e)$ c. $\frac{n + p}{r}$
   $nk + nw$ $gd - ge$ $\frac{n}{r} + \frac{p}{r}$
2. Write an expression for the area of the largest rectangle below in two ways.

   a. as length times width   b. as the sum of areas
   $k \cdot (3k + 16)$ $k \cdot 3k + k \cdot 16$
3. A person buys 45 envelopes at \$1.03 each. Explain how you can use the Distributive Property to calculate the total cost in your head.
4. Calculate in your head the total width of 5 windows that are each 39 inches wide. **195 in.**

In 5–10, expand the expression. **5.** $5m + 20$

5. $(m + 4)5$ 6. $-30x(x + 2 + 4n)$ 7. $12\left(k - \frac{1}{6}\right)$

8. $(2b + c)10b$ 9. $6(3v - 8w + 9z^3)$ 10. $-7a(a - b)$

11. Suppose the cost of a cell phone call is \$0.12 per minute. Two calls are made. One lasts 17 minutes and the other lasts 6 minutes. Find the total cost of the calls in two different ways.

12. Rewrite $\frac{24 + 6x}{8}$ as the sum of two fractions. Check your answer.

3. Answers vary. Sample answer:
$45(1.00 + 0.03) =$
$45 + 1.35 = \$46.35$

6. $-30x^2 - 60x - 120xn$
7. $12k - 2$
8. $20b^2 + 10bc$
9. $18v - 48w + 54z^3$
10. $-7a^2 + 7ab$
11. $0.12 \cdot (17 + 6)$;
$0.12 \cdot 17 + 0.12 \cdot 6 = \$2.76$

12. $3 + \frac{3x}{4}$; Let $x = 4$.
Then $\frac{24 + 6 \cdot 4}{8} = \frac{24 + 24}{8} = 6$ and
$3 + \frac{3 \cdot 4}{4} = 3 + 3 = 6$.

Accommodating the Learner ⬆

Give students this problem to solve. Suppose a farmer rents three farms on which she plants corn and soybeans. One farm consists of u acres of land, the second farm consists of v acres of land, and the third farm consists of w acres of land. She plants corn on the first two farms and harvests 184 bushels of corn per acre. She will earn \$3.30 per bushel. The farmer plants soybeans on the third farm and harvests 54 bushels per acre and earns \$6.42 per bushel. Explain how you would find how much she will earn.

$3.30 \cdot 184(u + v) + 6.42 \cdot 54(w)$

3 Assignment

Recommended Assignment
- Questions 1–24
- Question 25 (extra credit)
- Reading Lesson 2-2
- Covering the Ideas 2-2

Notes on the Questions

Question 2 This is an important question to discuss. The area representation of the distributive property is one that is applied in later lessons.

Question 4 Although the calculation is meant to be done by thinking of 39 as 40 − 1 and using the Distributive Property of Multiplication over Subtraction, it could also be done by thinking of 39 as 30 + 9 and using the Distributive Property of Multiplication over Addition.

Questions 13 and 14 These questions help to set up part of the next lesson.

Question 15 The key here is to treat $13\frac{1}{2}$ as $13 + \frac{1}{2}$.

Question 16 Part b generalizes Part a.

Questions 22 and 23 Many students may have studied how to solve sentences like these in early years, but here students are expected to make their decision by substitution, not by going through a solving process.

Question 25a Any number other than 0 and 1 is a counterexample.

Question 25b Any number other than 1 is a counterexample.

APPLYING THE MATHEMATICS

In **13** and **14**, complete each sentence to show examples of the Distributive Property.

13. $24(k + m) = 24\underline{\quad?\quad} + 24\underline{\quad?\quad}$ $k; m$

14. $10a + 80 = 10(\underline{\quad?\quad} + \underline{\quad?\quad})$ $a; 8$

15. For each hour of television, there is an average of $13\frac{1}{2}$ minutes of commercials. If you watch 9 hours of television in a week, how many minutes of commercials will you see? Explain how you can find the answer in your head.

16. You and your friend decide to start a dog-walking business and plan to charge $12 for each dog walked.

    a. You are scheduled to walk 13 dogs this week and your friend has scheduled 17 more appointments. Determine the total amount of money you will earn using two different methods.

    b. You are scheduled to walk 13 dogs this week. If your friend schedules x more appointments for the week, how much money will you earn?

20% of owned dogs were adopted from an animal shelter.

Source: www.thepetprofessor.com

15. Answers vary.
Sample answer:
$9 \cdot (13\frac{1}{2}) =$
$9 \cdot (13 + \frac{1}{2}) =$
$9 \cdot 13 + 9 \cdot \frac{1}{2} =$
$117 + 4.5 =$
121.5 min.

16a. $12 \cdot (13 + 17) =$
$12 \cdot 30 = \$360;$
$12 \cdot (13 + 17) =$
$12 \cdot 13 + 12 \cdot 17 =$
$156 + 204 = \$360$
16b. $(156 + 12x)$ dollars

REVIEW

17. The table below gives the number of films (up to 2006) in which the ten top-ranked actresses have starred. (**Lesson 1-6**)

Actress	Number of Films
Cate Blanchett	34
Patricia Clarkson	52
Toni Collette	32
Kirsten Dunst	52
Scarlett Johansson	27
Nicole Kidman	46
Julianne Moore	52
Samantha Morton	32
Michelle Pfeiffer	46
Kate Winslet	30

Source: Internet Movie Database

a. Find the mean number of films. 40.3 films

b. Find the mean absolute deviation. Explain what the mean absolute deviation means in this case. 9.3 films; On average, they have been within 9.3 films of their mean of 40.3.

---

18. Graph $y = (0.65x)^3$ and $y = 2^x$ on a graphing calculator with the following window settings: $0 \le x \le 60$ and $5 \le y \le 45$. **(Lessons 1-5, 1-3)**

    a. Create a table of values for both graphs with $x = -10, -5, 0, 5, 10,$ and 15.

    b. Are the expressions equivalent? Why or why not? **No; the expressions give different values for a given value of x.**

In 19 and 20, use the Associative and Commutative Properties of Multiplication to compute in your head. **(Lesson 1-1)**

19. $2 \cdot 11 \cdot 3 \cdot 1.5$ **99**

20. $8 \cdot 2 \cdot 7 \cdot 5$ **560**

21. A raffle to raise money for charity sells tickets for $4 each. The winner of the raffle will receive half of all the money raised from selling the tickets, and the other half will be given to the charity. If 721 tickets are sold, how much money will be given to the charity? **(Lesson 1-1)** **$1,442**

In 22 and 23, which of the numbers –2, 5, and 8 makes the sentence true? **(Lesson 1-1)**

22. $12 + 3n - 4 < 7$ **–2**

23. $11 \ge -3y + \frac{15}{3}$ **–2, 5, 8**

24. According to a study by the Kaiser Family Foundation, typical American teenagers spent an average of 12.5% of their days watching television in 2004. **(Previous Course)**

    a. How many hours does this represent in a day? **3 hr**

    b. How many hours does this represent in one week? **21 hr**

    c. How many days does this represent in one year? **45.625 days in a regular year, 45.75 days in a leap year**

EXPLORATION

25. Some people overgeneralize the Distributive Property. They think that because $6x + 3x = 9x$, both of the following must be true. Find a counterexample to each equation to show that it is false.

    a. $6x \cdot 3x = 18x$ **b.** $\frac{6x}{3x} = 2x$

18a.

x	$(0.65x)^3$	2^x
-10	-274.625	$\frac{1}{1,024}$
-5	-34.3281	$\frac{1}{32}$
0	0	1
5	34.3281	32
10	274.625	1,024
15	926.859	32,768

Teens spend the majority of their TV-watching time between the hours of 8 P.M. and 11 P.M.

Source: Nielsen Media Research

25a. Answers vary.
Sample answer:
$x = 2$

25b. Answers vary.
Sample answer:
$x = 2$

QY ANSWERS

1. $6x + 30$

2. C

The Distributive Property and Removing Parentheses   **71**

---

4   **Wrap-Up**

Ongoing Assignment

Put students in pairs. Have each student write an algebraic expression in the form $a(b \pm c)$. After exchanging papers with their partners, students should demonstrate their understanding of the Distributive Property by applying it to the problems created by their partners.

Project Update

If you have not had students look over the projects on pages 121 and 122, you might want to do so now. Project 5, Postal Rates, on page 122 relates to the content of this lesson.

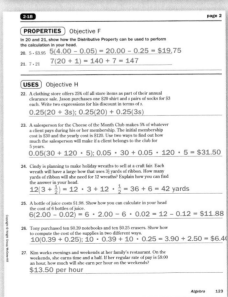

Lesson 2-2

GOAL

Add like terms using the Distributive Property of Multiplication over Addition.

SPUR Objectives

A Use the Distributive Property to expand and combine like terms.

H Apply the Distributive Property in real-world situations.

Materials/Resources

· Lesson Master 2-2A or 2-2B

· Resource Masters 21 and 22

HOMEWORK

Suggestions for Assignment

· Questions 1–33

· Question 34 (extra credit)

· Reading Lesson 2-3

· Covering the Ideas 2-3

Local Standards

1 Warm-Up

Show that *none* of the expressions below are equivalent to $3x + 4y$.

1. $7xy$
2. $7(x + y)$
3. $12xy$
4. $12(x + y)$
5. $3(x + 4)y$

Suggest that students use the values $x = 2$ and $y = 5$ to evaluate each expression. Then $3x + 4y = 26$, $7xy = 70$, $12xy = 120$, $12(x + y) = 84$, and $3(x + y) = 90$. So, none of the expressions are equivalent to $3x + 4y$.

Lesson 2-2

The Distributive Property and Adding Like Terms

Vocabulary

like terms

coefficient

factoring

▶ **BIG IDEA** By applying the Distributive Property, you can add or subtract like terms.

In Lesson 2-1, you learned that the Distributive Property can be used to remove parentheses by changing $c(a + b)$ into $ca + cb$. Now we will reverse the direction.

Adding Like Terms: From $ac + bc$ to $(a + b)c$

Algebraic expressions such as $x^2 + 3x + 5$ or $4a - 9b$ are made up of terms. The terms of $x^2 + 3x + 5$ are x^2, $3x$, and 5. Recall that a term is either a single number or a variable, or a product of numbers and variables. In an expression, addition separates terms. For instance, the terms of $4m^3 - 2m + 9.2m$ are $4m^3$, $-2m$, and $9.2m$. The terms of $-8k^2n + \frac{1}{3}k - 77$ are $-8k^2n$, $\frac{1}{3}k$, and -77.

The terms $-2m$ and $9.2m$ are called **like terms** because they contain the same variables raised to the same powers.

Like Terms	Unlike Terms
$3t$ and $40t$	$5t$ and $16t^2$ (different powers)
y^2 and $-19y^2$	$37x^3$ and y^3 (different variables)
$200u^5c^3$ and $8u^5c^3$	$9u^5c^3$ and $4u^{10}c$ (different powers)

Reversing the sides of the Distributive Property in Lesson 2-1 shows how to add or subtract like terms. For any real numbers a, b, and c, $ac + bc = (a + b)c$ and $ac - bc = (a - b)c$.

Here are the sums of two of the three pairs of like terms from the table above.

$$3t + 40t = (3 + 40)t \qquad y^2 + (-19y^2) = 1y^2 + -19y^2$$
$$= 43t \qquad\qquad = (1 + -19)y^2$$
$$= -18y^2$$

 QY

Mental Math

a. $-1(1 + -1)$ 0

b. $-1(1 + -1(1 + -1))$ -1

c. $-1(1 + -1(1 + -1(1 + -1)))$ 0

▶ **QY**

Find the sum of $200u^5c^3$ and $8u^5c^3$.

Background

Adding like terms. For centuries, the notion that you cannot add unlike terms kept some mathematicians from writing expressions that today are equivalent to our polynomial expressions. If you cannot add x^2 and x, how can you write $x^2 + x$? So it is more accurate to say that the numbers x^2 and x can be added, but there is no simpler form for the answer.

If you have 7 apples and 3 oranges, you *can* add them, not as apples and oranges, but as "pieces of fruit."

The analogous idea in mathematics is that you cannot simplify the sum $x + y$, but if $x = 5k$ and $y = 2k$, then you can simplify the sum to get $7k$.

Explaining the addition of fractions.
The general principle was stated in Lesson 2-1. $\frac{a + b}{c} = \frac{a}{c} + \frac{b}{c}$. In this lesson, you reverse the left and right sides and begin with two fractions and end up with one.

Notice that in combining $y^2 + -19y^2$, the first step was to rewrite y^2 as $1y^2$. Multiplying a number by 1 does not change its value. The following expression can be combined in a similar way.

$$5n - n = 5n - 1n$$
$$= (5 - 1)n$$
$$= 4n$$

When there are two or more collections of like terms in an expression, you can group the like terms together using the Commutative and Associative Properties of Addition.

Example 1

Write a simplified expression for the perimeter of the quadrilateral *QUAD*.

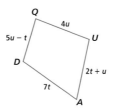

Solution The perimeter is the sum of the lengths of the sides.

$4u + (2t + u) + 7t + (5u - t)$

Group like terms, changing subtraction to addition.

$= (2t + 7t + -t) + (4u + u + 5u)$

Combine like terms using the Distributive Property. Notice that u is the same as $1 \cdot u$ and $-t$ is the same as $-1 \cdot t$.

$= (2t + 7t + -1t) + (4u + 1u + 5u)$

Add like terms.

$= 8t + 10u$

Check Pick values for t and u. We pick 10 for t and 25 for u because they are easy numbers to multiply. The values of the original and simplified expressions must be equal. Substitute 10 for t and 25 for u into the initial expression.

$4u + 2t + u + 7t + 5u - t = 4 \cdot 25 + 2 \cdot 10 + 25 + 7 \cdot 10 + 5 \cdot 25 - 10$
$$= 100 + 20 + 25 + 70 + 125 - 10$$
$$= 330$$

Substitute 10 for t and 25 for u into the simplified expression.

$8t + 10u = 8 \cdot 10 + 10 \cdot 25 = 80 + 250 = 330$

The values of the original and simplified expressions are equal, so it checks.

A number that is a factor in a term is called a **coefficient** of the other variables in the term. For instance in $-8k^2n$, -8 is the coefficient of k^2n. You can see from Example 1 that *like terms are combined by adding the coefficients.*

2 Teaching

Notes on the Lesson

Adding like terms: From $ac + bc$ to $(a + b)c$. Point out that "adding like terms" using the Distributive Property of Multiplication over Addition includes adding like terms by using the Distributive Property of Multiplication in reverse. The second example of adding like terms, $y^2 + -19y^2$, could be considered as subtraction: $y^2 - 19y^2$. Here we do not state a separate property, although you could speak about subtracting like terms: $ac - bc = (a - b)c$. Like terms are subtracted by subtracting the coefficients.

> ### Additional Example
> **Example 1** Write a simplified expression for the perimeter of quadrilateral *FOUR*.
>
>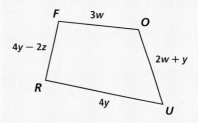
>
> $5w + 9y - 2z$

Notes on the Lesson

Guided Example 2 You might note that until the 1600s, adding f^2 and f was viewed as adding areas and lengths and thought to be incompatible.

Additional Example

Example 2 Combine like terms for $(3x^2 - x + 2) + 8(4x - x^2 + 5)$.

First remove parentheses.

$3x^2 - x + 2 + \underline{}^{?} x - \underline{}^{?} x^2$
$+ \underline{}^{?}$ 32, 8, 40

Group like terms, changing subtractions to additions.

$= (\underline{}^{?} x^2 + \underline{}^{?} x^2) + (\underline{}^{?} x$
$+ \underline{}^{?} x) + (\underline{}^{?} + \underline{}^{?})$ 3, −8, −1,
32, 2, 40

Add like terms.

$= \underline{}^{?} x^2 + \underline{}^{?} x + \underline{}^{?}$ −5, 31, 42

Notes on the Lesson

Explaining the addition of fractions.
Note that the Distributive Property explains why we add fractions by using common denominators. Without common denominators there is no easy way to add fractions.

It is very important to distinguish coefficients from exponents. For example, the Distributive Property applies to $3x + 11x$, but not to $x^3 + x^{11}$. To give a numerical example, $2 \cdot 10 + 3 \cdot 10 = (2 + 3)10 = 5 \cdot 10 = 50$, but $10^2 + 10^3 = 100 + 1{,}000$ or $1{,}100$ is not equal to 10^5 or $100{,}000$. *Different powers of the same number are not like terms.*

Sometimes the Distributive Property can be used twice to simplify an expression, first to remove parentheses and then to combine like terms.

GUIDED

Example 2

Combine like terms for $(4f^2 + f + 9) + 10(12f - f^2 - 3)$.

Solution First remove parentheses.

$= 4f^2 + f + 9 + \underset{120}{\underline{}^{?}} f - \underset{10}{\underline{}^{?}} f^2 - \underset{30}{\underline{}^{?}}$

Group like terms, changing subtractions to additions.

$= [\underset{4}{\underline{}^{?}} f^2 + (\underset{-10}{\underline{}^{?}} f^2)] + (\underset{1}{\underline{}^{?}} f + \underset{120}{\underline{}^{?}} f) + [\underset{9}{\underline{}^{?}} + (\underset{-30}{\underline{}^{?}})]$

Add like terms.

$= \underset{-6}{\underline{}^{?}} f^2 + \underset{121}{\underline{}^{?}} f + \underset{-21}{\underline{}^{?}}$

Be sure to check that the simplified expression is equivalent to the original expression by substituting a number for f into both expressions and making sure they are equal.

Explaining the Addition of Fractions

Adding fractions with the same denominator is an example of adding like terms. Below are two sums to consider: one is numeric and the other is algebraic. Dividing by a number (5 or m) is the same as multiplying by its reciprocal $\left(\frac{1}{5}\ \text{or}\ \frac{1}{m}\right)$.

$$\frac{3}{5} + \frac{4}{5} = 3 \cdot \frac{1}{5} + 4 \cdot \frac{1}{5} \qquad \frac{k}{m} + \frac{2}{m} = k \cdot \frac{1}{m} + 2 \cdot \frac{1}{m}$$
$$= (3 + 4) \cdot \frac{1}{5} \qquad\qquad\quad = (k + 2) \cdot \frac{1}{m}$$
$$= 7 \cdot \frac{1}{5} \qquad\qquad\qquad\quad = \frac{k + 2}{m}$$
$$= \frac{7}{5}$$

If the fractions do not have a common denominator, they must be changed to equivalent fractions that have a common denominator before they can be considered as like terms.

Accommodating the Learner ⬇

Place the following problem on an overhead. Gordon and Chuck are simplifying the following algebraic expression: $4y^2 - 2y + 6 + y^2 + 6y - 2$. Their work is shown.

Gordon
$(4 + 1)y^2 + (-2 + 6)y + (6 + -2)$
$= 5y^2 + 4y + 4$

Chuck
$4y^2 + (-2 + 6)y + (6 + -2)$
$= 4y^2 + 4y + 4$

Ask students to decide which person has done the work correctly. Students should then explain what the person making the mistake did incorrectly. **Gordon; Chuck combined successive terms, NOT like terms.**

Factoring

When $ac + bc$ is rewritten as $(a + b)c$, the original addition has been changed into a multiplication in which $(a + b)$ and c are factors. This process is called **factoring**. We say that c has been "factored out" of the expression. Notice that in this process, instead of removing parentheses, factoring introduces parentheses. For this reason, some people say that factoring "undoes" expansion.

Example 3

Factor 8 out of the expression $8x + 8y$.

Solution First write $8x + 8y = 8(\underline{\ ?\ } + \underline{\ ?\ })$. To get $8x$, there must be an x. To get $8y$, there must be a y.

$$8x + 8y = 8(x + y)$$

GUIDED

Example 4

Factor $3z^2$ out of the expression $3mz^2 - 6pz^2$.

Solution

$3mz^2 - 6pz^2 = 3z^2(\underline{\ ?\ } - \underline{\ ?\ })$ $m; 2p$

(*Hint:* Work backwards to see what $3z^2$ could be multiplied by to get each original term.)

Questions

COVERING THE IDEAS

1. Determine whether the term and $8m^2$ are like terms.
   a. $8m$ b. $8x^2$ c. m^2 d. $3m^2$

In 2–7, combine like terms.

2. $\frac{7}{11} + \frac{5}{4}$ $\frac{83}{44}$

3. $19x + -7x$ $12x$

4. $8y^3 + y^3 + 5y$ $9y^3 + 5y$

5. $(6x + 2y) + (2x + y)$ $8x + 3y$

6. $(9m^2p + 5mp^2 + 8) + (-4m^2 + 7mp^2)$ $9m^2p + 12mp^2 - 4m^2 + 8$

7. $\frac{x + 1}{3m} + \frac{4}{3m}$ $\frac{x + 5}{3m}$

8. Group the six terms below into three pairs of like terms.
   $5m^3n^2, -8.9m, 68m^2n, -m^2n, m, \frac{4}{9}m^3n^2$

1a. no

1b. no

1c. yes

1d. yes

8. $5m^3n^2$ and $\frac{4}{9}m^3n^2$; $68m^2n$ and $-m^2n$; $-8.9m$ and m

The Distributive Property and Adding Like Terms   **75**

Notes on the Lesson

Factoring. Point out that as noted in Lesson 2-1, factoring is the reverse process of expanding.

Additional Examples

Example 3 Factor 6 out of the expression $6d + 6e$. $6(d + e)$

Example 4 Factor $5x^2$ out of the expression $5wx^2 - 10vx^2$.

$5wx^2 - 10vx^2 = 5x^2(\underline{\ ?\ } - \underline{\ ?\ })$

$w, 2v$

Accommodating the Learner ⬆

Algebraic expressions containing fractions can often cause students to make errors. Write the following problem on the board: $\frac{1}{b}\left(2a + \frac{1}{a}\right) + \frac{1}{a}\left(\frac{1}{b} + \frac{1}{b^2}\right)$. Instruct students to first distribute $\frac{1}{b}$ and $\frac{1}{a}$. Next, ask them to change each term so that the fractions have common denominators. Finally, ask them to find the sum of the two fractions and reduce if possible. $\frac{2a^2b + 2b + 1}{ab^2}$

2-2

Recommended Assignment

- Questions 1–33
- Question 34 (extra credit)
- Reading Lesson 2-3
- Covering the Ideas 2-3

Notes on the Questions

Question 18 Some students will answer this question without using the Distributive Property. They will note that if $\frac{3}{10}$ goes to the driver, then $\frac{7}{10}$ goes to the company. Point out that they could subtract $F - 0.30F$ to obtain $0.70F$.

Question 20 This item is to emphasize that the variables in the Distributive Property can stand for expressions like $\sqrt{x}$.

9. Gregory measured his garden using the lengths h and f of his hands and feet. Write a simplified expression for the perimeter of his garden below. $26f + 3h$

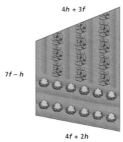

4h + 3f

7f − h

12f − 2h

4f + 2h

Fill in the Blanks In 10 and 11, factor the expression.

10. $16k - 16m = 16(\underline{\;?\;} - \underline{\;?\;})$ $k; m$

11. $2a^2 + 8b = 2(\underline{\;?\;} + \underline{\;?\;})$ $a^2; 4b$

In **12–14**, simplify the expression.

12. $27 + 10(z + 3) + 8z$ $18z + 57$

13. $p(3p + 1) + 5p^2$ $8p^2 + p$

14. $2x + 5(x - 4 + 3x) + (2 - 2x)$ $20x - 18$

15. Factor 5 out of $15ab + 40c - 10$. $5(3ab + 8c - 2)$

16. Factor $3y$ out of $9y^2 - 24xy$. $3y(3y - 8x)$

APPLYING THE MATHEMATICS

17. Frank, Susan, and Kazu collect stamps. Frank has f stamps, and Susan and Kazu each have 4 times as many stamps as Frank. Write an expression for the number of stamps they have altogether. $9f$

18. Some taxicab companies allow their drivers to keep $\frac{3}{10}$ of all the money they collect. The rest goes to the company. If a driver collects F dollars from the fares, write an expression for the company's share. $\frac{7}{10}F$

19. Find a counterexample to show that $6^x + 3^x = 9^x$ is not always true. Answers vary. Sample answer: let $x = 0$; $2 \neq 1$

20. Does $6\sqrt{x} + 3\sqrt{x} = 9\sqrt{x}$ for all values of x? Why or why not? Yes, since $6\sqrt{x}$ and $3\sqrt{x}$ are like terms summing to $9\sqrt{x}$.

Cabs contain a meter that indicates the fare based on the distance covered and other factors.

REVIEW

21. Timothy was asked to simplify $-4(-5 + 3n + -4m)$. His answer was $20 + 3n + -4m$. Write a note to Timothy explaining what he did wrong. **(Lesson 2-1)** Answers vary. Sample answer: Timothy, you did not distribute through all the terms!

76 Using Algebra to Explain

Extension

Suppose the dimensions of Jon's rectangular garden are ab feet by $(a + 2b)$ feet. Pana's rectangular garden is much bigger with dimensions $(3a + 5b)$ feet by $4ab$ feet. Write and simplify an algebraic expression for the area of Jon's garden. Write and simplify an algebraic expression for the area of Pana's garden. How would you find how many more square feet Pana's garden is than Jon's garden? Jon: $(a^2b + 2ab^2)$ ft²; Pana: $(12a^2b + 20ab^2)$ ft²; Subtract the areas of Jon's garden from Pana's.

22. Malia went out to dinner with two friends. They lost track of the number of sodas ordered. But before the bill came, they figured they owed $3x + 48$ dollars, where x represented the number of drinks. If they split the bill evenly, what expression represents how much Malia owes? (**Lesson 2-1**) $x + 16$ dollars

In 23 and 24, explain how to use the Distributive Property to calculate the cost in your head. (**Lesson 2-1**)

23. 8 footballs at $39.95 each Answers vary. Sample answer: $8(40 - 0.05) = 320 - 0.40 = \$319.60$

24. 20 bottles of water at $0.99 each Answers vary. Sample answer: $20(1 - 0.01) = 20 - 0.20 = \$19.80$

25. Suppose JI is 5 centimeters more than JM, and IM is 7 centimeters less than twice JM. Recall that JI represents the distance from J to I. (**Lesson 1-2**)

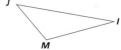

a. Write an expression for the length of each side of the triangle if $x = JM$. $JM = x$ cm; $JI = x + 5$ cm; $IM = 2x - 7$ cm

b. Write a simplified expression for the perimeter of $\triangle JIM$. $4x - 2$ cm

26. a. Describe the pattern below with one variable. $x^2 < x^3$

$$7^2 < 7^3$$
$$6.2^2 < 6.2^3$$
$$\left(\frac{11}{8}\right)^2 < \left(\frac{11}{8}\right)^3$$

b. Find an integer that is an instance of this pattern.

c. Find an integer that is a counterexample to the pattern.

d. Find a noninteger that is a counterexample to the pattern. (**Lesson 1-2**)

26b. Answers vary. Sample answer: $x = 2$

26c. Answers vary. Sample answer: $x = -1$

26d. Answers vary. Sample answer: $x = -0.5$

Matching In 27–30, match each algebraic expression to its English expression. (**Lesson 1-1**)

27. $2(x + 5)$ b

28. $2x + 5$ c

29. $x - 6$ a

30. $6 - x$ d

a. six less than a number

b. double the sum of five and a number

c. five more than double a number

d. take away a number from six

31. Suppose an apartment rents for $775 per month. Find the rent for the given time. (**Previous Course**)

a. 8 months $6,200

b. 3 years $27,900

c. 4.5 years $41,850

d. y years $9,300$y$

e. m months 775m$

Notes on the Questions

Questions 32 and 33 You might ask if any students can determine where the formula comes from. $4\ell w$ is the total area of the four walls, and one gallon of paint can cover 300 square feet.

So $\dfrac{4\ell w}{300} = \dfrac{\text{square feet to be painted}}{\frac{300 \text{ square feet}}{\text{gallon}}} =$ number of gallons needed. This number is multiplied by the price per gallon to get the total cost.

Question 34 Do not let students know that the pattern is not a hard one to find. Let them be surprised. (However, describing the pattern may be difficult.)

2-2

4 Wrap-Up

Ongoing Assignment

Write the following algebraic expression on the board: $(4xy^2 + -3x^2y + 2x) + (-5xy^2 + 7x^2y)$. Ask students to combine like terms. Students should write their answers on a piece of paper.

$-xy^2 + 4x^2y + 2x$

In 32 and 33, use the following information. The cost c of painting the four walls of a room is given by $c = \dfrac{p(4\ell w)}{300}$, where p is the price per gallon of paint and ℓ and w are the length and width of the room in feet. (**Previous Course**)

32. Find the cost of painting a bedroom with walls that are 16 feet by 8 feet and using paint that costs $29.95 per gallon. **about $51.11**

33. At $18.99 per gallon, what is the cost of painting a living room with walls that are 24 feet by 10 feet? **about $60.77**

In May 2004, the median hourly wage for house painters was $14.55.

Source: Bureau of Labor Statistics

EXPLORATION

34. Consider this sequence of sums of increasingly large multiples of x whose coefficients are alternately positive and negative.

Step 1	x
Step 2	$x + -2x$
Step 3	$x + -2x + 3x$
Step 4	$x + -2x + 3x + -4x$
Step 5	$x + -2x + 3x + -4x + 5x$

$\vdots$

a. Simplify the five lines that are shown. $x, -x, 2x, -2x, 3x$
b. What will be the simplified form of the 25th line? $13x$
c. What will be the simplified form of the 100th line? $-50x$
d. What is the simplified form of the nth line when n is even? $-\dfrac{n}{2}x$
e. What is the simplified form of the nth line when n is odd? $\dfrac{n+1}{2}x$

QY ANSWER

$208u^5c^3$

Lesson 2-3 Explaining Number Puzzles

▶ **BIG IDEA** Algebra explains why many number puzzles work and how to invent them.

The number puzzle at the right was sent by e-mail. Try it yourself.

> >From: <joe>
> >Re: I can guess your age
> >
> >Follow the steps below, and I
> >bet I can guess your age.
> >
> >1.) Write down your age.
> >2.) Add 3.
> >3.) Multiply by 5.
> >4.) Subtract your age.
> >5.) Add 9.
> >6.) Divide by 4.
> >7.) Subtract 6.
> >8.) The number you got
> >   is your current age!

Mental Math

a. In $\triangle ABC$, $m\angle A = 35°$ and $m\angle B = 105°$. What is $m\angle C$? **40°**

b. In $\triangle LMN$, $m\angle L = x$ and $m\angle M = 74°$. What is $m\angle N$? $(106 - x)°$

c. In $\triangle WYZ$, $m\angle W = r$ and $m\angle Y = s$. What is $m\angle Z$? $(180 - r - s)°$

The number puzzle raises some questions. Does it work for other ages? Will it work if you count your age in months? Will it work for your great-grandfather Odell? Will it work for the baby a mother is expecting in six months, who the family fondly refers to as $-\frac{1}{2}$ year old because she is half a year before her birth? Will it work for any age?

Explaining the Puzzle

The steps shown below are for a 16-year-old student.

Step 1 Write your age.	16	
Step 2 Add 3.	$16 + 3 = 19$	
Step 3 Multiply by 5.	$19(5) = 95$	
Step 4 Subtract your age.	$95 - 16 = 79$	
Step 5 Add 9.	$79 + 9 = 88$	
Step 6 Divide by 4.	$88 \div 4 = 22$	
Step 7 Subtract 6.	$22 - 6 = 16$	
The final result is the age.	16	

Lesson 2-3

GOAL
Show how algebra can explain how various number puzzles work.

SPUR Objective
G Use algebra to explain how number puzzles work.

Materials/Resources
· Lesson Master 2-3A or 2-3B
· Resource Masters 1 and 23–25
· Quiz 1

HOMEWORK
Suggestions for Assignment
- Questions 1–30
- Question 31 (extra credit)
- Reading Lesson 2-4
- Covering the Ideas 2-4

Local Standards

1 Warm-Up

If you have not assigned the reading from this lesson before class, you may want to have everyone in the class engage in the first puzzle. Each person should use his or her age and then go through the explanation.

Background

There are innumerable number patterns and puzzles. The ones that are in this lesson are either patterns in arrays of numbers or puzzles of the "pick a number" type, because at this point students may have only a small number of algebraic tools in their arsenal.

Three puzzles are detailed in the reading. The first is a "guess your age" puzzle. The surprise of this puzzle is that the rules involve the numbers 3, 5, 9, 4, and 6, but the number at the end equals the number you began with.

The second is a puzzle of a similar type is called "Seven Is Heaven." Here the number at the end equals 7 regardless of the number at the beginning.

The third puzzle (Example 2) is designed to show students how they can create a puzzle like the others in the lesson.

(continued on next page)

2-3

2 Teaching

Notes on the Lesson

Explaining the puzzle. As you explain the puzzle, consider putting arrows between the various steps: $A \rightarrow A + 3 \rightarrow 5(A + 3) = 5A + 15 \rightarrow \ldots$ and so on, so students understand that they are not solving equations. The arrows indicate that the expressions are not meant to be equivalent.

To use the outcome of the puzzle in a different way, you might want to subtract a different number in Step 7. For instance, if 10 is subtracted, then the result is 4 less than a person's age. Then you can add 4 to the number you get at the end to tell the age.

The "Seven Is Heaven" puzzle. This puzzle was invented for this lesson. There is no substitute for having students go through the puzzle using their own numbers. The appeal of this puzzle is that it uses the numbers 1, 2, 3, 4, 5, and 6 in order in the steps, but the answer at the end is 7. For extra credit, you might ask students what would need to be done to make an "Eight is Great" puzzle with the same characteristic.

Additional Example

Example 1 Work the puzzle below with a few numbers. Your answer should be 11. Then use a variable to create an expression to explain why the puzzle works. **Answers vary. Sample answers shown.**

Step 1 Begin with a number.
   Any number n
Step 2 Add 2.
   $n + 2$
Step 3 Multiply by 3.
   $3(n + 2) = 3n + 6$
Step 4 Multiply by 4.
   $4(3n + 6) = 12n + 24$
Step 5 Subtract 15.
   $12n + 24 - 15 = 12n + 9$
Step 6 Add 2.
   $12n + 9 + 2 = 12n + 11$
Step 7 Subtract 12 times your original number. $12n + 11 - 12n = 11$
Answer $= 11.$ **11**

Using algebra to explain the puzzle on page 79, we let the variable A stand for the age used in the first step. Now we follow the given directions, simplifying as we go by using the Distributive Property.

Step 1 Write your age. $\quad A$

Step 2 Add 3. $\quad A + 3$

Step 3 Multiply by 5. $\quad 5(A + 3) = 5A + 5 \cdot 3 = 5A + 15$

Step 4 Subtract your age. $\quad 5A + 15 - A = 4A + 15$

Step 5 Add 9. $\quad 4A + 15 + 9 = 4A + 24$

Step 6 Divide by 4. $\quad \frac{4A + 24}{4} = \frac{4A}{4} + \frac{24}{4} = A + 6$

Step 7 Subtract 6. $\quad A + 6 - 6 = A$

The algebra shows that any age works. The "trick" is really just an algebraic process. No matter what the original age is, the process will end with the same age from which you started.

The "Seven Is Heaven" Puzzle

In the next puzzle, the result is not the original number, but it is surprising in a different way.

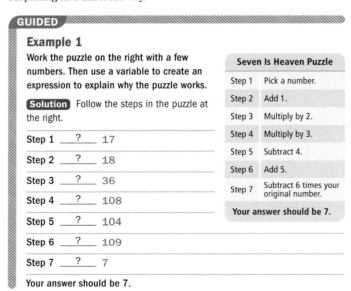

GUIDED

Example 1
Work the puzzle on the right with a few numbers. Then use a variable to create an expression to explain why the puzzle works.

Solution Follow the steps in the puzzle at the right.

Step 1 ___?___ 17
Step 2 ___?___ 18
Step 3 ___?___ 36
Step 4 ___?___ 108
Step 5 ___?___ 104
Step 6 ___?___ 109
Step 7 ___?___ 7

Your answer should be 7.

Seven Is Heaven Puzzle	
Step 1	Pick a number.
Step 2	Add 1.
Step 3	Multiply by 2.
Step 4	Multiply by 3.
Step 5	Subtract 4.
Step 6	Add 5.
Step 7	Subtract 6 times your original number.

Your answer should be 7.

Answers vary. Sample answers are given.

Accommodating the Learner

Some students are kinesthetic learners. Using algebra tiles or other objects, have them create a four-step addition, multiplication, division, and subtraction number puzzle that begins and ends with the same number. After students have created their puzzles, have them write each of the four steps algebraically.

In these cases, and in four other puzzles found in the questions, algebra justifies the results in the puzzles. The use of algebra demonstrates how one could create other puzzles like the number puzzles in this book.

Later in this course, we want students to be able to routinely check whether expressions such as $(x + 1)(x + 2)$ and $x^2 + 2$ are equivalent (they are not) by substituting values for their variables.

We show the process beginning with any number *n*.

Step 1	Begin with a number.	Any number n
Step 2	Add 1.	$n + 1$
Step 3	Multiply by 2.	$2(n + 1) = 2n + 2$
Step 4	Multiply by 3.	$3(2n + 2) = 6n + 6$
Step 5	Subtract 4.	$6n + 6 - 4 = 6n + 2$
Step 6	Add 5.	$6n + 2 + 5 = 6n + 7$
Step 7	Subtract 6 times your original number.	$6n + 7 - 6n = 7$
	Your answer should be 7.	7

Using Algebra to Create Number Puzzles

In Examples 2 and 3, we show how algebra can be used to create a number puzzle. This number puzzle will begin and end with the same number. Begin by choosing a variable to represent the starting number. A new expression is formed by performing an arithmetic operation on the existing expression. After several steps, carefully choose operations to return the expression to the variable.

Example 2
Create a number puzzle that begins and ends with the same number.

Solution We show the process and create one puzzle.

Changing

Begin with *n*.	n
Add 6.	$n + 6$
Multiply by 4.	$4(n + 6) = 4n + 24$
Divide by 2.	$\frac{4n + 24}{2} = \frac{4n}{2} + \frac{24}{2} = 2n + 12$
Subtract 19.	$2n + 12 - 19 = 2n - 7$

Returning

Add 7.	$2n - 7 + 7 = 2n$
Divide by 2.	$\frac{2n}{2} = n$
The answer equals *n*.	n

Additional Example
Example 2 Create a number puzzle that begins and ends with the same number. **Answers vary. Sample answer:**

Step 1 Begin with *n*. n

Step 2 Add 3. $n + 3$

Step 3 Multiply by 6.
$6(n + 3) = 6n + 18$

Step 4 Divide by 3. $\frac{6n + 18}{3}$
$= \frac{6n}{3} + \frac{18}{3} = 2n + 6$

Step 5 Subtract 5.
$2n + 6 - 5 = 2n + 1$

Step 6 Subtract 1.
$2n + 1 - 1 = 2n$

Step 7 Divide by 2. $\frac{2n}{2} = n$

Answer $= n$. n

Accommodating the Learner

Students are to create a puzzle similar to the ones found in this lesson. Students must follow the given guidelines. At least one variable must be used and the four operations +, −, ×, and ÷ must be used at least once. Parentheses and an exponent must be used at least once. The resulting answer must be −4. Students should list each step and model each step with an algebraic expression. Have students check that their puzzle works by providing an example.

2-3

Additional Example

Additional Example

Example 3 Create a number puzzle so that the answer is always 1.

Step 1: Begin with n. n

Step 2: Add 4.   ___?___ $n + 4$

Step 3: Multiply by 4. $4(n + 4) = $ ___?___
$4n + 16$

Step 4: Add $4n$.   ___?___ = ___?___
$4n + 16 + 4n, 8n + 16$

Step 5: Divide by 8.   ___?___ = ___?___
$\frac{8n + 16}{8}, n + 2$

Step 6: Subtract 1.   ___?___ = ___?___
$n + 2 - 1, n + 1$

Step 7: Subtract n.   ___?___ = ___?___
$n + 1 - n, 1$

GUIDED

Example 3

Create a number puzzle so that the answer always equals 6.

Solution

Step 1 Begin with n.	n	
Step 2 Subtract 4.	___?___	$n - 4$
Step 3 Multiply by 8.	$8(n - 4) = $ ___?___	$8n - 32$
Step 4 Add $8n$	___?___ = ___?___	$8n - 32 + 8n$; $16n - 32$
Step 5 Divide by 16.	___?___ = ___?___	$\frac{16n - 32}{16}$; $n - 2$
Step 6 Add 8.	___?___ = ___?___	$n - 2 + 8$; $n + 6$
Step 7 Subtract n.	___?___ = ___?___	$n + 6 - n$; 6

One of algebra's greatest strengths is the use of a variable to create algebraic expressions that can represent *all* the possibilities of a number puzzle, or even a real-life puzzle. This helps to explain mysteries and many other things in mathematics and the world.

Questions

COVERING THE IDEAS

1. Why would you use a variable in a number puzzle?

In 2–5, complete the number puzzle at the beginning of this lesson for the individual.

2. a person who is 50 years old The result is 50.

3. great-grandfather Odell, who is 97 years old The result is 97.

4. a baby expected to be born in half a year The result is $-\frac{1}{2}$.

5. a person who is 192 months old The result is 192.

In 6 and 7, complete the "Seven Is Heaven" puzzle on page 80 for a number x in the given range.

6. $250 < x < 500$ The result is 7. 7. $0 < x < 1$ The result is 7.

8. Will the "Seven Is Heaven" puzzle work for negative numbers? Explain why or why not.

9. Complete the "We're Number One!" puzzle at the right by starting with each number shown.
   a. 7   b. –2.9   c. n

1. Answers vary. Sample answer: Variables are used to see how the puzzle works for any number.

8. Answers vary. Sample answer: Yes, the properties that explain it are true for all real numbers.

9a. 7; –1; 6; 36; 41; 45; 15; 1

9b. –2.9; –10.9; –3.9; –23.4; –18.4; –14.4; –4.8; 1

9c. n; $n - 8$; $n - 1$; $6n - 6$; $6n - 1$; $6n + 3$; $2n + 1$; 1

We're Number One! Puzzle	
Step 1	Pick a number.
Step 2	Subtract 8.
Step 3	Add 7.
Step 4	Multiply by 6.
Step 5	Add 5.
Step 6	Add 4.
Step 7	Divide by 3.
Step 8	Subtract 2 times your original number.
Step 9	Your answer should be 1.

Extension

Have students refer to Questions 13 and 14 and consider the following "magic square" of order 4.

Ask students to find the sum of each column, row, and diagonal. Next have them add m to each cell and demonstrate that each column, row, and diagonal still give the same sum.

–7	0	5	4
6	3	–6	–1
–4	–3	8	1
7	2	–5	–2

10. Complete the "Double Trouble" puzzle at the right by starting with each number shown. **10a–c. See margin.**

   a. 17   b. 0.4   c. n

APPLYING THE MATHEMATICS

11. Create a number puzzle that begins and ends with the same number. **See margin.**

12. The "Seven Is Heaven" puzzle in Example 1 always ended with 7. Create an "Eight Is Great" puzzle that always ends with 8.

In 13 and 14, use the "magic square" at the right. In a magic square, the sums of any row, column, or diagonal are equal. In this magic square the sums are all 15.

13. Add 13 to every number in the magic square.
   a. Is the result still a magic square? **yes**
   b. By how much did the sum of the rows, columns, and diagonals change? **39**
   c. Add k to each of the numbers in the magic square. Is the result still a magic square? Explain your answer using algebra.

14. Multiply every number in the magic square by 7.
   a. Is the result still a magic square? **yes**
   b. By how much did the sum of the rows, columns, and diagonals change? **90**
   c. If you multiply each number in the magic square by m, will it still be a magic square? Explain your answer using algebra. **See margin.**

15. Refer to the card trick described on page 64. Make a table with 5 rows. In each row, give a number that the spectator might choose and the resulting number of cards in the small pile after Step 3 of the trick. **See margin.**

REVIEW

In 16–19, determine whether the terms are like or unlike. (Lesson 2-2)

16. k, $\frac{k}{6}$ 17. $-y$, $\frac{26}{y}$ 18. $22n$, $22n^2$ 19. $5d^2$, $-d^{-2}$
   like   unlike   unlike   unlike

20. The figure at the right consists of a big rectangle split into three rectangular parts. (Lesson 2-2)
   a. Write the area as length times width. $A = x \cdot 25$
   b. Write the area as the sum of three areas. $A = 8x + 11x + 6x$

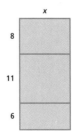

Explaining Number Puzzles   83

Double Trouble

Step 1	Pick a number.
Step 2	Subtract 11.
Step 3	Multiply by 3.
Step 4	Add 5 times your original number.
Step 5	Add 1.
Step 6	Divide by 4.
Step 7	Add 8.
Step 8	Your answer should be twice your original number.

6	7	2
1	5	9
8	3	4

12. Answers vary. Sample answer: change Step 6 of Seven Is Heaven to "Add 6."

13c. Answers vary. Sample answer: Yes, suppose the numbers in a certain row, column, or diagonal are x, y, and z, which add to 15. Their new sum is $(x + k) + (y + k) + (z + k) = x + y + z + 3k$. This will be the sum in every row, column, and diagonal.

3 Assignment

Recommended Assignment
- Questions 1–30
- Question 31 (extra credit)
- Reading Lesson 2-4
- Covering the Ideas 2-4

Notes on the Questions

Questions 2–8 The purpose of these questions is to point out how the generality of algebra shows that puzzles work for all numbers, including nonintegers and negative numbers.

Question 10 This puzzle is like the first number puzzle of the lesson in that the number at the end depends on the original number chosen.

Question 14 This explanation relies on the Distributive Property of Multiplication over Addition.

Question 15 This problem refers to the card trick described in the chapter opener, pages 64 and 65.

Additional Answers

10a. 17; 6; 18; 103; 104; 26; 34

10b. 0.4; −10.6; −31.8; −29.8; −28.8; −7.2; 0.8

10c. n; $n − 11$; $3n − 33$; $8n − 33$; $8n − 32$; $2n − 8$; $2n$

11. Answers vary. Sample answer: Step 1. Pick a number. Step 2. Subtract 11. Step 3. Multiply by 3. Step 4. Add 5 times your original number. Step 5. Add 1. Step 6. Divide by 8. Step 7. Add 4. Step 8. Your answer should be the number you picked.

14c. Answers vary. Sample answer: Yes, suppose the numbers in a certain row, column, or diagonal are x, y, and z, which add to 15. Their new sum is $mx + my + mz = m(x + y + z) = 15m$. This will be the sum in every row, column, and diagonal.

15. Answers vary. Sample answer:

Spectator's Choice	Number of Cards in Small Pile
10	$10 − 1 = 9$
11	$11 − 2 = 9$
12	$12 − 3 = 9$
13	$13 − 4 = 9$
14	$14 − 5 = 9$

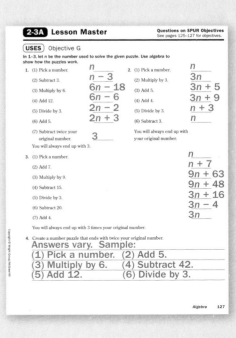

2-3

4 Wrap-Up

Ongoing Assignment

Tell students that you are thinking of a number n, and after performing a series of algebraic operations the resulting algebraic expression is $-4n - 7$. Ask students to explain how to algebraically manipulate the resulting algebraic expression so that the result is n. Have them test their answer by choosing a value for n.

Project Update

Project 1, Repeating Number Puzzle, and Project 2, A New Operation, on page 121 and Project 4, Magic Squares, on page 122 relate to the content of this lesson.

Additional Answers

22. $24x + 84$; $24(5) + 84 = 204$;
$4(3(2(5) + 7)) = 204$

23. $33n^2 - 132n$; $33(5)^2 - 132(5) = 165$;
$5(11(3(5 - 4))) = 165$

---

21. Write each expression as a single fraction. (Lesson 2-2)

a. $\frac{3}{5} + \frac{4}{3}$ $\frac{29}{15}$
b. $\frac{x}{2} + \frac{2x}{7}$ $\frac{11x}{14}$
c. $\frac{2}{5y} + \frac{4}{5y}$ $\frac{6}{5y}$

In 22 and 23, use the Distributive Property to simplify the expression. Check your answer by substituting 5 for the variable in both the original expression and your answer. (Lesson 2-1) 22–23. See margin.

22. $4(3(2x + 7))$
23. $n(11(3(n - 4)))$

24. A local coffee shop sells "Coffee Club" cups for $1.99. With the cup, each additional refill of coffee only costs $1.25. Let n = the number of refills purchased. (Lesson 1-4) 24a–b. See margin.

a. Make a table for 0, 1, 2, 3, 4, 5, and 6 refills purchased.

b. Graph your results from Part a.

c. Write an expression describing the cost of n refills.
$1.99 + 1.25n$ dollars

25. Write an expression for the amount of money each person has or owes after w weeks. (Lesson 1-1)

a. Eddie is given $100 and spends $4 per week. See margin.

b. Liseta owes $350 on a stereo and is paying it off at $5 per week. Liseta owes $-350 + 5w$ dollars

In 26–30, evaluate the expression. (Previous Course)

26. $-23 + 41$ 18
27. $-42 - (-87)$ 45
28. $(-8)(12)$ –96
29. $(-13)(-6)$ 78
30. $\frac{-24}{6}$ –4

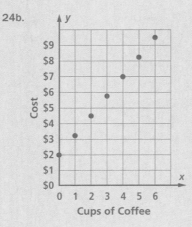

In the United States, it is estimated that as many as 70% of 18–24 year olds drink coffee in the morning.

Source: National Coffee Association of U.S.A., Inc.

EXPLORATION

31. The puzzle at the right involves a square array of numbers. Pick a number in the first row, then pick a number from the second row that is in a different column than the first number. Then choose the number in the third row that is not in either column as the first or second number. One example is 4, –24, and –15.

a. Multiply the three numbers together. What value do you get for the product? 1,440

b. Repeat the process. What do you notice?

c. The numbers in this puzzle at the right were chosen carefully. To see how, begin by replacing 3 with a and 4 with b. Then the other seven numbers can be expressed in terms of a and b. This has already been done for some cells in the diagram at the right. Fill in the remaining cells, and explain why the puzzle works. See margin.

8	4	–20
–24	–12	60
6	3	–15

31b. You get 1,440 every time.

?	b	–5a
?	–ab	?
2a	a	?

Additional Answers

24a.
n	Cost
0	$1.99
1	$3.24
2	$4.49
3	$5.74
4	$6.99
5	$8.24
6	$9.49

24b.

(graph)

25a. Eddie has $100 - 4w$ dollars

31c.
2b	b	–5b
–2ab	–ab	5ab
2a	a	–5a

Possible combinations have equal products

$(2b)(-ab)(-5a) =$
$(2b)(5ab)(a) =$
$(b)(-2ab)(-5a) = (b)(5ab)$
$(2a) = (-5b)(-2ab)(a) =$
$(-5b)(-ab)(2a) = 10a^2b^2.$

Lesson Master (2-3B)

page 2

2-3B Lesson Master

Questions on SPUR Objectives
See pages 125–127 for objectives.

USES Objective G

In 1–3, let n be the number used to solve the given puzzle. Use algebra to show how the puzzles work.

1. (1) Pick a number. n
(2) Add 2. $n + 2$
(3) Multiply by 15. $15n + 30$
(4) Subtract 51. $15n - 21$
(5) Divide by 3. $5n - 7$
(6) Add 11. $5n + 4$
(7) Subtract five times your original number. 4
You will always end up with 4.

2. (1) Pick a number. n
(2) Multiply by 5. $5n$
(3) Subtract 10. $5n - 10$
(4) Add 5. $5n - 5$
(5) Divide by 5. $n - 1$
(6) Add 1. n
You will always end up with your original number.

3. (1) Pick a number. n
(2) Subtract 12. $n - 12$
(3) Multiply by 4. $4n - 48$
(4) Add 12. $4n - 36$
(5) Divide by –2. $-2n + 18$
(6) Add three times your original number. $n + 18$
You will always end up with 18 more than your original number.

4. Create a number puzzle that ends with –4 times your original number. Answers vary. **Sample:**
(1) Pick a number. (2) Add 4.
(3) Multiply by 8. (4) Subtract 32.
(5) Divide by –2.

128   Algebra

Lesson 2-4 Opposites

Vocabulary

additive inverse

opposite

▶ **BIG IDEA** The opposite $-k$ of a number k has properties relating it to addition, multiplication, and subtraction: $-k + k = 0$; $-k = -1 \cdot k$; and $a - k = a + -k$.

The real numbers k and $-k$ are opposites. You have dealt with opposites in previous lessons. In this lesson, we look at some of the basic properties of opposites.

Opposites as Additive Inverses

Suppose you walk forward 10 steps and then walk backward 10 steps. We signal these opposite directions by calling the walk forward 10 and the walk backward −10. The result of doing these actions one after the other is to end in the same place from where you started. So $10 + -10 = 0$. When two numbers add to zero, they are called **additive inverses,** or **opposites.** Because they signal opposite actions, another name for additive inverse is opposite. So, if two real numbers x and y are opposites, then their sum is zero $(x + y = 0)$. Reversing this, if you know that $x + y = 0$, then x and y must be opposites $(x = -y$ or $y = -x)$.

 QY1

The numbers k and $-k$ are opposites regardless of the value of k. If $k = 5$, then $-k = -5$. If $k = -10$, then $-k = -(-10) = 10$. *When k is negative, $-k$ is positive.*

What is the opposite of $-k$? One way to denote the opposite of $-k$ is as $-(-k)$. Yet we know that the opposite of $-k$ is k. This tells us that these two expressions are equivalent. We call this the *Opposite of Opposites Property.*

Opposite of Opposites Property

For any real number a, $-(-a) = a$.

Mental Math

a. a. How many games must a team win to win a best-of-5 playoff series? 3

b. How many games must a team win to win a best-of-7 playoff series? 4

c. How many games must a team win to win a best-of-n playoff series? $\frac{1}{2}(n + 1)$

▶ **QY1**

What is the opposite of each number?

a. 3.5   **b.** $\frac{-17}{8}$

Background

The four properties identified in this lesson are of immense importance in rewriting expressions. The Opposite of Opposites Property is usually quite easy for students and requires little explanation. The Multiplication Property of −1, the Opposite of a Sum Property, and the Opposite of a Difference Property are helpful in dealing with tricky situations.

The opposite of a sum. Here we consider $-(a + b) = -a + -b$ as the special case of the Distributive Property, namely $c(a + b) = ca + cb$ when $c = -1$. Another approach avoids multiplication. You can think of $-(a + b)$ as that number which, when added to $a + b$, gives a sum of 0. Since $(a + b) + (-a + -b) = 0$, the opposite of the quantity $(a + b)$ is $-a + -b$. A third approach is in between: You think of the opposite sign as being distributed over the terms of the quantity. The last view is mentioned in the lesson.

Lesson 2-4

GOAL

Use the equivalence between multiplying by −1 and taking the opposite of a number to simplify algebraic expressions.

SPUR Objectives

B Use the Opposite of Opposites Property, the Opposite of a Sum Property, and the Opposite of a Difference Property to simplify expressions.

D Apply and recognize the following multiplication properties: Multiplicative Identity Property, Multiplicative Inverse Property, Multiplication Property of Zero, Multiplication Property of Equality, and Zero Product Property.

Materials/Resources

· Lesson Masters 2-4A and 2-4B
· Resource Masters 26 and 27

HOMEWORK

Suggestions for Assignment

• Questions 1–31
• Question 32 (extra credit)
• Reading Lesson 2-5
• Covering the Ideas 2-5

Local Standards

---

1 ▌**Warm-Up**

You might write or project the following.

1. Fill in the following table.

a	b	$-(a + b)$	$-a + -b$	$-a - b$
43	16	−59	−59	−59
−8	−3	11	11	11
$\frac{1}{2}$	$\frac{2}{3}$	$-\frac{7}{6}$	$-\frac{7}{6}$	$-\frac{7}{6}$
0	−51.3	51.3	51.3	51.3
−77	12	65	65	65

continued on next page

2. What do you notice about the three expressions, $-(a + b)$, $-a + -b$, and $-a - b$? The expressions seem to be equivalent.

Taking the Opposite by Multiplying by –1

One way of changing a number to its opposite is to multiply it by –1. The Distributive Property explains why this works. If the sum of two numbers is 0, then they must be opposites. Add k to $-1 \cdot k$ and see if the result is 0.

$$k + (-1) \cdot k = 1 \cdot k + (-1) \cdot k$$
$$= (1 + (-1))k$$
$$= 0k$$
$$= 0$$

So k and $-1 \cdot k$ are opposites. In symbols, this can be written $-1 \cdot k = -k$. We call this the *Multiplication Property of –1*.

2 Teaching

Notes on the Lesson

You might begin with the simple exercise: Does $-(-(-(-(-46))))$ equal 46, or does it equal –46? Here the number of opposite signs is 5, so the answer is –46. This leads to a simple yet important generalization of the Opposite of Opposites Property: If the number of opposite signs is even, then the value of the number is unchanged; If the number of opposite signs is odd, then the value of the number is changed to its opposite.

An example of the opposite of a sum. Ask students how they would check if the two expressions $800 - (a + b)$ and $800 + -a + -b$ are equivalent. (Substitute for a and b.)

Multiplication Property of –1
For any real number a, $a \cdot -1 = -1 \cdot a = -a$.

The Opposite of Opposites Property and the Multiplication Property of –1 can be used to rewrite and simplify algebraic expressions.

An Example of the Opposite of a Sum

Suppose Marisol has $800 in her savings account. She withdraws a dollars from her account. Deciding that this is not enough, she makes another withdrawal of b dollars. The amount of money left in her savings account can be expressed in several different ways. One way is to think that Marisol withdrew a total of $(a + b)$ dollars. So she has $800 - (a + b)$, or $800 + -(a + b)$ dollars left.

Another way is to think that Marisol withdrew a dollars, then withdrew b dollars. So she has $800 - a - b$, or $800 + -a + -b$ dollars left.

The fact that $-(a + b)$ is the same as $-a - b$ is due in part to the Distributive Property.

$$-(a + b) = -1(a + b) \qquad \text{Multiplication Property of –1}$$
$$= -1a + -1b \qquad \text{Distributive Property}$$
$$= -a + -b \qquad \text{Multiplication Property of –1}$$
$$= -a - b \qquad \text{Definition of Subtraction}$$

The opposite of a sum is the sum of the opposites of its terms.

The first cash dispenser in use was at Chemical Bank, Long Island, New York in 1969.

Source: www.atmwarehouse.com

Note-Taking Tips

The vocabulary words in this lesson can be very confusing, especially for your ELL students. As students enter the new vocabulary words into their notebooks, make sure they also include an example for each one. In the case of the Op-Op Property, students should include an example where the value of the variable is negative and one where the value of the variable is positive.

Opposite of a Sum Property
For all real numbers a and b, $-(a + b) = -a + (-b) = -a - b$.

For example, $-(15y + 3) = -15y - 3$.

Vocabulary Development

It is important that students do not think of $-a$ as a negative number but as the opposite of a. Impress upon students that the value of $-a$ is positive when the value of a is negative, negative when the value of a is positive, and zero when the value of a is zero.

The opposite of a difference. A key idea is that $a - b = a + -b$ even when b is a complicated expression like $5x^2 + 4x - 3$. Then $a - b = a - (5x^2 + 4x - 3)$.

$$= a + -(5x^2 + 4x - 3)$$
$$= a + -1 \cdot (5x^2 + 4x - 3)$$
$$= a - 5x^2 - 4x + 3$$

Obtaining correct signs when parentheses are removed will remain a problem for many students. These students often

need a great deal of practice before they achieve mastery, and constant reminders are needed even after mastery has been achieved. Thus, this is a skill we review throughout this chapter and in later chapters. We encourage you to move forward reasonably quickly because errors are often created in the rewriting from one step to the next. Students should be able to go immediately from $a - (5x^2 + 4x - 3)$ to $a - 5x^2 - 4x + 3$.

QY2

Opposite of a Difference

Suppose the expression in parentheses involves subtraction rather than addition. How can you rewrite its opposite? Again, the Distributive Property can be used.

$$-(a - b) = a + -b \qquad \text{Definition of Subtraction}$$
$$= -a + -(-b) \qquad \text{Opposite of a Sum Property}$$
$$= -a + b \qquad \text{Opposite of Opposites Property}$$

> **Opposite of a Difference Property**
>
> For all real numbers a and b, $-(a - b) = -a + b$.

Some problems involve subtracting an expression with two or more terms. Begin by rewriting the subtraction as adding the opposite.

Example 1

Simplify $4x - (3x + 7)$.

Solution Rewrite the subtraction as adding the opposite.

$$4x - (3x + 7) = 4x + -(3x + 7) \qquad \text{Definition of Subtraction}$$
$$= 4x + -3x + (-7) \qquad \text{Opposite of a Sum Property}$$
$$= x + -7 \qquad \text{Add like terms.}$$
$$= x - 7 \qquad \text{Definition of Subtraction}$$

STOP QY3

GUIDED

Example 2

Simplify $(x + 6) - 7(2x - 3)$.

Solution

$$(x + 6) + \underline{\;?\;} (2x - 3) \qquad \text{Definition of Subtraction } -7$$
$$= x + 6 + \underline{\;?\;} + \underline{\;?\;} \qquad \text{Distributive Property } -14x;\ 21$$
$$= \underline{\;?\;} + \underline{\;?\;} \qquad \text{Add like terms. } -13x;\ 27$$

Check When you are asked to simplify expressions, you can make a quick check to see if your answer is equivalent to the given expression by substituting a value for the variable. If the given expressions have one variable each, you can graph the expressions or generate a table of values to check that they are equivalent.

▶ **QY2**

Simplify $-(a^2 + 2b)$.

▶ **QY3**

Graph $y = 4x - (3x + 7)$ and $y = x - 7$ in the same window. Do both equations have the same graph?

Opposites 87

Notes on the Lesson

Examples 1 and 2 Use substitution to check the answer for each example. Remind students to use substitution as a way of checking whether the expressions are equivalent as they go through the question set.

You may want to extend the questions to include situations where trinomials and other polynomials are subtracted. For example,

1. Simplify $a + b - c + (a - b + c)$.
   $(2a)$
2. Simplify $a + b - c - (a - b + c)$.
   $(2b - 2c)$
3. Simplify $a + b - c - 2(a - b + c)$.
   $(-a + 3b - 3c)$

It is easy to make up more problems of this type to extend concepts further. If students have CAS capability, they can easily check their work.

> **Additional Examples**
>
> **Example 1** Simplify $7y - (2y + 11)$.
> $5y - 11$
>
> **Example 2**
> Simplify $(w - 3) - 2(4w + 2)$.
>
> $(w - 3) - 2(4w + 2)$
> $= (w + -3) + \underline{\overset{?}{\;\;}} (4w + 2)\ -2$
> $= w + -3 + \underline{\overset{?}{\;\;}} + \underline{\overset{?}{\;\;}}\ -8w,\ -4$
> $= \underline{\overset{?}{\;\;}} + \underline{\overset{?}{\;\;}}\ -7w,\ -7$
> $= \underline{\overset{?}{\;\;}} - \underline{\overset{?}{\;\;}}\ -7w,\ 7$

3 Assignment

Recommended Assignment

- Questions 1–31
- Question 32 (extra credit)
- Reading Lesson 2-5
- Covering the Ideas 2-5

Notes on the Questions

Question 1 The check part of this question is important.

Questions 7 and 8 Remind students that if they are confused, they can substitute a number for the variable and test the choices. Caution them that they should not substitute 0 for a variable. Ask why. (Because −0 = 0 so substituting 0 would not distinguish the choices.)

Additional Answers

17a.

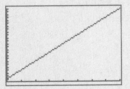

Yes, the expressions appear to be equivalent.

Questions

COVERING THE IDEAS

1. A bottle of apple juice contains 48 fluid ounces. You pour f ounces into a glass and drink it. Then you pour n ounces more into the glass.
   a. Express the amount of juice left in the bottle in two different ways. $48 - f - n$ oz and $48 - (f + n)$ oz
   b. Check that the two expressions in Part a are equal by letting $f = 12$ ounces and $n = 5$ ounces. $48 - 12 - 5 = 31$ oz and $48 - (12 + 5) = 31$ oz

2. Simplify $-(-(-w))$. $-w$

In 3–5, find the opposite of the expression.

3. $-2n$ $2n$

4. $6p - 8$ $-6p + 8$

5. $-2a^2 + 28a - 15$ $2a^2 - 28a + 15$

6. **Multiple Choice** The opposite of $-x$ is *not* A and D
   A $-x$. B x. C $-(-x)$. D $-(-(-(x)))$

7. **Multiple Choice** Which of the following is equal to $-(P + 7)$? C
   A $-P + 7$ B $P + -7$ C $-P + -7$ D $P - 7$

8. **Multiple Choice** Which expression does *not* equal $-(x - y)$? B
   A $-x + y$ B $-1x + -1y$ C $-x - (-y)$ D $y - x$

In 9–16, write an equivalent expression without parentheses.

9. $-(x + 15)$ $-x - 15$

10. $-(4n - 3m)$ $-4n + 3m$

11. $x - (x + 2)$ -2

12. $3y - 5(y + 1)$ $-2y - 5$

13. $(3k^4 + 4) - (7k^4 - 9)$

14. $-(5 + k^3) + (k^3 - 18)$ -23

15. $a^2 + b - c - (a^2 - b + c)$

16. $(-4a)(-a)$ $4a^2$

13. $-4k^4 + 13$
15. $2b - 2c$

APPLYING THE MATHEMATICS

17. Theo and Rafael completed the toothpick activity from Lesson 1-3. The expression Theo wrote for the number of toothpicks in the nth term was $2n + n + 1$, and the expression Rafael wrote was $4n - (n - 1)$.
    a. Graph $y = 2n + n + 1$ and $y = 4n - (n - 1)$ on your calculator. Do the expressions appear to be equivalent?
    b. Use the Opposite of a Difference Property to show the expressions are equivalent.

18. Evaluate each of the following expressions.
    a. $(-1)^6$ 1 b. $(-1)^8$ 1 c. $(-1)^7$ -1 d. $(-1)^9$ -1

19. **True or False** Justify your answer.
    a. $(-5)^3 = -5^3$ b. $(-5)^4 = -5^4$ c. $-(5^4) = -5^4$

88 Using Algebra to Explain

17a. See margin.

17b. $4n - (n - 1) =$
$4n - n + 1 = 3n + 1 = 2n + n + 1$

19a. True; they are both equal to -125.

19b. False; $(-5)^4$ is positive, -5^4 is negative.

19c. True; they are both equal to -625.

Research suggests that nutrients in apples and apple juice improve memory and learning.

Source: www.applejuice.org

Accommodating the Learner

Analyzing Errors: Ask students to describe the error(s) in the following example. Students should correct the example.

$2(x - 1) - 3(x - 2)$

$= 2(x + -1) + -3(x + -2)$ Definition of Subtraction

$= 2x + -2 + -3x + -2$ Distributive Property

$= -x + -4$ Opposite of a Difference Property

$= -x - 4$ Opposite of a Sum Property

20. **a.** Which powers of –1 are positive? even powers

    b. Which powers of –1 are negative? odd powers

    c. If –1 was changed to –3, would this change your answers to Parts a and b? Explain why or why not.

21. The command "about-face" in the military signals a soldier to rotate 180 degrees. Two commands of "about-face" result in the soldier facing in the original direction again. How does the table at the right relate to $(-1)^n$, where n is the number of about-faces?

Number of About-Faces	Facing Direction
1	Reverse
2	Forward
3	Reverse
4	Forward
.	.
.	.
.	.

22. Determine whether the number is positive, negative, or zero.

    a. $(-5)^{10}$ positive   **b.** $(-1)(-5)^{10}$ **c.** $(-1)^{10}(-5)^{10}$

    d. $(5)^{10}(-5)^{10}$ positive   **e.** $[5 + (-5)]^{10}$ zero   **f.** $(-1)^{10}(-5)$ negative

23. **Skill Sequence** Evaluate each expression.

    a. $-\frac{1}{2} \cdot -\frac{2}{3}$ $\frac{1}{3}$

    b. $-\frac{1}{2} \cdot -\frac{2}{3} \cdot -\frac{3}{4}$ $-\frac{1}{4}$

    c. $-\frac{1}{2} \cdot -\frac{2}{3} \cdot -\frac{3}{4} \cdot -\frac{4}{5}$ $\frac{1}{5}$

    d. $-\frac{1}{2} \cdot -\frac{2}{3} \cdot -\frac{3}{4} \cdot ... \cdot -\frac{9}{10}$ $-\frac{1}{10}$

REVIEW

24. **a.** Pick a number and complete the number puzzle below. 6

    Step 1 Subtract 1 from your number. 5; $n - 1$

    Step 2 Multiply this by 8. 40; $8(n - 1) = 8n - 8$

    Step 3 Add 20. 60; $8n - 8 + 20 = 8n + 12$

    Step 4 Divide by 4. 15; $2n + 3$

    Step 5 Subtract 5. 10; $2n + 3 - 5 = 2n - 2$

    Step 6 Divide by 2. 5; $n - 1$

    Step 7 Add 1. 6; $n - 1 + 1 = n$

    The result will be your original number.

    b. Let n be your original number. Develop an algebraic expression for each step of the puzzle. **(Lesson 2-3)**

20c. No. Answers vary. Sample answer: A negative number times a negative number is positive and a negative number times a positive number is negative.

21. Answers vary. Sample answer: we can think of "number of about-faces" as n and "facing direction" as $(-1)^n$, where a positive result is forward and a negative result is reverse.

22b. negative

22c. positive

Notes on the Questions

Question 20c Extend this problem. If –1 were replaced by $-\frac{3}{4}$, would the answers to Parts a and b change? (No, the property is one of all negative numbers.)

Question 22 The answers should be found without doing calculations.

Question 23d The answer should be found without writing all the fractions between $-\frac{3}{4}$ and $-\frac{9}{10}$.

Question 32 Remind students that "difference" is the answer to a subtraction problem.

2-4

4 Wrap-Up

Ongoing Assessment

This would be a good time to quiz the students on Lessons 2-1 through 2-3. The Distributive Property can be confusing, but it is essential that students understand when and how to use it. If they don't do well on the quiz, some reteaching might be necessary.

Caddies carry clubs, replace divots, rake sand traps or bunkers, look for lost balls, and clean the player's club after each time it is used.

Source: www.teachingkidbusiness.com

In 25–27, simplify the expression. (Lessons 2-2, 2-1)

25. $3(t + 5) + (4t - 7) + (-7t + 8)$ 16

26. $2(2v - 11w) + 3(v + 7w)$ $7v - w$

27. $\frac{7}{y} - \frac{4}{3y}$ $\frac{17}{3y}$

In 29 and 30, use the following situation. A golf caddie who works at Pine Oaks Country Club makes $15 per golfer, but he has to pay the country club a $12 equipment fee each day.

28. Write an expression for the amount a golf caddie makes if he caddies for g golfers each day. (Lesson 1-1) $15g - 12$ dollars

29. Write an expression for the amount a golf caddie makes after working 6 days, if he caddies for g golfers each day. (Lesson 2-2) $6(15g - 12) = 90g - 72$ dollars

30. Consider the sequence made with dots below. Each term is 1 row and 2 columns larger than the previous term. (Lesson 1-2)

   1   2   3

   ••   ••••   ••••••
         ••••   ••••••
                ••••••

   1 · 2   2 · 4   3 · 6

   a. Complete the table describing the number of dots for the next three terms.

n	1	2	3	4	5	6
dots	$1 \cdot 2 = 2$	$2 \cdot 4 = 8$	$3 \cdot 6 = 18$	? 32	?50	?72

   b. Write an expression for the number of dots required to make the nth term. $n(2n) = 2n^2$

31. a. Find two numbers, each greater than 1, with a product of 728.
    b. Find two numbers, each less than zero, with a product of 72.8.
    c. Find two numbers, each greater than 1, with a product of 7.28.
    (Previous Course) Answers vary. Sample answer: 1.3 and 5.6

EXPLORATION

32. The difference of two numbers is subtracted from their sum. What can be said about the answer? Explain how you explored this problem. See margin.

31a. Answers vary.
     Sample answer:
     13 and 56
31b. Answers vary.
     Sample answer:
     −1.3 and −56

QY ANSWERS

1. $-3.5, \frac{17}{8}$

2. $-a^2 - 2b$

3. yes

---

90   Using Algebra to Explain

Additional Answers

32. Answers vary. Sample answer: The answer is double one of the numbers. To see this, let the numbers be a and b. Then, we have $(a + b) - (a - b) = 2b$.

Lesson
2-5   Testing Equivalence

▶ **BIG IDEA**   You can test whether algebraic expressions are equivalent using substitution, tables, graphs, or properties.

One of the most powerful aspects of algebra is that it offers many different approaches to solving problems. It may seem to you that learning different ways to do the same thing is a waste of time, but it is not. The knowledge of different approaches increases your ability to undertake new and different situations or problems on your own.

In Chapter 1, you began working with one of the most important ideas in algebra: *equivalence*. This idea will be examined and reexamined throughout your study of mathematics. Numbers, graphs, and algebraic properties give us three different approaches for testing equivalence.

In Lesson 1-3, you were asked to write expressions to describe the number of toothpicks used to form patterns, as shown below.

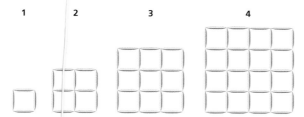

1   2   3   4

Suppose Yolanda and Suki created the following expressions to represent the number of toothpicks in the nth term.

Yolanda: $4n + 2n(n - 1)$

Suki: $n(n + 1 + n + 1)$

How can you tell if these expressions produce the same result for each value of n? You have seen a variety of methods used in this chapter. Some methods are more powerful than others.

> **Mental Math**
>
> **Estimate to the nearest integer.**
>
> a. $\frac{4}{5} + 2\frac{1}{10} + 7\frac{7}{8}$ 11
>
> b. $\frac{4}{5} - 2\frac{1}{10} + 7\frac{7}{8}$ 7
>
> c. $\frac{4}{5} - 2\frac{1}{10} - 7\frac{7}{8}$ -9

Testing Equivalence   **91**

Background

This lesson is a review of techniques from earlier lessons and a review of the idea of counterexample.

In Chapter 1, three methods were introduced to test whether expressions were equivalent: (1) substituting individual numbers for the variables in the expressions and checking whether their values are equal; (2) generating a table to see more values; and (3) creating graphs

from the expressions. Now we have a fourth method that can prove whether two expressions are equivalent: (4) using properties of numbers and operations.

Lesson
2-5

GOAL
Review various methods and properties to test equivalence.

SPUR Objectives
I Use a spreadsheet or table to test the equivalence of expressions.

J Use technology to test for equivalence of expressions.

Materials/Resources
· Lesson Master 2-5A or 2-5B
· Resource Masters 2 and 28–30
· Graphing calculator

> ### HOMEWORK
> **Suggestions for Assignment**
> • Questions 1–18
> • Question 19 (extra credit)
> • Reading Lesson 2-6
> • Covering the Ideas 2-6

> ### Local Standards

1 Warm-Up

Determine which two of these four expressions are equivalent:

A $x(x + 2) - 2(2 + x)$
B $(2 - x)(x + 2)$
C $x(x - 2) - 2(x - 2)$
D $2(x + 2) - x(2 + x)$ B and D

Discuss the method that can be used to determine the answer.

1. Substitution of any value for x other than 2 or 0 will indicate that only **B** and **D** can be equivalent.
2. Tables and graphs will also show that **B** and **D** are equivalent.
3. Use algebraic properties to show why
   B $(2 - x)(x + 2) = (2 - x)x + (2 - x)2 = 2x - x \cdot x + 4 - 2x$.
   D $2(x + 2) - x(2 + x) = 2x + 4 - 2x - x \cdot x$.

2 Teaching

Notes on the Lesson

There are no new properties introduced in this lesson, so it can be combined with a quiz over the first four lessons of the chapter.

This lesson can evolve from a discussion of the problems. You may want to have students form groups of 4. Have each of the four students be responsible for presenting one of the methods of Example 1 to the group. Then, the group should complete Guided Examples 2 and 3. Have students engage in a full-class discussion to show how properties can prove that expressions are equivalent.

Using graphs to test equivalence.
A nice technique when using graphs to check equivalence is to graph the second formula with the thick style (found to the left of the equals sign on the Y= screen on most calculators, or called "style" in some others). In sequential mode (the default), the thin graph will appear first, and then the thicker one if you press ENTER. This is very useful to see if two formulas are equivalent because the graphs are a different thickness.

Additional Example

Example 1 Test whether $3x(x + 2) + 5x$ and $x(3x - 1) + 12x$ are equivalent. Whether students use numbers, tables, graphs, or properties, the algebraic expressions are equivalent.

Example 1

Test whether $4n + 2n(n - 1)$ and $n(n + 1 + n + 1)$ are equivalent.

Method 1: Use numbers to test for equivalence. Choose $n = 1$. Evaluate each expression.

If $n = 1$, then $4n + 2n (n - 1) = 4 \cdot 1 + 2 \cdot 1(1 - 1) = 4$.

If $n = 1$, then $n(n + 1 + n + 1) = 1(1 + 1 + 1 + 1) = 4$, the number of toothpicks in the 1st term.

There are 12 toothpicks in the second term. Do both expressions have the value 12 when $n = 2$?

If $n = 2$, then $4n + 2n(n - 1) = 4 \cdot 2 + 2 \cdot 2(2 - 1) = 12$.

If $n = 2$, then $n(n + 1 + n + 1) = 2(2 + 1 + 2 + 1) = 12$, which checks.

You can repeat this process to test many numbers.

Technology can allow you to test many numbers at once, as seen in Method 2.

Method 2: Use tables to test equivalence. A graphing calculator can quickly make a table. Substitute x for n when entering the expressions into the calculator.

For Yolanda's expression enter into Y1:
$4x + 2x(x - 1)$.
For Suki's expression enter into Y2:
$x(x + 1 + x + 1)$.
We set a table starting at 1 with increments of 1.

The seven numbers located in the left column are each substituted into the two expressions. The results are automatically calculated and displayed in the second and third columns. In each case, the values of the expressions are equal, and they equal the numbers of toothpicks.

You can scroll up or down the left column of the table to see more values. So for these values of n, the expressions $4n + 2n(n - 1)$ and $n(n + 1 + n + 1)$ have the same value.

STOP QY

Method 3: Use graphs to test for equivalence. Use the formulas Y1 = $4x + 2x(x - 1)$ and Y2 = $x(x + 1 + x + 1)$. The table helps you decide on a viewing window. One window that fits the ordered pairs listed is $-1 \le x \le 10$, $0 \le y \le 120$.

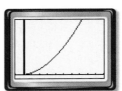

▶ QY

Two of the three expressions below are equivalent. Use the table feature on the graphing calculator to determine which are equivalent. Use at least three rows of your table to explain your answer. The screen below shows how the equations should be entered into the calculator.

a. $|x^2 + 1| \cdot (x - 3)$
b. $x^3 - 3x^2 + x - 3$
c. $(x^2 + 1) \cdot |x - 3|$

Extension

Sometimes algebraic expressions appear to be equivalent even when they are not. Students should consider the following two expressions $\frac{x^2 - x - 6}{x - 3}$ and $x + 2$. Have students fill in the following table and make a conjecture about the equivalence of the expressions.

x	−1	0	1	2
$\frac{x^2 - x - 6}{x - 3}$	1	2	3	4
$x + 2$	1	2	3	4

Next have students test equivalence by graphing. Set Y1 = $\frac{x^2 - x - 6}{x - 3}$ and Y2 = $x + 2$. Is their conjecture correct? Finally have students check equivalence using tables. Set the table start to −3 and the table increment to 1. Instruct the students to look carefully at the table values. What do they notice? Ask them why there seems to be a discrepancy at $x = 3$.

The graphs of the two expressions seem to be identical. But, even on a calculator, only a limited number of points are actually being graphed. How can you be sure the expressions are always equal? The answer is to use the properties of operations that are true for all real numbers.

Method 4: Use properties to test equivalence.

$$4n + 2n(n - 1) = 4n + 2n^2 - 2n \quad \text{Expand the expression.}$$
$$= 2n^2 + 2n \quad \text{Combine like terms.}$$
$$n(n + 1 + n + 1) = n(2n + 2) \quad \text{Combine like terms.}$$
$$= 2n^2 + 2n \quad \text{Expand the expression.}$$

In each case, the result is $2n^2 + 2n$. Since both expressions are equal to the same third expression, they are equal to each other (by the Transitive Property of Equality). Therefore, for any value of n,
$4n + 2n(n - 1) = n(n + 1 + n + 1)$.

Properties of operations are powerful because they can show that a pattern is true for all real numbers. But the other methods are useful too. Testing specific numbers, either by hand or in a table, can help you decide if two expressions *seem* equivalent. These methods can often help you detect a counterexample. Testing numbers is also a good way to catch your own mistakes.

GUIDED

Example 2

A common error that some students make is to think that $4x - x$ is equivalent to 4 for all values of x. Here are three ways to show that these expressions are not equivalent.

Solution

Method 1: Substitute a value for x to show that $4x - x$ is not equal to 4.

Method 2: Graph Y1 $= 4x - x$ and Y2 $= 4$. Are the graphs identical?

Method 3: Create a table of values for Y1 $= 4x - x$ and Y2 $= 4$.

You should find that for almost all values of x, the expressions do not have the same values. Therefore, $4x - x$ is not equivalent to 4. You could also simplify $4x - x$ to $3x$, which clearly is not 4 for every value of x.

Example 2
Method 1. Answers vary. Sample answer:
$x = 1$ gives $4x - x = 4(1) - 1 = 4 - 1 = 3 \neq 4$.

Method 2. The graphs are not identical.

Method 3.

Testing Equivalence **93**

Additional Example
Example 2 A common error that some students make is to think that $7x - x$ is equivalent to 7 for all values of x. Here are three ways to show that these expressions are not equivalent.

1 Substitute a value for x to show $7x - x$ is not equal to 7. Let $x = 3$. $7x - x = 7(3) - 3 = 21 - 3 = 18$. $18 \neq 7$

2 Graph Y1 $= 7x - x$ and Y2 $= 7$. Are the graphs identical? no

Create a table of values for Y1 $= 7x - x$ and Y2 $= 7$.
Answers vary. Sample answer:

x	Y1	Y2
−1	−6	7
−2	−12	7
0	0	7
1	6	7
2	12	7

Accommodating the Learner

The figure in the diagram is a large rectangle made up of a medium size rectangle and a smaller rectangle. Students are to find the area of the largest rectangle in two ways. First, students are to find the area by multiplying the length and width of the largest rectangle. Second, students are to find the area by adding the areas of the two smaller rectangles. Have students substitute a number to check the equivalence. Finally students should show the two areas are equivalent algebraically.

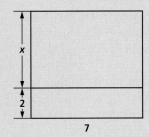

$7(x + 2) = 7x + 14$; $7 \cdot x + 7 \cdot 2 = 7x + 14$; Substitute 3 for x. Then $7(3 + 2) = 35 = 7 \cdot 2 + 7 \cdot 3$. Algebraically, the areas are equivalent by the Distributive Property.

2-5

Additional Examples

Example 3 Are $-x^4$ and $(-x)^4$ equivalent expressions? If so, explain. If not, provide a counterexample.

Pick a value for x. Suppose you pick 3. Then $-x^4 = -3^4$ and $(-x)^4 = (-3)^4$.

For -3^4, follow the order of operations and raise 3 to the fourth power before taking the opposite.

If $x = 3$, then $-x^4 = \underline{\quad?\quad} -3^4$

$= \underline{\quad?\quad} -81$

For $(-3)^4$, follow the order of operations and raise -3 to the fourth power.

If $x = 3$, then $(-x)^4 = \underline{\quad?\quad} (-3)^4$

$= (\underline{\;?\;})(\underline{\;?\;})(\underline{\;?\;})(\underline{\;?\;})$

$-3; -3; -3; -3$

$= \underline{\quad?\quad} 81$

Because $\underline{\;?\;}$ and $\underline{\;?\;}$ are not equal, the expressions are not equivalent.
$-81; 81$

Therefore, 3 is a counterexample.

Example 4 Use properties to show that $5(3a^2 - 2a) + 6(a - 3)$ is equivalent to $2(a - 9) + 3a(5a - 2)$.

$5(3a^2 - 2a) + 6(a - 3) =$
$15a^2 - 10a + 6a - 18$
by the Distributive Property

$= 15a^2 - 4a - 18$
by combining like terms

$2(a - 9) + 3a(5a - 2) =$
$2a - 18 + 15a^2 - 6a$
by the Distributive Property

$= 15a^2 - 4a - 18$
by combining like terms

GUIDED

Example 3

Are $-x^2$ and $(-x)^2$ equivalent expressions? If so, explain. If not, provide a counterexample.

Solution Pick a value for x. Suppose you pick 6. Then $-x^2 = -6^2$ and $(-x)^2 = (-6)^2$.

For -6^2, follow the order of operations and square 6 *before* taking the opposite.

If $x = 6$, then $-x^2 = \underline{\;?\;} -6^2$ Substitute.

$\qquad\qquad 6; 6 = -(\underline{\;?\;})(\underline{\;?\;})$ Evaluate powers first.

$\qquad\qquad = \underline{\;?\;} -36$ Simplify.

For $(-6)^2$, square -6.

If $x = 6$, then $(-x)^2 = \underline{\;?\;} (-6)^2$ Substitute.

$\qquad\qquad -6; -6 = (\underline{\;?\;})(\underline{\;?\;})$ Evaluate powers first.

$\qquad\qquad = \underline{\;?\;} 36$ Simplify.

Because $\underline{\;?\;}$ and $\underline{\;?\;}$ are not equal, the expressions are not equivalent. Therefore, 6 is a counterexample. $-36; 36$

Guided Example 3 used just one counterexample to show that $-x^2$ and $(-x)^2$ are not equivalent. Only one is necessary. However, to show that expressions *are* equivalent requires much more. You must show equality for *every* possible value of the variable. This is why using properties that apply to all numbers is so important.

Example 4

Use properties to show that $(2x^2 + 3) - 8(3x^2 + 4)$ is equivalent to $1 - 27x^2 - 30 + 5x^2$.

Solution Simplify each expression and check that the results are the same. Expand and combine like terms.

$(2x^2 + 3) - 8(3x^2 + 4) = 2x^2 + 3 - 24x^2 - 32$ Distributive Property
$\qquad\qquad\qquad\qquad\quad = -22x^2 - 29$ Combine like terms.

Now simplify $1 - 27x^2 - 30 + 5x^2$.

$1 - 27x^2 - 30 + 5x^2 = -22x^2 - 29$ Combine like terms.

Because both $(2x^2 + 3) - 8(3x^2 + 4)$ and $1 - 27x^2 - 30 + 5x^2$ equal $-22x^2 - 29$, we can say that

$(2x^2 + 3) - 8(3x^2 + 4) = 1 - 27x^2 - 30 + 5x^2$ by the Transitive Property of Equality.

Accommodating the Learner ⬆

Challenge your students to use their arithmetic skills. Which of the algebraic expressions is equivalent to $\dfrac{1}{1 + \frac{1}{1 + \frac{1}{x}}}$?

(*Hint:* Remember that when dividing fractions, one must multiply the numerator by the reciprocal of the denominator. For example, $\dfrac{1}{\frac{1}{x}} = 1 \cdot \dfrac{x}{1} = x$.)

a. x **b.** $\dfrac{x+1}{2}$ **c.** 1   **d.** $\dfrac{x+1}{2x+1}$ d

Questions

COVERING THE IDEAS

1. Refer to the sequence of toothpicks shown below and the table at the right.

Term Number	Number of Toothpicks
1	6
2	11
3	16

1   2   3

a. How many toothpicks would be used to make the 4th term? **21**

b. Dion and Ellis wrote the expressions below to give the number of toothpicks used to make the nth term. Test to see if these two expressions are equivalent for the values $n = 4, 5$, and 6. **1b–d. See margin.**

Dion: $1 + 3n + 2n$ Ellis: $6n - (n - 1)$

c. Use graphs with $0 \le n \le 10$ to test whether the two expressions in Part b are equivalent.

d. Simplify each expression in Part b to test whether they are equivalent.

In 2–4, test the two given expressions for equivalence by using a table or graph, or by simplifying the expressions.

2. $4n - 15$ and $4(n - 4) - 1$

3. $3x^2 + 6x(x + 2)$ and $3x^2 + 6x^2 + 2$

4. $(5 + x)^2$ and $25 + 10x + x^2$

    They are equivalent: $(5 + x)^2 = 25 + 5x + 5x + x^2 = 25 + 10x + x^2$

5. Is $3x^2$ equivalent to $(3x)^2$? If so, explain. If not, provide a counterexample. **no; Answers vary. Sample answer: $x = 2$**

2. They are not equivalent:
$4(n - 4) - 1 =$
$4n - 17 \ne 4n - 15$

3. They are not equivalent:
$3x^2 + 6x(x + 2) =$
$3x^2 + 6x^2 + 12x \ne$
$3x^2 + 6x^2 + 2$

APPLYING THE MATHEMATICS

6. Consider the expressions $x \cdot x$ and $2x$.

a. Copy and complete the table of values at the right.

b. Give two values of x for which $x \cdot x = 2x$.

c. Give two values of x for which $x \cdot x$ does *not* equal $2x$.

d. Graph $y = x \cdot x$ and $y = 2x$. Circle the points that correspond to your answer from Part b. **6b–d. See margin.**

x	$x \cdot x$	$2x$
-3	? 9	? -6
-2	? 4	? -4
-1	? 1	? -2
0	? 0	? 0
1	? 1	? 2
2	? 4	? 4
3	? 9	? 6

3 Assignment

Recommended Assignment
- Questions 1–18
- Question 19 (extra credit)
- Reading Lesson 2-6
- Covering the Ideas 2-6

Notes on the Questions

Question 1 Although Part d asks students to simplify each expression to *test* whether they are equivalent, emphasize that this strategy *determines* whether or not they are equivalent.

Questions 2 and 3 These questions exhibit common student errors in rewriting expressions.

Question 6 This question previews solving equations using graphs, the subject of Lesson 3-2.

Additional Answers

6d.

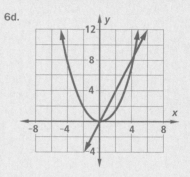

2-5A Lesson Master   Questions on SPUR Objectives
See pages 125–127 for objectives.

REPRESENTATIONS Objective I

In 1 and 2, consider the expressions $2x^2 + 1$ and $(2x)^2 - 1$.

1. Fill in the table. Then give two values of x for which $2x^2 + 1 = (2x)^2 - 1$.

x	$2x^2 + 1$	$(2x)^2 - 1$
-2	9	15
-1	3	3
0	1	-1
1	3	3
2	9	15

−1 and 1

2. Give a counterexample which shows that $2x^2 + 1$ is not equivalent to $(2x)^2 - 1$.   Sample: $x = 2$

In 3 and 4, consider the expressions $2(4n - 7) - (5n - 7)$ and $3(n + 2) - 13$.

3. Fill in the table. Do the expressions appear to be equivalent from the table?

x	$2(4n - 7) - (5n - 7)$	$3(n + 2) - 13$
-2	-13	-13
-1	-10	-10
0	-7	-7
1	-4	-4
2	-1	-1

yes

4. Simplify each expression to show whether or not they are equivalent.
$2(4n - 7) - (5n - 7) = 3n - 7$ and $3(n + 2) - 13 = 3n - 7$, so they are equivalent.

In 5 and 6, consider the expressions $2x^2 + 5(x + 1)$ and $2(x^2 + x - 1) + 3(x + 1)$.

5. Fill in the table. Do the expressions appear to be equivalent from the table?

x	$2x^2 + 5(x + 1)$	$2(x^2 + x - 1) + 3(x + 1)$
-2	3	-1
-1	2	-2
0	5	1
1	12	8
2	23	19

no

6. Simplify each expression to show whether or not they are equivalent.
$2x^2 + 5(x + 1) = 2x^2 + 5x + 5$ and $2(x^2 + x - 1) + 3(x + 1) = 2x^2 + 5x + 1$, so they are not equivalent.

Algebra   133

Additional Answers

1b.

Design Number	$1 + 3n + 2n$	$6n - (n - 1)$
4	21	21
5	26	26
6	31	31

1c.

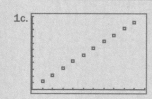

1d. Dion's expression is $1 + 3n + 2n = 5n + 1$. Ellis' expression is $6n - (n - 1) = 6n - n + 1 = 5n + 1$. They are equivalent.

6b. $x = 0$ and $x = 2$

6c. Answers vary. Sample answer: $x = 1$ and $x = -1$

2-5

Notes on the Questions

Question 8 Have students verify that the two expressions
$(3x − 2) + (3x − 2) + (3x − 2) + (3x − 2) + (3x − 2)$ and $5(3x − 2)$ are equivalent to $15x − 10$.

Question 9 You might ask how Manuel and Lina calculated the area. (Manuel begins with a 20-by-3x rectangle and subtracts the two parts that are cut out; Lina adds the two sides of the H and its middle.)

7. The perimeter of the square below can be written as $2x + 3 + 2x + 3 + 2x + 3 + 2x + 3$, or $4(2x + 3)$. Verify the two expressions are equivalent by using a table or graph, or simplifying each expression.
$2x + 3 + 2x + 3 + 2x + 3 + 2x + 3 = 8x + 12 = 4(2x + 3)$

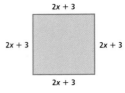

8. Write two equivalent expressions for the perimeter of the regular pentagon at the right. $3x − 2 + 3x − 2 + 3x − 2 + 3x − 2 + 3x − 2$ and $5(3x − 2)$

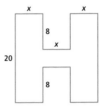

9. Manuel found the area of the "H" shape below to be $20(3x) − 2(8x)$, while Lina got $20x + 4x + 20x$. Are they equivalent?
   a. Use a table to find your answer. 9a–b. See margin.
   b. Use algebraic expressions to answer the question.
   c. Let $x = 5$. Find the area of the shape. 220 units^2

REVIEW

In 10–12, simplify the expression. (Lessons 2-4, 2-1)

10. $8b − 5(7b + 3)$ $-27b − 15$

11. $−1.4(2v − 4) + 3.6v$ $0.8v + 5.6$

12. $\frac{12m + 2}{3} − \frac{6m − 1}{3}$ $2m + 1$

13. Determine whether each expression is equivalent to $−(18 − 5x)$.
    (Lesson 2-4)

    a. $−18 − (−5x)$ yes
    b. $−9(2 − 5x)$ no
    c. $−18 − 5x$ no
    d. $−18 + 5x$ yes

9a. Answers vary. Sample answer:

x	$20(3x) − 2(8x)$	$20x + 4x + 20x$
0	0	0
1	44	44
2	88	88
3	132	132
4	176	176

9b. $20(3x) − 2(8x) = 60x − 16x = 44x = 20x + 4x + 20x$, which shows the expressions are equivalent.

14. a. Pick any number and do the following number puzzle. **2**

Step 1 Add 23 to your number. **25**

Step 2 Double the sum. **50**

Step 3 Subtract twice your original number. **46**

Step 4 Add 3. **49**

Step 5 Subtract 42. **7**

You will be left with 7.

b. Let n be your original number. Develop an algebraic expression for each step of the puzzle. **(Lesson 2-3)**

15. *Skill Sequence* Simplify each expression. **(Lesson 2-2)**

a. $p \cdot p \cdot p$ p^3

b. $p + p + p$ $3p$

c. $2p \cdot 2p \cdot 2p$ $8p^3$

d. $2p + 2p + 2p$ $6p$

16. Use the Distributive Property to find $5 \cdot 999{,}999$ in your head. **(Lesson 2-1)** First, multiply 5 times 1,000,000. Then, subtract 5 times 1 to get 4,999,995.

In 17 and 18, give a counterexample to show that the two expressions are *not* equivalent. (Lesson 1-3)

17. $6 + m$ and $2m - 3(m - 2)$

18. $\frac{y}{2} + \frac{3}{2}$ and $\frac{3y}{4}$

EXPLORATION

19. Two expressions used to calculate the area of the regular octagon below are $4ba$ and $\frac{1}{2}pa$, where p is the perimeter of the octagon. Explain how b and p are related and use this to demonstrate algebraically that the two expressions are equivalent.

$p = 8b, \ \frac{1}{2}pa = \frac{1}{2}(8b)a = 4ba$

14b. Answers vary.
Sample answer:
Step 1: $n + 23$;
Step 2: $2n + 46$;
Step 3: $2n + 46 - 2n = 46$;
Step 4: $46 + 3 = 49$;
Step 5: $49 - 42 = 7$

17. Answers vary.
Sample answer:
$m = 1, 6 + 1 = 7, 2(1) - 3(1 - 2) = 5$

18. Answers vary.
Sample answer:
$y = 0, \frac{3}{2} \neq 0$

QY ANSWER

Assume
Y1 $= |x^2 + 1| \cdot (x - 3)$,
Y2 $= x^3 - 3x^2 + x - 3$,
and
Y3 $= (x^2 + 1) \cdot |x - 3|$.
From the table it appears that Y1 and Y2 are equivalent. We also see that neither Y1 nor Y2 is equivalent to Y3.

X	Y1	Y2	Y3
−1	−8	−8	8
0	−3	−3	3
1	−4	−4	4

---

4 Wrap-Up

Ongoing Assignment

Have pairs of students each write an algebraic expression containing more than one term and exchange papers. Then have them write an equivalent algebraic expression and return the paper to the other student. Each should test to see if the two algebraic expressions are equivalent, and if not, should provide a counterexample.

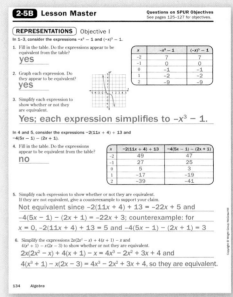

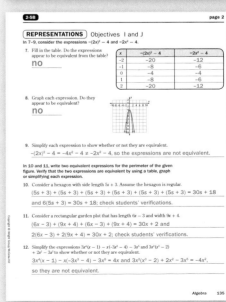

Lesson 2-6

GOAL

Use a computer algebra system (CAS) to test whether expressions are equivalent.

SPUR Objective

J Use technology to test for equivalence of expressions.

Materials/Resources

- Lesson Masters 2-6A and 2-6B
- Resource Masters 31 and 32
- Computer Algebra System (CAS)
- Quiz 2

HOMEWORK

Suggestions for Assignment

- Questions 1–19
- Question 20 (extra credit)
- Reading Lesson 2-7
- Covering the Ideas 2-7

Local Standards

1 Warm-Up

The Warm-Up for this lesson is designed to introduce students to the CAS technology.

1. Key in $x + x$ and press ENTER. Record your result. **$2 \cdot x$ or $2x$, depending on the technology**
2. Key in $a * a$ and press ENTER. Record the result. **a^2**
3. Key in $2 * (a - b)$ and press ENTER. Record the result. **Nothing happens.**
4. Key in EXPAND $(2 * (a - b))$ and press ENTER. Record the result. **$2 \cdot a - 2 \cdot b$**

Problem 2 has students use the alphabetical keys. Problem 3 is included to show that the technology often needs more specific instructions about what to do with an expression. Problem 4 shows that the EXPAND instruction will use the Distributive Property to remove parentheses.

Lesson 2-6 Equivalent Expressions with Technology

> ▶ **BIG IDEA** A computer algebra system (CAS) uses properties of operations to create equivalent expressions.

In this lesson, you will use a computer algebra system (CAS) to test whether expressions are equivalent. Then you will use it to explore a variety of equivalent forms for a single expression. A CAS does algebra just like a calculator does arithmetic. Among the many things that a CAS can do is simplify expressions and solve equations. It has been programmed to use the same algebraic properties that you have been learning. The first computer software with CAS capabilities was created in 1968 at MIT. Until then, mathematicians had to do even the most complicated algebraic calculations by hand.

Equivalent Formulas in Geometry

In geometry, it is not unusual to see different area formulas for the same type of figure. If the area is found using different formulas, will the results be the same? Where do different formulas come from?

Example 1

The picture below shows the area of a deck surrounding a rectangular swimming pool. The length of the entire region (pool and deck) is *L* and the width of the entire region is *W*. The distance across the deck is *x*.

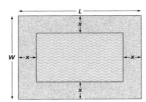

a. Find a formula for the area of the deck by splitting up the deck into 4 rectangles.

b. Split up the deck in another way to find its area.

Mental Math

a. 35 raffle tickets cost $10. What is the price per ticket? **29¢**

b. 60 raffle tickets cost $20. What is the price per ticket? **33¢**

c. *n* raffle tickets cost $15. What is the price per ticket? $\frac{15}{n}$ **dollars**

d. *y* raffle tickets cost *x* dollars. What is the price per ticket? $\frac{x}{y}$ **dollars**

Background

In this book, we do not expect students to have their own calculators equipped with CAS. But we do feel that it is important for students to know that such technology exists and to have experience using it. Evidence shows that the use of such technology does not result in poorer student performance on paper-and-pencil skills. On the contrary, the use of such technology confirms that algebra is important and provides students with a means for checking their work. This seems particularly helpful to slower students who are struggling with the language of variables.

Solutions Sonia and Roxy both found formulas for the area of the deck, but they are different.

a. Sonia's Method Sonia broke the deck region into four smaller rectangles and then added them. The length of Areas 2 and 4 can be found by taking the total length L and subtracting two lengths of x, or $L - 2x$. She found the areas of Areas 1 through 4 and added them together.

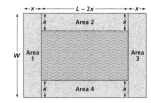

Area 1 $= W \cdot x = Wx$

Area 2 $= x \cdot (L - 2x) = x(L - 2x)$

Area 3 $= W \cdot x = Wx$

Area 4 $= x \cdot (L - 2x) = x(L - 2x)$

Sonia's Deck Area $= Wx + x(L - 2x) + Wx + x(L - 2x)$

b. Roxy's Method Roxy saw the area of the deck as the area of the pool and deck minus the area of the pool.

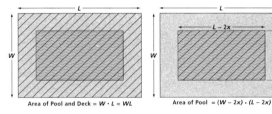

Area of Pool and Deck $= W \cdot L = WL$ Area of Pool $= (W - 2x) \cdot (L - 2x)$

Roxy's Deck Area $= WL - (W - 2x) \cdot (L - 2x)$

Sonia's and Roxy's methods lead to two expressions that appear to be different. But are they? A CAS can answer this question.

Is $Wx + x(L - 2x) + Wx + x(L - 2x)$ equivalent to $WL - (W - 2x) \cdot (L - 2x)$?

The approach that we use is one you saw in the last lesson. We work with the two expressions to see if the result is the same third expression.

2 Teaching

Additional Example

Example 1 The picture below shows a picture frame surrounding a rectangular photograph. The length of the frame is L and the width of the frame is W. The thickness of the frame is x.

a. Find a formula for the area of the frame by splitting up the frame into 4 rectangles.
$Lx + x(W - 2x) + Lx + x(W - 2x)$

b. Split up the frame in another way to find its area.
$WL - (L - 2x)(W - 2x)$

Accommodating the Learner

This lesson introduces students to computer algebra systems (CAS). It also introduces them to the expand command. Consider introducing students to some of the other instructions and features of CAS. Students enjoy working with technology and this is a good opportunity to show them some of the power that this tool provides.

ENGLISH LEARNERS
Vocabulary Development

Computer algebra system (CAS) may be a new term for most students. They may even think that the system they are about to use is the only system out there. Provide them with several examples of computer algebra systems or ask the students to do a little research.

2-6

Using a CAS to Test for Equivalence

Just as with any new technology, you need to learn the commands that your CAS uses. In this first activity, you will use the Distributive Property to expand multiplication expressions and to combine like terms. Most CAS make both of these changes to an expression by using the `expand` command. The expression that is to be changed appears in parentheses. For example, the command `expand(3(2x+50)+11)` does two operations. It first does the multiplication $3(2x + 50)$, which produces $6x + 150$. Then it adds $6x + 150 + 11$ to get $6x + 161$.

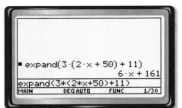

Activity 1

Use a CAS to expand the two expressions from Example 1 to determine whether they are equivalent. **Caution: You may need to enter** $W \cdot x$ **into your CAS so that the CAS will recognize** W **and** x **as separate variables.**

Step 1 Expand $Wx + x(L - 2x) + Wx + x(L - 2x)$, as shown below.

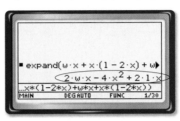

Step 2 Expand $WL - (W - 2x) \cdot (L - 2x)$, as shown below.

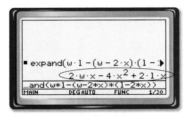

The CAS applied the properties of algebra and found that $Wx + x(L - 2x) + Wx + x(L - 2x)$ and $WL - (W - 2x) \cdot (L - 2x)$ are both equal to $2Wx - 4x^2 + 2Lx$. Therefore, they are equivalent to each other. Both Sonia's and Roxy's approaches will correctly find the area of the deck.

Activity 2

Find three expressions equivalent to $2a^2 + 4b$. In each case, use a CAS to verify the equivalence.

To form equivalent expressions, use the properties you have learned, but in reverse. Instead of trying to make the expression $2a^2 + 4b$ simpler, you need to make it more complicated. There are many approaches to take.

Expression 1 To find a first expression, notice that 2 and 4 are both divisible by 2. Therefore, one possibility is to "undo" the Distributive Property: $2a^2 + 4b = 2(a^2 + 2b)$.

Is $2(a^2 + 2b)$ an equivalent expression? Check using the expand command with a CAS. With some problems, you may find using a CAS is slower than doing it yourself. But a good check is one that uses a method different from the one originally used to get the answer.

Using expand gives the expression $2a^2 + 4b$.

Thus, $2(a^2 + 2b)$ is equivalent to $2a^2 + 4b$.

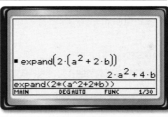

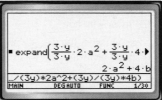

Expression 2 To find a second expression, apply the Identity Property of Multiplication. Multiplying a number by 1 does not change its value. The number 1 can take several forms, including $\frac{3y}{3y}$. Therefore, multiplying an expression by $\frac{3y}{3y}$ will result in an equivalent form. Is $\frac{3y}{3y} \cdot 2a^2 + \frac{3y}{3y} \cdot 4b$ an equivalent expression? Using the expand command gives $2a^3 + 4b$.

Thus, $\frac{3y}{3y} \cdot 2a^2 + \frac{3y}{3y} \cdot 4b$ is equivalent to $2a^2 + 4b$.

 QY1

> **QY1**
>
> Multiply $2a^2 + 4b$ by a different form of 1 to create another equivalent expression.

Expression 3 To find a third expression, apply the Identity Property of Addition and then rearrange the terms. The idea behind this method is to add a "clever" form of zero to the expression. This does not change its value, but produces an expression that looks very different from the original. Here we use $3a^2 + (-3a^2)$.

$$2a^2 + 4b + 3a^2 + -3a^2$$
$$= (2a^2 + 3a^2) + 4b - 3a^2$$
$$= 5a^2 + 4b - 3a^2$$

Add $3a^2 + -3a^2$, which is 0.
Group two of the like terms.
Add the first two like terms.

Is the new expression $5a^2 + 4b - 3a^2$ equivalent to $2a^2 + 4b$? Check using the expand command with a CAS.

Using the expand command gives the answer $2a^2 + 4b$.
Thus $5a^2 + 4b - 3a^2$ is equivalent to $2a^2 + 4b$.

 QY2

> **QY2**
>
> Create a new expression equivalent to $2a^2 + 4b$ by adding another form of zero.

Equivalent Expressions with Technology **101**

Notes on the Activity
Activity 2 Many students enjoy making simpler expressions more complicated. Activity 2 can be extended by having students create Expression 4, which combines the properties in Expressions 1, 2, and 3.

2-6

Notes on the Activity

Activity 3 Students will need practice creating equivalent algebraic expressions. Students should write down three or four algebraic expressions. These expressions should consist of no more than two terms. Have students start with the first algebraic expression and "undo" just one step. Using the CAS, have students check to see if the new expression is the same as the original one. Repeat this process with the other expressions.

Notes on the Questions

Question 2 CAS technology can be used to verify what the Distributive Property indicates should be the answer.

Questions 5, 6, and 8 With a CAS, equivalent expressions can be created using the FACTOR command. Other methods are to add and subtract the same number, or to multiply and divide by the same number.

Activity 3

Find at least four equivalent expressions for each of the following expressions. Try to use more than one property on each expression. See how complicated-looking you can make your expression while maintaining equivalence. Use a CAS to verify that your expressions are equivalent.

1–6. Answers vary. Sample answers are given.

1. $4(4a^2 - b^2)$
2. $-9m^2 + 12m - 8p$
3. $\frac{1}{2}m \cdot n + \frac{1}{4}$
4. $\frac{6y}{5x}$
5. $100p^2r^2$
6. $2\ell + 2w$

Questions

COVERING THE IDEAS

1. Write an expression equivalent to $5x(7x - 9y)$ by using the Distributive Property. $35x^2 - 45xy$

2. Are $6(x^3 - 5y) + 17x^2 + 12y$ and $6x^3 + 17x^2 - 18y$ equivalent? Why or why not?

3. Explain what the CAS did to simplify the expression on the screen below. 3–4. Answers vary. Sample answers are given.

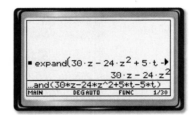

APPLYING THE MATHEMATICS

4. a. Find a third formula for the total area of the deck in Example 1.
   b. Show that it is equivalent to one of the other two formulas in the example. 4a.–b. See margin.

In 5–8, create three equivalent expressions.

5. $9k^2 - 3k$ 6. $13m^2 + 8m$ 7. $-24y$ 8. $16x^4 + 12xy + 20y$

9. Write a process you could use to convert the expression $5x - 7y$ into the equivalent expression $5(x - 2y) + 3y$. See margin.

10. Write an expression equivalent to $34wn + w^2$ using each property.
    a. Commutative Property of Addition $w^2 + 34wn$
    b. Commutative Property of Multiplication
       Answers vary. Sample answer: $34nw + w^2$

102   Using Algebra to Explain

Activity 3

1. $16a^2 - 4b^2$; $2b^2 + 16a^2 - 6b^2$; $\frac{12}{3}(4a^2 - b^2)$; $16(a^2 - \frac{1}{4}b^2)$

2. $-3m(3m - 4) - 8p$; $m^2 + 12m - (8p + 9m^2)$; $-9m^2 + 4(3m - 2p)$; $\frac{-36m^2 + 48m - 32p}{4}$

3. $\frac{1}{2}(mn + \frac{1}{2})$; $\frac{2mn + 1}{4}$; $0.5mn + (\frac{1}{2})^2$; $\frac{80m + 1}{4} - \frac{40m - mn}{2}$

4. $\frac{12y}{10x}$; $\frac{6x^5y^6}{5x^6y^5}$; $\frac{6y + 10}{5x} - \frac{2}{x}$; $1.2\frac{y}{x}$

5. $(10pr)^2$; $(9pr)^2 + \frac{19}{p^2r^2}(pr)^4$; $\frac{p^2r^2}{0.01}$; $101(pr)^2 - p^2r^2$

6. $2(\ell + w)$; $2q + 2\ell + 2w - 2q$; $\frac{8\ell + 5w}{4} + 0.75w$; $-(-(-(-(2\ell + 2w))))$

2. yes; By the Distributive Property the first expression is $6x^3 - 30y + 17x^2 + 12y$ or $6x^3 + 17x^2 - 18y$.

3. The CAS recognized that $5t$ and $-5t$ are additive inverses and applied the Additive Inverse Property.

5. $3k(3k - 1)$; $10k^2 - 3k - k^2$; $9k(k - \frac{1}{3})$

6. $m(13m + 8)$; $17m^2 + 7m - 4m^2 + m$; $4m(\frac{13}{4}m + 2)$

7. $-2 \cdot 3 \cdot 4y$; $6 + 6y - 3(10y + 2)$; $\frac{-120y^2}{5y}$

8. $4(4x^4 + 3xy + 5y)$; $20y + 2x(8x^3 + 6y)$; $4y(5 + 3x) + 16x^4$

Additional Answers

4a. Answers vary. Sample answer:
   $2xL + 2xW - 4x^2$.

4b. Answers vary. Sample answer:
   Sonia's expression $= Wx + x(L - 2x) + Wx + x(L - 2x) = Wx + xL - 2x^2 + Wx + xL - 2x^2 = 2Wx + 2xL - 4x^2$.

9. Answers vary. Sample answer: First, add $-3y$ and $3y$ to get $5x - 7y - 3y + 3y$. Then regroup terms to get $(5x - 10y) + 3y$. Finally, factor 5 out of the first part of the expression.

In **11** and **12**, test if the two expressions are equivalent by using a table. Then check your results by simplifying each expression. See margin.

11. $3n - 15, 3(n - 4) - 3$

12. $-2(a - 5), -2a - 5$

REVIEW

13. a. In your own words, state the Multiplication Property of –1.
   b. Give an example of this property. (**Lesson 2-4**)

14. Multiple Choice Which of the following must be negative?
   (**Lesson 2-4**) D

   A $-(-z)$ **B** $-(-6)$ **C** $-x$ **D** $-(-(-\frac{2}{5}))$

13a. Multiplying any real number by –1 gives the opposite of that number.

13b. Answers vary. Sample answer: $-5 \cdot -1 = 5$

15. Take a piece of paper. Fold it in half. The paper now has a thickness twice that of the original piece of paper. Fold the folded paper in half. The paper now has a thickness four times the original piece of paper. (**Lesson 1-2**)

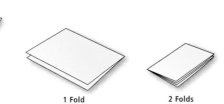

0 Folds   1 Fold   2 Folds

a. Complete the table for the thickness of a piece of paper that is folded 3 and 4 times.

Number of Folds	Thickness of Paper
0	1
1	$1 \cdot 2 = 2$
2	$1 \cdot 2 \cdot 2 = 4$
3	?
4	?

$1 \cdot 2 \cdot 2 \cdot 2 = 8$

$1 \cdot 2 \cdot 2 \cdot 2 \cdot 2 = 16$

b. If a piece of paper is folded six times, what is the thickness of the folded paper? 64 times the original thickness

c. Write an expression to describe the thickness of paper for n folds. 2^n

Equivalent Expressions with Technology   **103**

---

3 Assignment

Recommended Assignment

- Questions 1–19
- Question 20 (extra credit)
- Reading Lesson 2-7
- Covering the Ideas 2-7

Notes on the Questions

Question 15 A world record for folding a sheet of paper is often said to be 7 or 8 times, but this is incorrect. A world record was set by Britney Gallivan, then a high school junior, in January, 2002. She first folded gold foil, and then paper, 12 times. (A picture is at mathworld.wolfram.com/Folding.html.) In April, 2005, her success was mentioned on the prime time CBS television show Numb3rs. Another description of her work is at pomonahistorical.org/12times.htm.

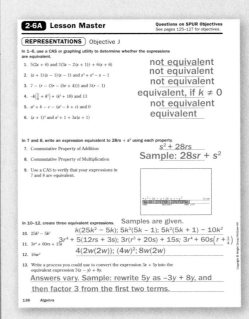

Additional Answers

11. Answers vary. Sample answer:

n	$(3n - 15)$	$3(n - 4) - 3$
–2	–21	–21
0	–15	–15
1	–12	–12
5	0	0
10	15	15

$3(n - 4) - 3 = 3n - 12 - 3 = 3n - 15$;
They are equivalent.

12. Answers vary. Sample answer:

a	$-2(a - 5)$	$-2a - 5$
–2	14	–1
0	10	–5
1	8	–7
5	0	–15
10	–10	–25

$-2(a - 5) = -2a + 10 \neq -2a - 5$. They are not equivalent.

2-6

4 Wrap-Up

Ongoing Assessment
Ask students to write two algebraic expressions that represent the area of the shaded region. Students should verify that the expressions are equivalent in two ways. They should simplify them by algebraically manipulating both expressions and by using a CAS.

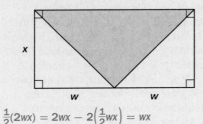

$$\tfrac{1}{2}(2wx) = 2wx - 2\left(\tfrac{1}{2}wx\right) = wx$$

Project Update
Project 3, Pascal's Triangle, on page 122 relates to the content of this lesson.

In 16 and 17, let $L =$ the length of a segment. Write an expression for the following. **(Lesson 1-1, Previous Course)**

16. one quarter the length   17. five and one half times the length

16. $\tfrac{1}{4}L$ 17. $5\tfrac{1}{2}L$

18. **Skill Sequence** Write each as a decimal. **(Previous Course)**
    a. 1 divided by 5 0.2
    b. 1 divided by 0.5 2
    c. 1 divided by 0.05 20
    d. 1 divided by 0.00005 20,000

19. Convert 0.325823224 to the nearest percent. **(Previous Course)** 33%

EXPLORATION

20. Use a CAS to determine which of these expressions are equivalent.

    A $x^3 + y^3$
    B $(x + y)^3$
    C $(x - y)^3$
    D $x^3 - y^3$
    E $(x + y)(x^2 - xy + y^2)$
    F $(x - y)(x^2 + xy + y^2)$
    G $(x + y)(x + y)(x + y)$
    H $(x - y)(x - y)(x - y)$

    A and E are equivalent. B and G are equivalent. C and H are equivalent. D and F are equivalent.

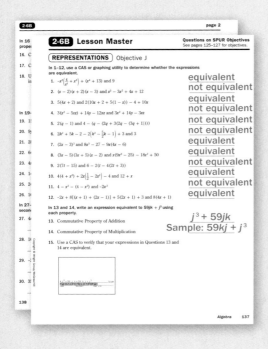

Lesson 2-7

Explaining Addition and Subtraction Related Facts

▶ **BIG IDEA** The Addition Property of Equality explains how addition and subtraction facts are related and helps solve equations of the form $a + x = b$.

A diagram called a *fact triangle* is shown at the right. Any pair of numbers in the triangle can be combined with addition or subtraction to produce the third number. The numbers 6, 8, and 14 produce the four related number facts listed below the triangle. You know that the first two facts are equivalent because $6 + 8 = 8 + 6$ by the Commutative Property of Addition.

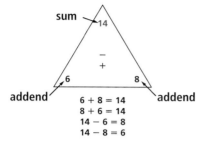

$6 + 8 = 14$
$8 + 6 = 14$
$14 - 6 = 8$
$14 - 8 = 6$

Fact triangles can be used to show addition/subtraction related facts with *any* kinds of numbers, including fractions and negative numbers. Here are two examples below. The fact triangle on the left uses fractions and the fact triangle on the right uses negative numbers. Each fact triangle has two addition facts and two subtraction facts.

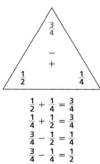

$\frac{1}{2} + \frac{1}{4} = \frac{3}{4}$
$\frac{1}{4} + \frac{1}{2} = \frac{3}{4}$
$\frac{3}{4} - \frac{1}{2} = \frac{1}{4}$
$\frac{3}{4} - \frac{1}{4} = \frac{1}{2}$

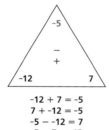

$-12 + 7 = -5$
$7 + -12 = -5$
$-5 - -12 = 7$
$-5 - 7 = -12$

🛑 **QY1**

Mental Math

a. 1 km ≈ $\frac{3}{5}$ mile, so
1 mile ≈ ___?___ km. $\frac{5}{3}$

b. 1 in. ≈ 2.5 cm, so
1 cm ≈ ___?___ in. 0.4

▶ **QY1**

a. What number goes in the empty corner of the fact triangle below?

b. Write the four related facts.

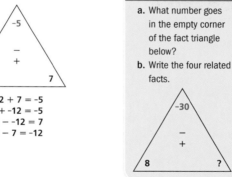

Background

Related facts. Students know that subtraction is related to addition. For example, $13 - 6 = 7$ because $6 + 7 = 13$. These are called *related facts.* The answer D (difference) to any subtraction problem $M - S$ (minuend minus subtrahend) can be checked by asking whether $D + S = M$.

Fact triangles. The representation used in this lesson, "fact triangles," is one that is

used in *UCSMP's Everyday Mathematics* to show related facts. The operations are indicated in the middle; in this lesson they are $+ -$ for addition and subtraction, and in Lesson 2-8 they are $\times \div$ for multiplication and division. We also use this fact triangle representation later in this book to show relationships among powers and among radicals.

continued on next page

Lesson 2-7

GOAL

Introduce the Addition Property of Equality and show how it explains the related addition and subtraction facts.

SPUR Objectives

C Use related facts to solve sentences.

E Apply and recognize the Additive Identity Property, Additive Inverse Property, and Addition Property of Equality.

Materials/Resources

· Lesson Masters 2-7A and 2-7B
· Resource Masters 6 and 33

HOMEWORK

Suggestions for Assignment
• Questions 1–25
• Question 26 (extra credit)
• Reading Lesson 2-8
• Covering the Ideas 2-8

Local Standards

1 Warm-Up

An addition or subtraction fact is given. Give the other three related facts.

1. $47 + 53 = 100$ $53 + 47 = 100$; $100 - 53 = 47$; $100 - 47 = 53$

2. $\frac{1}{3} - \frac{1}{5} = \frac{2}{15}$ $\frac{1}{3} - \frac{2}{15} = \frac{1}{5}$; $\frac{2}{15} + \frac{1}{5} = \frac{1}{3}$; $\frac{1}{5} + \frac{2}{15} = \frac{1}{3}$

3. $-11 + 12 = 1$ $12 + -11 = 1$; $1 - 12 = -11$; $1 - (-11) = 12$

4. $x + a = b$ $a + x = b$; $b - a = x$; $b - x = a$

5. $c - x = d$ $c - d = x$; $d + x = c$; $x + d = c$

Notice that if x were an unknown in Problems 4 and 5, then one of the related facts could be used to determine x.

2 **Teaching**

Notes on the Lesson

The Addition Property of Equality. You might begin by asserting the Addition Property of Equality. Students may think it is obvious, so ask: $45\% = \frac{9}{20}$ and $24\% = \frac{6}{25}$. If you add 45% and 24%, will you get 69%? If you add the two fractions, will the sum be equal to 69%? The answer is *Yes*, but some students may not be so sure.

Some teachers prefer not to use the Subtraction Property of Equality. They consider it a special case of the Addition Property of Equality, since every subtraction can be converted to an addition.

The Addition Property of Equality

You know from arithmetic that if you start with equal quantities and add the same amount to each, the resulting quantities are still equal. For example, we know that $4 + 3 = 7$.

Adding 5 to each side gives $4 + 3 + 5 = 7 + 5$.

$$12 = 12$$

Note that the value of each side changes from 7 in the first equation to 12 in the second equation. But in each case, the two sides of the equation are equal. The idea that adding a number to both sides produces another true equation is called the *Addition Property of Equality*. It is a basic property of addition.

> **Addition Property of Equality**
>
> For all real numbers a, b, and c, if $a = b$, then $a + c = b + c$.

By the Definition of Subtraction, $a - c = a + -c$ for all real numbers. Every subtraction can be converted to an addition. So if you wanted to subtract a number, say 40, from both sides of an equation, you could add –40 instead. For this reason, the Addition Property of Equality means also that there is a *Subtraction Property of Equality*.

> **Subtraction Property of Equality**
>
> For all real numbers a, b, and c, if $a = b$, then $a - c = b - c$.

The Related Facts Property of Addition and Subtraction

These properties also explain why related facts work. Write down a general addition fact. The sum of two numbers is a third number. The result is a related subtraction fact.

$$h + m = S$$
$$h + m - m = S - m \quad \text{Subtract } m \text{ from both sides.}$$
$$h = S - m$$

If instead you subtract h from both sides of the original addition fact, you get the other related subtraction fact.

$$h + m - h = S - h$$
$$m = S - h$$

In this way, algebra explains why fact triangles work. Either addend is equal to the sum minus the other addend. We call this the *Related Facts Property of Addition and Subtraction*.

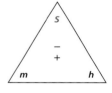

Why do fact triangles work? It can be argued that fact triangles work because subtraction is defined as the inverse operation of addition. This is true, but our definition of subtraction is that $a - b = a + -b$. So if $a - b = c$, then $a + -b = c$. Now, adding b to both sides of this equation (which can be done because of the Addition Property of Equality), $a + -b + b = c + b$, and so $a = c + b$.

The Addition Property of Equality. The Addition Property of Equality says that addition is a well-defined operation. That is, if we begin with equal quantities and add the same quantity to both sides, the sums will be equal quantities. We want to use the Addition Property of Equality to solve equations that are more complicated. The goal here is to show that related facts can be explained using the Addition Property of Equality.

Related Facts Property of Addition and Subtraction

For all real numbers a, b, and c,
if $a + b = c$, then $b + a = c$,
$c - b = a$, and $c - a = b$.

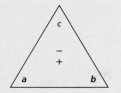

▶ QY2

Write the two related subtraction facts for $5a + x = k$.

 QY2

Example 1

Solve the equation $x + -8 = -30$
a. using a fact triangle (the Related Facts Property).
b. using the Subtraction Property of Equality.

Solutions

a. Draw a fact triangle. Place x and -8 at the lower corners. The sum at the top is -30, as shown at the right.
    The triangle shows that $x = -30 - (-8)$ is a related fact.
    $x = -30 - -8 = -30 + 8 = -22$

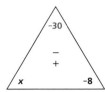

b. Subtract -8 from both sides.
    $$x + -8 = -30$$
    $$x + -8 - -8 = -30 - -8$$
    $$x + -8 + 8 = -30 + 8$$
    $$x = -22$$

Example 2

Solve the equation $-3.4 - y = 6.1$
a. using a fact triangle.   b. using properties.

Solutions

a. Because y is subtracted from -3.4, it must be that -3.4 is the sum. So put -3.4 in the upper corner and y in one of the lower corners. Put 6.1 in the third corner.
    $y = -3.4 - 6.1$
    $y = -3.4 + -6.1$
    $y = -9.5$

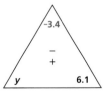

(continued on next page)

Explaining Addition and Subtraction Related Facts   **107**

Additional Examples

Example 1 Solve the equation $y + -3 = 21$

a. using a fact triangle (the Related Facts Property). Draw a fact triangle. Place y and -3 at the lower corners. The sum at the top is 21.

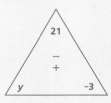

The triangle shows that $y = 21 - -3$ is a related fact. $y = 21 - (-3) = 21 + 3 = 24$

b. using the Subtraction Property of Equality. Subtract -3 from both sides.
    $$y + -3 = 21$$
    $$y + -3 - -3 = 21 - -3$$
    $$y + -3 + 3 = 21 + 3$$
    $$y = 24$$

Example 2 Solve the equation $4.7 - a = 5.3$

a. using a fact triangle.

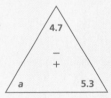

Because a is subtracted from 4.7, it must be that 4.7 is the sum. So put 4.7 in the upper shaded corner and a in one of the lower corners. Put 5.3 in the third corner. From the related facts,
    $a = 4.7 - 5.3$
    $= 4.7 + -5.3$
    $= -0.6$.

b. using properties. Use the Definition of Subtraction to rewrite the equation. Then use the Addition Property of Equality.
    $$4.7 - a = 5.3$$
    $$4.7 + -a = 5.3$$
    $$4.7 + -a + a = 5.3 + a$$
    $$4.7 = 5.3 + a$$
    $$4.7 + -5.3 = 5.3 + -5.3 + a$$
    $$-0.6 = a$$

2-7

Notes on the Lesson

Special numbers for addition. Fact triangles show that 0 is special. When 0 is one of the addends (numbers at the bottom vertices), the other two numbers are equal. When 0 is the sum (at the top), the other two numbers are additive inverses or opposites.

Additional Answers

2. $-5 + 82 = 77$, $77 - -5 = 82$, $77 - 82 = -5$;

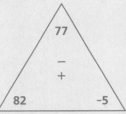

3. $-4 + 3\frac{7}{8} = -\frac{1}{8}$, $-\frac{1}{8} - -4 = 3\frac{7}{8}$, $3\frac{7}{8} + -4 = -\frac{1}{8}$;

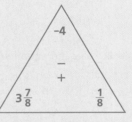

4. $5x + x = 6x$, $6x - x = 5x$, $6x - 5x = x$

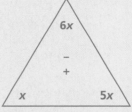

12. Answers vary. Sample answer: Jeremy walks 7 steps backward and then 7 steps forward.

13b. Answers vary. Sample answer:

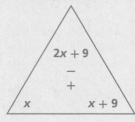

---

b.

$-3.4 - y = 6.1$	Write the equation.
$-3.4 + -y = 6.1$	Definition of Subtraction
$-3.4 + -y + y = 6.1 + y$	Add y to each side since we are looking for y and not the opposite of y.
$-3.4 = 6.1 + y$	Simplify.
$-3.4 - 6.1 = 6.1 - 6.1 + y$	Subtract 6.1 from each side.
$-9.5 = y$	Simplify.

Check Substitute -9.5 for y in the original equation.

Does $-3.4 - -9.5 = 6.1$?
$$-3.4 + 9.5 = 6.1$$
$$6.1 = 6.1 \text{ Yes.}$$

Special Numbers for Addition

Important properties can be seen from a fact triangle in which one of the numbers is zero. Two cases are possible.

Case 1: Zero is one of the addends.   **Case 2:** Zero is the sum.

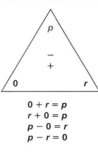

$0 + r = p$
$r + 0 = p$
$p - 0 = r$
$p - r = 0$

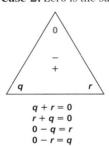

$q + r = 0$
$r + q = 0$
$0 - q = r$
$0 - r = q$

When 0 is an addend (Case 1), one of the related facts is $p - 0 = r$. This means that $p = r$. So the first related fact $0 + r = p$ can be rewritten as $0 + p = p$ or as $0 + r = r$. Adding 0 to a number keeps the *identity* of that number. So 0 is called the *additive identity*.

> **Additive Identity Property**
>
> For any real number a, $a + 0 = 0 + a = a$.

When 0 is the sum (Case 2), a related subtraction fact is $0 - q = r$.
$$0 + (-q) = r \qquad \text{Definition of Subtraction}$$
$$-q = r \qquad \text{Additive Identity Property}$$

Accommodating the Learner ⬇

Form groups of two students. On a piece of paper, have each student draw five fact triangles. In two of the three corners of each triangle have students place a number. Instruct them to vary the corners where they place the two numbers. Have students exchange papers. Instruct students to fill in the third corner of each triangle and write four related facts for each triangle.

Since $-q = r$, $q + r = 0$ becomes $q + (-q) = 0$. As you know from Lesson 2-4, q and $-q$ are *additive inverses*, or *opposites*. When you add two inverses, the sum is 0, the additive identity. Every number, including 0, has exactly one additive inverse.

Additive Inverse Property

For any real number a, $a + -a = -a + a = 0$.

Questions

COVERING THE IDEAS

1. What are the related facts for the fact triangle shown at the right? $0.23 + 0.44 = 0.67$, $0.44 + 0.23 = 0.67$, $0.67 - 0.44 = 0.23$, $0.67 - 0.23 = 0.44$

In 2–4, make a fact triangle to fit the equation. Then write the other three related facts. 2–4. See margin.

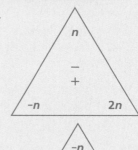

2. $82 + -5 = 77$
3. $-\frac{1}{8} - 3\frac{7}{8} = -4$
4. $x + 5x = 6x$

5. Solve the equation $y + (-6) = 14$ 5a. $y = 14 - -6 = 20$
   a. using a fact triangle (the Related Facts Property).
   b. using the Addition Property of Equality.

5b. $y - 6 = 14$,
so $y = y - 6 + 6$
$= 14 + 6 = 20$

6. a. Write the other three related facts of $7 - b = -8$.
   b. What is the value of b? 15

6a. $7 = -8 + b$ and
$7 - (-8) = b$

7. **Fill in the Blank** $0 + -10 = \underline{\ ?\ }$ -10

8. Why is zero called the additive identity?
Adding zero to a number results in the same number.
9. Give an example of two numbers that are additive inverses.
Answers vary. Sample answer: 629 and –629
10. What is another name for an additive inverse? opposite

11. What is the additive inverse of $-x$? x

APPLYING THE MATHEMATICS

12. Use $-7 + 7 = 0$ to describe a real situation. See margin.

13. Make a fact triangle where the sum is
   a. $\frac{5}{9}$.
   b. $2x + 9$. See margin.

13a. Answers vary.
Sample answer:

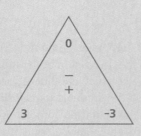

14. Write a note to a friend explaining how to make a fact triangle for $x + 10 = -19$. Put –19 at the top of your triangle and x and 10 at the two lower corners.
15. Show all possible fact triangles that can be made where two of the numbers are See margin.
   a. 3 and –3.
   b. n and $-n$.

15a.

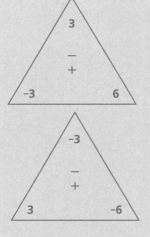

3 Assignment

Recommended Assignment
- Questions 1–25
- Question 26 (extra credit)
- Reading Lesson 2-8
- Covering the Ideas 2-8

Notes on the Questions
Question 13 This question shows the versatility of fact triangles.

Additional Answers

15b.

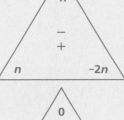

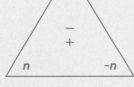

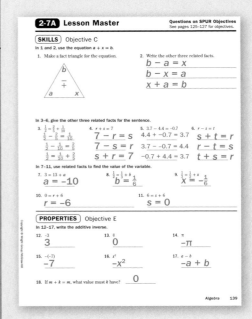

Notes on the Questions

Question 19 The idea of this question is to compare expressions students might get for answers, and then show they are equivalent.

16. Consider this expression:
$$-0.3 + 1.7 - 14.2 - 1.7 + 0.3 - 2.8 + 14.2$$
Use the Associative and Commutative Properties of Addition to first group the additive inverses together. Then evaluate the expression. $(-0.3 + 0.3) + (1.7 - 1.7) + (-14.2 + 14.2) - 2.8 = -2.8$

17. At 11:00 A.M., the temperature was 15°F. By the time the football game started at 7:00 P.M., the temperature had dropped to −4°F. By how much did the temperature drop? **19°F**

In the United States, there were a total of 1,071,775 high school football players during the 2005–2006 season.

Source: National Federation of State High School Associations

REVIEW

18. The figure below shows a rectangle with width $40 + a$ and height b. Find two different expressions that describe the area of the figure. Verify that the expressions are equivalent using properties. (**Lessons 2-5, 2-2, 2-1**) $40b + ab$ and $b(40 + a)$; $b(40 + a) = b \cdot 40 + ba = 40b + ab$

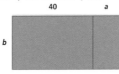

19. A farmer owns a piece of land that is 350 yards wide by 200 yards long, as shown below. She uses one part to harvest wheat and another to harvest corn. She does not use the brown part. Let $W =$ the area of the wheat field and $C =$ the area of the cornfield. The farmer decides to sell the wheat and corn fields. Write an expression for the area of the land she will own after the sale. (**Lesson 2-4**) Answers vary. Sample answer: $350 \cdot 200 - W - C$ yd^2

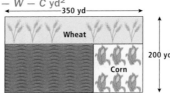

20. ***Skill Sequence*** Simplify without using a calculator. (**Lesson 2-4, Previous Course**)

  a. $23.7 + -23.7$ **0** b. $-(-23.7 + 23.7)$ **0** c. $-23.7(23.7 + -23.7)$ **0**

In 21 and 22, use the Distributive Property to write an equivalent expression. (**Lessons 2-2, 2-1**)

21. $-3p + 4p - 8$ $p - 8$ 22. $-2(3 - 4d)$ $-6 + 8d$

Extension

In groups of 3, have each student draw a fact triangle and write a sum at the top with two terms, one of which contains a variable, e.g. $3 + 2y$. Ask the students to pass their triangle to the left and then complete the triangle they receive. Pass left one more time and have each student write the set of three related facts.

23. Two times a number is increased by 5. The resulting quantity is tripled. If m is the original number, write the final result without parentheses. (**Lesson 2-1**) $6m + 15$

24. **Multiple Choice** Which formula was used to create the table at the right? (**Lessons 1-3, 1-1**) C

    A $y = 4x$ **B** $y = x + 2$

    C $y = 2x + 2$ **D** $y = 2x + 1$

x	y
0	2
1	4
2	6
3	8
4	10

25. Evaluate the following expressions. (**Lesson 1-1**)

    a. $n^3 - \dfrac{(-1)^n}{2 + n}$ for $n = -5$ $-\dfrac{376}{3}$

    b. $a\left(a + \dfrac{1}{a}\right)$ for $a = 2$ 5

EXPLORATION

26. A tetrahedron is a 3-dimensional solid whose four faces are equilateral triangles. A net to construct a tetrahedron is given below. A set of related facts has been formed within each triangle and at each vertex of the tetrahedron. Create a tetrahedron of your own with these properties. Describe the method you used to create it.

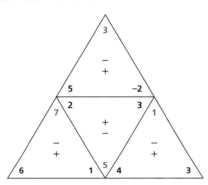

26. Answers vary. Sample answer:

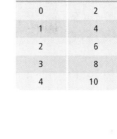

QY ANSWERS

1a. -38

1b. $8 + -38 = -30,$
$-38 + 8 = -30,$
$-30 - -38 = 8,$
$-30 - 8 = -38$

2. $k - x = 5a,$
$k - 5a = x$

2-7

4 Wrap-Up

Ongoing Assessment

Place several fact triangles on the board. Call on students to choose a triangle and give one related fact. Write the related fact under the triangle. Repeat the process until all related facts for each triangle are given.

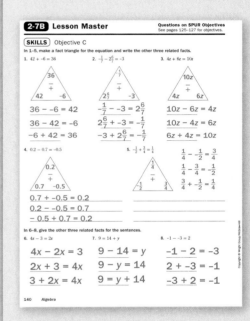

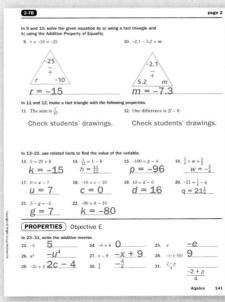

GOAL

Introduce the Multiplication Property of Equality and show how it explains the related multiplication and division facts.

SPUR Objectives

C Use related facts to solve sentences.

D Apply and recognize the Multiplicative Identity Property, Multiplicative Inverse Property, Multiplication Property of Zero, Multiplication Property of Equality, and Zero Product Property.

Materials/Resources

· Lesson Masters 2-8A and 2-8B
· Resource Masters 6 and 34

HOMEWORK

Suggestions for Assignment
• Questions 1–36
• Question 37 (extra credit)
• Reading Lesson 3-1
• Covering the Ideas 3-1

Local Standards

1 **Warm-Up**

You might write or project the following so that students can do these questions as they enter the classroom.

A multiplication or division fact is given. Give the three related facts.

1. $12 \cdot 34 = 408$ $34 \cdot 12 = 408$; $\frac{408}{34} = 12$; $\frac{408}{12} = 34$

2. $\frac{1}{2} \cdot \frac{3}{4} = \frac{3}{8}$ $\frac{3}{4} \cdot \frac{1}{2} = \frac{3}{8}$; $\frac{\frac{3}{8}}{\frac{3}{4}} = \frac{1}{2}$; $\frac{\frac{3}{8}}{\frac{1}{2}} = \frac{3}{4}$

3. $\frac{-78}{-6} = 13$ $\frac{-78}{13} = -6$; $-6 \cdot 13 = -78$; $13 \cdot -6 = -78$

4. $14x = 7$ $x(14) = 7$; $x = \frac{7}{14}$; $14 = \frac{7}{x}$

5. $\frac{5}{y} = 12$ $\frac{5}{12} = y$; $12y = 5$; $y(12) = 5$

6. $ax = b$; $a \neq 0$ $ba = x$; $x = \frac{b}{a}$; $a = \frac{b}{x}$

Explaining Multiplication and Division Related Facts

▶ **BIG IDEA** The Multiplication Property of Equality explains how multiplication and division facts are related and helps to solve equations of the form $ax = b$.

Related Facts for Multiplication

Fact triangles can also be used to represent related facts in multiplication and division. In a multiplication fact triangle, the number at the top is the product of the other two.

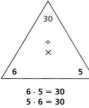

$6 \cdot 5 = 30$
$5 \cdot 6 = 30$
$30 \div 6 = 5$
$30 \div 5 = 6$

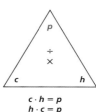

$c \cdot h = p$
$h \cdot c = p$
$p \div c = h$
$p \div h = c$

The related facts that can be obtained from these triangles are shown above. As with addition, the first two facts in each list are equivalent by the Commutative Property of Multiplication. Again, as with addition, the fact triangles work for any nonzero real numbers. Here are some other fact triangles and related facts with positive and negative numbers and with fractions.

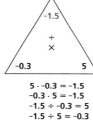

$5 \cdot -0.3 = -1.5$
$-0.3 \cdot 5 = -1.5$
$-1.5 \div -0.3 = 5$
$-1.5 \div 5 = -0.3$

$18 \cdot \frac{1}{2} = 19$
$\frac{1}{2} \cdot 18 = 9$
$9 \div \frac{1}{2} = 18$
$9 \div 18 = \frac{1}{2}$

Calculate.

a. $2 \cdot -5 - 10 + 60$ 40

b. $2 \cdot -5 - (10 + 60)$ –80

c. $2 \cdot (-5 - 10 + 60)$ 90

Background

This lesson is a companion to Lesson 2-7, using multiplication (and division) the way Lesson 2-7 used addition (and subtraction).

Corresponding properties of multiplication and addition. Students usually think of multiplication as repeated addition, but it is an operation in its own right. For example, we could not represent $\frac{1}{3} \times \frac{3}{4}$ or $\sqrt{2} \times \sqrt{3}$ as repeated addition.

The property of 0 in multiplication. Where multiplication differs from addition is that not all numbers have multiplicative inverses. Since $0 \cdot a = 0$ for all real numbers a, there is *no solution* to $0 \cdot x = 1$ or $0 \cdot x = y$ where $y \neq 0$. This is why you cannot divide by zero.

The Division Property of Equality. Changing division to multiplication is not as easy as changing subtraction to addition. In an equation such as $3.2x = 640$, it is simpler to divide both sides by 3.2 than to multiply both sides by the reciprocal of 3.2.

(continued on next page)

Just as you can add the same number to equal quantities and get equal quantities as a result, you can multiply (or divide) equal quantities by the same number and get equal quantities. For example, we know that $-0.3 \cdot 5 = -1.5$.

$$-0.3 \cdot 5 = -1.5$$

$10 \cdot -0.3 \cdot 5 = 10 \cdot -1.5$ Multiply each side by 10.

$\qquad -15 = -15$ Simplify.

This property is called the *Multiplication Property of Equality*.

Multiplication Property of Equality

For all real numbers a, b, and c, if $a = b$, then $ca = cb$.

Because $x \div c = x \cdot \frac{1}{c}$ for all values of x and c (provided c is not zero), every division can be converted to multiplication. So to divide both sides of an equation by c, you can multiply both sides by $\frac{1}{c}$. For this reason, the Multiplication Property of Equality means that there is also a *Division Property of Equality*.

Division Property of Equality

For all real numbers a, b, and all real nonzero numbers c, if $a = b$, then $\frac{a}{c} = \frac{b}{c}$.

The Related Facts Property of Multiplication and Division

The Multiplication Property of Equality also explains why related facts work. Write down a multiplication fact, as shown below.

$$8 \cdot 45 = 360$$

Now divide each side by 8. Do the computation on the left side only.

$$\frac{8 \cdot 45}{8} =$$
$$45 = \frac{360}{8}$$

The result is a related division fact. You can divide each side of the original fact by 45 to find the other related division fact.

$$8 = \frac{360}{45}$$

Related multiplication and division facts cannot be found if one of the numbers being multiplied is 0 because division of 0 is undefined. However, related facts can be found with nonzero numbers. We call this the *Related Facts Property of Multiplication and Division*.

The properties of multiplication are analogous to those for addition.

	Multiplication	Addition
Commutative	$xy = yx$	$a + b = b + a$
Associative	$x(yz) = (xy)z$	$a + (b + c) = (a + b) + c$
Identity	$xy = x$ if and only if $y = 1$.	$a + b = a$ if and only if $b = 0$.
Inverse	$xy = 1$ if and only if $x = \frac{1}{y}$. $\frac{1}{y}$ (reciprocal)	$a + b = 0$ if and only if $a = -b$. $-b$ (opposite)
Algebraic definition of inverse operation	$x \div y = x \cdot \frac{1}{y}$	$a - b = a + -b$
Related facts	If $xy = z$, with x, y, and $z \neq 0$, then $yx = z$, $x = \frac{z}{y}$, and $y = \frac{z}{x}$.	If $a + b = c$, then $b + a = c$, $a = c - b$, and $b = c - a$.

---

2 Teaching

Notes on the Lesson

You might wish to discuss the corresponding properties of multiplication and addition given in the Background as a lead-in to the lesson. This will enable you to review other material that has been covered in this chapter.

We assume students have seen equations of the form $ax = b$ in previous courses. If not, students will need more practice. You might give students these equations to solve by related facts and by using either the Multiplication or Division Property of Equality.

1. $5x = -40$ (Related facts $x = -\frac{40}{5} = -8$; multiply both sides by $\frac{1}{5}$ or divide both sides by 5 to obtain $x = -8$.)

2. $\frac{12}{r} = 18$ (Related facts $\frac{12}{18} = r$, so $r = \frac{2}{3}$; multiply both sides by r to obtain $12 = 18r$. Then divide both sides by 12 to obtain $\frac{12}{18} = r$.)

2-8

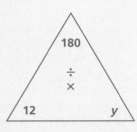
Related Facts Property of Multiplication and Division

For all nonzero real numbers a, b, and c, if $ab = c$, then $ba = c$, $\frac{c}{b} = a$, and $\frac{c}{a} = b$.

Multiplication equations can be solved by using related facts, or by performing the same operation on each side of the equation.

Example 1

Solve $16x = 192$.

Solution 1 Use a fact triangle.

The fact triangle shows $16x = 192$.

$16x = 192$

$192 \div 16 = x$

$12 = x$

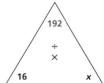

Solution 2 Divide each side by 16.

$16x = 192$

$\frac{16x}{16} = \frac{192}{16}$

$x = 12$

Solution 3 Multiply each side by $\frac{1}{16}$.

$16x = 192$

$\frac{1}{16} \cdot 16x = \frac{1}{16} \cdot 192$

$x = 12$

STOP QY1

The Role of Zero in Multiplication and Division

In many ways, the operations of addition and multiplication behave in similar ways. Both have commutative and associative properties. In both, fact triangles illustrate four related number facts. But there is one special case that arises for multiplication which has no parallel in addition. Zero is special in multiplication. You know that whenever 0 is multiplied by a number, the result is zero.

> **QY1**
>
> Solve $\frac{3}{5}x = 60$ by using
> **a.** a fact triangle.
> **b.** the Multiplication Property of Equality.

> **READING MATH**
>
> In some countries, zero is called the annihilator.

Multiplication Property of Zero

For any real number a, $a \cdot 0 = 0 \cdot a = 0$.

You have also learned that you cannot divide by 0. Another way of putting it is that a fraction cannot have zero in its denominator. This can be explained by using related facts.

Suppose you tried to divide 0 by 0. You write $\frac{0}{0} = b$. What is the value of b? Using related facts, you get $0 \cdot b = 0$. But any value of b would work to make the equation true. Since there is no unique value for $\frac{0}{0}$, we say it is undefined.

Now suppose you tried to divide some nonzero number a by 0. You write $\frac{a}{0} = b$. Then by related facts, you get $0 \cdot b = a$. The Multiplication Property of Zero says that a would have to be 0. But a was specifically indicated as being a nonzero number. So there is no value of b that makes the equation true.

Therefore, an attempt to divide a number by 0 can never give exactly one answer. And since operations must give a single answer and the same answer each time they are performed, division by zero is not allowed.

When zero is involved in multiplication or division, we do not draw a fact triangle. But zero can still be involved in sample multiplication equations. Three types of equations are possible.

Example 2

Solve each equation.

a. $0x = 0$
b. $0x = 4$
c. $13x = 0$

Solutions Each equation uses zero in a slightly different way.

a. Zero times x is zero. **All real numbers are solutions.**

b. Zero times x is a nonzero number. Since $0 \cdot x$ is always 0, it cannot be 4. **There is no solution.**

c. A nonzero number times x is zero. **There is exactly one solution, 0.**

Part c of Example 2 illustrates a simple fact.

Zero Product Property

If the product of two real numbers a and b is 0, then $a = 0$, $b = 0$, or both a and b equal 0.

Explaining Multiplication and Division Related Facts **115**

Additional Example

Example 3 Find the reciprocal of each number.

a. 1.125

b. $\frac{3}{11}$

c. −17

Solution

a. $\frac{1}{1.125}$ = $\frac{?}{\underline{}}$ · $\frac{9}{8}$

b. The reciprocal of $\frac{3}{11}$ is $\dfrac{1}{\frac{?}{?}}$ =

$1 \cdot \dfrac{?}{?} = \dfrac{11}{3} \cdot \dfrac{3}{11}, \dfrac{11}{3}$

c. The reciprocal of −17 is $\dfrac{?}{?}$ · $\dfrac{-1}{17}$

STOP QY2

Some Properties of the Number One

Another number that has special properties involving multiplication is 1.

There are two cases to investigate.

Case 1: One is a factor.

Whatever number you choose for the second factor, the result is that same number.

Case 2: One is the product.

What pairs of numbers multiply to give 1 as a result? They must be reciprocals, like 3 and $\frac{1}{3}$, or $\frac{2}{11}$ and $\frac{22}{4}$, or −8 and −0.125.

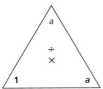
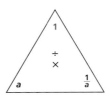

The two fact triangles above illustrate two properties of multiplication.

> **Multiplicative Identity Property**
>
> For any real number a, $a \cdot 1 = 1 \cdot a = a$.

The Multiplicative Identity Property is also true for zero, since $0 \cdot 1 = 1 \cdot 0 = 0$.

The second property involves the reciprocals or *multiplicative inverses* of a and $\frac{1}{a}$, whose product is 1.

> **Multiplicative Inverse Property**
>
> For any real number a, where $a \neq 0$, $a \cdot \frac{1}{a} = \frac{1}{a} \cdot a = 1$.

GUIDED

Example 3

Find the reciprocal of each number.

a. 1.5625   b. $\frac{4}{15}$ c. −34

▶ QY2

a. Find an equation (not in this lesson) that has no solution.

b. Find an equation (not in this lesson) that is true for every real number.

Solutions

a. The reciprocal of 1.5625 is $\frac{1}{1.5625}$. To find the decimal for $\frac{1}{1.5625}$, you can divide 1 by 1.5625 or find 1.5625^{-1} on your graphing calculator.
$$\frac{1}{1.5625} = \underline{\ ?\ }\ 0.64$$

b. The reciprocal of $\frac{4}{15}$ is $\underline{\ ?\ } = 1 \cdot \underline{\ ?\ } = \frac{15}{4}$. So taking the reciprocal inverts a fraction.

c. The reciprocal of –34 is $\underline{\ ?\ }$. $-\frac{1}{34}$

b. $\dfrac{\frac{1}{4}}{15}$, $\dfrac{15}{4}$

Questions

COVERING THE IDEAS

1. Write the related facts for the fact triangle shown below.

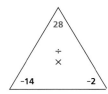

2. **a.** Make a fact triangle with the numbers 275, 25, and $\frac{1}{11}$.
   b. Write the four related facts.

3. If a, b, and c are not equal to zero and $a = bc$, find the other three related facts. $cb = a$, $\frac{a}{b} = c$, $\frac{a}{c} = b$

4. Use the equation $\frac{2}{3}p = 96$.
   a. Make a fact triangle for this equation.
   b. Use the fact triangle to solve the equation for p. $p = \frac{96}{\frac{2}{3}} = 144$
   c. Solve the equation using the Multiplication Property of Equality. $\frac{3}{2}(\frac{2}{3})p = \frac{3}{2}(96) = 144$
   d. Solve the equation using the Division Property of Equality.

5. **Fill in the Blank** If $a = b$, then $6a = \underline{\ ?\ }$. $6b$

In 6–8, find the reciprocal.

6. 0.8 1.25   7. –6 $-\frac{1}{6}$ 8. $\frac{4}{7}$ $\frac{7}{4}$

9. What number is the multiplicative identity? 1

10. **a.** If $ab = 1$, then what is true about a and b?
    b. If $ab = 0$, then what is true about a and b?

1. $28 = -2 \cdot -14$,
   $28 = -14 \cdot -2$,
   $\frac{28}{-14} = -2$, $\frac{28}{-2} = -14$

2a.
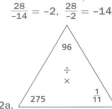

2b. $25 = 275 \cdot \frac{1}{11}$,
   $25 = \frac{1}{11} \cdot 275$,
   $25 \div 275 = \frac{1}{11}$,
   $25 \div \frac{1}{11} = 275$

4a.
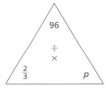

4d. $\dfrac{\frac{2}{3}p}{\frac{2}{3}} = \dfrac{96}{\frac{2}{3}} = 144$

10a. They are reciprocals of each other.

10b. $a = 0$, $b = 0$, or $a = 0$ and $b = 0$

Recommended Assignment
- Questions 1–36
- Question 37 (extra credit)
- Reading Lesson 3-1
- Covering the Ideas 3-1

Notes on the Questions
Question 6 You might have students write 0.8 as a fraction and find its reciprocal to verify the answer.

Question 10b Technically there is nothing you can say about *a and b*. You can say that either *a or b* equals 0.

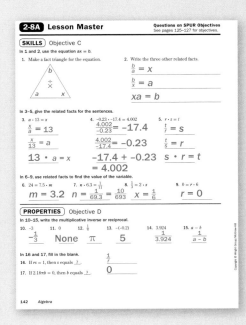

2-8

Notes on the Questions

Question 19 We assume in this course that students are familiar with the multiplication and division of positive and negative numbers.

11. Explain in your own words why 0 does not have a reciprocal.
Answers vary. Sample answer: Division by 0 is not defined.
12. What number(s) satisfy the following sentences?

   a. Zero times a number is eight. not satisfied by any number

   b. Zero times a number is zero. satisfied by all numbers

   c. Seven times a number is zero. satisfied by zero

In 13–16, solve the equation.

13. $4x = 0$ $x = 0$

14. $0y = \frac{1}{2}$ There are no solutions.

15. $0 \cdot a = 0$ Any number is a solution.

16. $3b - 3b = 0$ Any number is a solution.

APPLYING THE MATHEMATICS

In 17 and 18, what property is shown by the statement?

17. All the books on the table are free, so a book is free.
Multiplication Property of Zero
18. Since two packages of batteries cost $7.98, one package costs $3.99.
Multiplication or Division Property of Equality
19. Illustrate the rules for multiplying and dividing positive and negative numbers by drawing fact triangles. Label corners "pos" for positive number and "neg" for negative numbers. Draw all the possible triangles and give the rules that each triangle illustrates. See margin.

20. Explain why the fact triangle below is not possible.

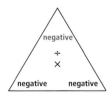

20. Answers vary. Sample answer: The product of two negative numbers is positive.

In 21 and 22, find the quotient by multiplying by the reciprocal.

21. $\dfrac{\frac{6}{7}}{\frac{3}{21}}$ 6

22. $\dfrac{\frac{9}{3}}{\frac{9}{8}}$ 24

23. A rectangle has a length of 50 centimeters and an area of 1 square centimeter.

   a. Is this rectangle possible? Yes, it is possible.

   b. If so, what is the width of the rectangle? If not, why is it not possible? The width of the rectangle is $\frac{1}{50}$ cm.

Additional Answers

19.

The product of two negative numbers or two positive numbers is positive. The product of a negative number and a positive number is negative.

24. Refer to the pattern in the table.

Quotient	$\frac{p}{10}$	$\frac{p}{1}$	$\frac{p}{0.1}$	$\frac{p}{0.01}$	$\frac{p}{0.001}$	$\frac{p}{0.0001}$
Equal Expression	0.1p	1p	10p	?	?	?

100p 1,000p 10,000p

a. Copy and complete the pattern in the table.

b. Use the pattern to rewrite $\frac{p}{0.000000001}$ as a multiple of p. 1,000,000,000p

25. Consider the formula $d = rt$, where d is distance, r is rate, and t is time.

a. Write the related facts for the formula. $d = tr, r = \frac{d}{t}, t = \frac{d}{r}$

b. Suppose Sam D. Yago is traveling from his home to Santa Clara, California, a distance of 160 miles. To the nearest mile, how long will the trip take him if he can average 42 miles per hour? **about 3.81 hr**

26. Meli went grocery shopping. Her least expensive purchase was a drink. She bought bread which cost twice as much as the drink, salad that was four times as much as the drink, and laundry detergent that was five times as much as the drink. Her bill came to $18. How much did each item cost Meli? **Her drink was $1.50, the bread $3.00, the salad $6.00, and the laundry detergent $7.50.**

REVIEW

27. The formula $P = 2a + 2b$ gives the perimeter P of a rectangle with sides a and b. Create a fact triangle using this formula, and list the other three related facts. **(Lesson 2-7) See margin.**

28. The measure of $\angle PQR$ equals 133°. Find y, the measure of $\angle SQR$. **(Lesson 2-7) 73°**

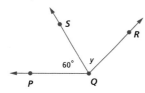

29. They are equivalent when $p = 6$, because $18p^2 + p = 18(6^2) + 6 = 654$ and $p^3 + 9p^2 + 19 = 9(6)^2 + (6)^3 + 19(6) = 654$.

29. Evaluate the expressions $18p^2 + p$ and $9p^2 + p^3 + 19p$ when $p = 6$. Are the expressions equivalent? Why or why not? **(Lessons 2-6, 1-3)**

30. a. Evaluate $-(-194) + -(-(-194))$. **0**

b. Explain how you found your answer. **(Lesson 2-4)**

30b. Answers vary. Sample answer: The second number is the opposite of the first.

Additional Answers

27.

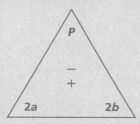

$P = 2b + 2a; 2a = P - 2b; 2b = P - 2a$

Question 24 For students who have had scientific notation (this includes students who have taken previous UCSMP courses), you might wish to change all the decimals to powers of 10. This will show that $10^n = \frac{1}{10^{-n}}$.

Question 25 Because the rate unit (say miles per hour) is the derived unit, for many people the primitive formula is not $d = rt$ but $r = \frac{d}{t}$.

Question 30 No computation is necessary on this problem. Because the addend on the right is the opposite of the addend on the left, the sum is zero.

Question 35 You might ask students to explain why this formula works. (The LH is area, and 7 represents 7 bricks in each square foot of wall.)

4 Wrap-Up

Ongoing Assessment

Form groups of three students. Using blank related multiplication and division fact triangles, have the first student place a number or variable in one of the corners. Pass the paper to the second student, who places a number or variable in a second corner. Pass the paper to the third student, who completes the triangle. Now pass the paper around a second time, and have each student write down a related fact.

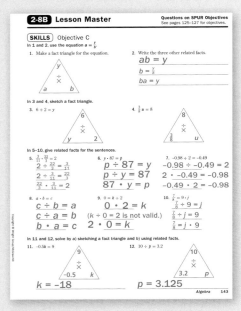

In 31–34, suppose that x is positive and y is negative. Tell whether the value of the expression is *always positive*, *sometimes positive*, or *never positive*. (Lessons 2-4, 1-1)

31. $\frac{x}{y}$ 32. $x \cdot y$ 33. $x - y$ 34. $x + y$

35. To estimate the number of bricks N needed in a wall, some bricklayers use the formula $N = 7LH$, where L and H are the length and height of the wall in feet. If a wall is to be 8.25 feet high and 27.5 feet long, about how many bricks would a bricklayer need? (Lesson 1-1) about 1,588 bricks

36. The value of Birchmere stock went down 1.64 on March 30. On March 31 and April 1 it went up 0.88 of a point each day. Find the net change in Birchmere stock over this 3-day period. (Previous Course) up 0.12

EXPLORATION

37. Find single values for a, x, w, and z that make all five of these equations true. (*Hint*: a, x, w, and z are all different numbers.)

$$a^2 = a$$

$$xw = x$$

$$z \cdot z = z + z$$

$$x + w = w$$

$$\frac{z}{a} = z$$

37. Answers vary. Sample answer: $a = 1$, $x = 0$, $w = 3$, $z = 2$

31. never positive
32. never positive
33. always positive
34. sometimes positive

Nearly 1 in 3 bricklayers are self-employed.

Source: Bureau of Labor Statistics

QY ANSWERS

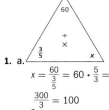

1. a.
$$x = \frac{60}{\frac{3}{5}} = 60 \cdot \frac{5}{3} =$$
$$\frac{300}{3} = 100$$

1. b. $\frac{3}{5}x = 60$ Multiply both sides by $\frac{1}{3}$, or $\frac{5}{3}$; the Multiplication Property of Equality tells us $\frac{5}{3} \cdot \frac{3}{5}x = \frac{5}{3} \cdot 60$, so $x = \frac{300}{3} = 100$.

2. Answers vary. Sample answers:
   a. $0 \cdot x = 17$
   b. $0 \cdot 3 \cdot x = 2 \cdot 0$

Chapter 2 Projects

1 Repeating Number Puzzle

An unusual number trick is performed as follows.

Your teacher asks Student A to jot down any three-digit number, and then to repeat the digits in the same order to make a six-digit number (for example, 546,546). The teacher asks Student A to pass the sheet of paper to Student B, who is requested to divide the number by 7.

"Don't worry about the remainder," your teacher claims, "because there won't be any." Student B is surprised to discover that your teacher is correct ($546{,}546 \div 7 = 78{,}078$). Without telling the teacher the result, Student B passes the paper on to Student C, who is told to divide the quotient by 11. Once again, your teacher states that there will be no remainder. This, in fact, is the case ($78{,}078 \div 11 = 7{,}098$).

With no knowledge of the answers obtained by these computations, your teacher directs a fourth Student D, to divide the last quotient by 13. Again, the quotient comes out even ($7{,}098 \div 13 = 546$). The final result is written on a slip of paper which is folded up.

Without opening it, the teacher passes the folded paper to Student A. The teacher says, "Open this and you will find your original three-digit number."

Prove that the trick works regardless of the digits chosen by the first student. Write out your explanation in several complete sentences. Include sufficient mathematical work to support your explanation. Make certain that you explain why the trick works in general (rather than showing it works for specific cases).

2 A New Operation

Addition and multiplication are both commutative and associative. Consider the operation # in which for all x and y, $x \mathbin{\#} y = xy + 2$. Some examples are shown below.

$$1 \mathbin{\#} 2 = 4 \quad 2 \mathbin{\#} 2 = 6 \quad 3 \mathbin{\#} 1 = 5 \quad 5 \mathbin{\#} 2 = 12$$

a. Is the operation # associative? Is it commutative?

b. Give an example of an operation that is *not* commutative.

c. Is there a number that is an identity for the operation #? In other words, is there a number n, so that $x \mathbin{\#} n$ always equals x?

Project Rubric

Advanced	Student correctly provides all of the details asked for in the project as well as additional correct independent conclusions.
Proficient	Student correctly provides all of the details asked for in the project.
Partially proficient	Student correctly provides some of the details asked for in the project or provides all details with some inaccuracies.
Not proficient	Student correctly provides few of the details asked for in the project or provides all details with many inaccuracies.
No attempt	Student makes little or no attempt to complete the project.

The projects relate to the content of the lessons of this chapter as follows:

Project	Lesson(s)
1	2-3
2	2-3
3	2-6
4	2-3
5	2-1

1 Repeating Number Puzzle

Verify that $7 \cdot 11 \cdot 13 = 1{,}001$. Consider the three-digit number abc. $abc(1{,}001) = abc(1{,}000 + 1) = abc{,}000 + abc = abc{,}abc$. Dividing $abc{,}abc$ in succession by 7, 11, and 13 results in the number abc. For example letting $a = 2$, $b = 5$, and $c = 8$ one gets $258(1{,}001) = 258(1{,}000 + 1) = 258{,}000 + 258 = 258{,}258$. Dividing $258{,}258$ in succession by 7, 11, and 13 results in 258.

2 A New Operation

It may be necessary to reinforce the concepts of additive and multiplicative identity as well as the commutative and associative properties. Students probably have not thought about whether all of the properties hold for every set of numbers. Yes, they know that $a - b$ is not the same as $b - a$, but have they thought about it in terms of a non-commutative set? Consider the set of integers, and re-explore the various properties with your students and find out if they hold within the set.

3 Pascal's Triangle

It might be helpful if students organize the data to be collected in a table. Have students build a table with 6 rows and 5 columns. Column headings could be titled Original Expression, Expanded Expression, Coefficients, Sum of Coefficients, and Number of Coefficients per Row. In the first column, under the heading Original Expression, place each of the following $(x + y)^2$, $(x + y)^3$, $(x + y)^4$, $(x + y)^5$, and $(x + y)^6$.

4 Magic Squares

Students may need to experiment with the idea of magic squares a little more because they only had a brief introduction to them in Lesson 2-3. Provide the students with the following two examples and discuss the reasons why these are magic squares.

2	3	1		$x + 1$	$x + 2$	x
1	2	3		x	$x + 1$	$x + 2$
3	1	2		$x + 2$	x	$x + 1$

If you have good posters from previous years, use them as models for students. Point out the things that make the poster good.

5 Postal Rates

Consider asking students to go online to pe.usps.gov/cpim/ftp/notices/Not123/Not123.pdf to download a document listing the current postal rates. Use the table for first class mail given in the document to support a discussion of how to find the postage for a letter weighing between 1 and 13 ounces.

3 Pascal's Triangle

Use a CAS to expand the expressions $(x + y)^2$, $(x + y)^3$, $(x + y)^4$, $(x + y)^5$, and $(x + y)^6$. For each expression, write down in a row the coefficients the CAS gives. For example: $(x + y)^2 = x^2 + 2xy + y^2 = 1 \cdot x^2 + 2 \cdot xy + 1 \cdot y^2$, so you should write **1 2 1**.

a. For each of the expressions above, compute the sum of all the coefficients in the row. For example, for $(x + y)^2$ you would calculate $1 + 2 + 1$, or 4. What seems to be the formula for this sum? Count the coefficients in each row. What seems to be the formula for this number?

b. There are many relationships among the coefficients you wrote down in Part a. For example, in every row there are repeating numbers. Describe the pattern behind these repetitions.

c. Another famous relationship explains how to use the coefficients in a row to figure out the row that comes after it. This relationship is named after the French mathematician Blaise Pascal (1623–1662). Can you figure out this relationship? Use it to predict the coefficients for $(x + y)^7$.

4 Magic Squares

In Lesson 2-3, you encountered magic squares. There are many methods you can use to construct your own magic squares. For example, the following is a magic square for any real numbers a, b, and c.

$a + c$	$a + b - c$	$a - b$
$a - b - c$	a	$a + b + c$
$a + b$	$a - b + c$	$a - c$

a. Choose three real numbers a, b, and c and check that the above method does give a magic square.

b. Explain algebraically why this method always gives a magic square.

c. Using the Internet or the library, find a method of constructing magic squares with more cells. Make a poster illustrating the method you found.

5 Postal Rates

In 2006, the cost to mail a first-class letter was $0.39 for the first ounce and $0.24 for each additional ounce up to 13 ounces. So people who mailed many letters would buy many $0.39 and $0.24 stamps. If you buy x $0.39 stamps and y $0.24 stamps, then the postage you have paid for is $0.39x + 0.24y$. For example, if you use one $0.39 stamp and three $0.24 stamps for a letter, you have paid a total of $1($0.39$) + 3($0.24$) = 1.11 for postage.

a. Which weights can be sent first class for less than $3 using these stamps?

b. What is the maximum weight you can send with these stamps without going over $10 for postage?

c. Explore the problem and find the postage beyond which it is *always* possible to use these stamps.

Notes

Chapter 2 Summary and Vocabulary

- With algebra, a wide variety of relationships among numbers can be explained. An important tool in these explanations is the **Distributive Property.** This property says that for all real numbers a, b, and c, $c(a + b) = ca + cb$. Moving from $c(a + b)$ to $ca + cb$ is called expanding the expression. Moving from $ca + cb$ to $c(a + b)$ is called factoring the expression $ca + cb$.

- In an equation, the expression on the left side is equivalent to the expression on the right. Algebraic properties provide a way of determining whether expressions are equivalent and, at the same time, explaining why they are equivalent. This makes the use of algebraic properties a more powerful method than using tables or graphs, which can suggest that expressions are equivalent but cannot prove them equivalent. Yet tables and graphs can be useful when algebraic methods are not available. Also, by using algebraic properties, you can create your own equivalent forms of algebraic expressions.

- Among the earliest properties you ever learned were the **related facts of addition and subtraction, and of multiplication and division.** The related facts properties and the other algebraic properties can also help explain why various number puzzles work. Algebra is a language that helps you better understand the world.

Vocabulary

2-2
like terms
coefficient
factoring

2-4
additive inverse
opposite

Theorems and Properties

Distributive Property of Multiplication over Addition (p. 66)
Distributive Property of Multiplication over Subtraction (p. 67)
Opposite of Opposites Property (p. 85)
Multiplication Property of –1 (p. 86)
Opposite of a Sum Property (p. 86)
Opposite of a Difference Property (p. 87)
Addition Property of Equality (p. 106)
Subtraction Property of Equality (p. 106)
Related Facts Property of Addition and Subtraction (p. 107)

Additive Identity Property (p. 108)
Additive Inverse Property (p. 109)
Multiplication Property of Equality (p. 113)
Division Property of Equality (p. 113)
Related Facts Property of Multiplication and Division (p. 114)
Multiplication Property of Zero (p. 115)
Zero Product Property (p. 115)
Multiplicative Identity Property (p. 116)
Multiplicative Inverse Property (p. 116)

Chapter 2

Summary and Vocabulary

The Summary gives an overview of the entire chapter and provides an opportunity for students to consider the material as a whole. Thus, the Summary can be used to help students relate and unify the concepts presented in the chapter.

Terms and symbols are listed by lesson to provide a checklist of concepts that students must know. Emphasize to students that they should read the vocabulary list carefully before starting the Self-Test on the next page. If students do not understand the meaning of a term, they should refer back to the indicated lesson.

Theorems and Properties covered in the chapter are listed below the Summary, with page references included to lead students back to the location in the chapter where the theorem or property is stated.

Self-Test

For the development of mathematical competence, feedback and correction, along with the opportunity for practice, are necessary. The Self-Test provides the opportunity for feedback and correction; the Chapter Review provides additional opportunities for practice. We cannot overemphasize the importance of these end-of-chapter materials. It is at this point that the material "gels" for many students, allowing them to solidify skills and understanding. In general, student performance should improve after these pages.

Assign the Self-Test as a one-night assignment. Worked-out solutions for all questions are in the Selected Answers section of the student book. Encourage students to take the Self-Test honestly, grade themselves, and then be prepared to discuss the test in class.

Advise students to pay special attention to those Chapter Review questions (pages 125–127) that correspond to the questions they missed on the Self-Test.

Additional Answers

1. $3w$

2. $\frac{6}{7}(4v + 78) = \frac{24v + 468}{7}$

3. $-5h - 8$

4. $3k + 30 - 11 - (-4k) = 7k + 19$

5. $-r$

6. $\frac{7x + 7}{6}$

7. $\frac{2 - 3}{3x} = -\frac{1}{3x}$

9. $L \cdot W$ of the entire rectangle
   $= x(x + 3 + 2)$; the sum of the areas
   of both rectangles $= 2x + x(x + 3)$.

13.

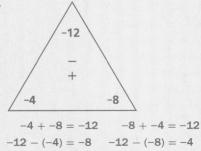

$-4 + -8 = -12 \qquad -8 + -4 = -12$
$-12 - (-4) = -8 \qquad -12 - (-8) = -4$

18. False; A negative number to an odd power
   is negative. $(-2)^5 = -32$ and $2^5 = 32$

Chapter **2** Self-Test

Take this test as you would take a test in class. You will need a calculator. Then use the Selected Answers section in the back of the book to check your work.

In 1–7, simplify the expression. 1–7. See margin.

1. $5w - 2w$

2. $\frac{6}{7}(3v + 78 + v)$

3. $-7h + 2(h - 4)$

4. $3(k + 10) - (11 - 4k)$

5. $-(-(-(r)))$

6. $\frac{5x + 7}{6} + \frac{2x}{6}$

7. $\frac{2}{3x} - \frac{1}{x}$

8. $7(20 - 0.02) =$
   $140 - 0.14 = \$139.86$

8. Carlos bought seven shirts at $19.98 each. Show how Carlos could use the Distributive Property to calculate the total cost of the shirts in his head.

9. Write two expressions to describe the total area of the figure below. See margin.

10. **Fill in the Blank** If $2 \cdot n = 4$, then $2 \cdot n \cdot 6 = \underline{\ ?\ }$. 24

11. Write the related facts for $C = \pi \cdot d$, where C is the circumference of a circle and d is its diameter. $C = d \cdot \pi$, $d = \frac{C}{\pi}$, $\pi = \frac{C}{d}$

12. If you know the circumference of a circle and want to find the diameter, which of the related facts from Question 11 should you use? $d = \frac{C}{\pi}$

13. Make a fact triangle for $-12 = -4 + -8$, and write the related facts.

In 14 and 15, find the opposite of the expression.

14. $-3p$ $3p$

15. $b + 2$ $-b - 2$

In 16 and 17, find the reciprocal of the expression.

16. -2.5 $\frac{1}{-2.50} = -\frac{2}{5}$

17. $\frac{4}{11d}$ $\frac{1}{\frac{4}{11d}} = \frac{11d}{4}$

18. **True or False** Is $(-2)^5 = 2^5$? Justify your response in one or two sentences. See margin.

---

19. Let n be any real number. Use algebra to show how the number puzzle below works.
   Step 1 Pick a number. n
   Step 2 Multiply by 10. $10n$
   Step 3 Add 30. $10n + 30$
   Step 4 Divide by 5. $2n + 6$
   Step 5 Subtract your original number. $n + 6$
   Step 6 Add 1. $n + 7$
   Step 7 Subtract 7. n
   You have your original number.

20. Use a graphing calculator to determine whether $w + (2w - 1) + 3(w + 6)$ and $6w - 5$ seem to be equivalent.

21. Use properties of operations to determine whether $w + (2w - 1) + 3(w + 6)$ and $6w - 5$ are equivalent. See margin.

22. Four siblings worked on a project. Darryl worked the shortest amount of time. Carol worked twice as long as Darryl. Beryl worked three times as long as Darryl, and Errol worked four times as long as Darryl. They decided to split up the $1,500 they earned from the project based on the amount of time each of them worked. How much did each sibling get? See margin.

23. Make a table to show that $2x + 1$ and $|-2x - 1|$ are not equivalent expressions. See margin.

13. $-12 = -8 + -4$, $-12 - (-4) = -8$,
   $-12 - (-8) = -4$; See margin for fact triangle.

20. No, they do not seem to be equivalent.

---

21. They are not equivalent. $w + (2w - 1)$
   $+ 3(w + 6) = 3w - 1 + 3w + 18 = 6w$
   $+ 17 \neq 6w - 5$

22. Let t be the amount of time Darryl worked.
   Then, Carol worked $2t$, Beryl worked $3t$, Errol
   worked $4t$. We solve $t + 2t + 3t + 4t =$
   1500. So, $t = 150$ dollars. Darryl got $150,
   Carol got $300, Beryl got $450, and Errol
   got $600.

23. Answers vary. Sample answer:

x	$2x + 1$	$|-2x + 1|$
-2	-3	3
-1	-1	1
0	1	1
1	3	3
2	5	5

Chapter 2 Chapter Review

SKILLS
PROPERTIES
USES
REPRESENTATIONS

SKILLS Procedures used to get answers

OBJECTIVE A Use the Distributive Property to expand and combine like terms. (Lessons 2-1, 2-2)

In 1–12, simplify the expression by distributing and/or combining like terms. 1–12. See margin.

1. $3(x + 4)$
2. $(2a - 1.3)10$
3. $5(3x + 7) - 11(x + 6)$
4. $\frac{2}{5}(10 + -15w + 4w)$
5. $4(y - 13) + 6(3y - 3y)$
6. $1.5x + -4x + 17x$
7. $7x + -2x + 13x$
8. $-6m + 5m + -m$
9. $\frac{3x}{4} - \frac{3}{8} + 2x$
10. $\frac{2x}{5} + \frac{4z}{5} - \frac{2x}{5}$
11. $\frac{n+1}{3} + \frac{5}{3}$
12. $\frac{3}{2x} + \frac{1}{x}$

OBJECTIVE B Use the Opposite of Opposites Property, the Opposite of a Sum, and the Opposite of a Difference Property to simplify expressions. (Lesson 2-4)

In 13–20, remove the parentheses and then combine like terms, if possible. 13–20. See margin.

13. $-(7a + 4)$
14. $-(3h - 7g + 8)$
15. $1 - (1 - z)$
16. $7x - (4x - 8)$
17. $1\frac{1}{2} - (\frac{3}{4} - y)$
18. $3(b - 2) - 5(3 + 2e)$
19. $(-2)^3$
20. $(-x)^4$

21. Evaluate each expression.
    a. $(-3)^4$ 81
    b. -3^4 -81
    c. $(-3)^5$ -243
    d. -3^5 -243

In 22–24, determine whether the expression is positive or negative. How do you know?

22. $-3(7.4)(-237)(-2)$
23. $(-1,135)4$
24. $x \cdot -x$ 22–24. See margin.

OBJECTIVE C Use related facts to solve sentences. (Lessons 2-7, 2-8)

In 25–27, identify all the real numbers that complete the sentence. 25. There are no solutions.

25. $0n = 3$
26. $-2 + k = 0$
27. $0g = 0$ 26. $k = 2$ 27. all real numbers

In 28–31, find the related facts for the sentence.

28. $d = cg$
29. $\frac{1}{2} = \frac{1}{6} + \frac{1}{3}$
30. $a + b = 5$
31. $317.23 = 1 \cdot 317.23$
28–31. See margin.

In 32–34, use related facts to find the value of the variable.

32. $2.6 = 13 + a$ $a = -10.4$
33. $56 = x \cdot 0.8$ $x = 70$
34. $0 = 1853.42b$ $b = 0$

PROPERTIES The principles behind the mathematics

OBJECTIVE D Apply and recognize the following multiplication properties: Multiplicative Identity Property, Multiplicative Inverse Property, Multiplication Property of Zero, Multiplication Property of Equality, and the Zero Product Property. (Lessons 2-4, 2-8) 36. $\frac{1}{0.513} \approx 1.949$

In 35–37, write the reciprocal of the number.

35. -5 $-\frac{1}{5}$
36. 0.513
37. $\frac{1}{8x}$ $8x$

38. Write the following statement in symbols: *The product of a number and its reciprocal is the multiplicative identity.* $a \cdot \frac{1}{a} = 1$

39. Of what property is this an example? If $w = x$, then $w - 1.7 = x - 1.7$. Subtraction Property of Equality

Chapter Review

The main objectives for the chapter are organized in the Chapter Review under the four types of understanding this book promotes—Skills, Properties, Uses, and Representations.

Whereas end-of-chapter material may be considered optional in some texts, in *UCSMP Algebra* we have selected these objectives and questions with the expectation that they will be covered. Students should be able to answer these questions with about 85% accuracy after studying the chapter.

You may assign these questions over a single night to help students prepare for a test the next day, or you may assign the questions over a two-day period. If you work the questions over two days, then we recommend assigning the *evens* for homework the first night so that students get feedback in class the next day, and then assigning the *odds* the night before the test because the answers are provided to the odd-numbered questions in the Selected Answers at the back of the book.

It is effective to ask students which questions they still do not understand and use the day as a total class discussion of the material that the class finds most difficult.

Resources
• Assessment Resources Chapter 2 Test, Forms A–D; Chapter 2 Test, Cumulative Form

Additional Answers

1. $3x + 12$
2. $20a - 13$
3. $4x - 31$
4. $4 - \frac{22}{5}w$
5. $4y - 52$
6. $14.5x$
7. $18x$
8. $-2m$
9. $\frac{22x - 3}{8}$
10. $\frac{4z}{5}$
11. $\frac{n}{3} + 2$
12. $\frac{5}{2x}$
13. $-7a - 4$
14. $-3h + 7g - 8$
15. z
16. $3x + 8$
17. $\frac{3}{4} + y$
18. $3b - 10e - 21$
19. -8
20. x^4
22. negative; Of the four factors three are negative, yielding a negative product.
23. negative; Of the two factors one is negative, yielding a negative product.
24. negative, unless $x = 0$; Of the two factors one is negative, yielding a negative product.

28. $d = gc, c = \frac{d}{g}$, and $g = \frac{d}{c}$
29. $\frac{1}{2} = \frac{1}{3} + \frac{1}{6}, \frac{1}{6} = \frac{1}{2} - \frac{1}{3}$, and $\frac{1}{3} = \frac{1}{2} - \frac{1}{6}$
30. $b + a = 5, a = 5 - b$, and $b = 5 - a$
31. $317.23 = 317.23 \cdot 1, \frac{317.23}{1} = 317.23$, and $1 = \frac{317.23}{317.23}$

Chapter **2** Review

Additional Answers

52. First, find 7 times 6. Then, subtract 7 times 0.05 to get $41.65.

53. First, find 36 times 100. Then, add 36 times 3 to get 3,708.

54. First, find 4 times 60. Then, subtract 4 times 1 to get 236.

55. $3.50(10 + 1) = $3.50(10) + $3.50(1) = $38.50

---

40. **Fill in the Blank** Multiplication by –1 changes a number to its ___?___.
    opposite or additive inverse

In 41–43, evaluate the expression $(x + 5)(x + 4)$ $(x + 3)$ for the given value of x.

41. $x = -3$ 0   42. $x = 3$ 336   43. $x = -2$ 6

OBJECTIVE E Apply and recognize the following properties: Additive Identity Property, Additive Inverse Property, and Addition Property of Equality. (Lesson 2-7)

44. *a* and *b* are opposites (or additive inverses).
44. If $a + b = 0$, how are a and b related?

45. If $a + b = a$, what is the value of b? 0

46. **Fill in the Blank** Let $r = t$. Then $r + 2.576 = t +$ ___?___. 2.576

In 47–49, write the additive inverse of the number.

47. -7.536 7.536 **48.** 0 0   **49.** $-(-x)$ $-x$

50. Write the following statement in symbols: *If two numbers are additive inverses, their sum is the additive identity.* $u + (-u) = 0$

OBJECTIVE F Use and apply the Distributive Property to perform calculations in your head. (Lesson 2-1)

51. In the sentence $2(r + w) = 2r + 2w$, what property has been applied?

In 52–55, explain how the Distributive Property can be used to do the calculations in your head.

52. $7 \cdot 5.95

53. $103 \cdot 36$

54. $4 \cdot 59$ 52–55. See margin.

55. the cost of 11 shirts if each one costs $3.50
51. Distributive Property of Multiplication over Addition

USES Applications of mathematics in real-world situations

OBJECTIVE G Use algebra to explain how number puzzles work. (Lesson 2-3)

In 56–58, let n be the number used to solve the number puzzle. Use algebra to explain the result.

56. **Step 1** Pick a number. n
    Step 2 Subtract 5. $n - 5$
    Step 3 Multiply by 4. $4n - 20$
    Step 4 Add 4. $4n - 16$
    Step 5 Divide by 2. $2n - 8$
    Step 6 Add 10. $2n + 2$
    Step 7 Subtract twice your original number. You will always end up with 2. 2

57. **Step 1** Pick a number. n
    Step 2 Multiply by 4. $4n$
    Step 3 Add 10. $4n + 10$
    Step 4 Add 2 more than your original number. $4n + 12$
    Step 5 Divide by 4. $n + 3$
    Step 6 Subtract 3. n
    You will always end up with your original number.

58. **Step 1** Pick a number. n
    Step 2 Add 11. $n + 11$
    Step 3 Multiply by 6. $6n + 66$
    Step 4 Subtract 12. $6n + 54$
    Step 5 Divide by 2. $3n + 27$
    Step 6 Subtract 30. $3n - 3$
    Step 7 Add 3. $3n$
    You will always end up with 3 times your original number.

OBJECTIVE H Apply the Distributive Property in real-world situations.
(Lessons 2-1, 2-2)

59. A $150,000 estate is to be split among 4 children, 2 grandchildren, and a charity. Each child gets the same amount, while the grandchildren get half as much. If the charity receives $5,000, how much will each child receive? **$29,000**

60. Two next-door neighbors' yards are pictured below. Find the total area of both yards.
$173(65 + 73) = 173 \cdot 138 = 23,874 \text{ ft}^2$

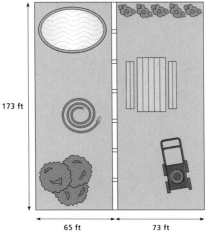

173 ft

65 ft   73 ft

61. Suppose a taxicab driver is allowed to keep $\frac{2}{5}$ of all fares collected. The remaining fares go to the company. If a driver makes F dollars in fares, what is the driver's share? $\frac{2F}{5}$

REPRESENTATIONS Pictures, graphs, or objects that illustrate concepts

OBJECTIVE I Use a spreadsheet or table to test the equivalence of expressions.
(Lesson 2-5)

62. Make a table of values to show that $3(2x + 4)$ and $6x + x + 12 - x$ are equivalent expressions. **See margin.**

63. Make a table of values to show that x^2 and $2x$ are not equivalent expressions. Circle a counterexample in the table. **Answers vary. Sample answer: For $x = 1$, $x^2 = 1$ but $2x = 2$.**

64. A table of values generated by two expressions is shown below. Do the expressions seem to be equivalent? Why or why not?

Expression 1		Expression 2	
x	y	x	y
−5	−4	−5	4
−4	−2	−4	2
−3	0	−3	0
−2	2	−2	2
−1	4	−1	4

They are not equivalent. The values for −5 and −4 are different for each expression.

OBJECTIVE J Use technology to test for equivalence of expressions.
(Lessons 2-5, 2-6)

In 65–67, use a CAS or a graphing calculator to determine whether the expressions are equivalent. **65–67. See margin.**

65. $n - (1 - (2 - (3 - n)))$ and $2n + 2$

66. $x^2 - 4x + 4$ and $(x - 2)(x - 2)$

67. $(x + 1)(x)(x - 1)$ and x^3

68. Suppose two different students use the formulas $A = \pi r^2$ and $A = \frac{\pi d^2}{4}$ to find the area of a circle. Remember, the diameter d of a circle is twice as long as the radius r. Use a graphing calculator or CAS to determine if the two formulas are equivalent. **They are equivalent.**

Assessment

Evaluation The *Assessment Resources* provide five forms of the Chapter 2 Test. Forms A and B present parallel versions of a short-answer format. Form C consists of four to six short-response questions that cover the SPUR objectives from Chapter 2. Form D offers performance assessment that covers a subset (or even just one) of the SPUR objectives for the chapter. The fifth type of test is a Chapter 2 Test, Cumulative Form. About 50% of this test covers Chapter 2, and the remaining 50% covers the previous chapter.

Feedback After students have taken the test for Chapter 2 and you have scored the results, return the tests to students for discussion. Class discussion on the questions that caused trouble for most students can be very effective in identifying and clarifying misunderstandings. You might want to have them note the items they missed and work either in groups or at home to correct them. It is important for students to receive feedback on every chapter test, and we recommend that students see and correct their mistakes before proceeding too far into the next chapter.

Additional Answers

62. Answers vary. Sample answer:

x	3(2x + 4)	6x + x + 12 − x
−3	−6	−6
0	12	12
1	18	18
5	42	42

65. They are not equivalent.

66. They are equivalent.

67. They are not equivalent.

3 Linear Equations and Inequalities

Chapter Overview	Local Standards	Pacing *(in days)*		
		Average	Advanced	Block
3-1 Graphing Linear Patterns **E** Solve problems involving equations of the form $y = ax + b$ using tables or graphs.		1	1	0.5
3-2 Solving Equations with Tables and Graphs **D** Use linear equations and inequalities of the form $ax + b = c$ or $ax + b < c$ to solve real-world problems. **E** Solve problems involving equations of the form $y = ax + b$ using tables or graphs.		1	0.5	0.5
3-3 Solving Equations by Creating Equivalent Equations **C** Apply the Addition and Multiplication Properties of Equality and Inequality.		1	0.5	0.75
QUIZ 1		0.5	0.5	0.25
3-4 Solving $ax + b = c$ **A** Solve and check linear equations of the form $ax + b = c$. **D** Use linear equations and inequalities of the form $ax + b = c$ or $ax + b < c$ to solve real-world problems.		1	0.5	0.5
3-5 Using the Distributive Property in Solving Equations **A** Solve and check linear equations of the form $ax + b = c$. **D** Use linear equations and inequalities of the form $ax + b = c$ or $ax + b < c$ to solve real-world problems.		1	1	0.5
3-6 Inequalities and Multiplication **C** Apply the Addition and Multiplication Properties of Equality and Inequality. **F** Graph all the solutions to a linear inequality.		1	1	0.75
QUIZ 2		0.5	0.5	0.25
3-7 Solving $ax + b < c$ **B** Solve and check linear inequalities of the form $ax + b < c$. **D** Use linear equations and inequalities of the form $ax + b = c$ or $ax + b < c$ to solve real-world problems. **F** Graph all the solutions to a linear inequality.		1	0.5	0.5
3-8 Solving Equations by Clearing Fractions **B** Solve and check linear inequalities of the form $ax + b < c$. **C** Apply the Addition and Multiplication Properties of Equality and Inequality. **D** Use linear equations and inequalities of the form $ax + b = c$ or $ax + b < c$ to solve real-world problems.		1	1	0.5
Self-Test		1	1	0.5
Chapter Review		2	2	1
Test		1	1	0.5
TOTAL		**13**	**11**	**7**

Differentiated Options Universal Access

	Accommodating the Learner	Vocabulary Development	Ongoing Assessment	Materials
3-1	pp. 131, 132		group, p. 134	scientific or graphing calculator, graph paper, motion detector
3-2			group, p. 138	graphing calculator, graph paper
3-3	pp. 140, 141	p. 141	written, p. 143	scientific or graphing calculator, Computer Algebra System (CAS)
3-4	pp. 145, 146		written, p. 148	graphing calculator
3-5	pp. 150, 151		group, p. 154	graphing calculator, graph paper
3-6	pp. 157, 159	p. 158	written, p. 161	scientific or graphing calculator, graph paper, Computer Algebra System (CAS)
3-7	pp. 163, 164		written, p. 166	scientific or graphing calculator
3-8	pp. 168, 170		written, p. 173	scientific or graphing calculator, Computer Algebra System (CAS)

Objectives

		Lessons	Self-Test Questions	Chapter Review Questions
Skills				
A	Solve and check linear equations of the form $ax + b = c$.	3-4, 3-5	1–3	1–12
B	Solve and check linear inequalities of the form $ax + b < c$.	3-7, 3-8	4–6, 14	13–16
Properties				
C	Apply the Addition and Multiplication Properties of Equality and Inequality.	3-3, 3-6, 3-8	8, 10, 15	17–22
Uses				
D	Use linear equations and inequalities of the form $ax + b = c$ or $ax + b < c$ to solve real-world problems.	3-2, 3-4, 3-5, 3-7, 3-8	9, 16, 17	23–28
Representations				
E	Solve problems involving equations of the form $y = ax + b$ using tables or graphs.	3-1, 3-2	11–13	29–31
F	Graph all the solutions to a linear inequality.	3-6, 3-7	7	32–35

Resource Masters Chapter 3

Resource Master 1, Graph Paper (page 2), can be used with Lessons 3-1, 3-2, 3-5, and 3-6. **Resource Master 2, Four-Quadrant Graph Paper** (page 3) can be used with Lessons 3-1, 3-2, 3-5, and 3-6. **Resource Master 4, Graphing Equations** (page 5) can be used with Lesson 3-1. **Resource Master 7, Number Lines** (page 8) can be used with Lessons 3-7 and 3-8.

Resource Master 35 Lesson 3-1

Warm-Up

Tell whether the table describes a constant-increase situation, a constant-decrease situation, or neither.

1.

x	y
1	2
3	5
6	8
10	11
15	14

2.

x	y
100	100
200	87
300	74
400	61
500	48

Additional Examples

1. Sharon bought a new home with a 5-foot deep pool in the backyard. The pool had 1 foot of water standing in it. When she began filling the pool, Sharon noticed that the water level of the pool rose 4 inches every hour. Let x equal the number of hours since she began filling the pool and y equal the depth of the water in the pool (in inches). We can model this situation with the equation $y = 4x + 12$. Graph this relationship.

2. In Problem 1, if the water level continues to rise at the same rate, how many hours will it take for the pool to reach a depth of 5 feet?

Resource Master for Lesson 3-1

Resource Master 36 Lesson 3-1

Question 1

Time x (hr)	Height y (in.)
0	18
1	
2	
3	
4	

Question 2

Suppose Miguel begins with $500 in an account and adds $20 per week.
a. Complete the table.
b. Graph the ordered pairs (w, t).
c. Write an equation that represents t in terms of w.
d. What is the domain of w?

Weeks (w)	Total (t)
0	
1	
2	
3	
4	

Resource Master for Lesson 3-1

Resource Master 37 Lesson 3-2

Warm-Up

Graph the equation $y = (x - 1)^2 - 2$ on the window $-5 \le x \le 5$, $-10 \le y \le 10$. Use the graph to answer these questions.
1. What is the smallest value of y that the trace key obtains?
2. What are the values of x where the value of y on the trace key is closest to zero?
3. Zoom in on the points in Problems 1 and 2 to obtain better estimates.

Additional Examples

1. Solve $10 = 3x + 4$ using a table.

2. Solve $-1 = 2x + 5$ using a graph.

3. Susie lives in a state where there is no sales tax. She bought 5 fountain drinks with a $10 bill and received $0.55 change. What was the price of one drink?

Question 25

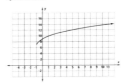

Resource Master for Lesson 3-2

Resource Master 38 Lesson 3-3

Warm-Up

Consider the equation $8x - 12 = 4$. What equation results from each action?

1. adding -12 to both sides
2. adding -8 to both sides
3. adding -4 to both sides
4. multiplying both sides by -8
5. multiplying both sides by $\frac{1}{8}$
6. adding 12 to both sides

Solving a Linear Equation Using a CAS

Step 1 Enter your equation into your CAS.

Step 2 Decide which operation to perform on each side. For example, to add 9 to both sides enter ⊞ 9.

Step 3 Do you get an equation that is simpler than the previous one? If the answer is "yes," continue until the equation is solved. If the answer is "no," re-enter the equation and try a different operation.

Step 4 You are finished solving the equation when the equation has the form *variable = number.*

Resource Master for Lesson 3-3

Resource Master 39 Lesson 3-4

Warm-Up

Bill wants to determine the weight of one of 7 identical packages. He has a balance with a 10-kilogram weight and many 500-gram weights. When he puts 5 of the packages on the scale and three of the 500-gram weights, it balances the 10-kilogram weight. What does each package weigh?

Additional Examples

1. Solve $-\frac{2}{9}x - 1 = 3$.

$$-\frac{2}{9}x - 1 + \underline{\quad} = 3 + \underline{\quad}$$
$$\underline{\quad} x = \underline{\quad}$$
$$-\left(\frac{2}{9}x\right) = \left(\frac{9}{2}\right)4$$
$$x = \underline{\quad}$$

2. When Sam works at a local college on Saturdays, he earns $8.20 per hour. He is also paid $5.00 for meals and $4.00 for transportation. Last Saturday, he received $68.45. How many hours did he work?

3. The area of the rectangle is 78 cm². What is the value of n?

Resource Master for Lesson 3-4

Resource Master 40 Lesson 3-5

Warm-Up

Solve each equation.

1. $5A = 40$
2. $-2B + 7B = 11$
3. $50C - 18C + 5 = -27$
4. $2(3D + 6) - D = 15$
5. $2(4 - E) - 3(5 - 2E) = 251$

Additional Examples

1. A $350,000 estate is to be split among four children, six grandchildren, and a charity. Each child gets the same amount while each grandchild gets half that amount. If the charity receives $35,000, how much will each child receive?

2. Solve $12y - y = 77$.

3. Solve $5(x + 2) = -35$.

4. A company charges $99.95 per weekend to rent a truck, with the first 100 miles free. After that the cost is $0.65 per mile. Therefore, if the truck is driven m miles (where $m \ge 100$), the total rental cost is $99.95 + 0.65(m - 100)$ dollars. Julie rented a truck for one weekend and paid $277.40. How many miles did Julie drive?

5. Solve $3(4m + 3) - (14m - 11) = 8$.

Resource Master for Lesson 3-5

Resource Master 41 — Lesson 3-6

Warm-Up
Place the appropriate <, =, or > sign between the numbers or expressions.

1. -50 _____ 36
2. 7 · -50 _____ 7 · 36
3. 0 · 50 _____ 0 · 36
4. -2 · -50 _____ 2 · 36

Suppose n is a negative number and p is a positive number. Place the appropriate <, =, or > sign between the expressions.

5. p _____ n
6. np _____ $n \cdot n$

Additional Examples
1. Solve $-5x \leq 35$ and check.

2. a. Solve $42 \geq 3x$.
   b. Graph the solution.
   c. Check your answer.

Resource Master for Lesson 3-6

Resource Master 42 — Lesson 3-6

Graphs and Inequalities on a Number Line

Exactly One Solution

$x = 3$

Infinitely Many Solutions

$x > 3$

$x \geq 3$

Double Inequality

-86   6,194

The Multiplication Property of Inequality
If $x < y$ and a is *positive*, then $ax < y$.

If $x < y$ and a is *negative*, then $ax > y$.

Resource Master for Lesson 3-6

Resource Master 43 — Lesson 3-7

Warm-Up
1. Find a positive number that is a solution to $31A + 5 < 6$.
2. Find a negative number that is a solution to both $-3x > 12$ and $-4x < 17$.

Additional Examples
1. An educational supply company does not charge for shipping orders of $450 or more. Mrs. Jenkins needs a microscope that costs $149.99 and she needs at least one-hundred twenty sets of micropipette ends, which are disposable and are a reoccurring expense for her Biology classes. Although she needs at least one-hundred twenty sets, she can use more. Micropipette end sets cost $1.98 each. If Mrs. Jenkins wants to avoid shipping charges, how many micropipette end sets should she buy?

2. Before the city pool closed for summer, the water level was 8 feet. The city maintenance man began emptying the pool. He noticed that the depth of the pool decreased 0.75 foot each hour. How many hours will it take to for the depth of the pool to be 0.5 foot or less?

Question 14

Resource Master for Lesson 3-7

Resource Master 44 — Lesson 3-8

Warm-Up
Give the least common multiple of the following numbers.

1. 2 and 5
2. 12 and 15
3. 4 and 6
4. 10 and 100
5. 6, 36, and 4

Additional Examples
1. Write an equation to describe the situation and solve it by clearing the fractions. The Smith family budget allows them to spend $\frac{1}{12}$ of the family income on recreation and give $\frac{1}{10}$ of the family's income to charities. The Smiths spent $13,200 in 2005 on recreation and charities together. What was the family's total income for 2005?

2. Solve $\frac{x}{7} - 2 > \frac{1}{2}$.

3. Solve $1.12n - 4 = 7.2$.

Activity 1

Multiplier	Resulting Equation	Fractions Cleared
2	$\frac{5(t - 420)}{3} = 540$	No
3	$\frac{5(t - 420)}{2} = 810$	No
6	$5(t - 420) = 1,620$	Yes

Resource Master for Lesson 3-8

Linear Equations and Inequalities

Pacing

Each lesson in this chapter is designed to be covered in one day. At the end of the chapter, you should plan to spend 1 day to review the Self-Test, 1 to 2 days for the Chapter Review, and 1 day for a test. You may wish to spend a day on projects and possibly a day is needed for quizzes. This chapter should therefore take 11 to 14 days. We strongly advise you not to spend more than 15 days on this chapter.

Using Pages 128–129

The opener describes the three most common ways of describing a numerical relationship among two quantities: with an equation, with a table, and with a graph. The equation is the *algebraic* description. The table is the *arithmetic* description, while the graph is the *geometric* description. It shows a relationship in a way that may not be obvious from the table.

Chapter 3 Projects

At the end of each chapter, you will find projects related to the chapter. At this time you might want to have students look over the projects on pages 174 and 175. You might want to have students tentatively select a project on which to work. Then, as students read and progress through the chapter, they can finalize their project choices.

Sometimes students might work alone; at other times, you might let them collaborate with classmates for a presentation and discussion. We recommend that you allow for diversity, and encourage students to use their imaginations when presenting their projects. As students work on projects throughout the year, they should see the many uses of mathematics in the real world.

▷ **Contents**

Stephen collects coins. He begins with 25 coins and each week is sent 10 new coins in the mail. After w weeks he will have $25 + 10w$ coins. Let t stand for the total number of coins he has at the end of w weeks. The size of Stephen's collection over these weeks can be described in a number of ways. Three of them are shown here.

Equation	Table		Graph

Equation

$$t = 25 + 10w$$

Table

w	t
0	25
1	35
2	45
3	55
4	65
⋮	⋮

Graph

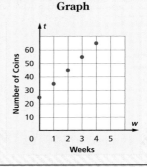

Chapter 3 Overview

This chapter and the next might be titled "Using Algebra to Solve." Both chapters are concerned with what many people believe to be the most important skill in elementary algebra, solving linear sentences. In this chapter, the equations and inequalities are those with the unknown variable on only one side. In Chapter 4, the unknown variables are on both sides.

The approach taken is multifaceted, not only in keeping with the diverse nature of the subject, but also the differing strengths of the students. Lessons 3-1 and 3-2 deal with solving linear equations using tables and graphs. These methods do not always lead to exact solutions and motivate the need for the more general algebraic methods found in Lessons 3-3 and 3-4.

continued on next page

The table lists the ordered pairs (0, 25), (1, 35), (2, 45), (3, 55), and (4, 65). All these pairs make the equation $t = 25 + 10w$ true. The equation $t = 25 + 10w$ is called a *linear equation* because all the points of its graph lie on the same line. For the same reason, $25 + 10w$ is called a *linear expression*.

Linear equations are the backbone of relationships among variables. In Chapter 1 you connected points to make graphs of algebraic expressions. In this chapter and the next, you will see more of their many applications.

129

These methods, based on the Addition and Multiplication Properties of Equality, are extended to inequalities in Lessons 3-6 and 3-7. Lesson 3-8 deals with more complex situations, but still involves the same general principles.

In the past, students in a first-year algebra course were not expected to have studied solving linear equations in earlier courses. Now it is not at all unusual for students to have spent some time in a preceding course examining the ideas of this chapter. Still, it is likely that the solving of linear inequalities and some of the theory will be new to students.

Lesson 3-1

GOAL

Generate a table of values from a linear equation and graph a line. Write an equation to describe a simple linear pattern. Answer questions about a situation from the graph, table, or equation.

SPUR Objective

E Solve problems involving equations of the form $y = ax + b$ using tables or graphs.

Materials/Resources

· Lesson Master 3-1A or 3-1B
· Resource Masters 1, 2, 4, 35, and 36
· Scientific or graphing calculator
· Graph paper
· Motion detector

HOMEWORK

Suggestions for Assignment
• Questions 1–20
• Question 21 (extra credit)
• Reading Lesson 3-2
• Covering the Ideas 3-2

Local Standards

1 Warm-Up

You might write or project the following so that students can do these questions as they enter the classroom.

Tell whether the table describes a constant-increase situation, a constant-decrease situation, or neither.

1.	x	y	2.	x	y
	1	2		100	100
	3	5		200	87
	6	8		300	74
	10	11		400	61
	15	14		500	48

1. Neither. It looks as if y is increasing at a constant amount, but x is not.
2. Constant decrease; y decreases 13 for every increase of 100 in x.

Lesson 3-1 Graphing Linear Patterns

Vocabulary

constant-increase situation
collinear
constant-decrease situation

▶ **BIG IDEA** Constant-increase and constant-decrease situations lead to linear graphs and are represented by linear equations.

Constant-Increase Patterns

The size of Stephen's coin collection described on pages 128 and 129 increases by 10 coins each week. It provides an example of a **constant-increase situation** because his collection grows by the same amount each week. The graph of every constant-increase situation consists of points that lie on the same line. We call these points **collinear.**

But notice that the graph does not include every point on the line. Because Stephen receives coins at specific whole-number intervals, the domain of w is the set of whole numbers. It does not make sense to connect the points on the graph because numbers such as $2\frac{1}{2}$ are not in the domain of w.

Constant-Decrease Patterns

A **constant-decrease situation** involves a quantity that decreases at a constant rate. In Example 1 below, the variable can be any positive real number between two whole numbers. The graph is no longer a set of separate or *discrete* points; it is connected or *continuous.*

Mental Math

Simplify.
a. $\frac{m}{x} + \frac{n}{x}$ $\frac{m+n}{x}$
b. $\frac{m}{x} - \frac{n}{kx}$ $\frac{km-n}{kx}$
c. $\frac{5}{x} + \frac{3}{kx}$ $\frac{5k+3}{kx}$

Example 1

After a flash flood, the level of water in a river was 54 inches above normal and dropping at a rate of 1.5 inches per hour. Let x equal the number of hours since the water started dropping and y equal the height, in feet, above normal of the lake. We can model this situation with the equation $y = 54 - 1.5x$. Graph this relationship.

Solution Find the lake level at various times and make a table. A table for 0, 1, 2, 3, and 4 hours is shown on the next page.

Flash floods result from a large amount of rain within a short amount of time and usually occur within 6 hours of a storm.

Background

Constant increase. Students will be familiar with the idea of models for operations, such as "putting together" for addition and "area" and "rate" for multiplication. Constant increase is a model for a linear function. If a situation has a constant increase in the dependent variable for a fixed increase in the independent variable, then the function is linear.

Constant decrease. A constant decrease situation can be viewed as a constant increase situation in which the increase in each interval is negative. A constant situation can also be viewed as a constant increase situation in which the increase in each interval is 0.

Time *x* (hr)	Height *y* (in.)	Ordered Pair (*x, y*)
0	54 − 1.5 • 0 = 54	(0, 54)
1	54 − 1.5 • 1 = 52.5	(1, 52.5)
2	54 − 1.5 • 2 = 51	(2, 51)
3	54 − 1.5 • 3 = 49.5	(3, 49.5)
4	54 − 1.5 • 4 = 48	(4, 48)

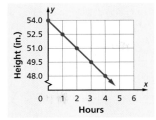

Plot the ordered pairs in the table and look for patterns. You should see that the five points lie on the same line. Time in hours can be any nonnegative real number, such as 1.75 or $3\frac{1}{2}$. This means that other points lie between the ones you have already plotted. So, draw the line through them for the domain $x \geq 0$.

Example 2

In Example 1, if the water level continues to drop at the same rate, how many hours will it take for the water level to fall to 3 feet above normal?

Solution Look at the graph from Example 1. The level of the water above the normal level is given by *y*. Find the point for 3 feet, or 36 inches, on the *y*-axis. The *x*-coordinate of this point is 12. This is shown by the arrows on the graph. The water will be 3 feet above normal after 12 hours.

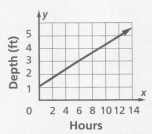

STOP QY

In Examples 1 and 2, notice that the ⌇ symbol appears on the graphs. This symbol indicates a break in the scale of the axis. It is often used so that patterns in graphs become more apparent.

Activity

You can create your own continuous graph using a motion detector that hooks up to a computer or your graphing calculator. These graphs are time-distance graphs. They plot the distance between the motion detector and a stationary solid object (like a wall) over time. If a person holds a motion detector and moves closer to or farther from a wall, those changes will be seen in the graph. An example of such a graph is shown at the right.

To create this graph, start about 5 feet away from the wall and move farther away from the wall at a constant speed.

(*continued on next page*)

▶ **QY**

Based on the graph in Example 2, when is the water level 42 inches above normal?

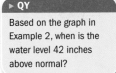

Notes on the Lesson

In Chapters 1 and 2, students have created graphs and dealt with patterns like the ones in this lesson. The difference here is that students are expected to move easily from one to the other. Students must be convinced that an equation and its graph are related.

Examples 1 and 2 have the students make a table and graph a constant-decrease situation.

The Activity uses calculator-based laboratory technology. If you can, project some students' results.

Additional Examples

Example 1 Sharon bought a new home with a 5-foot-deep pool in the backyard. The pool had 1 foot of water standing in it. When she began filling the pool, Sharon noticed that the water level of the pool rose 4 inches every hour. Let *x* equal the number of hours since she began filling the pool and *y* equal the depth of the water in the pool in inches. We can model this situation with the equation $y = 4x + 12$. Graph this relationship.

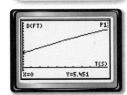

Example 2 In Additional Example 1, if the water level continues to rise at the same rate, how many hours will it take for the pool to reach a depth of 5 feet? **12 hr**

Accommodating the Learner ⬆

If you feel that students are proficient in graphing linear patterns, have them graph the line $y = x + 5$ and note the coordinates of the point where the line crosses the *y*-axis. Ask them to then graph the line $y = x + 2$ and note the coordinates of the point where this line crosses the *y*-axis. Finally ask them to graph the line $y = x + 10$. Ask them to *describe* the relationship between the constant term in the equation of a line and the point where the line crosses the *y*-axis.

Additional Answers

Activity
Step 2: For Graph A, start far from the detector and approach it at a constant pace. For Graph B, start nearby and walk away at a constant rate. For Graph C, start a fair distance from the detector, approach it at a constant rate, and then reverse direction and continue walking away from the detector at the original pace. For Graph D, start near the detector and walk away from it at a constant pace and reverse direction, eventually walking at the original pace. The distance from the motion detector changes.

3-1

3 Assignment

Recommended Assignment
- Questions 1–20
- Question 21 (extra credit)
- Reading Lesson 3-2
- Covering the Ideas 3-2

Notes on the Questions
Question 1 Ask students what it would mean if $x = -0.5$. If the stream had been dropping at 3 inches an hour before now, then this would be the height a half hour ago. Ask them if the value of y makes sense when $x = -0.5$. The value of y would be 19.5, indicating 19.5 inches above its normal level. For Part d, after you obtain the answer $x = 6$, ask what the equation predicts for the water level if $x = 7$. You get $y = -3$, so the stream is 3 inches below its normal level. The purpose of these questions is to point out that the values of x and y can make sense when they are negative.

Questions 2–10 These questions require graphs. Whether or not students are using graphing calculators, make certain that their graphs have accurate scales on both axes.

Note-Taking Tips
In their notebooks, have students write the following steps for graphing an equation.

Step 1: Make a table.
Step 2: Plot the ordered pairs.
Step 3: If the plotted points appear to be linear, draw a line through them.

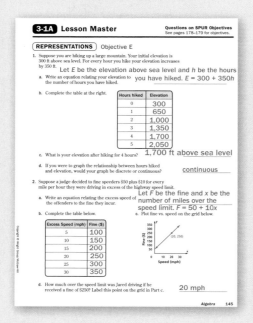

Step 1 Using a motion detector, create time-distance graphs as similar as possible to each graph below.

Graph A   Graph B   Graph C

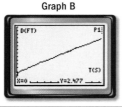

Graph D

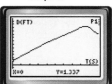

Step 2 Explain how you created each graph. Describe your starting point, direction, and speed while walking. Explain what quantity changes during the walk. **See margin on page 134.**

Questions

COVERING THE IDEAS

1. A flooded stream is 18 inches above its normal level. The water level is dropping 3 inches per hour. Its height y in inches above normal after x hours is given by the equation $y = 18 - 3x$. A table and a graph of the equation are shown at the right.

Time x (hr)	Height y (in.)
0	18
1	? 15
2	? 12
3	? 9
4	? 6

   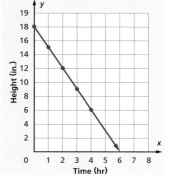

   a. Complete the table at the right.
   b. After how many hours will the stream be 12 inches above normal? **2 hr**
   c. How high above normal will the stream be after 3 hours? **9 in.**
   d. After how many hours will the stream be back to its normal level? **6 hr**

   2b. See margin.

2. Suppose Miguel begins with $500 in an account and adds $20 per week.

   a. Complete the table at the right, showing t, the total amount Miguel will have at the end of w weeks.
   b. Graph the ordered pairs (w, t).
   c. Write an equation that represents t in terms of w. $t = 500 + 20w$
   d. What is the domain of w? **the set of whole numbers**

Weeks (w)	Total (t)	
0	?	$500
1	?	$520
2	?	$540
3	?	$560
4	?	$580

Accommodating the Learner

If you feel that students are having difficulty with graphing at this point, ask them to make a human line graph. First, have them complete a table for the equation $y = x + 2$. Have them use the format shown. Then have them use the rows of desks in the classroom for a coordinate plane. Have the student in the first row, third seat stand up to represent the point $(1, 3)$; then have the student in the second row, fourth seat stand up to represent the point $(2, 4)$; then have the person in the third row, fifth seat rise representing the point $(3, 5)$. Students will see the line pattern forming. Repeat this activity with the equations $y = 2x - 1$ and $y = 3x - 2$.

x	$x + 2$	y
1	$(1) + 2$	3
2	$(2) + 2$	4
3	$(3) + 2$	5
4	$(4) + 2$	6
5	$(5) + 2$	7

3. A train consists of an engine that is 60 feet long and cars that are each 40 feet long. There is a distance of 2.5 feet between two cars and between the first car and the engine. Let T be the total length, in feet, of a train with c cars.

a. What is the total length of a train with 1 car? 102.5 ft

b. What is the total length of a train with 2 cars? 145 ft

c. **Multiple Choice** How are T and c related? C

    A $T = 60 + 40c$ B $T = 62.5 + 40c$

    C $T = 60 + 42.5c$ D $T = 62.5 + 42.5c$

d. Graph the equation you found in Part c for values of c from 1 to 5. See margin.

e. Find the length of the train if it has 12 cars. 570 ft

John Stevens built and operated the first steam locomotive in the United States in 1825.

Source: *The World Almanac*

APPLYING THE MATHEMATICS

4. A tree has a trunk with a 12-centimeter radius. The radius increases by 0.5 centimeter per year. Its radius y, in centimeters, after x years is described by $y = 12 + 0.5x$.

a. Make a table of values for this relationship.

b. Draw a graph of this situation. 4a–b. See margin.

c. After how many years will the radius equal 20 centimeters? 16 yr

5. a. Draw the graph of $y = 4x$. Choose your own values for x. 5a–b. See margin.

b. On the same grid from Part a, draw the graph of $y = -4x$.

c. At which points do the graphs of $y = 4x$ and $y = -4x$ intersect?

d. Describe any patterns you observe in these graphs.

5c. (0, 0)

5d. Answers vary. Sample answer: They are reflection images of each other over the y-axis.

6. A flooded stream is now 30 centimeters above its normal level. The water level is dropping at a rate of 3 centimeters per hour. Let x equal the number of hours from now and y equal the water level above normal after x hours.

a. Suppose the water level continues to drop at the same rate. Write an equation for y in terms of x. $y = 30 - 3x$

b. Graph your equation from Part a. See margin.

c. Use your graph to estimate when the stream is expected to drop to a level of 6 centimeters above normal. 8 hr

In 7–10, graph the equation using a graphing calculator, and determine whether the graph is linear. You may have to adjust the window to view the graph.

7. $y = -0.02(x - 3)$ linear   8. $y = \frac{1}{100}x^2$ not linear

9. $y = \frac{x - 3}{5} - x$ linear   10. $y = |x|$ not linear

Graphing Linear Patterns   133

Notes on the Questions

Question 7 Point out that when x is near zero, the values of y are very near zero. In a window larger than $-1 \leq y \leq 1$, the graph will coincide with the x-axis because it has been rounded to 0. Also, the graph will seem to be a broken line. But a trace of the points will show that they change at a constant rate.

Question 8 See above. An appropriate window will show the curve near the origin.

Question 9 The equation may not look like a linear equation, but it is.

Question 10 At this point, students should know that the graph is V-shape. If the window allows only positive values of x, or allows only negative values of x, then the graph will seem to be a line.

Question 21 You might have students vary the length L of the engine, the length R of each car, and the distance d between the cars, and obtain the general relationship $T = L + d + (R + d)c$, where c is the number of cars.

4a. Answers vary. Sample answer:

Years (y)	Radius (x)
0	12 cm
1	12.5 cm
2	13 cm
3	13.5 cm
4	14 cm

4b.
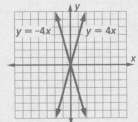

5a–b.
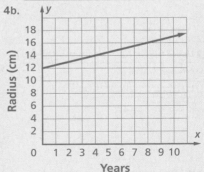

6b. See page 134 for answer.

Additional Answers

2b.
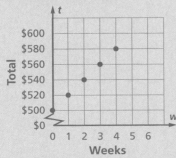

3d.
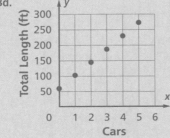

4 Wrap-Up

Ongoing Assessment

Have each student graph the line represented by the equation $y = 3x + 5$ and trade their graph with a partner. Have them compare the graph they receive with a graph of the equation that you provide on the board or overhead.

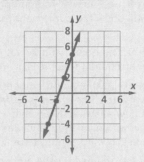

Project Update

If you have not had students look over the projects on pages 174 and 175, you might want to do so now. Project 1, Modeling Buying and Selling, on page 174, and Project 5, The Strength of Spaghetti, on page 175, relate to the content of this lesson.

Additional Answer

6b.

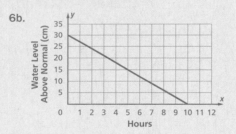

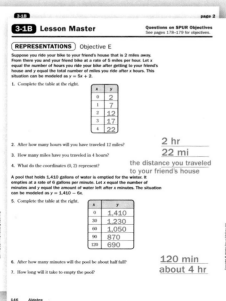

In 11–14, compute in your head. (Lesson 2-8)

11. $\frac{9}{11}h \cdot \left(\frac{9}{11}h \cdot \frac{11}{9h}\right)$ $\frac{9}{11}h$

12. $95{,}620 \cdot 657 - 95{,}620 \cdot 656$ 95,620

13. $85.69 \cdot 6.514 \cdot 0 \cdot 12$ 0

14. $\frac{4}{13} \cdot 9.85 \cdot \frac{13}{40}$ 0.985

In 15–17, use the table at the right and the formula $d = rt$ to calculate the following. (Lesson 2-8)

15. At top speed, how far can an ostrich run in 15 seconds? $\frac{1}{6}$ mi or about 0.17 mi

16. a. At top speed, how long will it take a cheetah to run 0.78 mile?

    b. How long will it take a cheetah to run 100 yards at top speed?

17. If a greyhound runs at top speed for 8 seconds and a giraffe runs at top speed for 17 seconds, which animal has run farther? giraffe

18. Consider the equation $-0.6(5x) = 90$. (Lesson 2-8)

    a. Simplify the left side of the equation. $-3x$

    b. Solve for x. $x = -30$

    c. Check your solution. $-0.6(5 \cdot -30) = -0.6(-150) = 90$

19. **Skill Sequence** Evaluate each expression. (Lesson 2-4)

    a. 6^2 36   b. -6^2 -36

    c. $(-6)^2$ 36   d. -6^3 -216

    e. $(-6)^3$ -216 f. $-(-6)^4$ $-1{,}296$

20. Is $x = -9$ a solution to $28 = -3x - 1$? Explain your reasoning. (Lesson 1-1) No. $-3(-9) - 1 = 27 - 1 = 26 \neq 28$.

21. In Question 3, approximate lengths are given for an engine, train cars, and the distance between them.

    a. Find the lengths of an engine and of a car for an actual train. Identify the type of train and where you found the information.

    b. Give an equation relating the total length T of the train and the number of cars c. $T = 64 + (85\frac{7}{12}c)$

16a. about 0.0111 hr or 40 sec

16b. about 2.92 sec

Fast Land Animals

Animal	Top Speed (mi/hr)
Cheetah	70
Ostrich	40
Greyhound	39
Giraffe	32

Source: American Museum of Natural History

21a. Answers vary. Sample answer: The ALP-46 Locomotive used by the New Jersey Department of Transit is 64 ft long. The Comet V Coach Car also used in New Jersey is 85 ft long. The HiLoMag train system uses 7 in. between cars.

QY ANSWER

after 8 hr

Activity Step 2 p. 132

For the first graph, start far from the detector and approach it at a constant pace. For the second graph, start nearby and walk away at a constant rate. For the third graph, start a fair distance from the detector, approach it at a constant rate, then reverse direction and continue walking away from the detector at the original pace. For the fourth graph, start near the detector and walk away from it at a constant pace and reverse direction eventually walking at the original pace.

Lesson 3-2

Solving Equations with Tables and Graphs

Vocabulary

solution to an equation

▶ **BIG IDEA** Tables and graphs lead to exact or approximate solutions to equations.

Consider an equation that contains one variable, such as $2 + x = 6$. A **solution to an equation** is a value of the variable that makes the equation true. For $2 + x = 6$, 4 is a solution because $2 + 4 = 6$.

 QY1

Solving with a Table and a Graph

In this lesson, you will learn two ways to solve equations: using a table and using a graph. We apply each way to solve $11 = 4x + 3$.

Mental Math

Evaluate.

a. 50% of $120P$ $60P$

b. 5% of $120P$ $6P$

c. 50% of $12P$ $6P$

d. 5% of $12P$ $0.6P$

Example 1

Solve $11 = 4x + 3$ using a table.

Solution Replace y with 11 and make a table of values for $y = 4x + 3$. Look in the table to the right to see what value of x gives a value of 11 for y.

Looking at the table, you can see that when $x = 2$, $y = 11$. Based on the table, you can conclude that **the solution to the equation $11 = 4x + 3$ is $x = 2$.**

x	$4x + 3$	y
1	$4(1) + 3$	7
2	$4(2) + 3$	11
3	$4(3) + 3$	15
4	$4(4) + 3$	19
5	$4(5) + 3$	23

▶ **QY1**

Is 5 a solution to $|-12m + 19| = 41$?

Example 2

Solve $11 = 4x + 3$ using a graph.

Solution As in Example 1, replace y with 11. Then graph $y = 4x + 3$ and look for the value of x that corresponds with the value of 11 for y. To do this, start at 11 on the y-axis. Move right to the line, and then move down to the x-axis. As in Example 1, $x = 2$ is the solution.

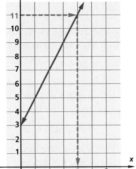

(continued on next page)

Background

The idea of this lesson is to begin formal equation-solving techniques. It is quite tedious to make a table or to draw a graph. Even with the use of a graphing calculator, the solution may not be evident because the pixels of the calculator may not coincide with integer or simple values of the variables.

Example 3 requires an important skill: creating an equation that describes the situation. Equations like these will be used throughout the rest of the course.

Extension

Have your students write and graph an equation for the standard income-tax deduction for a joint return based on the number of exemptions using the most recent tax tables available through the IRS (ignore limitations and exceptions).

Lesson 3-2

GOAL

Use tables and graphs to solve equations.

SPUR Objectives

D Use linear equations and inequalities of the form $ax + b = c$ or $ax + b < c$ to solve real-world problems.

E Solve problems involving equations of the form $y = ax + b$ using tables or graphs.

Materials/Resources

- Lesson Master 3-2A or 3-2B
- Resource Masters 1, 2, 4, and 37
- Graphing calculator
- Graph paper

HOMEWORK

Suggestions for Assignment

- Questions 1–24
- Question 25 (extra credit)
- Reading Lesson 3-3
- Covering the Ideas 3-3

Local Standards

1 Warm-Up

Present the following problems.

Graph the equation $y = (x - 1)^2 - 2$ on the window $-5 \le x \le 5$, $-10 \le y \le 10$ and use to answer the questions.

1. What is the smallest value of y that the trace key obtains? We found -1.998189; the smallest value of y on the graph is -2, when $x = 1$.

2. What are the values of x where the value of y on the trace key is closest to zero? We found $x = 2.4468085$ yields $y = 0.09325487$, and $x = -0.4255319$ yields $y = 0.03214124$. Actual values of x yielding $y = 0$ are $x = \sqrt{2} + 1 \approx 2.4142\ldots$ and $x = -\sqrt{2} + 1 \approx -0.4142\ldots$.

3. Zoom in on the points in Questions 1 and 2 to obtain better estimates.

3-2

2 Teaching

Notes on the Lesson

The Warm-Up can be used to point out that although in Examples 1 and 2 and a solution can be found from the table and from the hand-drawn graph, this is not always the case.

Situations leading to equations. The key here is for students to see the relationship between the given information and the equation by understanding the roles that subtraction and multiplication play in Example 3. Example 3 involves a constant-decrease situation because the amount of change goes down a constant amount for each taco. Students should be able to translate this kind of situation into an equation regardless of the numbers involved. This may not be easy at this point, but students should strive to make such translations automatic by the end of the chapter.

Additional Examples

Example 1 Solve $10 = 3x + 4$ using a table. $x = 2$

x	$3x + 4$	y
1	$3(1) + 4$	7
2	$3(2) + 4$	10
3	$3(3) + 4$	13
4	$3(4) + 4$	16
5	$3(5) + 4$	19

Example 2 Solve $-1 = 2x + 5$ using a graph. $x = -3$ when $y = -1$

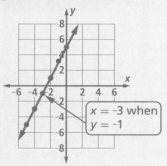

$x = -3$ when $y = -1$

Example 3 Susie lives in a state where there is no sales tax. She bought 5 fountain drinks with a $10 bill and received $0.55 change. What was the price of one drink? Let the cost of one drink be represented by d. Because $10.00 minus the cost of 5 drinks gave $0.55 in change, $10 - 5d = 0.55$. $d = 1.89$.

You can also see this on a graphing calculator. Most graphing calculators have a trace option. The trace option allows you to move a cursor along the graph. As the cursor moves, it lists the coordinates on the graph. The calculator screen at the right shows the cursor at (−0.8510638, −0.4042553). Move the cursor until the y-coordinate is as close as possible to 11. Remember that the x value is only an approximation for the solution if the y value is also an approximation.

Situations Leading to Equations

Real-world situations can often be translated into relationships among numbers. If you can represent these relationships with an equation, then the methods of this and the next lesson can lead to a solution.

Example 3

Khalid lives in Alaska where there is no sales tax. He bought 3 tacos with a $5 bill and received $0.77 in change. Define the variable and represent the relationship with an equation.

Solution Let t represent the unknown cost of one taco. Because $5 minus the cost of 3 tacos equals $0.77 in change, $5 - 3t = 0.77$ is the equation.

🛑 **QY2**

In 2006, the states without a sales tax were Alaska, Delaware, Montana, New Hampshire, and Oregon.

Source: Federation of Tax Administrators

Questions

COVERING THE IDEAS

1. Determine if the value of x is a solution for the equation.
   a. $11 - 9x = 47, x = 4$ no
   b. $3x^2 + 4x = 55, x = -5$ yes
   c. $-x^3 = 64, x = -4$ yes

In 2 and 3, solve by making a table for each equation and circling the row on the table that contains the solution. 2–3. See margin.

2. $6 = 2x + 2$

3. $-5a + 7 = -23$

In 4 and 5, solve by making a graph for each equation and drawing lines from the y-axis to the graph, and then to the x-axis to indicate the solution. 4–5. See margin.

4. $y = -3x - 4, y = 2$

5. $y = 5x - 18, y = -3$

6. a. With a graphing calculator, make a table for $y = 5(5x - 2)$ using the integers from –5 to 0. See margin.
   b. Adjust the table to solve $5(5x - 2) = -26$.
      $x = -0.64$; See margin for table.

▶ **QY2**

Todd has $250 in his savings account. If he has a job that pays $11 per hour, how many working hours will it take for him to have enough money to buy a $481 surfboard?

Additional Answers

2.

x	$2x + 2$
0	2
1	4
2	6
3	8

3.

a	$-5a + 7$
0	7
2	-3
4	-13
6	-23

4.

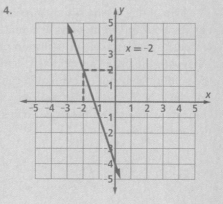

$x = -2$

In 7–9, define the variable and represent the relationship with an equation.

7. Solana lives where there is no sales tax. She bought five pieces of pizza for her friends with a $20 bill. She received $7.65 in change. What was the price of one piece of pizza?

8. Trevor is riding his bicycle across the United States. He started in a town on the East Coast and has already biked 630 miles. If he can ride 82 miles per day, how many days will it take him to complete the 3,210-mile journey?

9. The Coles are saving to send their child to college. They currently have $5,275 in the bank and are saving $950 per year. How many years will pass before they save $20,000? Let y be the number of years they save. Then, $5,275 + 950y = 20,000$.

7. Let p be the price of a piece of pizza. Then, $20 - 5p = 7.65$.

8. Let d be the number of days he rides. Then, $3,210 = 630 + 82d$.

APPLYING THE MATHEMATICS

10. Use a graph to solve $5 - 3t = 0.77$ from Example 3.
t appears to be around 1.4; See margin for graph.

11. Use a table to solve $250 + 11h = 481$ from QY2. See margin.

12. Use a table on a graphing calculator to solve $3x + 5 = -4$.

13. The graph at the right shows the equation $y = 6.2 - 2.15x$.
a. Draw dotted lines to show how to find an approximate solution to $3 = 6.2 - 2.15x$.
b. What is the approximate solution? about 1.5

In 14 and 15, use the information provided to write an equation involving the variable. Then use any method to find the value of the variable.

14. The perimeter of the rectangle at the right is 46 feet.
$32 + 2x = 46; x = 7$ ft

15. The perimeter of the triangle at the right is 97 meters.
$2(3x - 6) + 2x + 1 = 97; x = 13.5$ $(3x - 6)$ m

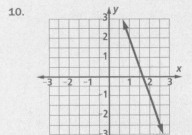

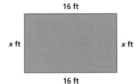

16 ft

x ft   x ft

16 ft

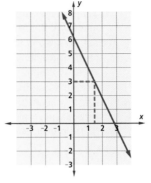

12.

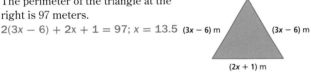

$(3x - 6)$ m $(3x - 6)$ m

$(2x + 1)$ m

REVIEW

In 16–18, graph the equation on a calculator. Does the graph appear to be a line? You may have to adjust the window to view the graph. (Lesson 3-1)

16. $y = 0.402(x - 3) + 1.97x - 0.567$ It is a line.

17. $h = 7 - 2t^2 + t$ It is not a line. 18. $y = 4x(5 + x)$ It is not a line.

Solving Equations with Tables and Graphs   **137**

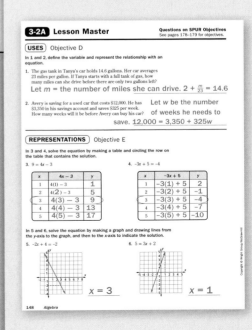
Additional Answers

5.

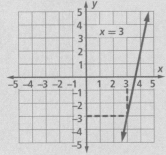

6a.

X	Y₁
-5	-135
-4	-110
-3	-85
-2	-60
-1	-35
0	-10
1	15

Y₁=-10

6b.

X	Y₁
-.68	-27
-.67	-26.75
-.66	-26.5
-.65	-26.25
-.64	-26
-.63	-25.75
-.62	-25.5

X=-.68

3-2

4 Wrap-Up

Ongoing Assessment

Have each student solve the equation $15 = 2x + 3$ by completing a table or a graph. Have his or her partner compare it with your table or graph on the board.

x	2x + 3	y	$x = 6$
2	2(2) + 3	7	
3	2(3) + 3	9	
4	2(4) + 3	11	
5	2(5) + 3	13	
6	2(6) + 3	15	

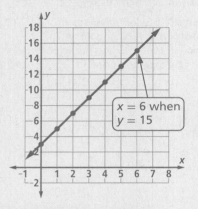

x = 6 when y = 15

Additional Answers

19a.

Years	Height (ft)
0	28
1	31.5
2	35
3	38.5

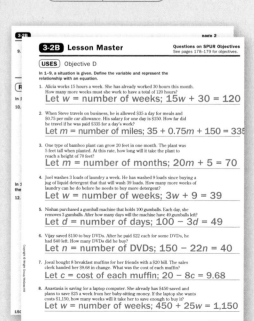

19. Sierra redwood trees are known to be among the world's tallest trees, growing an average of 3.5 feet each year until they mature. If a redwood tree is now 28 feet tall, its height h after y years is described by $h = 28 + 3.5y$. **(Lesson 3-1)** 19a–b. See margin.

    a. Make a table of values for this relationship.
    b. Draw a graph of this situation.
    c. How tall will the tree be in 21 years? **101.5 ft**
    d. How many years will it take the tree to grow to a height of 259 feet? **66 yr**

20. *Internet World Stats* reported in the summer of 2005 that there were about 220 million Internet users in North America. That number was growing by an average of 23 million users per year. Suppose this rate continues between 2005 and 2010. **(Lessons 3-1, 1-5)**

    a. Make a table showing the total number of millions of Internet users 0, 1, 2, 3, 4, and 5 years after 2005.
    b. Let x represent the number of years after 2005. What window on your graphing calculator would be most appropriate to view the graph?
    c. Draw the graph using your graphing calculator. See margin.

In 21 and 22, a number is given.
a. Find its opposite.
b. Find its reciprocal. **(Lessons 2-8, 2-5)**

21. 8.3 a. –8.3; b. $\frac{1}{8.3} \approx 0.12$ 22. $-\frac{26}{5}$ a. $\frac{26}{5}$; b. $-\frac{5}{26}$

In 23 and 24, evaluate the expression $\frac{a+b}{3} + 3(a - b)$ for the given values of a and b. **(Lesson 1-1)**

23. $a = 11$ and $b = -4$ 24. $a = 11x$ and $b = 55x$ **–110x**
    $\frac{142}{3}$ or about **47.33**

EXPLORATION

25. Use the graph below to solve $11 = 7 + 2\sqrt{x + 1}$. Draw dotted lines to show your method. **x = 3; See margin for graph.**

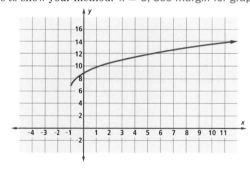

Many Sierra redwoods are between 250 and 300 feet tall, the tallest being about 325 feet high.

Source: California Department of Parks & Recreation

20a.

Years after 2005	Users (millions)
0	220
1	243
2	266
3	289
4	312
5	335

20b. Answers vary. Sample answer: x-min = 0; x-max = 11; y-min = 200; y-max = 360

QY ANSWERS

1. $m = 5$ is a solution because
   $|-12 \cdot 5 + 19| =$
   $|-60 + 19| = |-41|$
   $= 41$.

2. 21 hr

Additional Answers

19b.

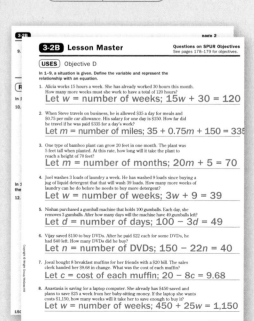

20c. Answers vary. Sample answer:

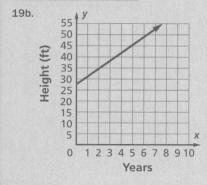

25.

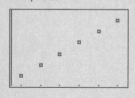
$y = 7 + 2\sqrt{x + 1}$

Lesson 3-3

Solving Equations by Creating Equivalent Equations

Vocabulary

equivalent equations

▶ **BIG IDEA** Performing the same arithmetic operations on both sides of an equation can create an equation that is easier to solve.

In the previous lesson, you used a table and a graph to find the solution to an equation of the form $ax + b = c$. Those methods allow you to visualize what it means to solve an equation. But in practice, they are sometimes awkward to use. Other times they yield solutions that are not exact. In this lesson, we discuss a method that enables you to find exact solutions to many types of equations.

Mental Math

a. If $x = 4z - 9y$, what is $3x$? $12z - 27y$

b. If $x = 4z - 9y$, what is $-x$? $9y - 4z$

c. If $x = 4z - 9y$, what is $x + 9y$? $4z$

Solving with a Balance

A balance illustrates the meaning of the "=" sign in an equation by placing equal weights on both sides. The scale will still balance as long as changes made to one side are also made to the other side. This is the idea behind solving an equation algebraically.

The equation $11 = 4x + 3$ is shown above with 11 identical 1-ounce weights on the left side and 3 one-ounce weights with 4 unknown weights on the right side. You can find the weight x of one box in two steps. Each step keeps the scale balanced.

Step 1 Remove 3 one-ounce weights from each side of the scale.

Step 2 Leave $\frac{1}{4}$ of the contents on each side.

From the original equation two more equations were formed.

$$11 = 4x + 3$$
$$8 = 4x$$
$$2 = x$$

These three equations are called *equivalent equations* because 2 is the solution to each of them. **Equivalent equations** are equations with exactly the same solutions.

Solving Equations by Creating Equivalent Equations   **139**

Background

For students who have previously solved linear equations algebraically, this lesson provides an opportunity to see how a CAS can be used to show the steps. For students who have *not* previously solved linear equations algebraically, this lesson shows the conceptual basis for doing the same things to both sides of an equation, and also shows solutions that they will be asked to emulate in the lessons that follow.

The Addition and Multiplication Properties of Equality. The Addition Property of

Equality and the Multiplication Property of Equality are the two fundamental properties that underlie the algebraic solving of equations. We assume that students have seen these properties in previous years. The balance scale is a good model for showing why these work: a and b are the original quantities that balance; if we add the same amount to them, subtract the same amount from them, or multiply or divide them by the same amount, the scale will still balance.

Lesson 3-3

GOAL

Through exploration on a computer algebra system (CAS), see what needs to be done to both sides of a linear equation in order to solve it.

SPUR Objective

C Apply the Addition and Multiplication Properties of Equality and Inequality.

Materials/Resources

- Lesson Master 3-3A or 3-3B
- Resource Master 38
- Quiz 1
- Scientific or graphing calculator
- Computer Algebra System (CAS)

HOMEWORK

Suggestions for Assignment

- Questions 1–19
- Question 20 (extra credit)
- Reading Lesson 3-4
- Covering the Ideas 3-4

Local Standards

1 Warm-Up

Use a CAS on this Warm-Up if it is available to students. Otherwise the Warm-Up can be done without a CAS.

Consider the equation $8x - 12 = 4$. What equation results from each action?

1. adding –12 to both sides $8x - 24 = -8$
2. adding –8 to both sides $8x - 20 = -4$
3. adding –4 to both sides $8x - 16 = 0$
4. multiplying both sides by –8 $-64x + 96 = -32$
5. multiplying both sides by $\frac{1}{8}$ $x - 1.5 = 0.5$ or $x - \frac{3}{2} = \frac{1}{2}$
6. adding 12 to both sides $8x = 16$

Now use the **SOLVE** command to solve each of the equations found in Questions 1–6. Each equation is equivalent to $x = 2$.

3-3

Notes on the Lesson

This lesson can be taught through its activity.

Notes on the Activity

Activity A CAS can solve an equation such as $8x - 12 = 4$ in one step, with an appropriate solve command. However, using that command disguises what has been done to both sides. Here we use a feature that is on many CAS, namely the ability to enter an equation and an action, and see what that action does to the equation.

It is also helpful to use a projector to display the Activity as you work through the steps.

Alternate Activity

If a CAS is not available, you may use algebra tiles for the same activity.

Use the following steps for solving the linear equation $8x - 12 = 4$ using algebra tiles: Lay out the pieces representing the equation and decide which operation to perform on each side (for instance, to add 12 to both sides add 12 green unit squares). If you get an equation that is simpler than the previous one, continue until the equation is solved. Otherwise, your operation was not the best choice. You are finished solving when the equation has the form *variable* = *number*.

Step 1: Lay out pieces to represent $8x - 12 = 4$.

x	x		R	R	R		G
x	x		R	R	R	=	G
x	x		R	R	R		G
x	x		R	R	R		G

Step 2: Add 12 green unit squares to each side.

x	x		R	R	R		G	G	G	G
x	x		R	R	R	=	G	G	G	G
x	x		R	R	R		G	G	G	G
x	x		R	R	R		G	G	G	G

Step 3: Group into 8 groups.

x	x		G G G G
x	x	=	G G G G
x	x		G G G G
x	x		G G G G

Step 4: $x = 2$

x	=	G G

Exploring $ax + b = c$ Equations with a Computer Algebra System (CAS)

The goal when solving equations of the form $ax + b = c$ is to add, subtract, multiply, or divide both sides of the equation to eventually get an equation of the form $x =$ a number. In the activity below, you will use a CAS to analyze the effect of performing various operations to the two sides of an equation.

Activity

Solve $8x - 12 = 4$.

Step 1 Enter $8x - 12 = 4$ into the calculator.

Step 2 Next enter ⊞12 to instruct your CAS to add 12 to both sides of the equation. The result is $8x = 16$, which is simpler than $8x - 12 = 4$. So adding 12 was a good choice.

Step 3 Enter ÷8 to divide each side by 8. The result is an equation that is as simple as possible. So $x = 2$.

STOP QY

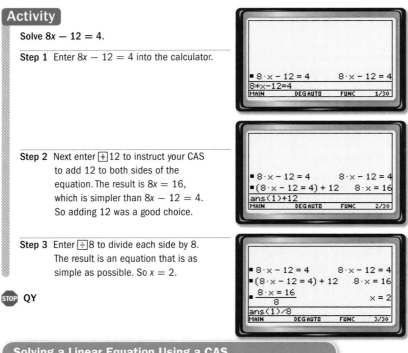

Solving a Linear Equation Using a CAS

Step 1 Enter your equation into your CAS.

Step 2 Decide which operation to perform on each side. For example, to add 9 to both sides enter ⊞9.

Step 3 Do you get an equation that is simpler than the previous one? If the answer is "yes," continue until the equation is solved. If the answer is "no," re-enter the equation and try a different operation.

Step 4 You are finished solving when the equation has the form *variable* = *number*.

▶ QY

Solve each question using a CAS.

a. $\frac{4}{7}z + \frac{2}{3} = \frac{1}{7}$

b. $-3y + 14 = 98$

Accommodating the Learner 🔽

If students seem to have difficulties with the CAS, have them use algebra tiles to solve $2x + 3 = 13$. Have students work as partners, one student manipulating the tiles and the other recording the results. Students should add three red unit squares to both sides, canceling the three green unit squares on the left and leaving only ten on the right. Then, students should group green unit squares in two groups of the same number of unit squares.

Each group contains 5 tiles, so $x = 5$. Have partners switch and solve the equation $3x + 2 = 32$ using the tiles, again with one student manipulating and the other recording. Ask students to explain the steps they take to solve the equation.

Questions

COVERING THE IDEAS

1. Why are the equations below called equivalent equations?

$2x + 5 = 11$ All three equations have the same solution, 3.
$2x = 6$
$x = 3$

2. **a.** What equation is represented by the diagram below? $3x + 1 = 7$

   b. What two steps can be taken with the weights on each side of the scale to find the weight of a single box?

   c. How much does a single box weigh? $x = 2$ oz

   2b. First, remove 1 oz from each side. Then, leave one-third of the weight on each side.

3. **a. Fill in the Blanks** When solving $5x - 27 = 13$, first ___?___ to each side, then ___?___ on both sides. **add 27; divide by 5**

   b. Solve $5x - 27 = 13$ and check your result. $x = 8$

4. Consider the steps used in the solution of $82n - 51 = 441$ below.

Given: $82n - 51 = 441$
Step 1 $82n = 492$
Step 2 $n = 6$

4a. 51 was added to both sides.
4b. Both sides were divided by 82.

   a. What was done to go from the given equation to Step 1?

   b. What was done to go from Step 1 to Step 2?

In 5–8, a pair of equations is given. Determine what was done to each side of the first equation to arrive at the second equation.

5. $4x - 11 = 12$ added 11
    $4x = 23$

6. $72 - 18t = 864$ subtracted 72
    $-18t = 792$

7. $\frac{3}{5}n = 30$
   $n = 50$ multiplied by $\frac{5}{3}$

8. $0.004v = 1.2$ divided by 0.004
   $v = 300$

9. What might be done first to each side of $75x - 100 = 800$ to begin the process of solving the equation?
Answers vary. Sample answer: Add 100.

APPLYING THE MATHEMATICS

10. In solving $5x + 430 = 315$, Paula instructed her CAS to divide both sides of the equation by 5.

   a. What result did she get? $x + 86 = 63$

   b. Is this a reasonable first step to solve the equation? If so, use it to solve the equation. If not, explain why. **yes, $x = -23$**

---

3   Assignment

Recommended Assignment

- Questions 1–19
- Question 20 (extra credit)
- Reading Lesson 3-4
- Covering the Ideas 3-4

Notes on the Questions

Question 9 The sample answer "Add 100" is not the only answer possible. In fact, any number could be added to (or subtracted from) both sides, and both sides could be multiplied (or divided) by any number other than zero. The question means: What might be done that would facilitate solving the equation? Most people would say "Add 100 to both sides," but "Divide both sides by 75" also leads to a simpler equation (though one that involves fractions). We see that second possibility, dividing both sides by the same number, in Question 10.

Question 10 Dividing by 5 is a reasonable first step because each term is divisible by 5.

Note-Taking Tips

You might ask the students to put the steps for solving equations using a CAS on index cards.

Accommodating the Learner ⬆

If you feel that students are comfortable solving equations using a CAS, have them try to solve $x^2 + 7x - 5 = 7$ using the CAS. Ask them to explain why they cannot solve this equation using the same methods on the CAS. If students are using graphing calculators that have a table function, show them how to input the equation. Have them first rewrite the equation in quadratic form $(x^2 + 7x - 12 = 0)$. Have them enter $x^2 + 7x - 12$ in the $y_1 =$ line. Have them apply the table function to see that both solutions are revealed at $y = 0$.

ENGLISH LEARNERS
Vocabulary Development

You may want to have your students add the terms *CAS* and *equivalent equations* to their vocabulary notebooks.

3-3

Notes on the Questions
Question 12 *Error Analysis* This common error can be avoided by first rewriting the equation as $4x + -32 = 20$.

11. In solving $-3y + 14 = 98$, Paula instructed her CAS to divide both sides by -3.

 a. What result did she get? $y + -\frac{14}{3} = -\frac{98}{3}$

 b. Is this a reasonable first step to solve the equation? If so, use it to solve the equation. If not, explain why.

12. A student showed the following work to solve $4x - 32 = 20$.

$$4x - 32 = 20$$
$$4x - 32 - 32 = 20 - 32$$
$$4x = -12$$
$$x = -3$$

 But substituting -3 in the original equation results in an equation that is not true. What did the student do wrong?

13. a. Solve $3x + 5y = c$ for x by hand or with a CAS. $x = \frac{c - 5y}{3}$

 b. Check your answer to Part a by substituting numbers for y and c and solving that equation.

REVIEW

14. a. Using the equation $y = 7x - 2$, complete the table at the right.
 (**Lesson 3-2**) 14b. $x = -2$

 b. Use the table to find a solution to the equation $7x - 2 = -16$

x	y
-2	? -16
-1	? -9
0	? -2
1	? 5
2	? 12

15. Jordan collects basketball cards. Last Sunday he had 200 cards. He then bought one pack of cards on each weekday, and two packs on Saturday. Jordan now has 284 cards. (**Lesson 3-2**)

 a. Define a variable and represent the relationship with an equation.

 b. Use a table or graph to find the number of cards in one pack. 12 cards

16. Consider the following situation. A bathtub has 11 gallons of water in it. Rachana adjusts the faucet so it is now filling at approximately 4.5 gallons per minute. (**Lesson 3-2**)

 a. Create a table and a graph showing the amount of water in the tub in terms of the amount of time that has passed from when Rachana adjusted the faucet. See margin.

 b. How much water will be in the tub after 7 minutes? 42.5 gal

 c. If the bathtub holds 56 gallons of water, how long does it take until the bathtub is full? 10 min

11b. Answers vary. Sample answer: No, subtracting 14 would have avoided fractions.

12. The student incorrectly subtracted 32 from both sides—it should have been added.

13b. Answers vary. Sample answer: Let $y = 2$, $c = 3$. $3x + 5(2) = 3$; $x = -\frac{7}{3}$ and $x = \frac{3 - 5(2)}{3} = -\frac{7}{3}$

15a. Let c be the number of cards in a pack. $200 + c + c + c + c + c + 2c = 284$ or $200 + 7c = 284$

Additional Answers

16a. Answers vary. Sample answer:

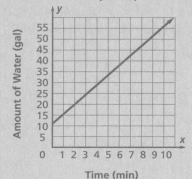

Time (min)	Amount of Water (gal)
0	11
1	15.5
2	20
5	33.5
7	42.5
10	56

3-3A Lesson Master
Questions on SPUR Objectives
See pages 178–179 for objectives.

PROPERTIES Objective C

1. a. What equation is modeled by the diagram below? $9 = 2x + 3$

 b. What two steps can be done on each side of the scale to find out how much a single box weighs? subtract 3; divide by 2

 c. If each round object weighs 1 oz, how much does a single box weigh? 3 oz

In 2 and 3, tell what was done to each side of the first equation to arrive at the second equation.

2. $-41 + 5x = 99$
 $5x = 140$
 add 41

3. $1.6 = 0.02a$
 $80 = a$
 divide by 0.02, or multiply by 50

4. Fill in the blanks to tell what operation should be performed on both sides to solve $-7x + 61 = 110$. Answers vary. Sample: add -61 to;
 First _____ both sides. Then _____ both sides. multiply by $-\frac{1}{7}$ on

5. Write the commands you would enter on a CAS to find the solution to $2.1 = 2.05k + 8.75$. $2.1 = 2.05k + 8.75$; $-8.75; /2.05$

6. In solving $-6y + 72 = -114$, Linda instructed her CAS to divide both sides by -6.

 a. What result did she get? $y - 12 = 19$

 b. Is this a reasonable first step to solve the equation? If so, use it to solve the equation. If not, explain why.
 Answers vary. Sample: Yes; next, add 12 to both sides of the equation to get $y = 31$.

7. Tell what was done to each step to solve the equation $72 - 18t = 864$.
 $72 - 18t = 864$
 $-18t = 792$
 $t = -44$
 Answers vary. Sample: Subtract 72 from both sides; divide both sides by -18.

Algebra 151

17. Death Valley, California once reached a record high of 134 degrees Fahrenheit. Suppose the temperature was 85 degrees at 9 A.M. and increased by 7 degrees every hour until 4 P.M., when it reached the record high. **(Lesson 3-1)**

    a. Use this information to complete the table at the right.

    b. Graph the data using the table. See margin.

18. Consider $\frac{3}{4}x = 16$. **(Lesson 2-8)**

    a. Solve this equation. $x = \frac{64}{3} \approx 21.33$

    b. Think of a real-world problem that can be solved with this equation.

19. Below is a dot plot of the number of mosquitoes caught in a trap over 15 days in Buckinghamshire, England. **(Lesson 1-7)**

    a. Is the shape symmetric, skewed right, skewed left, or uniform?

    b. Calculate the mean and mean absolute deviation of the data.

Time of Day		Temperature (°F)
9:00 A.M.	?	85
10:00 A.M.	?	92
11:00 A.M.	?	99
12:00 P.M.	?	106
1:00 P.M.	?	113
2:00 P.M.	?	120
3:00 P.M.	?	127
4:00 P.M.	?	134

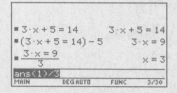

The average rainfall in Death Valley is about 1.65 inches per year.

Source: National Park Service

EXPLORATION

20. Enter $4(3x - 17) + 12 = 6(x + 2) + 6x - 68$ into your CAS as if you were going to solve the equation as in this section. Then press ENTER. 20a–c. See margin.

    a. Describe what the screen shows.

    b. Explain why. (*Hint:* Use algebra to simplify each side of the equation by hand.)

    c. Write down the other two equations that produce the same result when entered into a CAS.

18b. Answers vary. Sample answer: Together, Mr. Keto's class solves three quarters of an algebra problem every minute. How long will it take them to get through the 16 problems in their homework?

19a. symmetric

19b. The mean is about 19.73 mosquitoes, and the m.a.d. is 1.52 mosquitoes.

Solving Equations by Creating Equivalent Equations **143**

Additional Answers

17b.

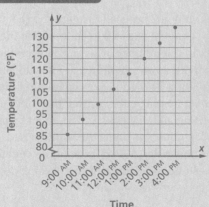

20a. The CAS returns "true."

20b. The equation is true for all values of x. Simplified, we have $12x - 56 = 12x - 56$.

20c. Answers vary. Sample answer: $2(x - 3) + 4(y + 9) = 2(x + y) + 2y + 30$; $\frac{1}{2}t - 7 = \frac{3t - 42}{6}$

---

4 Wrap-Up

Ongoing Assessment

Have each student solve the equation $3x + 5 = 14$ using the CAS. Have students write what they see on the computer screen. Check it against the correct answer.

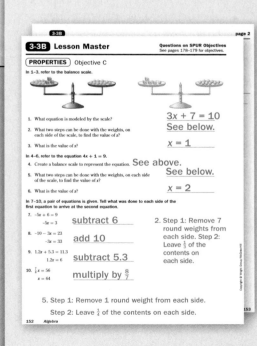

Project Update

Project 2, Appliances and Energy, on page 174 relates to the content of this lesson.

Lesson
3-4

Lesson
3-4 **Solving $ax + b = c$**

> ▶ **BIG IDEA** An equation of the form $ax + b = c$ can be solved in two major steps.

In 1637, the French philosopher and mathematician René Descartes started the practice of identifying known quantities by the letters a, b, and c from the beginning of the alphabet and unknown quantities by the letters x, y, and z from the end of the alphabet. Following the practice of Descartes, when we write "solving $ax + b = c$" we mean that a, b, and c are known numbers and x is unknown. For example, when $a = -\frac{3}{2}$, $b = -53$, and $c = 7$, we obtain the equation $-\frac{3}{2}x + -53 = 7$.

In general, any equation of the form $ax + b = c$, with a not equal to zero, can be solved in two steps. First add the opposite of b to both sides. Then multiply both sides by the reciprocal of a.

Mental Math

a. Which is greater, $\frac{1}{3}$ or 0.33? $\frac{1}{3}$

b. Which is greater, 1.4 or $\frac{33}{22}$? $\frac{33}{22}$

c. Which is greater, $-\frac{5}{4}$ or $-\frac{4}{5}$? $-\frac{4}{5}$

GUIDED

Example 1
Solve $-\frac{3}{2}x - 53 = 7$.

Solution

$$-\frac{3}{2}x - 53 = 7 \qquad \text{Write the equation.}$$

$$-\frac{3}{2}x - 53 + \underline{\ ?\ } = 7 + \underline{\ ?\ } \qquad \text{Add } \underline{\ ?\ } \text{ to each side. } 53; 53; 53$$

$$-\frac{3}{2}x = \underline{\ ?\ } \qquad \text{Simplify. } 60$$

$$-\frac{2}{3} \cdot -\frac{2}{3}\, \underline{\ ?\ } \left(-\frac{3}{2}x\right) = \underline{\ ?\ }\ (60) \qquad \text{Multiply each side by the reciprocal of } -\frac{3}{2}.$$

$$x = \underline{\ ?\ } \qquad \text{Simplify. } -40$$

Be sure to check your solution by substituting it back into the original equation.

Equations That Require Simplifying First

Equations are often complicated, but they can be simplified into ones that you can solve.

Descartes was a French scientist, mathematician, and philosopher. His statement, "I think; therefore I am," is very famous.

Source: *Discourse on Method*

Lesson
3-4

GOAL
Solve an equation of the form $ax + b = c$ regardless of the values of a, b, and c.

SPUR Objectives
A Solve and check linear equations of the form $ax + b = c$.

D Use linear equations and inequalities of the form $ax + b = c$ or $ax + b < c$ to solve real-world problems.

Materials/Resources
· Lesson Master 3-4A or 3-4B
· Resource Master 39
· Graphing calculator

HOMEWORK
Suggestions for Assignment
• Questions 1–29
• Questions 30 and 31 (extra credit)
• Reading Lesson 3-5
• Covering the Ideas 3-5

Local Standards

1 Warm-Up

Present the following problem.

Bill wants to determine the weight of one of 7 identical packages. He has a balance with a 10-kilogram weight and many 500-gram weights. When he puts 5 of the packages on the scale and three 500-gram weights, it balances the 10-kilogram weight. What does each package weigh? **1.7 kg, or 1,700 g**

Background

The power of algebra is in its generality. The same algorithm that solves an equation of the form $ax + b = c$ also solves variations such as $b + ax = c$, $c = ax + b$, or similar situations with subtraction or involving fractions or decimals. Do not expect immediate mastery. Although the algorithm does not change, the equations and their solutions look different enough to present difficulties for many students.

As students proceed through the rest of the chapter, you will need to advise them about the number of steps you want them to write down when they are solving an equation. It is good to keep in mind that the fundamental goal is getting the solution, not writing all the steps. At first, most teachers ask students to show the addition and multiplication to each side of the equation. As students' skills increase, writing down these steps can be dropped.

Example 2

When Val works at the zoo on Saturday, she earns $10.80 per hour. She is also paid $8 for meals and $3 for transportation. Last Saturday she received $83.90. How many hours did she work?

Solution Let h = the number of hours Val worked. In h hours she earned $10.80h$ dollars. So, $10.80h + 8 + 3 = 83.90$.

Next, 8 and 3 are added. The resulting equation has the form $ax + b = c$. Solve for h.

$10.80h + 11 = 83.90$	Write the equation.
$10.80h + 11 + -11 = 83.90 + -11$	Addition Property of Equality
$10.80h = 72.90$	Simplify.
$\frac{1}{10.80} \cdot 10.80h = \frac{1}{10.80} \cdot 72.90$	Multiplication Property of Equality
$h = 6.75$	Simplify.

Val worked 6.75 hours.

Check If Val worked 6.75 hours at $10.80 per hour, she earned $6.75 \cdot \$10.80$, or $72.90. Now add $8 for meals and $3 for transportation. The total comes to $83.90.

Zookeepers take care of wild animals in zoos and animal parks. They feed the animals, clean their living spaces, work to keep them healthy, and keep them cool in the summer months.

Source: Bureau of Labor Statistics

GUIDED

Example 3

The area of the largest rectangle is 94 square centimeters. What is the value of n?

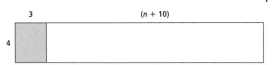

Solution Write an equation to represent the area. (*Hint:* You can use the sum of areas or the length and width of the big rectangle.) Then solve.

Area of left rectangle + Area of right rectangle = 94

$\underline{?} \cdot \underline{?} + \underline{?} \cdot \underline{?} = 94$	Write the equation. 4; 3; 4; $(n + 10)$
$12 + \underline{?} = 94$	Distributive Property $4n + 40$
$\underline{?}\,n + \underline{?} = 94$	Simplify. 4; 52
$\underline{?}\,n + \underline{?} + \underline{?} = 94 + \underline{?}$	Addition Property of Equality 4; 52; −52; −52
$\underline{?}\,(\underline{?}) = \underline{?}\,(\underline{?})$	Multiplication Property of Equality $\frac{1}{4}$; $4n$; $\frac{1}{4}$; 42
$n = \underline{?}$	Simplify. 10.5

Be sure to check your solution.

Accommodating the Learner

Students who are likely to have difficulty with problems like Examples 2 or 3 will need additional time. Plan for at least one additional day for these students. On the first day, have them practice only those problems like Example 1, and then have them write and study the note-taking tips in this section. You could introduce the other examples on the second day after students have had time to study the note-taking tips.

---

2 Teaching

Notes on the Lesson

It is important for students to realize that there are only two major steps in solving an equation of the form $ax + b = c$, as shown in Example 1. Other steps merely involve doing arithmetic.

Variations of $ax + b = c$. You may wish to have students identify a, b, and c in the various forms. You must point out that a is the coefficient of the unknown (for which you are solving), b is the constant on the same side of the equation as the unknown, and c is the constant on the other side of the equation. For instance, in $5W + 4 = 14$, $4 + 5W = 14$, or $14 = 4 + 5W$, $a = 5$, $b = 4$, and $c = 14$.

Additional Examples

Example 1 Solve $-\frac{2}{9}x - 1 = 3$.

$$-\frac{2}{9}x - 1 + \frac{\underline{?}}{1} = 3 + \frac{\underline{?}}{1}$$
$$-\frac{2}{9}\,\underline{?}\; x = \underline{?}\; 4$$
$$-\frac{9}{2}\,\underline{?}\;\left(-\frac{2}{9}x\right) = \left(-\frac{9}{2}\right)4$$
$$x = \underline{?}\; -18$$

Example 2 When Sam works at a local college on Saturdays, he earns $8.20 per hour.

He is also paid $5.00 for meals and $4.00 for transportation. Last Saturday he received $68.45. How many hours did he work? **Sam worked 7.25 hr.**

Example 3 The area of the rectangle is 78 cm². What is the value of n?

$2n + 1$

6

$\underline{?} \cdot \underline{?} = 78$	6; $2n + 1$
$\underline{?}\,n + 6 = 78$	12
$\underline{?}\,n + 6 + \underline{?} = 78 + \underline{?}$	12; −6; −6
$\underline{?}\,n = 72$	12
$n = \underline{?}$	6

3 Assignment

Recommended Assignment
- Questions 1–29
- Questions 30 and 31 (extra credit)
- Reading Lesson 3-5
- Covering the Ideas 3-5

Notes on the Questions
Question 3 Look back at Question 2. Ask students what has been done to both sides in Steps 1 and 2 in terms of a, b, and c. ($-b$ was added to both sides; both sides were multiplied by $\frac{1}{a}$.)

Question 4 The question may seem easy, but for many students it is not.

Questions 6–13 You may wish to ask students for the values of a, b, and c in each equation. (For example, in Question 7, $a = 11$, $b = -24$, and $c = 31$.) Questions 10–13 are particularly important so that students do not think that a, b, and c must be integers.

Note-Taking Tips
Have the students put the following steps in their notebook to solve problems involving multi-step equations with variables on one side:

1. Write an equation and simplify it as much as possible (until there are three terms at most).
2. Undo the constant term that is being added or subtracted from the side that has the variable.
3. Undo the coefficient that is being multiplied by the variable.
4. If the equation is in simplest form (x = answer), then check by replacing the variable with the answer to ensure that the answer yields a true equation.

Variations of $ax + b = c$

If an equation has the variable on the right side, as in $c = ax + b$, the solution can still be obtained by adding the opposite of b, and multiplying by the reciprocal of a. The Commutative Property of Addition also implies that $ax + b = c$ is equivalent to $b + ax = c$. For example, the following equations can be solved with the same major steps.

$$7 = \frac{3}{2}x - 53 \qquad -53 + \frac{3}{2}x = 7$$

$$\frac{3}{2}x - 53 = 7 \qquad 7 = -53 + \frac{3}{2}x$$

Questions

COVERING THE IDEAS

1. a. **Fill in the Blanks** When solving $7t - 57 = 97$, first add __?__ to both sides. Then __?__ each side by __?__. 57; multiply; $\frac{1}{7}$
   b. Solve and check $7t - 57 = 97$. $t = 22$; $7(22) - 57 = 154 - 57 = 97$

2. Steps in solving $73y - 432 = 1{,}101$ are shown here.
   Given: $73y - 432 = 1{,}101$

   Step 1 $73y = 1{,}533$

   Step 2 $y = 21$

   a. What was done to arrive at Step 1? 432 was added to each side.
   b. What was done to arrive at Step 2? Each side was multiplied by $\frac{1}{73}$.

In 3 and 4, the equation is in the form $ax + b = c$. Find the values of a, b, and c.

3. $73y - 432 = 1{,}101$
   $a = 73$; $b = -432$; $c = 1{,}101$

4. $17 - 4y = 88$
   $a = -4$; $b = 17$; $c = 88$

5. **Multiple Choice** How do the solutions to $50x - 222 = 60$ and $60 = 50x - 222$ compare? A
   A They are equal.
   B They are opposites.
   C They are reciprocals.
   D None of these are true.

In 6–13, solve and check the equation. See checks at the right.

6. $6x + 42 = 126$ $x = 14$
7. $31 = 11A - 24$ $A = 5$
8. $-20y - 2 = 8$ $y = -\frac{1}{2}$
9. $18 = 16 + 5B$ $B = \frac{2}{5}$
10. $7 + \frac{3}{5}d = -5$ $d = -20$
11. $2.4n - 2.4 = 2.4$ $n = 2$
12. $1.06P + 3.25 = 22.86$
    $P = 18.5$
13. $200 = 4 - \frac{7}{2}m$ $m = -56$

6. $6(14) + 42 =$
   $84 + 42 = 126$

7. $11(5) - 24 =$
   $55 - 24 = 31$

8. $-20\left(-\frac{1}{2}\right) - 2 =$
   $10 - 2 = 8$

9. $16 + 5\left(\frac{2}{5}\right) =$
   $16 + 2 = 18$

10. $7 + \frac{3}{5}(-20) =$
    $7 - 12 = -5$

11. $2.4(2) - 2.4 =$
    $4.8 - 2.4 = 2.4$

12. $1.06(18.5) + 3.25$
    $= 19.61 + 3.25 =$
    22.86

13. $4 - \frac{7}{2}(-56) =$
    $4 + 196 = 200$

Accommodating the Learner

If you feel that students are comfortable solving equations using these methods, have them explore the table function on a graphing calculator to solve the equation $2x + 7 = 29$. They should enter $2x + 7$ in the $Y1 = $ " line. Then use the table function to find the solution. They may need to set the table to accept their values for x instead of using automatic values. Students will discover that 11 is the value for x that gives a y value of 29.

14. Write directions to teach a friend how to solve the equation given in Question 6 in a step-by-step process, but do not tell your friend the exact equations. Answers vary. Sample answer: Add -42 to both sides, and then multiply both sides by $\frac{1}{6}$.

APPLYING THE MATHEMATICS

In 15–17, a situation is given.
a. Write an equation of the form $ax + b = c$ to describe the situation. Be sure to identify what the unknown variable represents.
b. Solve the equation and answer the question.

15. Ms. Toshio bought gas for $2.39 per gallon and a drink for $1.50. The total bill was $31.15 before sales tax. How many gallons of gas did she buy? 15a–b. See margin.

16. Bena lives in Delaware, where there is no sales or meals tax. She bought three chicken sandwiches with a $10 bill and received $1.45 change. What was the price of one sandwich? 16a–b. See margin.

17. Eighty students from a school went to the taping of a television program. They filled 7 rows of seats and there were 3 students in the eighth row. How many seats were in each row? 17a–b. See margin.

The average price per gallon of unleaded gasoline in 2004 in the United States was $1.92.

Source: U.S. Department of Energy

18. **Skill Sequence** Solve for n in each equation.

a. $17n + 38 = 4$
   $n = -2$
b. $-2n + 15 = 7$
   $n = 4$
c. $3n + a = 9$
   $n = 3 - \frac{a}{3}$

In 19–22, solve and check the equation.

19. $\frac{11}{17}x + \frac{17}{11} = 11\frac{11}{17}$

20. $0.003 = 0.02y - 0.1$

21. $\frac{4}{3}\left(a - \frac{1}{2}\right) = 3\frac{1}{3}$

22. $2.08 + 4.2n = 41.56$

19. $x = \frac{1,889}{121} \approx$
    $15.61; \frac{11}{17}\left(\frac{1,889}{121}\right)$
    $+ \frac{17}{11} = \frac{1,889}{187} + \frac{17}{11}$
    $= 11\frac{11}{17}$

20. $y = 5.15;$
    $0.02(5.15) - 0.1$
    $= 0.103 - 0.1 =$
    0.003

21. $a = 3; \frac{4}{3}\left(3 - \frac{1}{2}\right)$
    $= \frac{4}{3}\left(\frac{5}{2}\right) = 3\frac{1}{3}$

22. $n = 9.4; 2.08 +$
    $4.2(9.4) = 2.08 +$
    $39.48 = 41.56$

REVIEW

23. Consider the balance below. (Lesson 3-3)

a. What equation is shown? $7x + 1 = 15$
b. What two steps can be done with the weights on the balance to find the weight of a single box?
c. How much does a single box weigh? 2 oz

23b. Remove 1 oz from each side. Leave one-seventh of the weight on each side.

Additional Answers

15a. Let g be the number of gallons the driver bought. Then, $1.50 + 2.39g = 31.15$.

15b. g is about 12.4 gallons

16a. Let p be the price of one sandwich. Then, $3p + 1.45 = 10$.

16b. $p = \$2.85$

17a. Let r be the number of seats in a row. Then, $3 + 7r = 80$.

17b. $r = 11$ seats

Notes on the Questions
Questions 15–17 Repeatedly emphasize that students should be able to solve a problem regardless of the numbers in it. Here we modify **Example 2** by changing the numbers. Some students can answer these questions without setting up an equation. More power to them! But emphasize that when the numbers are complicated, solving the equation is the easier route.

Questions 30 and 31 These questions discuss the general algorithm for solving equations of the form $ax + b = c$.

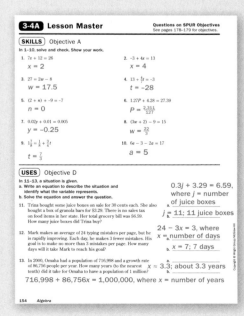

3-4

4 Wrap-Up

Ongoing Assessment

Have each student solve the following equations using any method in Chapter 3. Have students pair up and exchange papers to check.

1. Solve $\frac{1}{2}x - 7 = -15$. x = -16

2. Solve $27 = 15 + 6x$. x = 2

3. When Kim works at an ice cream shop on Saturdays she earns $6.50 per hour. She is also paid $3.00 for meals and $8.00 for transportation. Last Saturday she received $79.25. How many hours did she work? Kim worked 10.5 hr.

Project Update

Project 3, Integer Solutions to Linear Equations, and Project 4, Combining Linear Equations, on pages 174 and 175 relate to the content of this lesson.

24. **True or False** Determine whether the given equation is equivalent to $\frac{1}{2}x + 1 = 21$. (Lesson 3-3)

a. $x + 2 = 42$ true

b. $-x + 2 = -38$ true

c. $x = 40$ true

d. $\frac{1}{4}x + \frac{1}{4} = \frac{21}{4}$ false

25. a. Graph the following set of points: {(1, 2), (3, 4), (5, 6), (7, 8), (9, 10)}. (Lessons 3-1, 1-4)

b. These points are collinear. The point (99, 63a + 10) is on that line. What is a? $a = \frac{10}{7} \approx 1.43$

c. **Fill in the Blank** The point $(m, \underline{\ ?\ })$ is also on this line. m + 1

In 26–28, apply the Distributive Property to rewrite the expression with fewer terms. (Lessons 2-4, 2-2, 2-1)

26. $7p + q - 7(q + 6p)$ –35p – 6q

27. $-(a - b) + 2(a + b)$ a + 3b

28. $3(-2n - 5) - 2(-3n + 5)$ –25

29. Suppose $y = 11 - (9 - 14x)$. If x is 9, what is y? (Lesson 1-1) y = 128

EXPLORATION

30. Solve the general equation $ax + b = c$ for x. $x = \frac{c - b}{a}$

31. Consider equations of the form $ax + b = c$, where $a \neq 0$.

a. Write a program for a calculator or a computer that accepts values of a, b, and c as input and gives the value of x as output.

b. Run your program with different values of a, b, and c that lead to both positive and negative solutions. 31a–b. See margin.

25a.

Additional Answers

31a. Answers vary. Sample answer: (for a TI-73 or TI-84):
Disp "AX + B = C"
Disp "A = "
Input A
Disp "B = "
Input B
Disp "C = "
Input C
ClrScreen
(C − B)/A → X
Disp "X = ", X
Pause

31b. Answers vary. Sample answer: For a positive result, try A = 2.4, B = −11, and C = 19. For a negative result, try A = 99, B = 88, and C = 77.

Lesson 3-5

Using the Distributive Property in Solving Equations

> **BIG IDEA** By collecting like terms or expanding expressions, you can transform many equations into the form $ax + b = c$.

Solving Equations by Collecting Like Terms

We need to solve $c + c + \frac{1}{2}c + \frac{1}{2}c + \frac{1}{2}c + 15{,}000 = 260{,}000$ in Example 1. It takes only one step more to solve this equation than to solve an equation in the form of $ax + b = c$. The first step is to simplify the left side of the expression. Simplifying sides of equations is common in solving equations.

Mental Math

a. How many cups is $\frac{1}{3}$ of 2 cups? $\frac{2}{3}$ cup

b. How many cups is $\frac{1}{3}$ of 4 cups? $1\frac{1}{3}$ cups

c. How many cups is $\frac{1}{3}$ of n cups? $\frac{n}{3}$ cups

Example 1

A \$260,000 estate is to be split among two children, three grandchildren, and a charity. Each child receives the same amount, while each grandchild receives half that amount. If the charity receives \$15,000, how much will each child receive?

Solution First identify the unknown. Let $c =$ the portion a child receives. Then $\frac{1}{2}c$ is a grandchild's portion of the estate.

Now translate the given information into an equation.

$$c + c + \tfrac{1}{2}c + \tfrac{1}{2}c + \tfrac{1}{2}c + 15{,}000 = 260{,}000$$

Step 1 Use the Distributive Property to add the like terms.

$$3\tfrac{1}{2}c + 15{,}000 = 260{,}000$$

Now the equation is in the form $ax + b = c$ and can be solved in two steps.

Step 2 Add –15,000 to each side. Rewrite $3\frac{1}{2}$ as 3.5 to make the computation easier.

$$3.5c + 15{,}000 + {-15{,}000} = 260{,}000 + {-15{,}000}$$
$$3.5c = 245{,}000$$

Step 3 Multiply each side by $\frac{1}{3.5}$.

$$c = 70{,}000$$

Each child will receive \$70,000.

(continued on next page)

Background

The equations here illustrate two major applications of the Distributive Property: collecting like terms and removing parentheses. Examples 1 and 2 require collecting terms, while Examples 3 through 5 involve removing parentheses. In each case, the idea is for students to apply the Distributive Property to reduce the equation to one of the type $ax + b = c$.

Lesson 3-5

GOAL

Use the Distributive Property in solving linear equations.

SPUR Objectives

A Solve and check linear equations of the form $ax + b = c$.

D Use linear equations and inequalities of the form $ax + b = c$ or $ax + b < c$ to solve real-world problems.

Materials/Resources

· Lesson Master 3-5A or 3-5B
· Resource Masters 1, 2, and 40
· Graphing calculator
· Graph paper

HOMEWORK

Suggestions for Assignment
• Questions 1–25
• Questions 26 and 27 (extra credit)
• Reading Lesson 3-6
• Covering the Ideas 3-6

Local Standards

1 Warm-Up

Solve each equation.

1. $5A = 40$ $A = 8$
2. $-2B + 7B = 11$ $B = \frac{11}{5}$
3. $50c - 18c + 5 = -27$ $c = -1$
4. $2(3D + 6) - D = 15$ $D = \frac{3}{5}$
5. $2(4 - E) - 3(5 - 2E) = 251$ $E = \frac{129}{2}$

3-5

2 Teaching

Notes on the Lesson

In this lesson, students should practice solving equations and discussing what they have done. This can be done in small groups or as the class as a whole. Examples should be reviewed to serve as models for solutions.

Example 1 When students solve equations like the one in Example 1, make sure they do not lose track of the original problem. The check in Example 1 is *not* of the equation, but with the information given in the original problem.

Example 2 This example is intended to teach students that $9y - y$ does not simplify to 9.

Additional Examples

Example 1 A $350,000 estate is to be split among four children, six grandchildren, and a charity. Each child gets the same amount while each grandchild gets half that amount. If the charity receives $35,000, how much will each child receive? **$45,000**

Example 2 Solve $12y - y = 77$. **$y = 7$**

Example 3 Solve $5(x + 2) = -35$. **$x = -9$**

Check Each grandchild receives half as much as a child. This amount is $35,000. So the two children, three grandchildren, and the charity will receive $2 \cdot 70,000 + 3 \cdot 35,000 + 15,000$ dollars.
Does $2 \cdot 70,000 + 3 \cdot 35,000 + 15,000 = 260,000$? Yes.

Notice that in Example 1 we check the result not by substituting into the original equation, but by checking if the numbers work in the original statement of the problem.

Sometimes the use of the Distributive Property will result in an equation that requires only one step for its solution.

Example 2

Solve $9y - y = 40$.

Solution

Write the equation.

$9y - y = 40$

Many students like to rewrite y as $1 \cdot y$ to make the use of the Distributive Property more obvious.

$9y - 1y = 40$	$y = 1 \cdot y$
$(9 - 1)y = 40$	Distributive Property
$8y = 40$	Combine like terms.
$\frac{8y}{8} = \frac{40}{8}$	Divide each side by 8.
$y = 5$	Simplify.

Check

Substitute 5 for y in the original equation.

Does $9(5) - 5 = 40$?
$45 - 5 = 40$?
$40 = 40$? Yes.

Solving Equations by Removing Parentheses

You can use the Distributive Property to remove parentheses that appear in equations.

Example 3

Solve $2(x + 3) = 7$.

Accommodating the Learner ⬆

Have students who are performing above average on solving equations check solutions to equations on a graphing calculator. Have them graph the line $y_1 = 2x + 7$ on the graphing calculator and use the trace function to move along the line and find that when $x = 11$, $y = 29$. This is the solution to $2x + 7 = 29$. They could also graph $y_2 = 29$ and find the point of intersection of the two graphs on their calculator. **(11, 29)**

Solution

$$2(x + 3) = 7 \qquad \text{Write the equation.}$$
$$2x + 6 = 7 \qquad \text{Distributive Property}$$
$$2x + 6 - 6 = 7 - 6 \qquad \text{Subtraction Property of Equality}$$
$$2x = 1 \qquad \text{Simplify.}$$
$$\frac{2x}{2} = \frac{1}{2} \qquad \text{Division Property of Equality}$$
$$x = \frac{1}{2} \qquad \text{Simplify.}$$

Check

Is $2(\frac{1}{2} + 3) = 7$?
$$2(3\frac{1}{2}) = 7$$
$$7 = 7 \text{ Yes.}$$

Example 4

A company charges $29.95 each day to rent a truck, with the first 50 miles free. Subsequently, the cost is $0.60 per mile. Therefore, if the truck is driven m miles (where $m \geq 50$), the total rental cost is $29.95 + 0.60(m - 50)$ dollars. Isabel rented a truck for one day and paid $100.15. How many miles did Isabel drive?

Solution

Let the total cost equal $100.15 to determine how far the truck was driven.

$$29.95 + 0.60(m - 50) = 100.15$$
$$29.95 + 0.60m - 0.60 \cdot 50 = 100.15$$
$$29.95 + 0.60m - 30 = 100.15$$
$$0.60m - 0.05 = 100.15$$
$$0.60m = 100.20$$
$$m = 167$$

The truck was driven 167 miles.

STOP QY

In the U.S., one in five households moves every year, or 20% of the population.

Source: www.ourtownamerica.com

GUIDED

Example 5

Solve $2(3k + 4) - (9k - 7) = 6$.

(continued on next page)

Notes on the Lesson

Example 4 For Example 4, you might wish to ask students how they could check the answer. (If the truck is driven 167 miles, then the total rental cost is $29.95 + 117 miles · $0.60/mile = $29.95 + $70.20 = $100.15, so 167 miles is the correct answer.)

Guided Example 5 Decide for yourself whether all these steps are needed in a student solution. Must students put in the step where −15 is added to both sides? Should students think of that step as adding −15 or subtracting 15? Either is acceptable. You might also decide whether, in going from $-3k = -9$ to $k = 3$, you want students to think of dividing both sides by −3, as done here, or as multiplying both sides by $-\frac{1}{3}$. Either way is acceptable.

Additional Examples

Example 4 A company charges $99.95 per weekend to rent a truck, with the first 100 miles free. After that the cost is $0.65 a mile. Therefore, if the truck is driven m miles (where $m \geq 100$), the total rental cost is $99.95 + 0.65(m - 100)$ dollars. Julie rented a truck for one weekend and paid $277.40. How many miles did Julie drive? **373 mi**

Example 5 Solve.
$$3(4m + 3) - (14m - 11) = 8$$

$$\underline{\frac{?}{12}} m + 9 - 14m \underline{\frac{?}{+11}} = 8$$

$$\underline{\frac{?}{-2}} m + \underline{\frac{?}{20}} = 8$$

$$-2m + 20 \underline{\frac{?}{-20}} = 8 - 20$$

$$\underline{\frac{?}{-2m}} = \underline{\frac{?}{-12}}$$

$$m = \underline{\frac{?}{6}}$$

Accommodating the Learner

Have students simplify the expression $2(x + 4)$. Remind them that when a number is in front of a set of parentheses the implied operation is multiplication, and that they should distribute the 2 to each of the terms inside the parentheses to get $2x + 8$. Then have students simplify the expression $7x - 2x + 15$. Remind them that in simplifying, if there are any terms that are "like terms" they need to be combined by adding the coefficients. This expression simplifies to $5x + 15$.

3-5

Recommended Assignment
- Questions 1–25
- Questions 26 and 27 (extra credit)
- Reading Lesson 3-6
- Covering the Ideas 3-6

Notes on the Questions
Question 7 This question is like Example 2.

Question 11 This question is like Example 1.

Question 12 This question is like Example 4.

Solution

$$2(3k + 4) - (9k - 7) = 6$$ Write the equation.

$$\underline{} = 6$$ Distributive Property $6k + 8 - 9k + 7$

$$-3 \underline{}k + 15 = 6$$ Add like terms.

$$-3 \underline{}k + 15 - 15 = 6 - 15$$ $\underline{}$ Subtract 15 from each side.

$$-3 \underline{}k = \underline{} \quad -9$$ Add like terms.

$$\frac{-3k}{-3} \underline{?} = \underline{?} \quad \frac{-9}{-3}$$ Divide each side by –3.

$$k = \underline{?} \quad 3$$ Multiplication Property of Equality

Check Substitute 3 for k in the original equation.

Does $2(3 \cdot \underline{} + 4) - (9 \cdot \underline{} - 7) = 6$? 3; 3

Questions

COVERING THE IDEAS

In 1–10, solve the equation.

1. $3r + r = 8$ 2
2. $2x + 3x - 7 = 23$ 6
3. $14 = 3(x + 2)$ $\frac{8}{3}$
4. $2(4x - 9) = -2$ 2
5. $9 = 2(x + 2) + 2$ $\frac{3}{2}$
6. $5y - 3(5 - 2y) = -15$ 0
7. $42 = t - 7t$ –7
8. $3x - (x + 4) = 22$ 13
9. $13(t + 1) - 3(2 + 4t) = 38$ 31
10. $6(\frac{1}{2}b + 3) + 4(12 - b) = \frac{5}{6}$ $\frac{391}{6} \approx 65.17$

11. The winner of a car race received a prize of $150,000. Ten percent went to the driver and the rest was split among the 4 owners and the head mechanic, with the head mechanic getting half as much as the owners.

   a. Let E be the amount each owner received. Write an equation that can be solved to determine E.

   b. Find E and the amount the head mechanic received. $E = \$30,000$ and the head mechanic received $15,000.

12. In 2005, the federal income tax T for a single person whose taxable income I was between $7,300 and $29,700 was given by $T = 730 + 0.15(I - 7,300)$. This can be translated as $730 plus 15% of the amount over $7,300. If a single person paid $2,150 in income tax, what was the person's taxable income to the nearest dollar? $16,767

11a. Answers vary. Sample answer:
$15,000 + 4E + \frac{1}{2}E = 150,000$

Race cars can reach speeds in excess of 230 mph.

Source: National Aeronautics and Space Administration

APPLYING THE MATHEMATICS

13. The area A of a trapezoid with parallel bases b_1 and b_2 and height h is given by the formula $A = 0.5h(b_1 + b_2)$, as shown at the right.

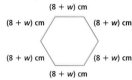

a. If $h = 6$ in., $b_2 = 4$ in., and $b_1 = 8$ in., calculate A. **36 in²**

b. If $A = 26$ in², $h = 4$ in., and $b_2 = 5$ in., calculate b_1. **8 in.**

c. If $A = 48$ in², $h = 4$ in., and $b_1 = 8$ in., calculate b_2. **16 in.**

14. If the perimeter of the rhombus at the right is 940 centimeters, find y.
$\frac{221}{6} \approx 36.83$ cm

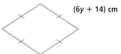

$(6y + 14)$ cm

15. Find the value of w in the regular hexagon at the right if each side has length $(8 + w)$ cm and the perimeter is 186 centimeters. **23 cm**

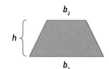

$(8 + w)$ cm
$(8 + w)$ cm $(8 + w)$ cm
$(8 + w)$ cm $(8 + w)$ cm
$(8 + w)$ cm

16. Find the value of z if the area of the rectangle at the right is 96 square miles. **6.5 mi**

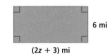

6 mi

$(2z + 3)$ mi

17. Suppose you have $100,000 to invest. You decide to put part of the money in a certificate of deposit (CD) that pays 6% annual interest and the rest in a savings account that pays 4% per year. If d dollars are invested in the CD, then $E = 0.06d + 0.04(100{,}000 - d)$ gives the interest earned E in one year. How much should you put in each place to earn $4,800 in the first year?
$40,000 in the CD, $60,000 in the savings account

REVIEW

In 18–20, solve and check the equation. **(Lesson 3-4)**

18. $\frac{4}{7}d + 9 = -11$ 19. $6.21 = 3.4 + -c$ 20. $\frac{1}{2}t + 4 = -2$

18. $d = -35;\ \frac{4}{7}(-35) + 9 = -20 + 9 = -11$

19. $c = -2.81;\ 3.4 + -(2.81) = 3.4 + 2.81 = 6.21$

20. $t = -12;\ \frac{1}{2}(-12) + 4 = -6 + 4 = -2$

21. There had already been 5 inches of snow on the ground when it started snowing at midnight. Snow continued to fall throughout the night, accumulating at three-quarters of an inch per hour. **(Lesson 3-4)**

a. How much snow was on the ground at 4 A.M.? **8 in.**

b. Winterville Junior High cancels school when there are more than 10 inches of snow on the ground. At what time was school canceled? **6:40 A.M.**

In the U.S., snow depth is usually reported to the nearest 1 inch. 24-hour snowfall is reported to the nearest 0.1 inch.

Source: National Oceanic & Atmospheric Administration

Using the Distributive Property in Solving Equations **153**

Notes on the Questions

Questions 13–16 We assume students have seen this vocabulary in previous courses. The usage here is to remind students of these terms. You might ask students to describe (if not define) each of the figures. Question 13: A *trapezoid* is a quadrilateral (4-sided polygon) with *at least* one pair of parallel sides. (Our definition is the one preferred by geometers.) Question 14: A *rhombus* is a quadrilateral with all sides of the same length. Question 15: A *regular hexagon* is a 6-sided polygon with all sides of the same length and all angles of the same measure. (The angles are not needed here.) Question 16: A *rectangle* is a quadrilateral with four right angles.

Question 17 In explaining the origin of the equation, an important idea is that if two numbers add up to 100,000 and one of them is d, then the other is $100{,}000 - d$.

Question 27 It is the sales tax that makes this a more difficult algebra problem, for if there were no sales tax, then the most expensive jeans you could afford would be the solution to $x + 20 = 64$.

Extension

Have students write and solve two problems using Example 1 and Example 4 for the pattern.

3-5

4 Wrap-Up

Ongoing Assessment

Divide students into pairs. Have each student write and solve an equation similar to Guided Example 5, with at least two sets of parentheses. Have students exchange papers and solve the equation their partner wrote. Students will have solved at least two equations. Repeat the process as many times as necessary.

22. Sareeta is planning a party and she wants to serve sandwiches to her guests. Each sandwich costs $4.50. **(Lessons 3-4, 3-1)**
    a. Labeling the *x*-axis *Number of Sandwiches* and the *y*-axis *Total Cost,* draw a graph to represent possible costs for the sandwiches. Use $0 \le x \le 20$.
    b. Suppose Sareeta paid $50 for the sandwiches and received $0.50 in change. How many sandwiches did she buy? (Assume there is no sales tax.) **11**

22a.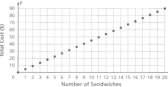

23. Sherman was twice as late arriving home today as he was yesterday. If he is supposed to be home at 5:00 P.M. each day and didn't arrive until 7:30 P.M. today, at what time did he get home yesterday? **(Lesson 3-3)** 6:15 P.M.

24. The perimeter of the triangle below is 54 yards. Find *x* and the length of the shortest side. **(Lesson 3-2)**

24. 7.5; so the shortest side is 14.5 yd.

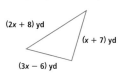

$(2x + 8)$ yd

$(x + 7)$ yd

$(3x - 6)$ yd

25. The equation $3\frac{1}{2}c = 245{,}000$ in Example 1 was solved by changing $3\frac{1}{2}$ to 3.5 then multiplying both sides by $\frac{1}{3.5}$. The equation can also be solved by multiplying by the reciprocal of $3\frac{1}{2}$. What is the reciprocal of $3\frac{1}{2}$? **(Lesson 2-8)** $\frac{2}{7}$

EXPLORATION

26. a. Solve the equation $mx + (m + 1)x = 8mx + 4$ for *x*.
    b. Check your solution by substituting a number for *m* and solving the resulting equation.

27. You have $64 and you want to buy a pair of jeans and a $20 T-shirt. There is a 7% sales tax. If *x* represents the cost of the jeans, then the equation $x + 20 + 0.07(x + 20) = 64$ shows how much you can spend on jeans. What is the price of the most expensive jeans you can afford? **$39.81**

26a. $\dfrac{-4}{6m - 1}$ or $\dfrac{4}{1 - 6m}$

26b. Answers vary. Sample answer: Let $m = 2$. Solve $2x + 3x = 8(2x) + 4$; $x = -\dfrac{4}{11}$ and $\dfrac{-4}{6m-1} = \dfrac{-4}{6(2) - 1} = -\dfrac{4}{11}$

Consumers in the United States spent about $329 billion on clothing and shoes in 2004.

Source: The World Almanac and Book of Facts

QY ANSWER

$134.95

154 Linear Equations and Inequalities

3-5B Lesson Master
Questions on SPUR Objectives
See pages 178–179 for objectives.

(SKILLS) Objective A

In 1–15, solve and check. Show your work.

1. $8x + -12x = 32$
   $x = -8$
2. $-41 = 6x + 7 - 18x$
   $x = 4$
3. $3(a + 10) = 15$
   $a = -5$

4. $\frac{5}{6}(12 - 5b) = 35$
   $b = -6$
5. $10 = \frac{5}{6}m - \frac{5}{6}m$
   $m = -12$
6. $\frac{7}{9}n + n = 4\frac{8}{9}$
   $n = 4$

7. $3.4c - (5c + 1) = -12.2$
   $c = 7$
8. $0.45(d - 1.2) + 0.67 = 5.53$
   $d = 12$
9. $-9e + 3.1 + 5e - 7.1 = 8$
   $e = -3$

10. $6(x - 1) - (x + 2) = -18$
    $x = -2$
11. $15 - 3(2 - f) - f = 19$
    $f = 5$
12. $99 = \frac{3}{4}(g + 2) + 12(g + 2)$
    $g = 6$

13. $-12 = -(3h - 1) + 4(2 - h)$
    $h = 3$
14. $7(k + 3) - 6(k + 3) = -6$
    $k = -9$
15. $6.1(x - 8) + 2.3(8 - x) = 7.6$
    $x = 10$

158 Algebra

3-5B page 2

(USES) Objective D

In 16–20, a situation is given.
a. Write an equation to describe the situation and identify what the variable represents if necessary.
b. Solve the equation and answer the question.

16. Braden, Brooke, and Brett work at a bike shop. Braden works *h* hours a week. Brooke works 5 more hours than Braden in a week. Brett works twice as many hours as Braden in a week. How many hours does Braden work in a week if altogether they work a total of 33 hours?
    a. $h + (h + 5) + 2h = 33$, where h = number of hours
    b. $h = 7$; 7 hours

17. Nancy has 60 feet of fencing to enclose a run for her dog, Daisy. She wants the run to be twice as long as it is wide. What dimensions should she use for the dog run?
    a. $2(2w) + 2w = 60$, where w = width
    b. $w = 10$; 10 ft wide, 20 ft long

18. Philip purchased *x* pairs of shoes for the school year. He also purchased jeans and T-shirts. The number of jeans is 3 more than the number of pairs of shoes and the number of T-shirts is twice as many as the number of pairs of jeans. How many shoes did he purchase if he purchased a total of 17 items?
    a. $s + (s + 3) + 2(s + 3) = 17$, where s = number of pairs of shoes
    b. $s = 2$; 2 pairs

19. Gary is planning to build a wooden deck shaped like a trapezoid. For cost reasons, he wants the area to be 240 square feet. The height of the trapezoid will be 12 feet and the shorter side will be 16 feet shorter than the longer side. Use the formula $A = 0.5h(b_1 + b_2)$ to find the length of the shorter and longer sides of the deck.
    a. $240 = 0.5(12)(x + (x - 16))$
    b. $x = 28$; shorter side = 12 ft, longer side = 28 ft

20. A deck is built around a pool. What is the value of *x* if the perimeter of the deck is 84 feet?
    $(3x + 5)$ ft
    a. $6(3x + 5) = 84$
    b. The value of *x* is 3.

Algebra 159

Lesson 3-6
Inequalities and Multiplication

▶ **BIG IDEA** Multiplying each side of an inequality by a positive number keeps the direction of the inequality; multiplying each side by a negative number reverses the direction of the inequality.

$x > y$ $3x > 3y$

Graphs and Inequalities on a Number Line

An **inequality** is a mathematical sentence with one of the verbs < ("is less than"), > ("is greater than"), ≤ ("is less than or equal to"), or ≥ ("is greater than or equal to").

Even though they look similar, equations and inequalities are different in important ways. Consider $x = 3$, $x > 3$, and $x \geq 3$. The equation $x = 3$ has just one solution, while the inequalities $x > 3$ and $x \geq 3$ have infinitely many solutions. Their graphs at the right show these differences.

In the graph of $x > 3$ on a number line, the 3 is marked with an open circle because 3 does not make the sentence $x > 3$ true. The number 3 is the **boundary point** between the values that satisfy $x > 3$ and those that do not. Numbers just a little larger than 3 such as 3.01 and $3\frac{34}{10,000}$ are solutions, as are larger numbers like 1 million. The graph of $x \geq 3$ does include 3 because the sentence $3 \geq 3$ is true. Another way to write $x \geq 3$ is to use set-builder notation. It is written as $\{x: x \geq 3\}$ and is read as "the set of all x such that x is greater than or equal to 3."

When solving real-world problems, you must often decide what domain makes sense for the situation. Inequalities are common in the world. For example, let x = a Fahrenheit temperature at which water is in solid form (ice). Then, since water freezes below 32°F, $x < 32$, as graphed at the right. The open circle at 32 shows that all numbers to the left of 32 are graphed, but not 32 itself.

Vocabulary

inequality
boundary point
interval
endpoint

Mental Math

Estimate to the nearest dollar.

a. 20% tip on a $49.56 bill $10

b. 20% tip on a $149.56 bill $30

c. 20% tip on a $249.56 bill $50

Exactly One Solution

$x = 3$

Infinitely Many Solutions

$x > 3$

$x \geq 3$

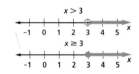

32

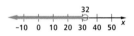

Lesson 3-6

GOAL
Review the vocabulary and basic properties of inequalities and apply them to the solution of inequalities of the form $ax < b$.

SPUR Objectives
C Apply the Addition and Multiplication Properties of Equality and Inequality.

F Graph all the solutions to a linear inequality.

Materials/Resources
· Lesson Master 3-6A or 3-6B
· Resource Masters 1, 2, 41, and 42
· Quiz 2
· Scientific or graphing calculator
· Computer Algebra System (CAS)
· Graph paper

HOMEWORK
Suggestions for Assignment
- Questions 1–25
- Question 26 (extra credit)
- Reading Lesson 3-7
- Covering the Ideas 3-7

Local Standards

1 Warm-Up

Place the appropriate <, =, or > sign between the numbers or expressions.

1. –50 __?__ 36   <

2. 7 · –50 __?__ 7 · 36   <

3. 0 · 50 __?__ 0 · 36   =

4. –2 · –50 __?__ 2 · 36   >

Suppose n is a negative number and p is a positive number. Place the appropriate <, =, or > sign between the expressions.

5. p __?__ n >   **6.** np __?__ $n \cdot n$ <

Background

This lesson is likely to have parts that are review (particularly if they have had previous UCSMP courses) and parts that are new. The language of endpoints, intervals, and the graphing of inequalities on a number line is meant to be review. It precedes a discussion of the one aspect of solving inequalities that differentiates them from solving equations, the Multiplication Property of Inequality, which we split into two parts. The easier Addition Property of

Inequality is discussed in the next lesson, but you may wish to bring it up now.

Inequality symbols. We use the term "inequality" to include sentences with any of the four signs <, ≤, >, or ≥, but we also include the ≠ sign here as a sign of inequality even though there are few rules for operating with inequalities of the form $a \neq b$.

3-6

2 Teaching

Notes on the Lesson

Graphs of inequalities on a number line. A common error is to graph the solutions to an inequality such as $x > 3$ as a set of dots beginning with 4 and proceeding through 5, 6, and so forth. Emphasize that the graph of an inequality such as $x > 3$ is a continuous ray starting at 3 without the endpoint 3, and that the graph of $x \geq 3$ includes that endpoint. To emphasize this idea, you might ask students for the smallest number on the graph of $x > 3$. Is it 3.1? 3.01? It is none of these. There is no smallest number.

Additional Answers

Activity

1.

2.

3.

4.

5.
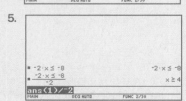

STOP QY

Some situations lead to *double inequalities*. Let E = the elevation of a place in the United States. Elevations in the United States range from 86 meters below sea level (in Death Valley) to 6,194 meters above sea level (at the top of Denali, also known as Mt. McKinley). So, $-86 \leq x \leq 6{,}194$. This double inequality is graphed below.

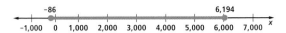

Draw dots on –86 and 6,194 to show that those numbers are included in the solution.

The graph of $-86 \leq x \leq 6{,}194$ is an *interval*. An **interval** is a set of numbers between two numbers a and b, which are called the **endpoints** of the interval. When the endpoints are included in the interval, it is described by $a \leq x \leq b$. If the endpoints are not included, the $\leq$ is replaced by $<$, giving $a < x < b$.

> **▶ QY**
>
> Write the solutions to the inequality $x < 32$ in set-builder notation.

The height of Mt. McKinley (Denali) is 20,320 feet.

Source: U.S. Geological Survey

Activity

The inequalities in 1–7 below are very similar. Use a CAS to solve each one. Record the operation you do to both sides and the inequality that results. A CAS screen for the first problem is shown. 1–7. See margin.

1. $2x < 8$ 2. $2x < -8$ 3. $2x \leq 8$ 4. $-2x < 8$

5. $-2x \leq -8$ 6. $2x > 8$ 7. $-2x \geq 8$

In 8 and 9, give what you expect the solution to be. Use a CAS to check your answer. 8–9. See margin for screens.

8. $4m > -20$ $m > -5$ 9. $-10w \leq 62$ $w \geq -6.2$

10. The inequalities you solved in 1–9 can be grouped into two categories whose solution processes are somewhat different. What are the two categories? **Answers vary. Sample answer: Inequalities with the variable being multiplied by a positive number or by a negative number**

The Multiplication Property of Inequality

Here are some numbers in increasing order. Because the numbers are in order, you can put the inequality sign ($<$) between any two of them.

$$-10 < -6 < 0 < 5 < 15$$

Additional Answers

Activity

6.
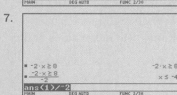

7.
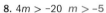

8.
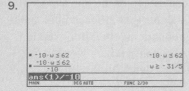

9.
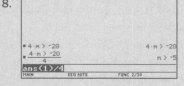

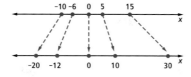

Now multiply these numbers by some fixed *positive* number, say 2.

$$-20 \quad -12 \quad 0 \quad 10 \quad 30$$

The order stays the same, as shown in the number line at the right.

You could still put a $<$ sign between any two of the numbers. This illustrates that if $x < y$, then $2x < 2y$. In general, multiplication by a positive number maintains the order of a pair or a list of numbers.

Multiplication Property of Inequality (Part 1)

If $x < y$ and a is *positive*, then $ax < ay$.

Here is the same list of numbers we used earlier.

$$-10 < -6 < 0 < 5 < 15$$

Now we multiply these numbers by -2 and something different happens.

$$20 \quad 12 \quad 0 \quad -10 \quad -30$$

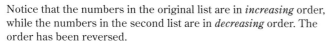

Notice that the numbers in the original list are in *increasing* order, while the numbers in the second list are in *decreasing* order. The order has been reversed.

If you multiply both sides of an inequality by a *negative* number, you must change the direction of the inequality. This idea can be generalized.

Multiplication Property of Inequality (Part 2)

If $x < y$ and a is *negative*, then $ax > ay$.

Changing from $<$ to $>$, or from $\leq$ to $\geq$, or vice-versa, is called *changing the sense of the inequality.* You have to change the sense of an inequality when you are multiplying both sides by a negative number. Otherwise, solving $ax < b$ is similar to solving $ax = b$.

Solving Inequalities

To solve an inequality of the form $ax < b$, you must isolate the variable on one side (just like solving an equation). Be careful to notice whether you multiply or divide each side by a positive number or a negative number.

Notes on the Lesson

The Multiplication Property of Inequality. There are many ways of visualizing the Multiplication Property of Inequality. One of these is given in this lesson after the Activity. The key is that the negative numbers proceed in absolute value in a direction opposite that of the positive numbers. If the two number lines and the arrows connecting the numbers are drawn accurately, then the arrows lie on concurrent lines. In the first illustration, the lines intersect above the top line. In the second illustration, the lines intersect between the parallel lines. In both cases, the point of intersection is on the line through the points with coordinate 0.

Solving inequalities. Even though the goal in solving an inequality is to isolate the variable, as in solving equations, some students will have difficulty applying the ideas of equations here. Emphasize the ways in which solving inequalities differs from solving equations. The solutions to inequalities usually cannot be listed, even with an infinite list such as 4, 5, ... So, either a graph or an equivalent, simple inequality must be given as the solution. The check is very important to help students grasp the essential aspects of the inequality.

Accommodating the Learner

Review the inequality symbols before beginning this lesson. If students are having trouble with the concept of between, have the students form a single file line across the front of the room. Have them line up from left to right according to order of birth and then ask the ones who were born before a certain date but after a certain date to step forward. (For example: Students born before October 5, 1993, but after April 5, 1993, step forward.)

3-6

Notes on the Lesson

In Example 1, to solve $-7x \geq 126$, we multiply both sides by the reciprocal of -7, which is $-\frac{1}{7}$. Just as -7 is negative, so is $-\frac{1}{7}$. Numbers and their reciprocals must have the same sign because their product is the positive number 1.

Additional Examples

Example 1 Solve $-5x \leq 35$ and check. $x \geq -7$; check $(-5)(-7) = 35$, $(-5)(-6) = 30$, which is less than 35

Example 2a. Solve $42 \geq 3x$ $x \leq 14$

b. Graph the solution.

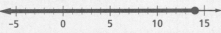
-5   0   5   10   15

c. Check your answer. $42 = 3(14)$; $42 \geq 3(13)$, $42 \geq 39$

Example 1

Solve $-7x \geq 126$ and check.

Solution Multiply both sides by $-\frac{1}{7}$, the reciprocal of -7. Since $-\frac{1}{7}$ is a negative number, Part 2 of the Multiplication Property of Inequality tells you to change the sense of the inequality sign from $\geq$ to $\leq$.

$-7x \geq 126$	Write the inequality.
$-\frac{1}{7} \cdot -7x \leq -\frac{1}{7} \cdot 126$	Multiply each side by $-\frac{1}{7}$.
$x \leq -\frac{126}{7}$	Simplify.
$x \leq -18$	Simplify.

Check

Step 1 Substitute -18 for x. Does $-7 \cdot -18 = 126$? Yes.

Step 2 Try a number satisfying $x < -18$. We use -20. Is $-7 \cdot -20 \geq 126$? Yes, $140 \geq 126$.

The two-step check of an inequality is important. The first step checks the boundary point in the solution. The second step checks the sense of the inequality.

> ▶ **READING MATH**
>
> Inequalities with variables are open sentences. When the variable is replaced with a number, the inequality is either true or false.

GUIDED

Example 2

a. Solve $20 \geq 4x$.

b. Graph the solution.

c. Check your answer.

Solutions

a.
$20 \;\; \geq \;\; 4x$	Write the inequality.
$\frac{1}{4} \cdot 20 \;\underline{\;?\;}\; \frac{1}{4} \cdot 4x$	Multiply each side by $\frac{1}{4}$. $\geq$
$5 \;\underline{\;?\;}\; x$	Simplify. $\geq$

This can be rewritten as $x \;\underline{\;?\;}\; 5$. $\leq$

b. Graph the solution on the number line.

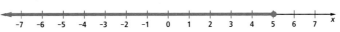
-7 -6 -5 -4 -3 -2 -1 0 1 2 3 4 5 6 7 x

c. **Step 1** Check the boundary point by substituting 5 for x.

Does $\underbrace{\;?\;}_{20} = 4(\underbrace{\;?\;}_{5})$? Yes

ENGLISH LEARNERS

Vocabulary Development

Have students add definitions found in this section to their vocabulary notes. Be sure they include the following: inequality, boundary point, endpoint, and interval. ELL students may have difficulty with *approximately equal to* and *Fahrenheit*.

Step 2 Check whether the sense of the inequality is correct. Pick some number from the shaded region in Part b. This number should also work in the original inequality. We choose 0.

Is __?__ ≥ 4(__?__)? Yes, __?__ ≥ __?__. 20; 0; 20; 0

Since both steps worked, the solution to 20 ≥ 4x can be described by the sentence __?__. $x \le 5$

Examples 1 and 2 showed solutions of two types of inequalities.

Multiplication Property of Inequality (in words)

You may multiply both sides of an inequality by the same *positive* number without affecting the set of solutions to the sentence. You can also multiply both sides by a *negative* number, but then you must also *change the sense of the inequality*.

Questions

COVERING THE IDEAS

In 1 and 2, consider the situation. a. Write an inequality that describes the situation. b. Identify the boundary point for the inequality. c. Graph the solution set of the inequality.

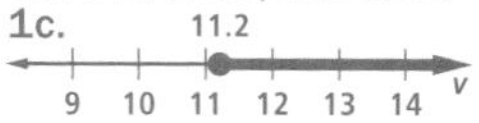

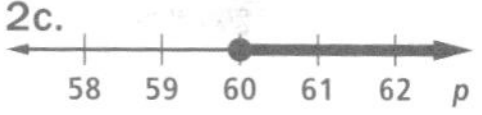

1. To successfully leave Earth's orbit, a satellite must be launched at a velocity of at least 11.2 kilometers per second. Let v be the launch velocity of a satellite in kilometers per second.

2. To obtain a passing grade on the Spanish exam, Marlene needs to answer at least 60 percent of the test items correctly. Let p be the percentage of items answered correctly.

3. Wakana's dog w weighs over 120 pounds, but not more than 130 pounds. Graph the possible values of w on a number line.

In 4 and 5, graph the inequality on a number line.

4. $x < 2\frac{1}{5}$

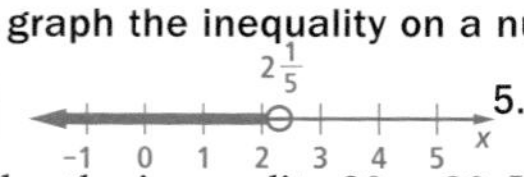

5. $y \le -3$

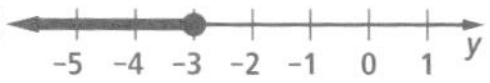

6. Consider the inequality 20 < 30. What true inequality results if you multiply both sides of the inequality by the given number?
   a. 6 **120 < 180**
   b. $\frac{1}{2}$ **10 < 15**
   c. −4 **−80 > −120**

In 7–12, solve the inequality. Then check your answer.

7. $15x > 5$
8. $-32 < 2n$
9. $\frac{4}{5}y \le 20$
10. $-\frac{3}{2}z \le 1$
11. $-3a \le -6$
12. $7b \ge 6$

The SBS-4 communications satellite is deployed from the space shuttle payload bay.

Source: National Aeronautics and Space Administration

Inequalities and Multiplication **159**

(Answer column)

1a. $v \ge 11.2$; 1b. 11.2
1c.
[number line: 9 10 11 12 13 14, point at 11.2, shaded right, v]

2a. $p \ge 60$; 2b. 60
2c.
[number line: 58 59 60 61 62, point at 60, shaded right, p]

3.
[number line: 120 122 124 126 128 130, open circle at 120, closed at 130, w]

7. $x > \frac{1}{3}$; $15(\frac{1}{3}) = 5$; Pick $x = 1$. $15(1) = 15 > 5$

8. $n > -16$; $2(-16) = -32$; Pick $n = 0$. $2(0) = 0 > -32$

9. $y \le 25$; $\frac{4}{5}(25) = 20$; Pick $y = 0$. $\frac{4}{5}(0) = 0 \le 20$

10. $z \ge -\frac{2}{3}$; $-\frac{3}{2}(-\frac{2}{3}) = 1$; Pick $z = 0$. $-\frac{3}{2}(0) = 0 \le 1$

11. $a \ge 2$; $-3(2) = -6$; Pick $a = 4$. $-3(4) = -12 \le -6$

12. $b \ge \frac{6}{7}$; $7(\frac{6}{7}) = 6$; Pick $b = 1$. $7(1) = 7 \ge 6$

---

3 Assignment

Recommended Assignment
- Questions 1–25
- Question 26 (extra credit)
- Reading Lesson 3-7
- Covering the Ideas 3-7

Notes on the Questions
Question 8 Some students become confused when the variable is on the right side. They could solve the equivalent inequality $2n > -32$. Switching the sides is not to be confused with doing something to both sides of the inequality; this is *rewriting* the inequality. Because of this confusion, our general practice is to keep the variable on the right side until the very end. Then, when the solution is described (in this case $-16 < n$), rewrite the solution so that the variable is on the left side ($n > -16$).

Accommodating the Learner ⬆

Have students who are comfortable working with inequalities write the following expressions algebraically using the proper inequality symbols.

1. Sam had at most $20 in his pocket.
   $S \le 20$

2. When rounded to the nearest tenth, the length of the wire must be 12.5 centimeters. **$12.45 \le x < 12.54$**

3. Susie must maintain a balance of at least $200 in her checking account to avoid any fees. **$b \ge 200$**

3-6

Notes on the Questions

Question 13 This question helps students understand the second part of the Multiplication Property of Inequality.

Question 14 The inequality sign will not switch when you take the reciprocals if one of the numbers is negative and one is positive. For example, $-5 < 2$, and also $-\frac{1}{5} < \frac{1}{2}$. (The inequality sign does not change.)

Question 17 The domain of the unknown is the set of whole numbers, so a graph of the inequality is most accurately a (finite) set of points.

13. Consider the following list of numbers. $\frac{1}{2}$, $\frac{1}{3}$, $\frac{1}{4}$, $\frac{1}{5}$, $\frac{1}{6}$
    a. Place an appropriate symbol between each pair of consecutive numbers ($<$, $\leq$, $\geq$, or $>$). $\frac{1}{2} > \frac{1}{3} > \frac{1}{4} > \frac{1}{5} > \frac{1}{6}$
    b. Multiply each number in the list by -8, then place an appropriate symbol between each pair of consecutive numbers ($<$, $\leq$, $\geq$, or $>$) in the new list. $-4 < -\frac{8}{3} < -2 < -\frac{8}{5} < -\frac{4}{3}$
    c. Did the direction of the symbols change in Part b? Why or why not? Yes, because we multiplied by a negative number.

APPLYING THE MATHEMATICS

14. Consider the following list of numbers. 10, 20, 30, 40, 50
    a. Place an appropriate symbol between each pair of consecutive numbers ($<$, $\leq$, $\geq$, or $>$). $10 < 20 < 30 < 40 < 50$
    b. Create a new list by taking the reciprocal of each number, then place an appropriate symbol between each pair of consecutive numbers ($<$, $\leq$, $\geq$, or $>$) in the new list.
    c. Did the direction of the symbols change in Part b? Why or why not?

14b. $\frac{1}{10} > \frac{1}{20} > \frac{1}{30} > \frac{1}{40} > \frac{1}{50}$

14c. Yes, because larger positive numbers have smaller reciprocals.

15. **Fill in the Blanks** If $6 \leq m \leq 6.2$, then $\underline{\quad?\quad} \leq 5m \leq \underline{\quad?\quad}$. 30; 31

In 16 and 17, read the problem situation. a. Write an inequality describing the situation. b. Solve the inequality.

16. An engineer is designing a rectangular parking lot that is to be 75 feet wide. According to the city building code, the area of the lot can be at most 6,250 square feet. What is the allowable length of the lot?

16a. Let ℓ be the length of the parking lot. Then, $75\ell \leq 6{,}250$.

16b. $\ell \leq \frac{250}{3}$ ft

17. A concert hall is being designed to seat at least 2,200 people. Each row will have 80 seats. How many rows of seats will the hall have?

17a. Let r be the number of rows. Then, $80r \geq 2{,}200$.

17b. $r \geq 27.5$ rows

REVIEW

18. The boxes are of unknown equal weight W. (**Lesson 3-5**)

18a. $4 + 2W = 12$

    a. What equation is pictured by the balance above?
    b. What two steps can be done with the weights on the balance to find the weight of a single box?
    c. How much does each box weigh? $W = 4$ oz

18b. First, remove 4 oz from each side. Then, take half of the boxes on the left side away and half of the ounces on the right side away.

In 19 and 20, solve the equation. (Lesson 3-5)

19. $-4(3x - 1.5) + 7 = 39$ **20.** $2(a + 5) - 3(5 + \frac{1}{2}a) = -19$

19. $x = -\frac{13}{6}$

20. $a = -28$

21. Grafton went to the store to buy bottles of soda and bags of chips for a party. He bought bottles of soda for $1.99 each and bags of chips for $2.99 each. He bought twice as many bags of chips as bottles of soda. After paying with two twenty-dollar bills, he received $0.15 in change. (Lessons 3-5, 3-3)

 a. Define a variable and write an equation describing the situation. Let p be the number of bottles of soda Grafton buys. Then, $1.99p + 2.99(2p) + 0.15 = 40$.

 b. How many bottles of soda and bags of chips did Grafton buy? 5 bottles of soda, 10 bags of chips

22. Multiple Choice How do the solutions to $2x - 111 = 35$ and $-35 = 2x + 111$ compare? (Lessons 3-4, 2-8, 2-4) B

 A They are equal. **B** They are opposites.

 C They are reciprocals. **D** none of the above

In 23 and 24, a fact triangle is given. Write the related facts and determine the value of *x*. (Lesson 2-7)

23.

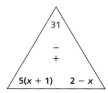

24.

23. $5(x + 1) + (2 - x) = 31$, $(2 - x) + 5(x + 1) = 31$, $31 - 5(x + 1) = 2 - x$, and $31 - (2 - x) = 5(x + 1)$; $x = 6$

24. $6(3x + 13) = 42$, $6 + (3x + 13) = 42$, $6 = \frac{42}{3x + 13}$, and $3x + 13 = \frac{42}{6}$; $x = -2$

25. Tomás drove at an average speed of 61 miles per hour for $3\frac{1}{4}$ hours. About how many miles did he travel? (Previous Course) 198.25 mi

EXPLORATION

26. A rectangle is 12 units by *w* units.

 a. Find the values of *w* that would make the area of the rectangle greater than 84 square units. $w > 7$

 b. Find the values of *w* that would make the area of the rectangle less than or equal to 216 square units. $w \leq 18$

 c. Write a sentence to explain what the inequality $60 \leq 12w < 108$ means in relation to the rectangle.

 d. Solve the inequality in Part c and explain its meaning. $5 \leq w < 9$, which means the width is at least 5 units, but less than 9 units.

26c. We know the area of the rectangle with length 12 units and width *w* is at least 60 square units but less than 108 square units.

w

12

QY ANSWER

$\{x: x < 32\}$

3-6

4 Wrap-Up

Ongoing Assessment

Graph each inequality on a number line.

1. $x \leq 4$

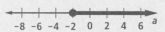

-8 -6 -4 -2 0 2 4 6 8 *x*

2. $a \geq -2$

-8 -6 -4 -2 0 2 4 6 *a*

3. $-4 \leq r \leq 5$

-5 -4 -3 -2 -1 0 1 2 3 4 5 6 *r*

4. $x < 1$

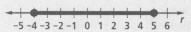

-8 -7 -6 -5 -4 -3 -2 -1 0 1 2 *x*

5. $b > 0$

-2 -1 0 1 2 3 4 5 6 7 *b*

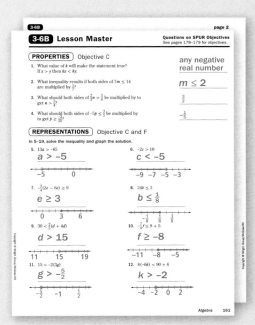

Lesson

3-7

GOAL

Solve sentences of the form $ax + b < c$ and recognize situations that lead to such sentences.

SPUR Objectives

B Solve and check linear inequalities of the form $ax + b < c$.

D Use linear equations and inequalities of the form $ax + b = c$ or $ax + b < c$ to solve real-world problems.

F Graph all the solutions to a linear inequality.

Materials/Resources

· Lesson Master 3-7A or 3-7B
· Resource Masters 7 and 43
· Scientific or graphing calculator

HOMEWORK

Suggestions for Assignment
• Questions 1–28
• Questions 29 and 30 (extra credit)
• Reading Lesson 3-8
• Covering the Ideas 3-8

Local Standards

1 Warm-Up

1. Find a positive number that is a solution to $31A + 5 < 6$. any number between 0 and $\frac{1}{31}$, for instance, 0.02

2. Find a negative number that is a solution to both $-3x > 12$ and $-4x < 17$. any number between −4 and −4.25

Lesson

3-7   Solving $ax + b < c$

> **BIG IDEA**   Inequalities of the form $ax + b < c$ can be solved in two steps, similar to those used in solving $ax + b = c$.

If you are x years old and an older friend's age is y, then you can write the inequality $x < y$ to compare the ages.

Six years from now you will still be younger than your friend. The inequality that compares your ages then is $x + 6 < y + 6$.

In general, H years from now you will still be younger than your friend. This is written as $x + H < y + H$.

These examples illustrate the *Addition Property of Inequality*.

Addition Property of Inequality

For all real numbers a, b, and c, if $a < b$, then $a + c < b + c$.

The Addition Property of Inequality can be represented with a balance, as shown below. Suppose a and b represent the weights of two packages where $a < b$.

If the same weight c is added to each side of the balance at the right, then $a + c < b + c$.

Inequalities containing $>$, $\geq$, or $\leq$ signs work in the same way. Thus, sentences with $=$, $<$, $>$, $\leq$, or $\geq$ can all be solved in the same way.

Addition Property of Inequality (in words)

You may add the same number to both sides of an inequality or equation without affecting the set of solutions to the sentence.

Mental Math

$n \| p$ and $m\angle 1 = 140°$.

a. What is $m\angle 2$? 40°

b. What is $m\angle 3$? 40°

Background

The steps used in solving $ax + b < c$ (add $-b$ to both sides, then multiply both sides by $\frac{1}{a}$) $\geq$ are the same for inequalities as for the corresponding equations $ax + b = c$. Thus this lesson also provides practice in solving linear equations. But the checks are different, requiring checking both the boundary point and the direction of the inequality.

Remember that $b - a = b + -a$, so you can convert any subtraction expression to an addition expression. This means you may subtract the same number from each side of an inequality or equation without affecting its solutions.

Solving Inequalities with Positive Coefficients

The process of solving inequalities of the form $ax + b < c$ is quite similar to that of solving equations.

Example 1

A crate weighs 7 kilograms when empty. An orange weighs about 0.3 kilogram. For shipping, the crate and oranges must weigh at least 70 kilograms. How many oranges should be put in the crate?

Solution Let n be the number of oranges. Then the weight of n oranges is $0.3n$. The weight of the crate with n oranges is $0.3n + 7$, so the question can be answered by solving the inequality $0.3n + 7 \geq 70$.

This is of the form $ax + b \geq c$ and is solved the same way as $ax + b = c$.

$0.3n + 7 + -7 \geq 70 + -7$ Add -7 to both sides.

$\qquad 0.3n \geq 63$ Simplify.

$\qquad \dfrac{0.3n}{0.3} \geq \dfrac{63}{0.3}$ Divide each side by 0.3.

$\qquad n \geq 210$ Simplify.

At least 210 oranges should be put in the crate.

Check

Step 1 Check the boundary of $n \geq 210$.

Is $0.3(210) + 7 = 70$?
$\qquad 70 = 70$ Yes

Therefore, 210 is the boundary point.

Step 2 Pick a number that satisfies the inequality $n \geq 210$. We choose 250.

Is $0.3(250) + 7 \geq 70$?
$\qquad 82 \geq 70$ Yes

Since both Steps 1 and 2 produce true statements, $n \geq 210$ describes the solutions to the original inequality.

The United States produced almost 295 million boxes of oranges in 2004.

Source: U.S. Department of Agriculture

Solving $ax + b < c$ **163**

3-7

2 Teaching

Notes on the Lesson

Addition Property of Inequality. If you are x years old and a friend's age is y, and you are younger, then $x < y$, and six years from now you will still be younger: $x + 6 < y + 6$. Also, three years ago, you were younger: $x - 3 < y - 3$. So whether you add or subtract the same number to both sides of an inequality, the sense of the inequality stays the same.

Additional Example

Example 1 An educational supply company does not charge for shipping orders of $450 or more. Mrs. Jenkins needs a microscope that costs $149.99 and she needs at least one hundred-twenty sets of micropipette ends, which are disposable and are a reoccurring expense for her Biology classes. Although she needs at least one hundred-twenty sets she can use more. Micropipette end sets cost $1.98. If Mrs. Jenkins wants to avoid shipping charges, how many micropipette end sets should she buy? **at least 152**

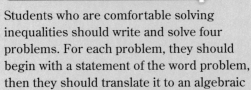

Accommodating the Learner ↑

Students who are comfortable solving inequalities should write and solve four problems. For each problem, they should begin with a statement of the word problem, then they should translate it to an algebraic inequality, and finally, they should find the solution. Have students write one problem using each of these expressions: at most, at least, no more than, and between but not including.

3-7

Notes on the Lesson

Example 2 Because students know they must reverse the sense of the inequality when they *multiply* both sides by a negative number, they may think that they should also reverse the sense when they *add* a negative number to both sides. Use Example 2 to note that adding the same number to both sides does not change the sense of the inequality.

Additional Example

Example 2 Before the city pool closed for summer the water level was 8 feet. The city maintenance man began emptying the pool. He noticed that the depth of the pool decreased 0.75 foot each hour. How many hours will it take for the depth of the pool to be 0.5 foot or less? **at least 10 hours**

Note-Taking Tips

You could have students write the following steps for solving inequality problems in their notes.

1. Write an inequality in algebraic form then simplify by combining like terms.
2. Undo the constant term that is being added or subtracted on the side with the variable.
3. Undo the multiplication or division last, remembering that if you multiply or divide by a negative number, the inequality symbol changes.

Solving Inequalities with Negative Coefficients

Remember the Multiplication Property of Inequality when solving inequalities with negative coefficients. Example 2 is about drought, a natural phenomenon that affects many communities.

Example 2

Suppose that during a particularly dry summer, the level of water in a local reservoir decreased 1.5 feet each week. At the start of summer, the water level was 60 feet. When the water level is 30 feet or less, a "water emergency" is put into effect, with various water conservation measures enacted. When will a water emergency be in effect?

Solution First, express the problem as an inequality. Let x represent the number of weeks from the start of summer. Since the water level is initially 60 feet and the water level decreases 1.5 feet each week, the water level in week x is $60 - 1.5x$. A water emergency is put into effect when the water level is 30 feet or less. The problem is solved with the inequality $60 - 1.5x \leq 30$. Solve this inequality.

$60 - 1.5x + \text{-}60 \leq 30 + \text{-}60$ Add -60 to each side.

$-1.5x \leq -30$ Simplify.

$-1.5x \cdot -\frac{1}{1.5} \geq -30 \cdot -\frac{1}{1.5}$ Multiply each side by $-\frac{1}{1.5}$.
       Reverse the inequality sign.

$x \geq 20$ Simplify.

Here is a graph of the solutions.

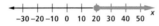

STOP QY

The worst drought in 50 years affected at least 35 states during the long hot summer of 1988. Rainfall totals over the Midwest, Northern Plains, and the Rockies were 50–85% below normal.

Source: National Weather Service

> ▶ **QY**
>
> Check that $\{x: x \geq 20\}$ is the set of solutions to Example 2 using the two-step check in Example 1.

Questions

COVERING THE IDEAS

1. Use the symbol $>$ to state the Addition Property of Inequality.

2. a. What inequality is suggested at the right?
   b. What is the solution to the inequality? $W > 2$ oz

1. For real numbers a, b, and c, if $a > b$, then $a + c > b + c$.

2a. $3 + 4W > 11$

Accommodating the Learner ⬇

You should divide the assignment for students who are having difficulty with writing inequalities in algebraic form. First, they should study the following list of common words and phrases used in inequalities: at most ($\leq$), at least ($\geq$), no more than ($\leq$), more than ($>$), less than ($<$), between ($a < x < b$); and secondly, they should study the note-taking tips.

In 3–6, solve, graph, and check the inequality. **3–6. See margin for graphs and checks.**

3. $3x + 4 < 19$ $x < 5$

4. $6 \leq 4b + 10$ $b \geq -1$

5. $5 \leq -3n + 2 - 7n + 203$ $n \leq 20$

6. $-101 - 102x < 103$ $x > -2$

7. T-shirts can be ordered from the Sports Central catalog for $7.50 each, with a shipping fee of $4 for the order. A team wants to spend $300 on shirts to give away to fans. How many shirts can they buy? **39 shirts**

APPLYING THE MATHEMATICS

In 8–13, solve the inequality.

8. $6(-4x - 23) - 73 < 77$ $x > -12$

9. $-0.2y + \frac{1}{2} \geq 0.48$ $y \leq 0.1$

10. $15 \geq 12 + \frac{1}{3}a$ $a \leq 9$

11. $\frac{-5d}{6} + 30 < 120$ $d > -108$

12. $11 - 5(16 - 7p) \geq 49$ $p \geq \frac{118}{35}$

13. $594 > -2(q - 9) + 3(7 - 8q) - 17$ $q > -22$

14. Using the graph of $y = 13x - 20$ at the right, find each of the following for $13x - 20 \leq 45$.
   a. the boundary point $x = 5$
   b. a value of x in the solution set
   c. a value of x *not* in the solution set
   d. an inequality using x that describes all solutions
   14b. Answers vary. Sample answer: $x = 3$
   14c. Answers vary. Sample answer: $x = 6$
   14d. $x \leq 5$

During sporting events, T-shirts are often launched into crowds with slingshots.

15. Using the table of values for $y = -9.6x - 41.4$ below, find each of the following for $-9.6x - 41.4 > -108.6$.

x	-3	-1	1	3	5	7	9	11	13
y	-12.6	-31.8	-51	-70.2	-89.4	-108.6	-127.8	-147	-166.2

   a. the boundary point $x = 7$
   b. a value of x in the solution set Answers vary. Sample answer: $x = 3$
   c. a value of x *not* in the solution set Answers vary. Sample answer: $x = 11$
   d. an inequality using x that describes all solutions $x < 7$

16. Use the formula $C = \frac{5}{9}(F - 32)$ to determine which Celsius temperatures are below $68°F$. $C < 20$

Solving $ax + b < c$ **165**

3 Assignment

Recommended Assignment
- Questions 1–28
- Questions 29 and 30 (extra credit)
- Reading Lesson 3-8
- Covering the Ideas 3-8

Notes on the Questions

Question 7 Students may wonder why they cannot just solve the equation $7.50t + 4.00 = 300.00$, find $t = 39.4$, and use that to answer the question. They must know that the answer is $t \leq 39$, so it is easier to begin with $7.50t + 4.00 \leq 300.00$.

Questions 8, 12, and 13 The solutions can be checked with a CAS using the SOLVE command, and the removing of parentheses can be checked with the EXPAND command.

Question 16 If students know the benchmark that $20°C = 68°F$, this question can be answered without solving an inequality. Otherwise, this can be a very difficult question for students to answer in a mathematically precise way. If they substitute 68 for F, they will find that $68°F = 20°C$. Then they must use a value greater than or less than 68 to find whether the answer is greater than or less than 20.

Question 28 This is a review in preparation for the next lesson.

Questions 29–30 To vary the question, you might ask students for five inequalities equivalent to $11 - x < 5$.

Additional Answers

3. 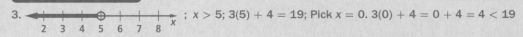 ; $x > 5$; $3(5) + 4 = 19$; Pick $x = 0$. $3(0) + 4 = 0 + 4 = 4 < 19$

4. ; $b \geq -1$; $4(-1) + 10 = -4 + 10 = 6$; Pick $b = 0$. $4(0) + 10 = 0 + 10 = 10 \geq 6$

5. ; $n \leq 20$; $-3(20) + 2 - 7(20) + 203 = 5$; Pick $n = 0$. $-3(0) + 2 - 7(0) + 203 = 205 \geq 5$

6. ; $x > -2$; $-101 - 102(-2) = -101 + 204 = 103$; Pick $x = 0$. $-101 - 102(0) = -101 < 103$

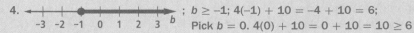

3-7

4 Wrap-Up

Ongoing Assessment
Have each student solve and graph on a number line the inequality $-2x - 5 < -11$. $x > 3$

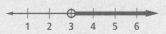

1 2 3 4 5 6

3-7B Lesson Master Questions on SPUR Objectives
See pages 178–179 for objectives.

(SKILLS) Objective B
In 1–9, solve the inequality and check your answer. Show your work.

1. $5x - 7 < 3$
$x < 2$

2. $11 - 2a < 19$
$a > -4$

3. $\frac{2}{3}(15c + 5) > -28$
$c > -5$

4. $100 \le 12.6d + 24.4$
$d \ge 6$

5. $26.8 < 13.4 - 6.7x$
$x < -2$

6. $-5(m - \frac{3}{10}) + \frac{6}{5}(14m + 7) > \frac{1}{2}$
$m > -1$

7. $-\frac{3}{4}k - \frac{1}{5} > \frac{1}{3}$
$k < -\frac{25}{9}$

8. $2m - 5(m + 2) \ge 8$
$m \le -6$

9. $6(n - 1) - 2n \le 26$
$n \le 8$

(USES) Objective D
In 10–14, a situation is given.
a. Write an inequality to describe the situation.
b. Solve the inequality and answer the question.

10. A gallon of paint covers up to 400 square feet. Tuck already has 2 gallons of paint to use. What is the least number of gallons Tuck needs to purchase to cover a total area less than 2,800 sq ft?
a. $400(2 + x) < 2,800$, where x = the number of gallons of paint
b. $x < 5$; 4 gallons

164 Algebra

3-7B page 2

11. A child needs to be at least 54 inches tall to use the slide at the public pool. Eliese is 40 inches tall and has been growing at an average rate of 2.5 inches a year. In about how many years will Eliese be able to use the slide at the public pool?
a. $40 + 2.5x \ge 54$, where x = the number of years
b. $x \ge 5.6$; in about 6 years

12. A small truck has the capacity to hold 1,168 pounds. Markus went to the garden supply store to purchase bags of soil that weigh 40 pounds each. He also purchased bags of mulch that weigh 10 pounds each. He bought twice as many bags of mulch as bags of soil. If he weighs 190 pounds, what is the greatest number of bags of soil and mulch that he can carry in his truck?
a. $40x + 10(2x) + 190 \le 1,168$, where x = the number of bags of soil
b. $x \le 16.3$; 16 bags of soil, 32 bags of mulch

13. Hailey will drive no more than 1,400 miles to get to her vacation destination. She has already driven 130 miles. If she drives the same number of miles for 2 days, what is the greatest number of miles she needs yet to drive each day to reach her destination? Round to the nearest whole mile.
a. $2x + 130 \le 1,400$, where x = the number of miles
b. $x \le 635$; 634 miles

14. Douglas practices piano the same number of hours each day Monday through Friday. He doesn't practice on Saturday, but practices 3 more hours on Sunday than he does on Monday. He should practice more than 15 hours a week. What is the least number of hours he should practice on Monday? Round up to the nearest whole hour. $5x + (x + 3) > 15$, where x is
a. the number of hours he practices on Monday
b. $x > 2$; 3 hours

(REPRESENTATIONS) Objective F
In 15–17, solve the inequality and graph the solution.

15. $\frac{2}{7}(14r + 21) \ge 33$
$r \ge 4$

16. $2.3w - 1.4(w - 1) > 9.5$
$w > 9$

17. $5(3x - 1) - 2(2 - x) \le -77$
$x \le -4$

Algebra 165

---

17. A membership to Jenny's Gym costs $22 per month plus an initial $49.95 fee to join. If Arturo has $300 budgeted to join and pay monthly fees, for how many months can he be a member? **11 mo or fewer**

18. You are allowed to fly with a suitcase that weighs no more than 50 pounds. Suppose your suitcase and clothes total 35.2 pounds, and your shoes weigh 3.7 pounds per pair. How many pairs of shoes can you bring on the flight? **4 pairs or fewer**

19. Compare and contrast the solutions to $-7w - 1 \le -15$ and $7w + 1 \le 15$.

20. a. Solve the sentence $ax + b < c$ for x when $a > 0$. $x < \frac{c - b}{a}$
    b. How does the result from Part a change if $a < 0$?
    If $a < 0$, $x > \frac{c - b}{a}$

REVIEW

21. Consider the inequality $8 > -2$. What inequality (if any) results if you multiply both sides of the inequality by each number? **(Lesson 3-6)** 21d. No inequality results.
    a. 100
       800 > -200
    b. -5 $-40 < 10$
    c. $\frac{1}{2}$ $4 > -1$
    d. 0

22. The area of the foundation of a rectangular building is not to exceed 15,000 square feet. The width of the foundation is to be 150 feet. Write an inequality that should be solved to find how long the foundation can be. **(Lesson 3-6)**
    Let ℓ be the length of the foundation. Then, $150\ell \le 15,000$.
In 23–25, solve the inequality. **(Lesson 3-6)**

23. $5j > 17$ $j > \frac{17}{5}$

24. $4.2 < 8.4k$ $k > 0.5$

25. $\frac{5}{6}x \le 12$ $x \le \frac{72}{5}$

26. Solve and check $3x + (-5x) + 12(x - 15) = -4$. **(Lesson 3-5)** $x = 17.6$

27. Nomar gets paid $2 per pizza that he delivers in his car. He also gets paid $0.31 for every mile he drives while making deliveries. Last month he delivered 512 pizzas. If his monthly paycheck was $1,482.80, how many miles did he drive last month delivering pizzas? **(Lesson 3-4)** 1,480 mi

28. **Skill Sequence** Simplify the expression. **(Previous Course)**
    a. $\frac{5}{6} + \frac{1}{9}$ $\frac{17}{18}$
    b. $\frac{5}{6}c + \frac{1}{9}c$ $\frac{17}{18}c$
    c. $\frac{5c}{6} + \frac{c}{9}$ $\frac{17}{18}c$

EXPLORATION

29. Create five inequalities of the form $ax + b < c$ equivalent to $x < 24$.

30. Create five inequalities of the form $ax + b < c$ equivalent to $x > 4$. Answers vary. Sample answer: $x + 25 > 29$; $x - 1 > 3$; $7x + 11 > 39$; $-x < -4$; $-5x - 20 < -40$

166 Linear Equations and Inequalities

Some people recommend that a person participate in an aerobic activity at least 3–5 times per week for 20–30 minutes per session as part of a healthy lifestyle.

Source: Aerobics and Fitness Association of America

19. Except for 2, which is a solution to both, every real number is a solution to exactly one of these inequalities.

29. Answers vary. Sample answer:
$x + 3 < 27$;
$x - 10 < 14$;
$5x + 5 < 125$;
$-x > -24$;
$-3x + 2 > -70$

QY ANSWER

$x = 20$: 30 = 30;
$x > 20$ ($x = 30$): 15 < 30

Extension

You may want to have students use the skills learned in Lesson 3-2 to solve inequalities by graphing boundary lines in a coordinate plane. You could have them shade the half plane and instruct them to use a dotted boundary line if the inequality is > or < and a solid line if it is ≥ or ≤.

Lesson
3-8

Solving Equations by Clearing Fractions

> **BIG IDEA** Equations with fractions can be transformed into equivalent equations without fractions.

Choosing a Multiplier to Clear Fractions

With the techniques you have learned, you can solve any linear equation. However, when you want to solve an equation containing fractions, for example $\frac{t}{3} + \frac{t}{2} - 350 = 270$, you may want to *clear the fractions* before you do anything else. The Multiplication Property of Equality allows you to do this. If you make a wise choice of a number by which to multiply both sides, the result will be an equation with no fractions.

We will examine the results of different multipliers for the equation $\frac{t}{3} + \frac{t}{2} - 350 = 270$, as shown below. For example, to tell a CAS to multiply both sides of the equation by 2, type $(t/3+t/2-350 = 270)*2$ ENTER.

Mental Math

Let *n* be any real number. Determine if the statement is *always*, *sometimes but not always*, or *never true*.

a. $\frac{n}{3}$ is greater than *n*.

b. *n* is greater than −*n*.

c. 5*n* is equal to −5*n*.

a. sometimes but not always

b. sometimes but not always

c. sometimes but not always

Multiply by 2.	Multiply by 3.	Multiply by 6.
		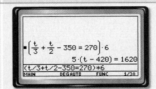
The CAS transformed the equation into $\frac{5(t-420)}{3} = 540$. But there is still a fraction in the equation. So 2 is not a useful multiplier.	Again, the result is an equation that has fractions. So 3 is also not a good multiplier.	Success! When 6 is a multiplier, the result is $5(t - 420) = 1,620$, an equation that has no fractions and is equivalent to $\frac{t}{3} + \frac{t}{2} - 350 = 270$.

Background

We offer a method in this lesson which quickly creates equivalent equations without fractions. This alternative is particularly attractive to those who are unsure of their skill in manipulating fractions. The method involves multiplying both sides of the original equation by a number that will eliminate all fractions. The goal is to multiply by the smallest number that is large enough to clear out the fractions. The CAS allows experimenting with various numbers and

should convince students that the least common multiple of the denominators is the best multiplier to use.

There are two reasons for *multiplying through*. If the sentence contains fractions or decimals, then multiplying by a judicious whole number will result in a sentence without fractions or decimals. If all the coefficients and constants in a sentence are multiples of the same number, then dividing by a judicious whole number will result in a sentence with smaller numbers to deal with.

Lesson
3-8

GOAL

Apply the Multiplication Property of Equality or Inequality to clear out fractions or decimals in solving equations or inequalities.

SPUR Objectives

B Solve and check linear inequalities of the form $ax + b < c$.

C Apply the Addition and Multiplication Properties of Equality and Inequality.

D Use linear equations and inequalities of the form $ax + b = c$ or $ax + b < c$ to solve real-world problems.

Materials/Resources

· Lesson Master 3-8A or 3-8B
· Resource Masters 7 and 44
· Scientific or graphing calculator
· Computer Algebra System (CAS)

HOMEWORK

Suggestions for Assignment

• Questions 1–27
• Question 28 (extra credit)
• Reading Lesson 4-1
• Covering the Ideas 4-1

Local Standards

1 Warm-Up

The Activity introducing the lesson can be used as a Warm-Up. If it is done the preceding day, then here is another Warm-Up.

In 1–5, give the least common multiple of the following numbers.

1. 2 and 5 10
2. 12 and 15 60
3. 4 and 6 12
4. 10 and 100 100
5. 6, 36, and 4 36

2 Teaching

Notes on the Activity

This CAS activity has two goals. First is to introduce a useful strategy in solving equations (and inequalities); namely, to begin by multiplying both sides of an equation by some number in order to make the coefficients more manageable. Second is to help students learn how to choose the number to be the multiplier.

With the equation in this activity, $\frac{t}{3} + \frac{t}{2} - 350 = 270$, one way of solving is to treat it as if t were not multiplied by fractions but whole numbers. It is an equation of the type found in Lesson 3-5.

Apply the Distributive Property.

$$\left(\frac{1}{3} + \frac{1}{2}\right)t - 350 = 270$$

Add the fractions.

$$\frac{5}{6}t - 350 = 270$$

Now it is an equation of the form $ax + b = c$, and can be solved by the method of Lesson 3-4. Add 350 to both sides and then multiply both sides by $\frac{6}{5}$.

Alternate activity. Find the least possible positive multiplier that will clear the fractions in the equation $\frac{x}{4} + \frac{x}{5} - 50 = -48$. **20**

On some CAS machines you must use the `expand` or `simplify` command to cause the multiplication to be carried out. You may need to type `expand((t/2 + t/3 - 350 = 270)*6)` or `simplify((t/2 + t/3 - 350 = 270)*6)` to multiply both sides by 6. So one multiplier that clears fractions in $\frac{t}{3} + \frac{t}{2} - 350 = 270$ is 6. But there are others, as you will see in the following activity.

Activity

Step 1 The table below shows the effect of three different multipliers on the equation $\frac{t}{3} + \frac{t}{2} - 350 = 270$. Experiment to find three more multipliers that clear the fractions. Record your results in the table.

Multiplier	Resulting Equation	Fractions Cleared?	
2	$\frac{5(t-420)}{3} = 540$	No	
3	$\frac{5(t-420)}{2} = 810$	No	
6	$5(t-420) = 1,620$	Yes	
?	?	?	12; $10(t-420) = 3,240$; Yes
?	?	?	18; $15(t-420) = 4,860$; Yes
?	?	?	24; $20(t-420) = 6,480$; Yes

Step 2 Consider the multipliers you tried in Step 1. Describe the relationship between the multipliers that eliminate fractions and the original equation $\frac{t}{3} + \frac{t}{2} - 350 = 270$.

Step 3 Use what you have learned about multipliers in Steps 1 and 2 to find an equation equivalent to $\frac{5n}{6} + \frac{n}{4} + \frac{2n}{3} = 42$ that contains no fractions.

   a. Predict a value by which you could multiply each side of the equation to clear the fractions.

   b. Test your prediction using a CAS. Multiply each side of the equation $\frac{5n}{6} + \frac{n}{4} + \frac{2n}{3} = 42$ by the value and write down the results.

Step 2. Note that the fractions are eliminated when the multiplier is a multiple of every denominator.

Step 3. Answers vary. Sample answer: 12 gives $10n + 3n + 8n = 504$.

Accommodating the Learner

Before beginning the lesson have students solve the equation $\frac{x}{3} = 2$. Point out that as long as they multiply both sides of the equation by the same number, in this case 3, the value of x does not change and the equality of the equation is not disrupted. Then have them solve $\frac{x}{5} = \frac{2}{3}$ by multiplying both sides of the equation by 15.

Clearing Fractions in Equations

In the preceding activity you saw how to clear fractions in an equation. The idea is to multiply both sides of the equation by a common multiple of the denominators. The result is an equation in which all of the coefficients are integers.

Example 1

In 2004 the Washington Redskins and the Cleveland Browns had the highest earnings in the National Football League (NFL). The Redskins accounted for $\frac{1}{12}$ of the league's income and the Browns accounted for $\frac{1}{15}$ of the league's income. Their combined income was $129 million. What was the total league income for 2004?

a. Write an equation to describe the situation.

b. Solve by clearing the fractions.

In 2005, the average NFL team was worth $733 million.
Source: Forbes

Solution 1

a. Let T be the NFL's total earnings, in millions of dollars.

Redskins' earnings + Browns' earnings = 129

$\frac{1}{12}T + \frac{1}{15}T = 129$

b. Multiply each side by a common multiple of 12 and 15. We use 60.

$60\left(\frac{1}{12}T + \frac{1}{15}T\right) = 60 \cdot 129$	Multiply each side by 60.
$5T + 4T = 7,740$	Distributive Property
$9T = 7,740$	Combine like terms.
$T = 860$	Divide each side by 9.

The total income for the NFL in 2004 was $860 million.

Solution 2

b. Add the fraction coefficients.

$\frac{1}{12}T + \frac{1}{15}T = 129$	Write the equation.
$\frac{5}{60}T + \frac{4}{60}T = 129$	Find equivalent fractions with the same denominator.
$\frac{9}{60}T = 129$	Add like terms.
$60 \cdot \frac{9}{60}T = 60 \cdot 129$	Multiply each side by 60 to clear the fractions.
$9T = 7,740$	Simplify.
$T = 860$	Divide each side by 9.

 QY1

▶ **QY1**

Use a CAS to solve $\frac{1}{12}T + \frac{1}{15}T = 129$.

Notes on the Lesson

Choosing a multiplier to clear fractions. The general idea in solving any equation is to use common sense in deciding how to solve. If the constants and/or coefficients are fractions, then multiply both sides by a number large enough to get rid of the fractions. If the coefficients are decimals, then multiply by the power of 10 that is large enough to get rid of places to the right of the decimal point. If the constants and coefficients on both sides of the equation are multiples of the same number, then divide by that number.

Clearing fractions in equations. It is important that students never lose sight that both sides of the sentence must be multiplied by the same number. Sometimes, in using the Distributive Property, students will think that because they did two (or more) multiplications on one side, they do not have to multiply on the other side. To emphasize this point, you might make the multiplier quite explicit, perhaps showing it in a second color if you write or project a solution on a board.

Additional Example

Example 1 Write an equation to describe the situation and solve it by clearing the fractions. The Smith family budget allows them to spend $\frac{1}{12}$ of the family income on recreation and give $\frac{1}{10}$ of the family's income to charities. The Smiths spent $13,200 in 2005 on recreation and charities together. What was the family's total income for 2005? Let $x =$ the family's total 2005 income; $\frac{1}{12}x + \frac{1}{10}x = 13,200$; $x = $72,000$

3-8

Example 2 Solve $\frac{x}{7} - 2 > \frac{1}{2}$.

$\underline{\quad?\quad}\frac{x}{7} - 2 > \underline{\quad?\quad}\frac{1}{2}$ 14; 14

$\underline{\quad?\quad} \cdot \frac{x}{7} - \underline{\quad?\quad} \cdot 2 > 7$ 14; 14

$\underline{\quad?\quad}x - \underline{\quad?\quad} > 7$ 2; 28

$\underline{\quad?\quad}x > \underline{\quad?\quad}$ 2; 35

$x > \underline{\quad?\quad}$ $17\frac{1}{2}$

Example 3 Solve $1.12n - 4 = 7.2$.
$n = 10$

Note-Taking Tips

You could have students write the procedure for clearing fractions on index cards.

1. Find the LCD for all fractions in the equation or inequality.
2. Multiply both sides of the equation or inequality by the positive whole number LCD.
3. Simplify and make sure fractions are cleared.
4. Continue solving.

Clearing Fractions in Inequalities

When solving an inequality, you can multiply to clear fractions just like you do when solving an equation.

> **GUIDED**
>
> **Example 2**
> Solve $\frac{x}{4} - 8 > \frac{1}{6}$.
>
> **Solution** The two denominators in the sentence are 4 and 6. The least common denominator is $\underline{\quad?\quad}$. So multiply each side of the inequality by $\underline{\quad?\quad}$. 12; 12
>
> $$\underline{\quad?\quad}\left(\frac{x}{4} - 8\right) > \underline{\quad?\quad} \cdot \frac{1}{6} \quad \text{12; 12}$$
> $$\underline{\quad?\quad} \cdot \frac{x}{4} + \underline{\quad?\quad} \cdot 8 > 2 \quad \text{12; 12}$$
> $$\underline{\quad?\quad}x - \underline{\quad?\quad} > 2 \quad \text{3; 96}$$
> $$\underline{\quad?\quad}x > \underline{\quad?\quad} \quad \text{3; 98}$$
> $$x > \underline{\quad?\quad} \quad \frac{98}{3}$$

> **To Clear Fractions in an Equation or Inequality**
>
> 1. Choose a common multiple of all of the denominators in the sentence.
> 2. Multiply each side of the sentence by that number.

STOP **QY2**

▶ **QY2**

To clear the fractions, what number could you use to multiply each side of $\frac{m}{6} - \frac{3}{8}m \leq 5$?

Clearing Decimals

Like fractions, decimals can be cleared from an equation to give a simpler equation with integer coefficients. A decimal can be thought of as a fraction whose denominator is a power of 10. For example, 0.4 can be written as $\frac{4}{10}$, so the "denominator" of 0.4 is 10. Similarly, the "hidden denominators" of 9.38 $\left(\text{or } 9\frac{38}{100}\right)$ and 6.022 $\left(\text{or } 6\frac{22}{1,000}\right)$ are 100 and 1,000, respectively.

> **Example 3**
> Solve $5.85n - 9 = 2.7$.
>
> **Solution** The equation involves two decimals: 5.85 and 2.7. Their "hidden denominators" are 100 and 10. Since 100 is divisible by both 100 and 10, multiply each side of the equation by 100.

> **Accommodating the Learner** ⬆
>
> If you feel that students are comfortable clearing fractions, have them clear the fractions in a variable-only equation. Have them solve the equation $\frac{x}{a} + \frac{b}{c} = \frac{d}{e}$ for x.
>
> $x = \frac{dac - bae}{ce}$

$$5.85n - 9 = 2.7 \qquad \text{Write the equation.}$$
$$100(5.85n - 9) = 100 \cdot 2.7 \qquad \text{Multiply each side by 100.}$$
$$585n - 900 = 270 \qquad \text{Simplify.}$$
$$585n - 900 + 900 = 270 + 900 \qquad \text{Add 900 to each side.}$$
$$585n = 1{,}170 \qquad \text{Simplify.}$$
$$\frac{585n}{585} = \frac{1{,}170}{585} \qquad \text{Divide each side by 585.}$$
$$n = 2 \qquad \text{Simplify.}$$

Questions

COVERING THE IDEAS

1. Suppose $\frac{3}{5}w + 2 = 26$.

   a. Multiply each side of the equation by 5. $3w + 10 = 130$
   b. Solve the resulting equation. $w = 40$
   c. Check your answer. $\frac{3}{5}(40) + 2 = 26; 24 + 2 = 26$

2. Consider the equation $\frac{m}{9} + \frac{m}{3} = 16$.

   a. Multiply each side by 9 and solve the resulting equation.
   b. Multiply each side by 27 and solve the resulting equation.
   c. What conclusions can you make from your work in Parts a and b? Multiplying both sides of an equation by the same number does not change the solution.

3. Consider the equation $0.152 = 0.3m - 0.43$.

   a. What are the "hidden denominators" in the equation?
   b. Multiply each side by 100 and solve the resulting equation.
   c. Convert the decimals in the equation to fractions and solve the resulting equation. $\frac{152}{1,000} = \frac{3}{10}m - \frac{43}{100}; m = 1.94$
   d. What conclusions can you make from your work in Parts b and c? Converting decimals to fractions does not change the solution.

In 4 and 5, an inequality and a number are given.
a. Write the inequality that results if both sides of the inequality are multiplied by the given number.
b. Solve the inequality.
c. Graph the solution set on a number line.
d. Check your work.

4. $\frac{3n}{2} - \frac{n}{4} < 6; 4$ 4a. $6n - n < 24$; 4b. $n < 4.8$

5. $\frac{2}{3}a + \frac{a}{5} \geq 21; 15$ 5a. $10a + 3a \geq 315$; 5b. $a \geq \frac{315}{13}$

2a. $m + 3m = 144$; $m = 36$
2b. $3m + 9m = 432$; $m = 36$
3a. 1,000; 10; and 100
3b. $15.2 = 30m - 43$; $m = 1.94$

4c.
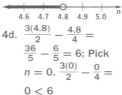

4d. $\frac{3(4.8)}{2} - \frac{4.8}{4} =$
$\frac{36}{5} - \frac{6}{5} = 6$; Pick $n = 0$. $\frac{3(0)}{2} - \frac{0}{4} =$
$0 < 6$

5c.

5d. $\frac{2}{3}\left(\frac{315}{13}\right) + \frac{\left(\frac{315}{13}\right)}{5}$
$= \frac{210}{13} + \frac{63}{13} = 21$;
Pick $a = 30$. $\frac{2}{3}(30)$
$+ \frac{30}{5} = 20 + 6 =$
$26 \geq 21$

3 **Assignment**

Recommended Assignment
- Questions 1–27
- Question 28 (extra credit)
- Reading Lesson 4-1
- Covering the Ideas 4-1

Notes on the Questions
Question 3 For the answer to Part a, refer to Example 3 for the meaning of "denominators." Notice that multiplying by 100 does *not* get rid of all decimals. Ask students whether multiplying by 10 or 1,000 might be more appropriate. (Multiplying by 10 gets rid of the decimal coefficient of *m* and could be preferred for that reason. Multiplying by 1,000 gets rid of all decimal places to the right of the decimal point.)

Question 4 Some students might want to multiply both sides by 8, the product of 2 and 4. This will work, of course, but the coefficients will be larger than those obtained by multiplying both sides by 4.

3-8

Notes on the Questions

Questions 10–13 You might want to show the solutions to any of these sentences that would result if one did not multiply both sides by the same number.

Question 14 The names are meant to be puns on the plants known as the philodendron and the rhododendron.

Question 28 This is a classic problem in the history of mathematics, and should be discussed in detail in class.

In 6–13, solve and check the sentence.

6. $\frac{3}{7}x + 2 = \frac{2}{5}$ $-\frac{56}{15}$

7. $\frac{3}{4}y - \frac{1}{3} = 5$ $y = \frac{64}{9}$

8. $0.05n + 3.75 = 22.50$ $n = 375$

9. $40,000 = 138,000 - 2,000c$ $c = 49$

10. $\frac{d}{3} + \frac{3d}{5} < \frac{3}{4}$ $d < \frac{45}{56}$

11. $1 - \frac{n}{10} \geq -\frac{4}{5}$ $n \leq 18$

12. $5 - \frac{t}{3} = -7$ $t = 36$

13. $\frac{m}{5} - \frac{1}{13} \geq \frac{3}{22}$ $m \geq \frac{305}{286}$

14. Philo Dendrum owns $\frac{3}{8}$ of the stock in Blossom Industries and his wife Rhoda Dendrum owns $\frac{1}{4}$ of it. This means that they receive $\frac{3}{8}$ and $\frac{1}{4}$, respectively, of the dividends paid to the stockholders.

   a. Last year the Dendrums together earned $25,400 from the stock. What was the total amount of dividends paid to the stockholders? **$40,640**

   b. How much did stockholders other than Philo and Rhoda receive in dividends? **$15,240**

APPLYING THE MATHEMATICS

15. When solving $4,000 = 8,000 - 2,000x$, a student first multiplies both sides by $\frac{1}{1,000}$. Is this a good idea? Why or why not? **Yes, because it simplifies the equation.**

In 16 and 17, solve the sentence.

16. $\frac{1}{6}\left(\frac{17}{3} - \frac{y}{4}\right) < -7$

   $y > \frac{572}{3}$

17. $\frac{x}{6} + \frac{17}{36} - \frac{x}{4} = -7$

   $x = \frac{269}{3}$

REVIEW

18. What inequality is suggested by the balance below? What is the solution to the inequality? (**Lesson 3-7**) $5 + 3W > 7$; $W > \frac{2}{3}$ oz

In 19–21, solve and check the inequality. (**Lesson 3-7**)

19. $5t - 3(7t + 1) < 93$ $t > -6$

20. $77 \leq -3n + 29$ $n \leq -16$

21. $5y - 16 > 49$ $y > 13$

22. Use the formula $C = \frac{5}{9}(F - 32)$ to determine which Fahrenheit temperatures are between $50°C$ and $70°C$. (**Lessons 3-7, 1-1**) **22. $122 < F < 158$**

Nine of the top ten greatest one-day point gains on the Dow Jones Industrial Average occurred in 2000 or later.

Source: Dow Jones & Company, Inc.

6. $x = -\frac{56}{15}$; $\frac{3}{7}\left(\frac{-56}{15}\right) + 2 = -\frac{8}{5} + 2 = \frac{2}{5}$

7. $y = \frac{64}{9}$; $\frac{3}{4}\left(\frac{64}{9}\right) - \frac{1}{3}$
   $= \frac{16}{3} - \frac{1}{3} = 5$

8. $n = 375$; $0.05(375) + 3.75 = 18.75 + 3.75 = 22.5$

9. $c = 49$; $138,000 - 2,000(49) = 40,000$

10. $d < \frac{45}{56}$; $\frac{\frac{45}{56}}{3} + \frac{3\left(\frac{45}{56}\right)}{5}$
    $= \frac{15}{56} + \frac{27}{56} = \frac{3}{4}$;
    Pick $d = 0$. $\frac{0}{3} + \frac{3(0)}{5}$
    $= 0 < \frac{3}{4}$

11. $n \leq 18$; $1 - \frac{18}{10} =$
    $-\frac{4}{5}$; Pick $n = 0$. 1
    $-\frac{0}{10} = 1 \geq -\frac{4}{5}$

12. $t = 36$; $5 - \frac{36}{3} =$
    $5 - 12 = -7$

13. $m \geq \frac{305}{286}$; $\frac{\left(\frac{305}{286}\right)}{5} - \frac{1}{3} =$
    $\frac{61}{286} - \frac{1}{3} = \frac{3}{22}$; Pick $m = 5$.
    $\frac{5}{5} - \frac{1}{13} = \frac{12}{13} \geq \frac{3}{22}$

---

23. Find the value of w in the pentagon below if the perimeter is 105 meters. (**Lessons 3-5, 1-1**) $w = 9$

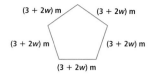

(3 + 2w) m   (3 + 2w) m
(3 + 2w) m   (3 + 2w) m
(3 + 2w) m

24. Felipe has been trying to lower his cell phone bill by limiting the length of his calls to an average of 2.5 minutes. His calls on November 30th were 2, 3, 6, 1, 1, 2, 1, 3, 4, 1, and 7 minutes long. (**Lessons 3-4, 1-7**)

   a. Was his average call less than 2.5 minutes long? no

   b. What is the mean absolute deviation for the calls?
   about 1.62 min

In 25–27, combine like terms. (**Lesson 2-2**)

25. $\frac{5}{t} + \frac{-4}{7t}$ $\frac{31}{7t}$

26. $\frac{3x + y}{3} - \frac{2z + 8y}{5}$ $\frac{15x - 19y - 6z}{15}$

27. $\frac{4x^2}{9} - \frac{7x^2}{18}$ $\frac{x^2}{18}$

EXPLORATION

28. Diophantus, a Greek mathematician who lived in the third century, was the first known person to use variables to stand for unknown numbers. About 200 years after his death, an algebraic riddle was written to honor him. Here is one version of that riddle, written as a rhyming poem. Decipher the riddle to find an equation and solve the equation to determine how long Diophantus lived. $D = \frac{1}{6}D + \frac{1}{12}D + \frac{1}{7}D + 5 + \frac{1}{2}D + 4$; 84 yr

"Here lies Diophantus." The wonder behold

Through art algebraic, the stone tells how old.

"God gave him his boyhood one-sixth of his life,

One-twelfth more as youth while whiskers grew rife;

And then yet one-seventh ere marriage begun;

In five years there came a bounding new son.

Alas, the dear child of master and sage

Met fate at just half his dad's final age.

Four years yet his studies gave solace from grief,

Then leaving scenes earthly he, too, found relief."

In 2006, about 22% of people in the world owned a cellular phone.

Source: International Telecommunication Union

QY ANSWERS

1. $T = 860$

2. Answers vary. Sample answer: 24

Solving Equations by Clearing Fractions **173**

3-8

4 Wrap-Up

Ongoing Assessment

Have students clear the fractions or decimals. Do not solve the resulting equation or inequality.

1. $\frac{x}{2} + \frac{y}{3} = \frac{1}{6}$ $3x + 2y = 1$

2. $\frac{5x}{7} + 2 = 1$ $5x + 14 = 7$

3. $\frac{1}{2}x + \frac{2}{3} = 3$ $3x + 4 = 18$

4. $\frac{x}{3} - \frac{3}{5} < \frac{1}{2}$ $10x - 18 < 15$

5. $7.32x + 2.25 = 1.7$
   $732x + 225 = 170$

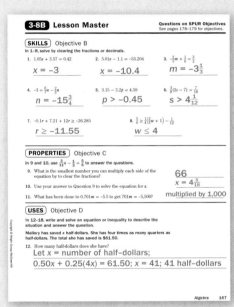

Chapter 3

The projects relate to the content of the lessons of this chapter as follows:

Project	Lesson(s)
1	3-1
2	3-3
3	3-4
4	3-4
5	3-1

1 Modeling Buying and Selling

Students who like working with technology will enjoy this project. If students who choose this project are having trouble getting started, suggest that they write a variable representation for the total spent on new CDs and the total earned by selling old CDs. Remind students to tackle just one part of the project at a time.

2 Appliances and Energy

Suggest that students create a form to use for each refrigerator. They should include a place to list the size, price, yearly energy cost, an equation describing its total cost over its lifespan, a graph of the equation, and the total cost over a 10-year period. Students will be able to access their information more easily if they use a form for each refrigerator to organize the findings.

Chapter 3 Projects

1 Modeling Buying and Selling

Sue visits the CD store to sell some of her old CDs and buy used ones. The store will give her $2 for every CD she sells to them, and each CD costs $4 to buy. Sue also has $20 to buy used CDs in addition to any money she gets from selling her old ones.

a. Find an equation relating x, the number of CDs she buys; y, the number of CDs she sells; and z, the amount of money she has left afterwards.

b. Use three-dimensional graphing software or a graphing calculator to graph this equation. Describe the shape of the graph.

c. If Sue doesn't sell any CDs but still buys x CDs, your equation from Part a can be reduced to a linear equation. Graph this equation. Is this a constant-increase or constant-decrease situation? What inequality must be satisfied by x?

d. Repeat Part c for if Sue sells 5 CDs. What do you notice about the lines from Parts c and d? Explain.

2 Appliances and Energy

Visit a store or Web site where appliances are sold. New major appliances like refrigerators are tested for their expected energy consumption per year. That information is available to consumers to aid them in their decisions. Pick a range of sizes of refrigerators (for example, 16 to 21 cubic feet) and find the price and expected yearly energy cost for at least four different models. For each model, develop an equation that describes its total cost over its lifespan. Graph these equations. Is the least expensive model always the most economical? Which model is the best value if it is kept for 10 years?

174   Linear Equations and Inequalities

Project Rubric

Advanced	Student correctly provides all of the details asked for in the project as well as additional correct independent conclusions.
Proficient	Student correctly provides all of the details asked for in the project.
Partially proficient	Student correctly provides some of the details asked for in the project or provides all details with some inaccuracies.
Not proficient	Student correctly provides few of the details asked for in the project or provides all details with many inaccuracies.
No attempt	Student makes little or no attempt to complete the project.

3 Integer Solutions to Linear Equations

You have seen that equations of the form $ax + b = c$ always have one solution when a is nonzero. But even if a, b, and c are integers, the solution may not be an integer. Write a program for a graphing calculator or computer to solve $ax + b = c$ when a, b, and c are entered. Roll a die three times to determine values for a, b, and c, and use your program to solve for x. Record these values in a table and repeat the process until you have solved 20 equations. What percentage of solutions are integers? Is this result surprising? (Note that you can broaden this project by writing a program on your computer which generates and solves the equations.)

4 Combining Linear Equations

If a and d are nonzero, then the equations $ax + b = c$ and $dx + e = f$ always have one solution for x. What happens if you add these two equations together, that is, add the left sides together and the right sides together? Do you get a linear equation? When does it have a solution? What if you subtract one equation from the other? Using a CAS, multiply the two equations together. Do you get a linear equation? Explain.

5 The Strength of Spaghetti

Support a strand of uncooked spaghetti on each end, leaving a gap of about 7 inches. Unfold a paper clip. Hook one end over the spaghetti. Hook the other end through the rip of a small paper cup. Drop pennies into the cup one by one until the spaghetti "bridge" breaks. Record the number of pennies it takes to break the bridge. Repeat this process for bridges made with 2, 3, 4, 5, 6, and 7 strands of spaghetti. Each time, record the number of strands and the number of pennies that broke the bridge. Draw a line that approximates your data. Using your graph, predict how many pennies it will take to break a bridge made of 12 strands.

3 Integer Solutions to Linear Equations

Students may choose to complete this project on a graphing calculator. They will find it helpful to review the steps involved in writing a program, the definition of *integers*, and how to find percentages before beginning this project. Suggest that students create a table before getting started. They should include headings a, b, c, solution, and integer with space to test 20 equations. Have them provide a space at the bottom to answer the questions.

4 Combining Linear Equations

Suggest that students create a separate form to report results from adding the equations, subtracting the equations, multiplying the equations, and answering the project questions. If students are having trouble getting started, suggest that they choose at least 10 sets of values for a, b, c, d, e, and f. Encourage them to try some sets of values that have $a = d$.

5 The Strength of Spaghetti

Suggest that students create a chart to record the results of the experiment. They should include two columns, one with the number of pennies and the other with the number of spaghetti strands. Have them extend their table to include twelve strands of spaghetti so that they may make predictions for eight through twelve strands.

Notes

Chapter 3

Summary and Vocabulary

The Summary gives an overview of the entire chapter and provides an opportunity for students to consider the material as a whole. Thus, the Summary can be used to help students relate and unify the concepts presented in the chapter.

Terms and symbols are listed by lesson to provide a checklist of concepts that students must know. Emphasize to students that they should read the vocabulary list carefully before starting the Self-Test on the next page. If students do not understand the meaning of a term, they should refer back to the indicated lesson.

Theorems and Properties covered in the chapter are listed below the Summary, with page references included to lead students back to the location in the chapter where the theorem or property is stated.

Additional Answers

Self-Test, p. 177

1. $t = 4.5$. First, add 5 to both sides. Then divide by 4.

2. $t = -4$. First, distribute to get $10 + 5t = -10$. Then subtract 10 from both sides and divide by 5.

3. $f = \frac{109}{7}$. First, distribute and combine like terms to get $101 = 13f - 8 - 6f = 7f - 8$. Then add 8 to both sides and divide by 7.

9. Let $2x$ be the value of the grand prize. Then, $x + x + x + 2x = 3,500$. Combining like terms gives $5x = 3,500$, and dividing by 5 gives $x = 700$, so the grand prize is $1,400.

Chapter 3 — Summary and Vocabulary

○ **Constant-increase** and **constant-decrease situations** can be described by algebraic expressions of the form $ax + b$ (where x is changing) and equations of the form $ax + b = c$. Since the points (x, y) that satisfy the equation $y = ax + b$ lie on a line, we call the expressions *linear expressions* and the equations *linear equations*.

○ There are many ways to solve an equation of the form $ax + b = c$. A **table of values** of the expression $ax + b$ may give a value that equals c. A **graph** of $y = ax + b$ may reach the value c at a point whose x-coordinate can be determined. For example, to solve $3x - 46 = 17$, you can make a table of values of $3x - 46$ for various values of x and check if 17 appears as a value of y. You can graph $y = 3x - 46$ and check if it crosses the line $y = 17$. Graphs and tables may be created by hand, but they are easily produced with the aid of technology.

○ Tables and graphs can picture how a quantity is changing, but they are not reliable methods for finding an exact solution to a linear equation. A sure method is to use the **Addition and Multiplication Properties of Equality** to change the given equation into a simpler equation. For example, to solve $3x - 46 = 17$, you might add 46 to each side, resulting in $3x = 63$. Then multiply each side by $\frac{1}{3}$, resulting in $x = 21$. The solution 21 checks in the original equation.

○ **Linear inequalities** can be solved by finding equivalent inequalities in much the same way that equivalent equations can be found to solve linear equations. For example, $-3x - 46 < 17$ is solved by adding 46 to each side and then dividing each side by -3 to get $x > 21$. Notice that when multiplying or dividing by a negative number, the inequality sign is reversed.

○ To remove fractions from an equation, you can find a common multiple of the denominators and then multiply each side by that multiple.

Theorems and Properties

Multiplication Property of Inequality (Parts 1 and 2) (p. 157)	Addition Property of Inequality (p. 162)

Vocabulary

3-1
constant-increase situation
collinear
constant-decrease situation

3-2
solution to an equation

3-3
equivalent equations

3-6
inequality
boundary point
interval
endpoint

Additional Answers

11.

Months	Money in account
0	$350
1	$330
2	$310
3	$290
8	$190

12.

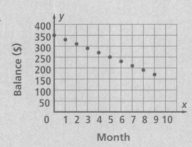

Chapter

3 Self-Test

Take this test as you would take a test in class. You will need a calculator. Then use the Selected Answers section in the back of the book to check your work.

In 1–3, solve and check the equation.

1. $4t - 5 = 13$ **1–3. See margin.**

2. $5(2 + t) = -10$

3. $101 = 13f - 2(4 + 3f)$

In 4–6, solve the inequality.

4. $3(x - 4) \geq 12$ $x \geq 8$

5. $5x + 14 < -26$ $x < -8$

6. $26 - 2x > 10$ $x < 8$

7. Match the solutions to Questions 4–6 with the graphs below.

a.

Question 6

b.
Question 4

c.
Question 5

8. Solve $\frac{n}{4} - \frac{n}{8} = 3$ by clearing fractions.
$2n - n = 24$ so, $n = 24$

9. A school held a fund-raising raffle that had three winners and one grand-prize winner. The value of the grand prize was twice the value of the other prizes combined. Together the prizes had a value of \$3,500. What was the value of the grand prize? **See margin.**

10. Write down the steps you should take to solve the equation $-15 = -2x + 7$ for x. Solve the equation and check your answer.

10. Subtract 7 from both sides; divide both sides by −2; $x = 11$. Answers vary. Sample answer: $-15 = -2(11) + 7$ $-15 = -15$

In 11–13, use the following situation. Allison has \$350 in her checking account and she withdraws \$20 each month to pay for her school lunch ticket. After m months she has $t = 350 - 20m$ dollars in the account. **11–12. See margin.**

11. Make a table of values for the relationship.

12. Make a graph from the table.

13. When will Allison have \$190? **after 8 months**

14. Make a table to solve the inequality $30 < 2x - 6$. **14–16. See margin.**

15. Which commands would you enter on a CAS to find solutions to the inequality $5 - 3x > 17$? What are the solutions?

16. Toni is collecting leaves for a school science project. She needs to have 37 different types of leaves for the project. Toni already has 9 leaves and she plans on collecting 7 more each weekend. When will Toni have enough leaves to complete her project?

17. In 2006, the United States Postal Service charged \$0.39 for the first ounce and \$0.24 for each additional ounce for first-class mail.

a. Write an equation for the price P of a first class letter that weighs w ounces.

b. Use your equation from Part a to find the weight of a package that costs \$3.27 to ship.

17a. $P = 0.39 + 0.24(w - 1)$

17b. Let $P = 3.27$. Then solve $3.27 = 0.39 + 0.24(w - 1)$ by subtracting 0.39 from both sides, which implies $2.88 = 0.24(w - 1)$. Then divide by 0.24, which implies $w - 1 = 12$. So $w = 13$ oz.

Additional Answers

Chapter Review, p. 178

19. Sample answer: You could enter $(2x - 3 = 7) + 3$. The result would be $2x = 10$.

20. Sample answer: You could enter $(0.45 \cdot x = 7.989)/0.45$. The result would be $x = 17.753333$.

21. Yes. The student multiplied both sides by −1, which changes the sense of the inequality.

Additional Answers

14.

x	$2x - 6$
12	18
14	22
16	26
18	30
20	34

15. Subtract 5, then divide by −3. The solution is $x < -4$.

16. Let w be the number of weekends Toni collects. Toni has enough leaves when $9 + 7w \geq 37$. Subtracting 9 and dividing by 7 gives $w \geq 4$. So, she must collect for at least 4 weeks.

Chapter Review

The main objectives for the chapter are organized in the Chapter Review under the four types of understanding this book promotes—Skills, Properties, Uses, and Representations.

Whereas end-of-chapter material may be considered optional in some texts, in *UCSMP Algebra* we have selected these objectives and questions with the expectation that they will be covered. Students should be able to answer these questions with about 85% accuracy after studying the chapter.

You may assign these questions over a single night to help students prepare for a test the next day, or you may assign the questions over a two-day period. If you work the questions over two days, then we recommend assigning the *evens* for homework the first night so that students get feedback in class the next day, and then assigning the *odds* the night before the test because the answers are provided to the odd-numbered questions in the Selected Answers at the back of the book.

It is effective to ask students which questions they still do not understand and use the day as a total class discussion of the material that the class finds most difficult.

Resources

• Assessment Resources: Chapter 3 Test, Forms A–D; Chapter 3 Test, Cumulative Form; Comprehensive Test, Chapters 1–3

29a.

Years	Radius (cm)
0	12
1	12.5
2	13
3	13.5
x	$12 + 0.5x$

Chapter **3** Chapter Review

SKILLS Procedures used to find answers

OBJECTIVE A Solve and check linear equations of the form $ax + b = c$.
(Lessons 3-4, 3-5)

In 1–12, solve and check the equation.

1. $4t + 3 = 15$ $t = 3$
2. $5x + -3x + 6 = 12$ $x = 3$
3. $(4 + n) + -10 = -4 + 5$ $n = 7$
4. $-470 + 2r = 1,100$ $r = 785$
5. $0.9y + 11.2 + 1.7y = 131.2$ $y = 46.15$
6. $5(s + 4) = 85$ $s = 13$
7. $4,000W - 8,000 = 12,000$ $W = 5$
8. $21 = 2x + 3(2 + x)$ $x = 3$
9. $\frac{2}{3}z + 14 = 4$ $z = -15$
10. $16 = \frac{3}{4}x + 22$ $x = -8$
11. $3(w + 4) - 4(2w - 2) = 7$ $w = 2.6$
12. $\frac{n}{5} - \frac{2n}{11} = 6$ $n = 330$

OBJECTIVE B Solve and check linear inequalities of the form $ax + b < c$.
(Lessons 3-7, 3-8)
13. $x < 94$ 14. $d < 1$
In 13–16, solve and check the inequality.
13. $2x + 11 < 199$ 14. $-3 + d + 6 < 4$
15. $-28 \le 18 - 3y - 7$ 16. $4 < -16t + 7t + 5$
     $y \le 13$ $t < \frac{1}{9}$

PROPERTIES The principles behind the mathematics

OBJECTIVE C Apply the Addition and Multiplication Properties of Equality and Inequality. (Lessons 3-3, 3-6, 3-8)

29b.

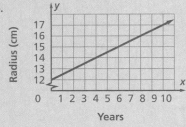

30b.

Weeks (x)	Water Level in feet (y)
0	6.1
1	5.9
2	5.7
3	5.5
x	$6.1 - 0.2x$

In 17 and 18, explain what has been done to both sides of the first equation to get the second equation. 17. 17 was added to each side.

17. If $17d - 17 = 22$, then $17d = 39$.
18. If $\frac{11}{12}b = \frac{2}{3}$, then $11b = 8$.
    Each side was multiplied by 12.
In 19 and 20, write a command you would enter in a CAS to complete the next step in solving the equation. Then predict the output of the CAS.
19.–20. See margin.
19.

20.

21. Given the inequality $-x \ge 4$, Desiree writes $x \le -4$ as the next step. Is she correct? Why or why not? See margin.

22. To solve $5y + 38 < 50$, Kaya subtracts 38 from both sides. What inequality should she get? $5y < 12$

USES Applications of mathematics in real-world situations

OBJECTIVE D Use linear equations and inequalities of the form $ax + b = c$ or $ax + b < c$ to solve real-world problems. (Lessons 3-2, 3-4, 3-5, 3-7, 3-8)

23. If the temperature is $-12°C$, by how much must it increase to become hotter than $14°C$? **more than 26°C**

24. Monica has $250 in the bank and has a job that pays her $9 per hour. She deposits all the money she earns into a savings account. How long will it take her to save a total of $439? **21 hr**

25. Bo Constrictor earns $7.80 per hour at the zoo. He also receives weekly a $25 meal allowance, $15 for transportation, and $7.50 for dry cleaning. Last week he was paid a total of $297.10. How many hours did he work last week? **32 hr**

26. A $98,100 estate is to be split among four children and a grandchild after $5,000 in estate expenses are paid. Each child gets the same amount and the grandchild gets half that amount. How much will each receive? **See margin.**

27. Saudi Arabia has about one-fourth of the world's oil reserves. The rest of the Middle East has approximately two-fifths of the world's oil reserves. Together they have about 660 billion barrels. How many barrels are estimated to be in the world's oil reserve?
approximately 1,015 billion barrels

28. A small cup is 2 inches high. When stacked, each cup adds $\frac{3}{32}$ inch to the height of the stack. How many cups are in a stack that is $5\frac{3}{8}$ inches high? **37 cups**

REPRESENTATIONS Pictures, graphs, or objects that illustrate concepts

OBJECTIVE E Solve problems involving equations of the form $y = ax + b$ using tables or graphs. (Lessons 3-1, 3-2)

29a–b. See margin.
29. A tree now has a trunk with a radius of 12 centimeters. The radius is increasing by 0.5 centimeter per year. Its radius y after x years is described by $y = 12 + 0.5x$.

   a. Make a table of values for this relationship.

   b. Use the table to draw a graph.

   c. How many years will it take for the tree trunk to reach a radius of 15 centimeters? **6 yr**

   d. What will the radius be in 8 years? **16 cm**

30. In the summer of 2005, the Chicago area had its worst drought on record. On July 3, the level of the Fox River was 6.1 feet and dropping 0.2 foot per week. Let y be the level of the river after x weeks.

   a. Suppose the river continues to drop at the same rate. Write an equation for y in terms of x. $y = 6.1 - 0.2x$

   b. Make a table of values for this relationship.

   c. Use the table to draw a graph.
30b-c. See margin.
31. Darnell has $55 in the bank and is adding $20 every week. Let b be his balance after w weeks. 31a–d. See margin.

   a. Write an equation for b in terms of w.

   b. Make a table of values for this relationship.

   c. Make a graph from the table.

   d. When will he have $175 in the bank? Explain how you found your answer.

OBJECTIVE F Graph all the solutions to a linear inequality. (Lessons 3-6, 3-7)

In 32–35, graph all solutions to each inequality on a number line. 32–35. See margin.

32. $x \geq -4.3$ **33.** $d < 3\frac{1}{2}$

34. $2 < 5 - a$ **35.** $4m + 6 > -2$

Assessment

Evaluation The *Assessment Resources* provide four forms of the Chapter 3 Test. Forms A and B present parallel versions of a short-answer format. Form C consists of four to six short-response questions that cover the SPUR objectives from Chapter 3. Form D offers performance assessment that covers a subset (or even just one) of the SPUR objectives for the chapter.

Feedback After students have taken the test for Chapter 3 and you have scored the results, return the tests to students for discussion. Class discussion on the questions that caused trouble for most students can be very effective in identifying and clarifying misunderstandings. You might want to have them note the items they missed and work either in groups or at home to correct them. It is important for students to receive feedback on every chapter test, and we recommend that students see and correct their mistakes before proceeding too far into the next chapter.

Additional Answers

31c.

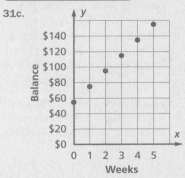

31d. Answers vary. Sample answer: After 6 weeks, find $175 on the y-axis and draw a horizontal line to the graph, then a vertical line down to the x-axis to find when Darnell has $175.

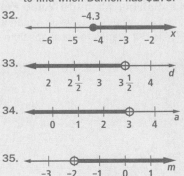

Additional Answers

30c.

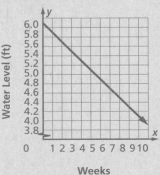

31a. $b = 55 + 20w$

31b.

Weeks	Balance
0	$55
1	$75
2	$95
3	$115

Chapter

4 More Linear Equations and Inequalities

Chapter Overview

	Local Standards	Pacing (in days)		
		Average	Advanced	Block
4-1 Solving Percent Problems Using Equations D Solve percent problems. J Solve real-world problems involving percents.		1	0.5	0.5
4-2 Horizontal and Vertical Lines I Use tables and graphs to solve real-world problems involving linear situations. K Graph horizontal and vertical lines.		1	1	0.5
4-3 Using Tables and Graphs to Solve I Use tables and graphs to solve real-world problems involving linear situations. L Use graphs to solve problems involving linear equations.		1	0.5	0.75
QUIZ 1		0.5	0.5	0.25
4-4 Solving $ax + b = cx + d$ A Solve and check equations of the form $ax + b = cx + d$. F Apply and recognize Addition and Multiplication Properties of Equality and Inequality when solving linear sentences. H Use linear equations and inequalities of the form $ax + b = cx + d$ or $ax + b < cx + d$ to solve real-world problems.		1	1	0.5
4-5 Solving $ax + b < cx + d$ B Solve and check compound inequalities of the form $ax + b < cx + d$. F Apply and recognize Addition and Multiplication Properties of Equality and Inequality when solving linear sentences. H Use linear equations and inequalities of the form $ax + b = cx + d$ or $ax + b < cx + d$ to solve real-world problems.		1	1	0.5
4-6 Situations That Always or Never Happen G Recognize when sentences have no solution or every real number as a solution. M Use graphs to model sentences that have no solution or every real number as a solution.		1	0.5	0.75
QUIZ 2		0.5	0.5	0.25
4-7 Equivalent Formulas C Find equivalent forms of formulas and equations.		1	0.5	0.5
4-8 Compound Inequalities, *And* and *Or* B Solve and check compound inequalities of the form $ax + b < cx + d$.		1	1	0.5
4-9 Solving Absolute Value Equations and Inequalities E Solve absolute value equations and inequalities involving linear expressions. N Use graphs to solve absolute value inequalities of the form $|ax + b| < c$ or $|ax + b| > c$.		1	1	0.5
Self-Test		1	1	0.5
Chapter Review		2	2	1
Test		1	1	0.5
TOTAL		14	12	7.5

Differentiated Options Universal Access

	Accommodating the Learner	Vocabulary Development	Ongoing Assessment	Materials
4-1	pp. 183, 184		written, p. 187	scientific or graphing calculator
4-2	pp. 189, 190	p. 191	group, p. 195	scientific or graphing calculator
4-3	pp. 197, 198		oral, p. 201	scientific or graphing calculator
4-4	pp. 204, 205	p. 204	group, p. 209	scientific or graphing calculator
4-5	pp. 211, 212		oral, p. 215	scientific or graphing calculator
4-6	pp. 217, 218	p. 218	written, p. 220	scientific or graphing calculator
4-7	pp. 222, 223		groups, p. 226	scientific or graphing calculator
4-8	pp. 228, 229	p. 229	written, p. 233	scientific or graphing calculator
4-9	pp. 236, 237		written, p. 239	scientific or graphing calculator

Objectives

		Lessons	Self-Test Questions	Chapter Review Questions
Skills				
A	Solve and check equations of the form $ax + b = cx + d$.	4-4	4-6	1–8
B	Solve and check compound inequalities of the form $ax + b < cx + d$.	4-5, 4-8	7, 8	9–16
C	Find equivalent forms of formulas and equations.	4-7	15	17–22
Properties				
D	Solve percent problems.	4-1	20	23–28
E	Solve absolute value equations and inequalities involving linear expressions.	4-9	9	29–34
F	Apply and recognize Addition and Multiplication Properties of Equality and Inequality when solving linear sentences.	4-4, 4-5	2, 3	35–39
G	Recognize when sentences have no solution or every real number as a solution.	4-6	10	40–43
Uses				
H	Use linear equations and inequalities of the form $ax + b = cx + d$ or $ax + b < cx + d$ to solve real-world problems.	4-4, 4-5	18, 19	44–47
I	Use tables and graphs to solve real-world problems involving linear situations.	4-2, 4-3	17	48–50
J	Solve real-world problems involving percents.	4-1	1, 12	51–53
Representations				
K	Graph horizontal and vertical lines.	4-2	14	54–58
L	Use graphs to solve problems involving linear equations.	4-3	11	59–62
M	Use graphs to model sentences that have no solution or every real number as a solution.	4-6	16	63–66
N	Use graphs to solve absolute value inequalities of the form $|ax + b| < c$ or $|ax + b| > c$.	4-9	13	67, 68

Resource Masters Chapter 4

Resource Master 1, Graph Paper (page 2) can be used as needed.

Resource Master 2, Four Quadrant Graph Paper (page 3), can be used with Lessons 4-2, 4-3, 4-5, 4-8, and 4-9.

Resource Master 3, Centimeter Grid (page 4) can be used with Lesson 4-1.

Resource Master 7, Number Lines (page 8) can be used with Lesson 4-8.

Resource Master 45 Lesson 4-1

Warm-Up

1. What percent of 60 is 12?
   A 120%   B 5%   C 50%
   D 20%   E 25%

2. 12 is what percent of 3?
   A 25%   B 250%   C 400%
   D 300%   E 40%

3. Suppose 3% of x is 10 and 10% of y is 3. How are x and y related?
   A They are equal.
   B They are reciprocals.
   C The product of x and y is 10,000.

Additional Examples

1. 4% of what number is 76?
2. What percent of 210 is 33.6?
3. Chauncey wants to buy a pair of jeans costing $44.50. He knows he will be charged 4.5% sales tax on the jeans. Find the total cost of the jeans including the sales tax.
4. A bicycle normally costs $425, but is on sale for 20% off. What is the sale price?

Resource Master for Lesson 4-1

Resource Master 46 Lesson 4-1

Accommodating the Learner

1. Compare the following pairs of numbers using <, >, or =.
   a. $\frac{12}{13}$ _____ 92%
   b. $0.32\frac{1}{2}$ _____ $32\frac{1}{2}$%
   c. 0.6 _____ 6%
   d. 0.176 _____ 17.6%
   e. 40% _____ 0.4
   f. 37% _____ 3

2. a. Write a ratio and a percent to describe the parts of each rectangle.

   b. Shade $\frac{1}{3}$ or $33\frac{1}{3}$% of each figure.

Resource Master for Lesson 4-1

Resource Master 47 Lesson 4-2

Warm-Up

1. You have been asked to graph the point $(2, \square)$. You can't read the second coordinate because it is covered. What can you say about where that point would be graphed?

2. You have been asked to graph the point $(\square, -11.4)$. Now the first coordinate is covered. What can you say about where that point would be graphed?

Additional Examples

1. Give an equation describing all points on the line graphed below.

   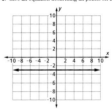

2. a. Graph $x = -15$ on a number line.
   b. Graph $x = -15$ on a coordinate plane.

3. Ricky is taking $1,400 with him to college for spending money. If he spends $100 per week, how many weeks will his money last?

Resource Master for Lesson 4-2

Resource Master 48 Lesson 4-3

Warm-Up

Refer to the Example on page 196.

1. What is the charge to make h copies of Acme Copiers in one month?
2. What is the cost to make h copies at Best Printers in one month?
3. Use the expressions in 1 and 2 to write an equation to determine the number of copies in a month for which the cost of both firms will be the same.

Additional Example

You are looking at new cell phone plans. You are trying to decide between two companies. Flash Cellular charges $65 a month for the first 400 minutes and then $0.03 for each additional minute. Horizon Cellular charges $60 a month for the first 400 minutes and then $0.04 for each additional minute. Describe the break-even point—the situation for which the costs are the same.

Number of Minutes (x)	Flash Cellular's Price (65 + 0.03x)	Horizon Cellular's Price (60 + 0.04x)
0		
50		
150		
250		
350		
450		
550		
650		

Resource Master for Lesson 4-3

Resource Master 49 Lesson 4-4

Warm-Up

Begin with Equation 1 in the Activity: $3z - 4 = 5z - 23$. There are numerous options for the first step in solving the equation. What equation results from each of the following operations on both sides of the original equation?

1. Add $-5z$ to both sides.
2. Add 4 to both sides.
3. Subtract 4 from both sides.
4. Subtract $3z$ from both sides. Solve the equation.

Additional Examples

1. Solve $7a + 2 = 42 - 3a$ using a CAS.
2. Solve $21x - 9 = 11x - 39$.
3. Solve $-13 - (x - 2) = -3(x - 3)$.
4. The length and width of a rectangle are $x + 4$ and $x - 3$, respectively. The lengths of the three sides of a triangle are x, x, and $x + 6$. Determine the value of x for which the perimeters of both figures will be equal.

Resource Master for Lesson 4-4

Resource Master 50 Lesson 4-4

Accommodating the Learner

The following problem has at least one error in its solution. Locate and correct each error. Write a brief description of the error(s) encountered.

$-6(x - 2) - (x + 3) = (2x - 8) - 9$
$-6x + 12 - x + 3 = (2x - 8) - 9$
$-7x + 15 = 2x - 1$
$-9x = -16$
$x = \frac{16}{9}$

Question 31

Resource Master for Lesson 4-4

Resource Master 51 · Lesson 4-5

Warm-Up

1. Find all solutions to the sentence.
   a. $-20x + 50 = 150$
   b. $-20x + 50 < 150$
   c. $-20x + 50 \geq 150$

2. Check your answers to all three sentences from Problem 1.

Additional Examples

1. The Bethel Company needs to ship items ordered by customers online. Quick Delivery charges a monthly service charge of $40 a month and $5 per package. On-Time Delivery charges a monthly service charge of $50 per month and $4.50 per package. Initially, Quick Delivery will be the more economical carrier. Due to the large volume of packages that need to be shipped each month, On-Time Delivery will become the more economical choice at some point during the month. When will On-Time Delivery become the more economical choice?

2. Solve $8 - 6x \leq -4x + 12$.

3. Twelve more than eight times a number n is less than four times the number. Find the number.

Resource Master for Lesson 4-5

Resource Master 52 · Lesson 4-6

Warm-Up

1. a. Solve $4(3A + 5) \geq 3(4A + 5)$.
   b. Check your answer to Part a by graphing $Y_1 = 4(3x + 5)$ and $Y_2 = 3(4x + 5)$. Explain how the graph verifies the answer.

Additional Examples

1. Solve $7x - 10 - 3x = 2(2x - 4)$.
2. Solve $7q + 1 > 60q - 4 - 53q$.

Comparing Situations

Years Worked	Job 1	Job 2
0	$30,000	$28,000
1	$35,000	$33,000
2	$40,000	$38,000
3	$45,000	$43,000
4	$50,000	$48,000
5	$55,000	$53,000
6	$60,000	$58,000

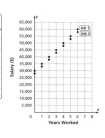

Resource Master for Lesson 4-6

Resource Master 53 · Lesson 4-7

Warm-Up

1. Consider the formula $A = p + pr$, which gives the amount A (in dollars) after one year in a bank account that started with p dollars and which has an annual yield of r.
   a. Solve this formula for p.
   b. Solve this formula for r.
   c. Check your answer to either Part a or b.

2. Find three formulas relating the unit cost C of an item, the number n of items purchased, and the total cost T.

Additional Examples

1. Solve $C = 2\pi r$ for the variable r. C is the circumference of a circle with radius r.
2. A formula for the area of a sphere is $A = 4\pi r^2$. Solve the formula for r. Explain what you do in each step.
3. Use a graphing calculator to graph $-7x + 3y = 18$.

Accommodating the Learner

Find the perimeter P, of the running track in terms of r and t. Solve for r in terms of P and t. If $P = 400$ m and $t = 100$ m, what is the value of r? Use $\pi = 3.14$ and round your answer to the nearest hundredth. If $t = 115$ meters, what would the radius be?

Running Track

Resource Master for Lesson 4-7

Resource Master 54 · Lesson 4-8

Warm-Up

1. Find a number A that is a solution to $10 < A < 10.01$.
2. Find a number B that is a solution to $B - 3 > 4$ but *not* a solution to $B - 4 > 5$.
3. Find a number C that is a solution to $-62 \geq C \geq -64$ but *not* a solution to $-64 < C \leq 64$.

Additional Examples

1. Let $A =$ the set of numbers for which $x \leq 6$. Let $B =$ the set of numbers for which $x > -4$. Graph the set $A \cap B$. Describe the set with an *and* or an *or* statement.

2. Anita has three recipes for making brownies. The first recipe makes 4 servings, the second makes 8 servings, and the third makes 12 servings. Anita knows that it is not recommended to scale a recipe either up or down beyond four times its original serving size. If s represents the serving size, then the first recipe's serving-size scaled interval is $1 \leq s \leq 16$, the second recipe's serving-size scaled interval is $2 \leq s \leq 32$, and the third recipe's serving-size scaled interval is $3 \leq s \leq 48$. Which interval satisfies all three recipes?

3. Solve and graph $-5 < 3x - 8 \leq 1$.

4. Solve $5z - 4 < z$ or $7z + 18 < z$. Solve each inequality separately.

Resource Master for Lesson 4-8

Resource Master 55 · Lesson 4-8

Accommodating the Learner

Let $A = \{3, 4, 5, \ldots, 11\}$ and $B = \{-4, -2, 0, 2, 4, 6, 8\}$. Using the Venn diagram given, illustrate $A \cap B$ by shading the intersection. Repeat the process for $A \cup B$.

The Language of Compound Sentences

Normal Temperatures

$t \geq 40°$ and $t \leq 120°$

The graph is an interval.

Abnormal Temperatures

$t < 40°$ and $t > 120°$

The graph is two rays without their endpoints.

Describe the Intervals $a \leq x \leq b$

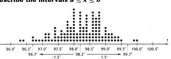

Resource Master for Lesson 4-8

Resource Master 56 · Lesson 4-9

Warm-Up

1. Give the two numbers whose distance from 100 is equal to 43.
2. The answers to Problem 1 are the solutions to which of these sentences?

   A $|x - 100| = 43$

   B $|x - 43| = 100$

   C $|x - 43| < 100$

   D $|x - 100| < 43$

3. A box is supposed to hold 100 clips. A store will accept one of these boxes if it holds from 100 to 104 clips.
   a. Write the acceptable number of clips n in a double inequality.
   b. Write the acceptable number of clips in the form $a \pm b$.
   c. Write the acceptable number of clips in a sentence involving absolute value.

Additional Example

1. Graph $y_1 = |x + 4|$ and $y_2 = 3$. Use the graph and algebraic properties to solve $|x + 4| = 3$.

Resource Master for Lesson 4-9

Resource Master 57 · Lesson 4-9

Additional Example

2. Solve $|3x - 6| < 21$.

Think: $|x| < a$ means $-a < x < a$.

$3x - 6 =$ _____   or $3x - 6 =$ _____
$x =$ _____   or $x =$ _____

Now decide whether the solutions occur for the values of x that are less or greater than the two values you just found. Use the table or graph to help you decide.

x	$|3x - 6|$
-9	
-5	
1	
7	
9	
11	

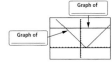

So the solution to $|3x - 6| < 21$ is _____.

Resource Master for Lesson 4-9

Resource Master 58 · Lesson 4-9

Solving $|x| = a$

x	$|x|$
-4	4
-3	3
-2	2
-1	1
0	0
1	1
2	2
3	3
4	4

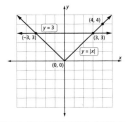

Resource Master for Lesson 4-9

More Linear Equations and Inequalities

Pacing

Each lesson in this chapter is designed to be covered in one day. At the end of the chapter, you should plan to spend 1 day to review the Self-Test, 1 to 2 days for the Chapter Review, and 1 day for a test. You may wish to spend a day on projects and possibly a day is needed for quizzes. This chapter should therefore take 12 to 15 days. We strongly advise you not spend more than 16 days on this chapter; there is ample opportunity to review ideas in later chapters.

Using Pages 180–181

The opener describes the three most common ways of describing a numerical relationship between two quantities: with a table (an arithmetic description), with a graph (a geometric description), and with an equation (an algebraic description).

A way of analyzing the light-bulb situation without algebra is to note that it costs 32¢ more for a regular bulb for each 100 hours of light. How long does it take the compact fluorescent (CF) bulb to make up the original $1.47 difference? Divide $1.47 by 0.32 to get 4.59 · 100 hours, or about 459 hours. That is the number that is approximated in the graph, and it is a reasonable value given what is in the table.

The algebraic solution to the equation and inequalities emulates this arithmetic process, giving us the inequality $1.47 > 0.32h$, the inequality $1.47 < 0.32h$, or the equation $1.47 = 0.32h$. To solve those sentences, we divide both sides by 0.32, and this means that the value of h is either found or bounded by 1.47 divided by 0.32.

> ## Contents
>

A lightbulb manufacturer produces two kinds of bulbs: regular bulbs and new compact fluorescent (CF) bulbs. The CF bulbs are more energy efficient than regular bulbs, since they produce the same amount of light but use less electricity. However, CF bulbs cost more than regular bulbs. Would the money a person saves in electricity make up for the higher initial cost of the CF bulb? This question and other related questions can be answered by using tables, by drawing graphs, and by solving linear equations and inequalities.

180

Chapter 4 Overview

This chapter extends the content of Chapter 3, beginning with simpler equations, and then considering linear equations and inequalities with the unknown on both sides. While your students may have seen the ideas of this chapter, the ideas are so important that they should not be skipped.

Lesson 4-1 shows how to use equations to solve common problems involving percent. Lesson 4-2 discusses horizontal and vertical lines as an introduction to graphing in Lesson 4-3. The purpose of Lesson 4-3 is to show the arithmetic and geometric approaches to solving equations that tables and graphs represent, and to show the types of problems that lead to equations with variables on both sides.

(continued on next page)

$$a + bx > c + dx$$
$$a + bx < c + dx$$
$$a + bx = c + dx$$

Hours (h)	CF Bulb Cost	Regular Bulb Cost
0	$1.99	$0.52
100	$2.15	$1.00
200	$2.31	$1.48
300	$2.47	$1.96
400	$2.63	$2.44
500	$2.79	$2.92
600	$2.95	$3.40
700	$3.11	$3.88
800	$3.27	$4.36
900	$3.43	$4.84
1,000	$3.59	$5.32

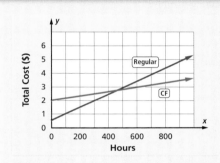

Equations and Inequalities

	CF Bulb Cost	Regular Bulb Cost
When is the regular bulb cheaper?	$1.99 + 0.16h > 0.52 + 0.48h$	
When is the CF bulb cheaper?	$1.99 + 0.16h < 0.52 + 0.48h$	
When are the costs the same?	$1.99 + 0.16h = 0.52 + 0.48h$	

In this chapter, you will use all these ways to solve linear sentences and study how they are related to each other.

181

Lessons 4-4 and 4-5 are the heart of the chapter, discussing the important skills of solving general linear equations and general linear inequalities. The special cases of when these sentences have no solution or many solutions are discussed in Lesson 4-6. Lesson 4-7 discusses solving a linear equation for one variable in terms of another.

The last two lessons apply linear equations and inequalities to solving more complicated sentences. Lesson 4-8 discusses the union and intersection of one-variable inequalities. Lesson 4-9 applies these concepts to the solving of sentences involving absolute value.

Lesson

4-1

Lesson

4-1

Solving Percent Problems Using Equations

GOAL

Solve three basic percent problems by translating them into equations.

SPUR Objectives

(The SPUR Objectives for all of Chapter 4 are found in the Chapter Review on pages 245–249.)

D Solve percent problems.

J Solve real-world problems involving percent.

Materials/Resources

· Lesson Master 4-1A or 4-1B
· Resource Masters 3, 45, and 46
· Scientific or graphing calculator

HOMEWORK

Suggestions for Assignment

- Questions 1–28
- Question 29 (extra credit)
- Reading Lesson 4-2
- Covering the Ideas 4-2

Local Standards

---

1 Warm-Up

You might write or project the following so that students can do these questions as they enter the classroom.

1. What percent of 60 is 12? **D**
  A 120%   **B** 5%   **C** 50%
  D 20%   **E** 25%

2. 12 is what percent of 3? **C**
  A 25%   **B** 250%   **C** 400%
  D 300%   **E** 40%

3. Suppose 3% of x is 10 and 10% of y is 3. How are x and y related? **C, because $x = \frac{1,000}{3}$ and $y = 30$**
  A They are equal.
  B They are reciprocals.
  C The product of x and y is 10,000.

▶ **BIG IDEA**   Many types of questions involving percents can be answered by solving an equation of the form $ax = b$.

The word **percent** (often written as the two words per cent) comes from the Latin words "per centum," meaning "per 100." So 7% literally means 7 per 100, the ratio $\frac{7}{100}$, or the decimal 0.07. The symbol % for percent is only a little more than 100 years old.

Putting Percent Problems into the Form $p \cdot q = r$

Recall that to find a percent p of a given quantity q you simply multiply q by p. For example, to find 12% of 85, multiply $0.12 \cdot 85 = 10.2$. To find $5\frac{1}{4}$% of $3,000, calculate $0.0525 \cdot 3,000 = \$157.50$. This gives a straightforward method for solving many percent problems. Just translate the words into an equation of the form $p \cdot q = r$, where p is the percent in decimal or fraction form, q is the initial quantity, and r is the resulting quantity.

Example 1
7% of what number is 91?

Solution

7% of what number is 91?

$0.07 \cdot \quad q \quad = 91$ Change 7% to 0.07.

$\frac{0.07q}{0.07} = \frac{91}{0.07}$ Divide each side by 0.07.

$q = 1,300$ Simplify.

Check 7% of $1,300 = 0.07 \cdot 1,300 = 91$. It checks.

Background

Three types of percent problems. Examples 1, 2, and 3 illustrate the types of percent problems discussed in this lesson. Example 1 requires solving an equation. Example 2 is a division problem—divide the part by the whole: $38.4 \div 160 = 0.24 = 24\%$, as shown in the solution on page 183. Example 3 uses the Distributive Property to change a percent increase from an addition situation to a multiplication situation. Approaching the problems as separate entities has the advantage of reducing the amount of algebra and getting to the heart of the arithmetic. The disadvantage is, that it requires learning different strategies. Still, it is a strategy that we have used in previous UCSMP courses.

Example 2

What percent of 160 is 38.4?

Solution

What percent of 160 is 38.4?

$$p \cdot 160 = 38.4 \quad \text{Translate into an equation.}$$

$$\frac{p \cdot 160}{160} = \frac{38.4}{160} \quad \text{Divide each side by 160.}$$

$$p = 0.24 \quad \text{Simplify. This is the solution to the equation.}$$

$$p = 24\% \quad \text{Rewrite the solution as a percent.}$$

Check 24% of 160 = 0.24 · 160 = 38.4. It checks.

Percent Add-Ons and Discounts

Percents are very common in business, science, statistics, and even everyday shopping. In the next example, the Distributive Property gives a useful approach to a common situation.

Example 3

Ian, Cassady, Quincy, and Dylan ate at a local restaurant. The meal cost $36.50 without a tip. The bill states, "An 18% gratuity (tip) will be added for parties of 4 or more people." Find the total cost of the meal and tip.

Solution 1 Let M be the cost of the meal. We know M = $36.50, but we ignore that for a while. Note that total cost = cost of meal + cost of tip.

total cost = 100% · M + 18% · M   18% of $36.50

= 118% · M   Distributive Property

= 1.18 · 36.50   Rewrite 118% as 1.18.

= 43.07   Multiply.

So the total cost was $43.07.

An average of one out of five meals consumed by Americans—4.2 meals per week—is prepared in a commercial setting.

Source: Meal Consumption Behavior

Solution 2 Find the amount of the tip and then add it to the $36.50 meal cost.

tip = 18% · 36.50   18% of $36.50

= 0.18(36.50)   18% = 0.18

= 6.57   Simplify.

total cost = 36.50 + 6.57 = 43.07

Again, the total cost was $43.07.

Solving Percent Problems Using Equations   **183**

2 Teaching

Notes on the Lesson

The key in solving simple percent problems is to convert situations into equations of the form $a \cdot b = c$, thus illustrating the power of algebra.

Changing between percent and decimal forms is critical. Remind students that the % symbol means "multiply by 0.01." Thus, to change from a percent to a decimal, move the decimal point two places to the left as you would when multiplying by 0.01. To change from a decimal to percent, reverse the operation. Students can check this reasoning with percents that they already know—for instance, 50% = 0.5.

Additional Examples

Example 1 4% of what number is 76? **1,900**

Example 2 What percent of 210 is 33.6? **16%**

Example 3 Chauncey wants to buy a pair of jeans costing $44.50. He knows he will be charged 4.5% sales tax on the jeans. Find the total cost of the jeans including the sales tax. **$46.50**

Accommodating the Learner

Ask students to compare the following pairs of numbers using <, >, or =.

a. $\frac{12}{13}$ __?__ 92% >   b. $0.32\frac{1}{2}$ __?__ $32\frac{1}{2}\%$ =

c. 0.6 __?__ 6% >   d. 0.176 __?__ 17.6% =

e. 40% __?__ 0.4 =   f. 37% __?__ 3 <

Once students get these done correctly, ask them to write three examples of their own.

4-1

Notes on the Lesson

Stress the importance of using estimation to check answers, as in the check to Example 2. In Example 3, the cost should be larger than $36.50. Since 25% of $36 is $9, the cost should not be as much as $45. Example 4 is important because it involves only changing the subtraction to a multiplication.

STOP QY

The use of the Distributive Property in Solution 1 of Example 3 enables the total cost to be found with just one calculation. This idea is used in Example 4 to quickly calculate the price for an item on sale.

If a meal cost $21.16 with a 15% tip, what was the cost before the tip?

GUIDED

Example 4

A dishwasher normally costs $320, but it is on sale for 15% off. What is the sale price?

Solution Let P be the regular price. Then the discount is 15% · P, or $0.15P$.

Sale price = regular price − discount

$= \underline{\ ?\ } - \underline{\ ?\ }$ Translate into an equation. P; 0.15P

$= \underline{\ ?\ } - \underline{\ ?\ }$ Multiplicative Identity Property 1P; 0.15P

$= \underline{\ ?\ }$ Combine like terms. 0.85P

We know $P = 320. So the sale price is $\underline{\ ?\ }(\underline{\ ?\ }) = \$\underline{\ ?\ }$.

Another way to think about the sale price is that when 15% of the price is removed, 100% − 15%, or 85% of the price remains. 0.85; 320; 272

Additional Example

Example 4 A bicycle normally costs $425, but is on sale for 20% off. What is the sale price? **$340**

Markups and Discounts

If an item is discounted x%, you pay $(100 - x)$% of the original or listed price.

If an item is marked up or taxed x%, you pay $(100 + x)$% of the original or listed price.

Questions

COVERING THE IDEAS

1. 123% of 780 is what number? **959.4**

2. 40% of what number is 440? **1,100**

3. What percent of 4.7 is 0.94? **20%**

4. What number is 62% of 980? **607.6**

5. Suppose a shirt is on sale for 10% off its original price of $23.50.
   a. What percent of the original price does the customer pay? **90%**
   b. How much does the customer pay before tax? **$21.15**

Accommodating the Learner ⬇

Ask students to write a ratio and a percent to describe the shaded regions of each figure.

$\frac{3}{10} = 30\%$ $\frac{1}{4} = 25\%$ $\frac{1}{6} \approx 16.7\%$

Once students have completed this task correctly, place the following figures on an overhead. Instruct students to shade in $33\frac{1}{3}\%$ of each figure.

6. Suppose a dinner costs D dollars and you wish to give a 20% tip.
   a. What is the amount of the tip? **0.2D**
   b. What is the total cost of the meal with tip? **1.2D**

7. A table is being sold at "40% off." If the price of the table before the sale was T dollars, what is the sale price? **0.6T**

8. An electronics store owner buys a television from the manufacturer, and then adds 45% of that cost to get the price the customer pays. If a TV sells for $499, what was the price the store owner paid? **$344.14**

9. The total cost of a digital camera including an 8.5% sales tax is $215. How much tax was paid on this purchase? **$16.84**

Digital-camera sales surpassed $4 billion in 2004.

Source: *Twice*

10. The Cupertinos bought a new car. The total amount they paid was $28,250.75 including the 8% sales tax. What was the price before the sales tax was added? **$26,158.10**

11. Consider the sales receipt at the right. Determine the sales-tax rate as a percent. **7.25%**

Ian's Computer Store
2217 Smithville Road
Middleboro, Ohio 42155

– CASH RECEIPT –
9/30/2004 1:29:07 PM

Ref ID: 4727-1324

AMOUNT   15.85
TAX   1.15
- - - - - - - - - - -
TOTAL:

CASH:

CHANGE:

THANK YOU
To Reorder Call: (714) 449-8211
MADE IN THE USA

12. Clearwater High School expects a 4% increase in enrollment next year. There are 1,850 students enrolled this year.
    a. How many students will the school gain? **74 students**
    b. What is the expected enrollment next year? **1,924 students**

13. According to the 2000 census, 73% of the 221 million U.S. residents age 15 and older had been married at least once. How many U.S. residents over 15 had *never* been married?
    59,670,000 U.S. residents

APPLYING THE MATHEMATICS

In 14 and 15, use the following information. Sucrose, or common table sugar, is composed of carbon, hydrogen, and oxygen. Suppose an experiment calls for 68.4 grams of sucrose.

14. If 4.2% of the weight of sucrose is carbon, how many grams of carbon are in the 68.4 grams? **about 2.87 g**

15. If 35.2 grams of the 68.4 grams are oxygen, what percent of the weight of sucrose is oxygen? **about 51.5%**

Solving Percent Problems Using Equations **185**

3 Assignment

Recommended Assignment
- Questions 1–28
- Question 29 (extra credit)
- Reading Lesson 4-2
- Covering the Ideas 4-2

Notes on the Questions

Question 1 We include percents greater than 100% because they are important not only for taxes and increases in price, but also for the exponential growth that students will study later. They will then need to convert these percents into decimals, as they need to do here.

Question 5 The idea of Part a is for students to note that 10% off means one pays 90%, and that the Distributive Property does not need to be used in solving the equation that gives the answer to Part b.

Questions 7–11 Each of these questions involves an important consumer skill.

Questions 14 and 15 These should be assigned together.

4-1A Lesson Master

Questions on SPUR Objectives
See pages 245–249 for objectives.

PROPERTIES Objective D

1. 82 is 40% of what number? **205**
2. A computer costs $1,200 after a 20% discount. What was its original price? **$1,500**
3. To the nearest percent, 11 is what percent of 70? **16%**
4. To the nearest tenth what number is 52% of 162? **84.2**
5. 15 is what percent of 45? **33.3%**
6. 45 is what percent of 15? **300%**
7. What number is 20% of 205? **41**
8. You go out to dinner and pay a 15% tip equal to $4.50. How much did the meal cost? **$30**
9. To the nearest whole number, 23% of 578 is what number? **133**

USES Objective J

10. In 2006, there were 299,400,000 Americans. If this number represented 4.58% of the world's population, how large was the world's population in 2006? **6,537,117,904**
11. The "Spanish Flu" pandemic of 1918–1919 was among the greatest worldwide disasters. It is not known exactly how many people died, but estimates range from 50 million to 100 million people. If these numbers represent 2.5% and 5% of the world's 1918 population, how large was the world's population at that time? **2 billion**
12. Estimated receipts for the US government for fiscal year 2006 were $2.2 trillion. About $976.8 billion of this money came from individual income tax. What percent of the 2006 receipts came from individual income tax? **44.4%**
13. Oxygen accounts for approximately 23.113% of the mass of Earth's atmosphere. According to the National Center for Atmospheric Research, the total mass of the atmosphere is 5.1480×10^{18} kg. What is the total mass of the oxygen in the atmosphere? **1.1899×10^{18} kg**

Algebra 169

Notes on the Questions

Question 25 By this time, students might begin to realize that an equation relating c to n will involve multiplying by 4, since there are 4 more cubes in each term than the preceding. You might probe students to see how many have realized that.

Question 26 This question helps to set up Lesson 4-2.

Question 27 One reason for a question like this is to show students that a problem may look difficult but be quite easy if they look for patterns.

Question 29 This relationship can be used to simplify some calculations of percents. For instance, it is easier to think of 50% of 18 than 18% of 50.

Note-Taking Tips

Students often make a mistake when they change 0.05% to a decimal. Often they will write 0.05 rather than 0.0005. Emphasize that the % symbol means hundredths and they must move the decimal place two places to the left. Have students write several examples in their notebooks.

16. On a mathematics test there were eight A's, twelve B's, ten C's, two D's, and zero F's. What percent of the students earned A's? **25%**

17. Consider the following situation. Jorge works at a clothing store in the local mall. As an employee, he receives a 20% discount on clothes. He spent $118.50 at the store.

    a. What was the regular price of the clothes Jorge bought before the discount was figured? **$148.13**

    b. Suppose a student answers Part a in the manner shown below. Show why the student's answer is not correct.

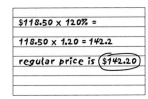

```
$118.50 x 120% =

118.50 x 1.20 = 142.2

regular price is ($142.20)
```

17b. The regular price is not 120% of the sale price. The sale price is 80% of the regular price.

In 2002, about 40 million households in the United States had DVD players.

Source: Consumer Electronics Association

18. A DVD player originally cost $150. It is on sale for $72.50. What is the percent of the discount, rounded to the nearest tenth of a percent? **51.7%**

REVIEW

In 19–21, solve and check the equation. **(Lesson 3-8)**

19. $\frac{k}{7} + 18 = \frac{19}{2}$
$k = -59.5$

20. $\frac{u}{12} - \frac{u}{2} = 35$
$u = -84$

21. $\frac{a+3}{4} + 3 = \frac{1}{2}$
$a = -13$

22. Penelope Nichols spends half her monthly income on housing and food, and budgets the other half as follows: $\frac{1}{4}$ on clothes, $\frac{1}{3}$ on entertainment, and $\frac{1}{4}$ on transportation. She saves the remaining $40. What is her monthly income? **(Lesson 3-8)** **$480**

23. Rebecca works at a clothing store that pays her $7.25 per hour plus 9% of the cost of the clothes that she sells. If she works for 8 hours, what is the cost of the clothing she must sell if she wants to earn at least $87? **(Lesson 3-7)** **$322.23**

24. **Multiple Choice** Which graph below shows the solutions of $6 < -4n + 10$? **(Lesson 3-7)** **A**

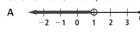
A

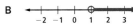
B

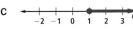
C

D

25. Consider the sequence made with cubes below. (Lessons 3-2, 1-4)

1   2   3

a. How many cubes will be needed to make the 4th term? 13 cubes

b. Write an equation for the number c of cubes that are in the nth term. Answers vary. Sample answer: $4n - 3$

c. Using your equation from Part b, find the term number that contains 33 cubes. 9

26. Trina timed her commute to school every morning for two weeks. Her times, in minutes, were 15, 22, 17, 12, 14, 16, 20, 21, 21, and 19. Compute the m.a.d. of Trina's commute. (Lesson 1-7)
    2.9 min

27. Evaluate $(w + 4.7)(2.6 - w)(w + 7.1)$ when $w = -4.7$.
    (Lesson 1-1) 0

28. A recipe calls for $\frac{1}{4}$ tablespoon of vanilla. If Sally wants to make $\frac{2}{3}$ of the recipe, how much vanilla will she use? (Previous Course)
    $\frac{1}{6}$ tbs

EXPLORATION

29. Jerome noticed that 40% of 50 is equal to 50% of 40 and concluded a% of b is always equal to b% of a. Explain why this works for any positive values of a and b. Answers vary. Sample answer: $a\%$ of $b = \frac{a}{100} \cdot b = \frac{ab}{100} = \frac{b}{100}a = b\%$ of a.

QY ANSWER

$18.40

4 **Wrap-Up**

Ongoing Assessment

In 2005, approximately 99 billion aluminum cans were sold in the United States. Of those 99 billion cans approximately 51.4 billion cans were recycled. Ask students to figure the percent of cans that were recycled. In 2005, it took about 3.2% of a pound of aluminum to make a can. Ask students to figure out how many pounds of aluminum it took to make 99 billion cans.

About 52% were recycled; 3,168,000,000 lb

Lesson
4-2

Horizontal and Vertical Lines

Vocabulary

horizontal line, $y = k$

vertical line, $x = h$

GOAL

Graph horizontal and vertical lines and show how these graphs can help in solving problems.

SPUR Objectives

I Use tables and graphs to solve real-world problems involving linear situations.

K Graph horizontal and vertical lines.

Materials/Resources

- Lesson Master 4-2A or 4-2B
- Resource Masters 2 and 47
- Scientific or graphing calculator

HOMEWORK

Suggestions for Assignment
- Questions 1–27
- Question 28 (extra credit)
- Reading Lesson 4-3
- Covering the Ideas 4-3

Local Standards

---

1 Warm-Up

You might write or project the following so that students can do these questions as they enter the classroom.

1. You have been asked to graph the point (2, __?__). You can't read the second coordinate. What can you say about where the point is graphed? It will be on a vertical line through (2, 0).

2. You have been asked to graph the point (__?__, –11.4). Now the first coordinate is covered. What can you say about where that point would be graphed? It will be on a horizontal line through (0, –11.4).

▶ **BIG IDEA** Every horizontal line has an equation of the form $y = k$; every vertical line has the form $x = h$.

Equations for Horizontal Lines

In Lesson 2-3, you saw several number puzzles in which you began with a number and then performed a series of calculations to get a final answer. The puzzling part came from the surprising relationship between the starting number and the final result. Below you see ordered pairs for two of these puzzles in a table and on a graph. For each puzzle, the points lie on a line. In the "I Can Guess Your Age Puzzle," the result is always the same as the starting number. The line that is graphed has equation $y = x$.

I Can Guess Your Age Puzzle	
Starting Number (*x*)	Result (*y*)
3	3
10	10
–8	–8

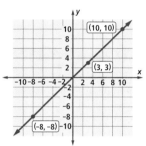

But the "Seven Is Heaven" graph is different.

Seven Is Heaven Puzzle	
Starting Number (*x*)	Result (*y*)
3	7
10	7
–1	7

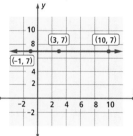

The points lie on a *horizontal line*. For all of these points, the *y*-coordinate equals 7. In short, $y = 7$. Every *horizontal line* has an equation of this type.

Mental Math

△**ABC** is equilateral.

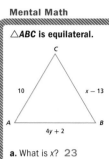

a. What is *x*? 23

b. What is *y*? 2

Background

Horizontal and vertical lines are not complicated, but their equations can create problems for students. The first inclination students have is to believe mistakenly that the graph of $x = h$ is parallel to the *x*-axis and the graph of $y = k$ is parallel to the *y*-axis.

The equation $x = h$ involves two different uses of variables: *x* is indeed a number that in theory could represent many values in a situation while *h* is a constant, a variable that represents only one value. Because *x* and *h* are equal, students need to realize

that *x* also takes on only one value. Similar difficulties occur with $y = k$.

Suppose a student is asked to graph $x = 3$. How is a student to know whether the graph is a *point* on a number line or a *vertical line*? Generally, the context tells you. If you are graphing lines, then you are in two dimensions, so the graph of $x = 3$ is a line. If you are graphing solutions to an equation in one variable, then the graph is a point on the number line.

(continued on next page)

Equation of a Horizontal Line

Every **horizontal line** has an equation of the form *y* = *k*, where *k* is a real number.

Example 1

Find an equation describing all points on the line graphed at the right.

Solution The points are on a horizontal line that crosses the *y*-axis at 2. An equation for the line is y = 2.

Check Two of the points on the line have coordinates (1, 2) and (−3, 2). These numbers satisfy the equation *y* = 2.

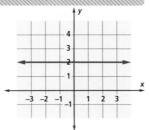

Equations for Vertical Lines

A vertical line is drawn at the right.

Notice that the *x*-coordinate of the ordered pairs is 4.5 regardless of the *y*-coordinate. Thus an equation for the line is *x* = 4.5. This means *x* is fixed at 4.5, but *y* can be any number.

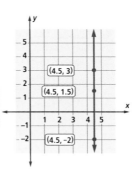

Equation of a Vertical Line

Every **vertical line** has an equation of the form *x* = *h*, where *h* is a real number.

An equation with only one variable, such as *x* = −4.5 or *y* = 7, can be graphed on a number line (in which case its graph is a point), or on a coordinate plane (in which case its graph is a line). The directions or the context of the problem will usually tell you which type of graph to draw.

Example 2

a. Graph *x* = −20 on a number line.

b. Graph *x* = −20 on a coordinate plane.

Solutions

a. Draw a number line. Mark the point with coordinate equal to −20, as shown below. The graph of *x* = −20 on a number line is the single point with coordinate −20.

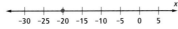

(continued on next page)

Horizontal and Vertical Lines   **189**

---

2 Teaching

Notes on the Lesson

Equations for horizontal lines. The set of points (*x*, *y*) with *y* = *k* for a particular value of *k* is sometimes used as the *definition* of "horizontal line." Similarly, the set of points (*x*, *y*) with *x* = *h* is sometimes used as the definition of "vertical line."

Some students may need to remember that the word *horizontal* comes from *horizon*. Horizontal lines are parallel to the horizon.

Additional Examples

Example 1 Give an equation describing all points on the line graphed below.

y = −3

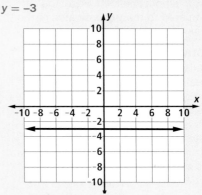

Example 2

a. Graph *x* = −15 on a number line.

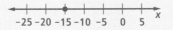

b. Graph *x* = −15 on a coordinate plane.

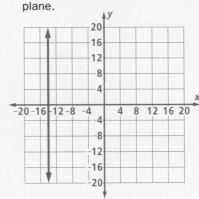

The distinction can be made symbolically by using *set-builder notation*. {*x*: *x* = 3}, read "the set of numbers *x* such that *x* equals 3," consists of the single number 3. {(*x*, *y*): *x* = 3}, read "the set of ordered pairs *x*, *y*, such that *x* equals 3," consists of all ordered pairs whose first coordinate is 3.

Accommodating the Learner

Send a volunteer up to the overhead projector and ask him or her to graph a vertical or horizontal line. The student should label at least two points on the line. Have the student call on a classmate to give an equation of the line graphed. If the second student is correct, he or she should give another equation of a vertical or horizontal line to the student standing at the overhead projector. Ask the student to use the overhead projector to graph this equation and label at least two points.

4-2

Notes on the Lesson

Example 3 Here we graph $y = 300$ and $y = 900 - 50x$. They intersect at the value of x for which $900 - 50x = 300$. This is a difficult concept for students but one that will be seen many times throughout the remainder of the year. You might have students replicate this graph on their graphing calculators.

Additional Example

Example 3 Ricky is taking $1,400 with him to college for spending money. If he spends $100 per week, how many weeks will his money last? **14 wk**

Activity The Activity on page 191 provides a nice application of horizontal lines. It may help students to realize that $y = k$ is horizontal, because k is being compared to the y-coordinates of the other points.

Note-Taking Tips

Students often have a difficult time keeping vertical and horizontal lines straight. Tell them that horizontal lines are parallel to the horizon, and all points on a horizontal line are the same distance from the x-axis. Tell them that vertical lines are straight up and down, and all points on a vertical line are the same distance from the y-axis.

---

b. Draw a coordinate grid. Plot points whose x-coordinate is -20. Some points are $(-20, 10)$, $(-20, 4)$, and $(-20, -8)$. Draw the line through these points.

The graph of $x = -20$ in a coordinate plane is the vertical line that crosses the x-axis at -20.

Horizontal Lines and Linear Patterns

Horizontal lines can be helpful in solving equations or inequalities.

Example 3

At the beginning of a vacation, Matt has $900 in his savings account. As long as he has at least $300 in his account, he does not have to pay a service fee. Each morning he withdraws $50 from an ATM for spending money. How many days can he withdraw $50 per day without paying a service fee?

Solution 1 Let $x =$ the number of days after Matt's vacation began. Let $y =$ the amount of money in his bank account. Then $y = 900 - 50x$.

Day (x)	Balance (y)
0	900
4	700
8	500
12	300
16	100

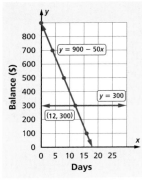

The table of (x, y) values can be used to graph $y = 900 - 50x$. Also graphed is $y = 300$ to represent the balance that he must keep to avoid a service fee. As long as the point for Matt's balance is at or above the $y = 300$ line he does not have to pay a service fee. The lines appear to intersect at $x = 12$, so for the first 12 days, Matt's balance is high enough to avoid paying a service fee.

Solution 2 Translate "Matt's balance is at least $300" into an inequality and solve. Let $x =$ the number of days Matt has been on vacation. In x days, he will have withdrawn $50x$ dollars, so we want to know when $900 - 50x \geq 300$.

The first modern day ATM in the United States was introduced to consumers in 1971 by Chemical Bank.

Source: Cash Technologies, Inc.

190   More Linear Equations and Inequalities

Accommodating the Learner ⬆

Group the students by threes. Instruct each group to describe two realistic situations that could be modeled by a vertical line. Instruct each group to describe two realistic situations that could be modeled by a horizontal line. Have students write their equations on a piece of paper and graph each of them. Often in a realistic setting, the entire line doesn't make sense in the context of the problem.

Ask students whether they should include the entire line or just part of it. Have students erase that part of each line which does not apply to each of the situations.

$$900 - 50x - 900 \geq 300 - 900 \quad \text{Subtract 900 from each side.}$$

$$-50x \geq -600 \quad \text{Collect like terms.}$$

$$\frac{-50x}{-50} \leq \frac{-600}{-50} \quad \text{Divide each side by } -50.$$
Change the sense of the inequality.

$$x \leq 12 \quad \text{Simplify.}$$

For the first 12 days, Matt does not have to pay a service charge.

Deviation from the Mean

For statistical data in a scatterplot, a horizontal line at the mean can help to show how the data relate to the average value. The hourly temperatures in Flagstaff, Arizona, on a June day are shown in the graph below.

Related to each temperature is its deviation from the mean, which is the difference between the actual temperature and the mean temperature.

For example, when $h = 15$ (3 P.M.), the temperature was 82.9°F, giving a deviation of $82.9 - 68.1 = 14.8$°F from the mean. At $h = 3$ (3 A.M.), the deviation was $52 - 68.1 = -16.1$°F.

Activity

Use the table and graph of the temperatures at Flagstaff on a June day. Notice that the values on the vertical axis begin at 45. The interval $0 < y < 45$ is compressed on the graph since there are no data in that interval.

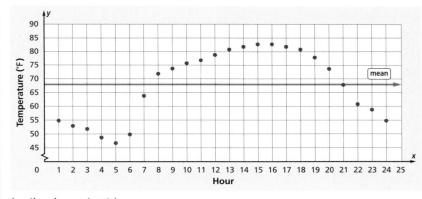

(continued on next page)

Horizontal and Vertical Lines   **191**

Notes on the Activity

Remind students they can produce the results seen in this Activity using their calculator.

1. Press STAT.

2. Press ENTER to select EDIT.

3. If there is any old data in column L1, use DEL → ENTER for each value. Using arrow keys do the same for L2.

4. Key in data from the table. In L1 key in 1–24. After each entry press ENTER. In L2 key in all temperatures from the table.

5. Press Window – Use these settings:

   Xmin – Use the least hour – in this case 1.

   Xmax – Use the greatest hour – in this case 24.

   Xscl – use 1.

   Ymin – Use a whole number that is less than the lowest temperature; in this case, 40 is good.

   Ymax – Use the same logic but pick a number greater than the highest temperature. In this case use 85.

   Yscl – use 5.

6. Press GRAPH to view the points on a graph.

7. Graph the mean line. Press y = and set $Y_1 = 68.1$.

8. Press GRAPH to view all points plus the mean line.

Vocabulary Development

While the equations of horizontal lines ($y = k$) and vertical lines ($x = h$) are *equations of a line,* they are special cases of other forms of equations for lines that students will see throughout this course. The general forms are slope-intercept form $y = mx + b$, the point-slope form $y - y_1 = m(x - x_1)$, and the standard form $Ax + By = C$.

4-2

Hour (h)	Temperature (°F)
1	55
2	53.1
3	52
4	48.9
5	46.9
6	50
7	64
8	72
9	73.9
10	75.9
11	77
12	79
13	81
14	82
15	82.9
16	82.9
17	82
18	81
19	78.1
20	73.9
21	68
22	61
23	59
24	55

1. What is the equation of the horizontal line that is graphed? $y = 68.1$
2. Give the deviation from the mean at 7 A.M. and 8 A.M. $-4.1°F; +3.9°F$
3. For which two hours was the deviation $+5.8°F$? 9, 20
4. The temperatures t are described by the interval $\underline{\ ?\ } \leq t \leq \underline{\ ?\ }$.
5. The deviations d are described by the interval $\underline{\ ?\ } \leq d \leq \underline{\ ?\ }$.
6. The deviation is positive when h, the number of hours since midnight, is in the interval $\underline{\ ?\ } \leq h \leq \underline{\ ?\ }$. 8; 20
7. The deviation is negative when $h \leq \underline{\ ?\ }$ or $h \geq \underline{\ ?\ }$. 7; 21
8. The maximum deviation and the maximum absolute deviation are $\underline{\ ?\ }$ and $\underline{\ ?\ }$ respectively. Why is the minimum deviation not equal to the minimum absolute deviation? 14.8; 21.2; the point closest to the mean is lower than the mean, so the minimum absolute duration is less than the minimum deviation.

Sometimes deviations are taken from a number other than the mean. For instance, it is common in golf to give the player's results not by the score, but by how the score deviates from par. (*Par* is the expected number of strokes a golfer should take on the hole.) For example, in the 2006 U.S. Open, par was 70 strokes for 18 holes. Some scores in the last round were; Jim Furyk 0 (his score was 70), Ryuji Imada +4 (score: 74), Jeff Sluman −1 (score: 69), and Vijay Singh +3 (score: 73). In other sports, the deviation of a team's score from its opponent's score is described with statements like "We're down by 3 points!"
Activity: 4. 46.9°; 82.9°; 5. −21.2°, 14.8°

Questions

COVERING THE IDEAS

1. a. List three ordered pairs whose y-coordinate is 4.
   Answers vary. Sample answer: (0, 4), (−3, 4), and (−0.6, 4)
   b. Graph your points from Part a and draw a line through them.
   c. Write the equation of your line from Part b. $y = 4$

In 2 and 3, write an equation for each graph.

2. $y = -2$

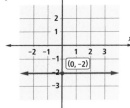

3. $x = -4$

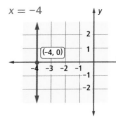

1b.

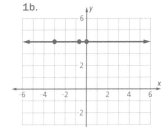

192   More Linear Equations and Inequalities

Extension

Students can use their calculator to find how the mean of the data in L2, 68.1, was calculated using the mean(command.

1. 2ND → LIST.
2. Use arrow keys to MATH.
3. Select mean.
4. Screen will show mean(
5. 2ND → L2.
6. right paren → ENTER.
7. 68.1 will show.

4. **Fill in the Blank** All points on a horizontal line have the same __?__-coordinate. *y*

5. **Fill in the Blank** All points on a vertical line have the same __?__-coordinate. *x*

In 6 and 7, an equation is given.

   a. Graph all points on a number line that satisfy the equation.

   b. Graph all points in the coordinate plane that satisfy the equation.

6. $x = 2$ 7. $y = 1.5$ **See margin.**

8. At the beginning of the year, Kylie has $580 in her savings account. As long as she has $200 in her account she does not have to pay a service fee. How long can she withdraw $20 per week without paying a service fee? **19 wk**

In 9–11, the graph shows the annual snowfall on Mt. Hood near Portland, Oregon. The mean snowfall is 98.5 inches per year. This information is important for the water supply in the region, and also for people who like to ski on Mt. Hood.

9. a. Let *S* be the snowfall in year *y*. What is an equation of the line that is graphed? $S = 98.5$

   b. Which year had the greatest absolute deviation from the mean? **1997**

10. a. Which year's snowfall was closest to the mean? **1998**

   b. What does that tell about its absolute deviation from the mean?

11. a. In which two consecutive years was the deviation negative? **2000 and 2001**

   b. Was this good or bad news for Portland residents? Explain your answer.

In 12 and 13, write an equation for the line containing the given points.

12. (–9, 12), (–4, 12), (0.04, 12)   13. (–6, –3), (–6, 4), (–6, 22)
    $y = 12$ $x = –6$

14. a. Write an equation for the horizontal line through (7, –13). $y = –13$

   b. Write an equation for the vertical line through (7, –13). $x = 7$

15. **Fill in the Blanks** Horizontal lines are parallel to the __?__-axis and perpendicular to the __?__-axis. *x; y*

6a.

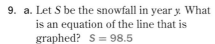

6b.

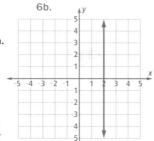

S

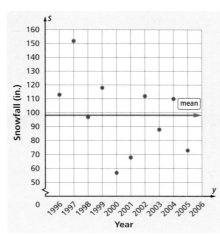

Snowfall (in.) / Year

10b. Answers vary. Sample answer: The deviation from the mean in 1998 was small.

11b. Answers vary. Sample answer: Bad news; snow depths below normal could affect snow tourism and also result in lower water supply from runoff.

Horizontal and Vertical Lines   **193**

---

3 **Assignment**

Recommended Assignment
- Questions 1–27
- Question 28 (extra credit)
- Reading Lesson 4-3
- Covering the Ideas 4-3

Notes on the Questions
Question 8 Some students will be able to answer this question without a table, graph, or equation. Point out that the numbers are simple so this question could be done "by feel," but if the numbers were more complicated, it might be useful to describe the sentence algebraically. (Here if *w* is the number of weeks, then we want to know when $580 - 20w \leq 200$.)

Questions 9–11 Notice how important the line $y = 98.5$ is in this situation. On this line, the value of *x* may vary but the value of *y* stays the same.

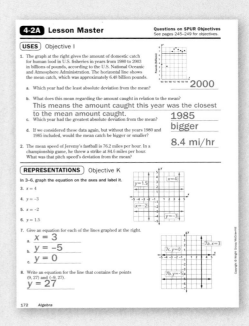

Additional Answers

7a.

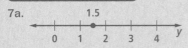

7b.

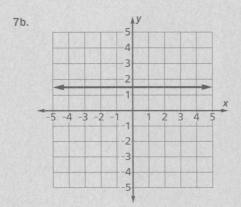

Notes on the Questions

Question 17 These are like the lines one gets when graphically solving a system of equations in two variables.

16. **Matching** Match each table with the appropriate graph.

a.

x	y
−3	1
−2	0
−1	−1
0	−2
1	−3
2	−4

ii

b.

x	y
−3	1
−3	2
−3	3
−3	4
−3	5
−3	6

iii

c.

x	y
−4	−5
−2	−5
0	−5
2	−5
4	−5
6	−5

i

i.
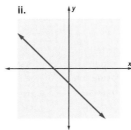

ii.
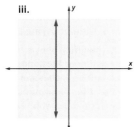

iii.
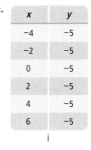

APPLYING THE MATHEMATICS

17. Predict where the lines $y = 5$ and $x = 7$ will intersect without graphing. (7, 5)

18. The table at the right gives information about a set of data values that has a mean of 53. Complete the table.

Value	Deviation
45	? −8
42	? −11
? 52	−1
? 66	13
? 60	7

19. The temperature in Acapulco, Mexico does not vary greatly whereas in a desert location like Reno, Nevada, the temperature can change greatly over the course of a day. Suppose that at 7 A.M. the temperature in Acapulco was 80°F and in Reno it was 65°F. If the Acapulco temperature stayed steady all morning, and the Reno temperature rose 5°F per hour, when were the temperatures in the cities the same? 10 A.M.

20. Write an equation for a line through the points $(4, m)$, $(0, m)$, $(6, m)$, and $(-8, m)$. $y = m$

194 More Linear Equations and Inequalities

21. A furnace repair service charges $35 for travel time plus $70 per hour to repair furnaces. Lloyd's Smoothie Emporium needs its furnace repaired, but Lloyd is willing to spend no more than $315 on the repair.

   a. Write an equation that relates the repair cost y to the time spent x. $y = 35 + 70x$

   b. Draw a graph of the equation that you wrote in Part a.

   c. On the same coordinate axes as in Part b, draw the line $y = 315$ to represent the money that Lloyd is willing to spend on the repair.

   d. Use your graph to determine the maximum number of hours that the furnace repairperson could work and still keep Lloyd's bill under $315. 4 hr

   e. Check your answer to Part d by solving an inequality.
      Solving $35 + 70x \le 315$ yields $x \le 4$ hr.

21b.

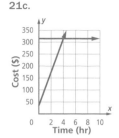

21c.

REVIEW

22. In 2006, the seating capacity in Fenway Park was 38,805 people. If 28,486 people show up for a baseball game, what percent of the stadium is full? Round your answer to the nearest percent. (**Lesson 4-1**) 73%

23. After a 6% sales tax, it cost the Clarences $17,000 for a car. What was the amount before the tax was applied? (**Lesson 4-1**) $16,037.74

24. The Sholitons bought a farm, but they did not know the capacity of the heating-oil storage tank. At one point, the tank was $\frac{1}{8}$ full. After a delivery of 450 gallons, the tank's gauge showed that it was $\frac{7}{8}$ full. How many gallons of oil does the tank hold? (**Lesson 3-8**) 600 gal

25. Last year the Guptas paid $18,550 in income taxes, more than one fourth of their earned income. (**Lessons 3-7, 3-6**)

   a. Let I = the Guptas earned income last year. Write a sentence that describes the situation above. $18{,}550 > \frac{1}{4}I$

   b. Solve the sentence. $I < 74{,}200$

26. Solve $2(x + 1) + 7 = 5x$. (**Lesson 3-3**) $x = 3$

27. Graph $y = -5x - (1 + x)$. (**Lesson 3-1**) See margin.

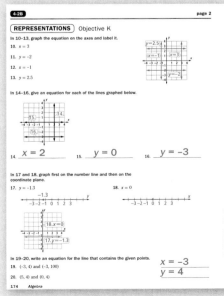

Major League Baseball's oldest ballpark, Fenway Park, is located in Boston, Massachusetts.

Source: Major League Baseball

EXPLORATION

28. Find a set of data with numbers that lend themselves to finding the mean. Find the mean. Then find the deviations. Describe the advantages and disadvantages of using deviations rather than the actual values. See margin.

Horizontal and Vertical Lines   **195**

Additional Answers

27.

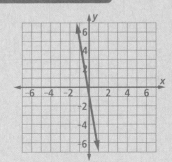

28. Answers vary. Sample answer: Waiting times at a doctor's office, in minutes: 5, 13, 12, 2, 19, 11, 10, 8. Mean = 10. Deviations (in order): −5, 3, 2, −8, 9, 1, 0, −2. Deviations make comparisons easier, but it is often helpful to study the actual values when trying to draw conclusions about data.

4-2

4 Wrap-Up

Ongoing Assessment

Group the students in pairs. One of the students should write the equation of a vertical or horizontal line on a piece of paper and pass the paper to the second student. The second student should graph the equation. Together, students should check to see if the equation is graphed correctly. Repeat the process starting with the second student.

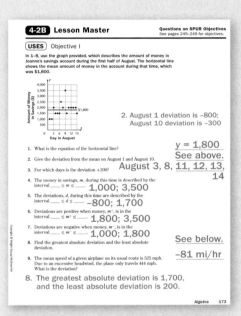

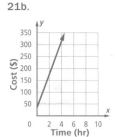

Lesson 4-3

Lesson 4-3

Using Tables and Graphs to Solve

GOAL

Show how tables and graphs can be used to solve equations of the form $ax + b = cx + d$.

SPUR Objectives

I Use tables and graphs to solve real-world problems involving linear situations.

L Use graphs to solve problems involving linear expressions.

Materials/Resources

· Lesson Master 4-3A or 4-3B
· Resource Masters 2 and 48
· Scientific or graphing calculator
· Quiz 1

HOMEWORK

Suggestions for Assignment
• Questions 1–16
• Question 17 (extra credit)
• Reading Lesson 4-4
• Covering the Ideas 4-4

Local Standards

1 Warm-Up

You might write or project the following so that students can do these questions as they enter the classroom. Refer to the Guided Example on this page.

1. What is the charge to make h copies of Acme Copiers in one month? $250 + 0.01h$
2. What is the cost to make h copies at Best Printers in one month? $70 + 0.03h$
3. Use the expressions in 1 and 2 to write an equation whose solution will tell you the number of copies in a month for which the cost for the two copy firms will be the same. $250 + 0.01h = 70 + 0.03h$

▶ **BIG IDEA** Tables and graphs are often useful for comparing values from two or more situations.

GUIDED

Example

You are the manager of an office. Your company needs to lease a copy machine. You must choose between two office supply firms. Acme Copiers offers a copier for $250 per month with an additional charge of $0.01 per copy.

Best Printers offers the same machine for $70 per month with a per-copy charge of $0.03.

Describe the *break-even point,* the situation for which the costs are the same.

Solution 1 Use a table. The cost of the machine depends upon the number of copies made. To compare, you must look at prices for many situations.

1. Let $x = $ the number of copies made per month.

   Price for x copies from Acme Copiers $= 250 + 0.01x$

   Price for x copies from Best Printers $= 70 + 0.03x$

   Use your calculator to make a table showing the costs for 0; 2,000; 4,000; 6,000; ...; 20,000 copies per month. Use the table to draw conclusions about which company's pricing plan best suits your needs.

Number of Copies (x)	Acme Copiers Price 250 + 0.01x	Best Printers Price 70 + 0.03x
0	? 250	? 70
2,000	? 270	? 130
4,000	? 290	? 190
6,000	? 310	? 250
8,000	? 330	? 310
10,000	? 350	? 370
12,000	? 370	? 430
14,000	? 390	? 490
16,000	? 410	? 550
18,000	? 430	? 610
20,000	? 450	? 670

Mental Math

a. Half a serving of soup is 150 mL. How many mL are 2 servings? 600 mL

b. How many mL are 3 servings? 900 mL

c. How many mL are 4 servings? 1,200 mL

Background

There are only six questions before the Review questions in this lesson. This is because each question takes time. That is one of the points of this lesson. Although tables and graphs can help a person *understand* a situation, they are not always efficient. An efficient way is given in Lesson 4-4.

2. When $x \geq$? , Acme's price is lower. When $x \leq$? , Best's price is lower.
10,000; 8,000

3. From this table you cannot tell the exact break-even point. However, it seems to occur between ? copies and ? copies. 8,000; 10,000

4. Another table with x between the values in Step 3 above may yield a solution. Complete this table.

Number of Copies (x)	Acme Copiers Price 250 + 0.01x	Best Printers Price 70 + 0.03x
8,000	? 330	? 310
8,500	? 335	? 325
9,000	? 340	? 340
9,500	? 345	? 355
10,000	? 350	? 370

5. The break-even point occurs when $x =$? and the price is ? .
9,000 $340

6. It is important to describe the two variables for the break-even point.

   a. The x value: How many copies are made when Best and Acme charge the same amount? ? 9,000

   b. The y value: What is the amount charged by each copier when the prices are the same amount? ? $340

A graph can help you interpret the information in a table and can help answer many questions.

Solution 2 Use a graph.

1. Let the prices be as in Step 1 of Solution 1.

   Graph $y_1 = 250 + 0.01x$ on the window $0 \leq x \leq 20,000, 0 \leq y \leq 500$.

   Graph $y_2 = 70 + 0.03x$ on the same window.

2. Use the INTERSECT command to determine the point at which the graphs intersect. (? , ?) 9,000; 340

3. What do the coordinates of the point of intersection mean?

   The x-coordinate, ? , means ? . 9,000; both companies charge the same amount for 9,000 copies

   The y-coordinate, ? , means ? . 340; the two companies both charge $340 at the break-even point.

One of the challenges of finding solutions using tables or graphs is that the result is a coordinate point with both an x and a y value. You need to pay close attention to the question you are being asked to determine whether the x- or the y-coordinate is the final answer.

Accommodating the Learner

Students may not be comfortable setting the proper window to see the portion of the graph that is needed to answer a question. Have students practice finding an appropriate window to locate the point of intersection of each of the following pairs of linear equations. Once students have found an appropriate window, ask them to use the CALC command followed by the INTERSECT command to find the point of intersection.

Continue to hit ENTER key until you see the point of intersection on your screen.

a. Y1 = 5x + 400; Y2 = –3x + 80
   x = –40, y = 200
b. Y1 = $-\frac{1}{2}x$ + 100; Y2 = $\frac{3}{4}x$ – 10
   x = 88, y = 56
c. Y1 = 0.7x + 111.2; Y2 = –1.3x – 89.8
   x = –100.5, y = 40.85

2 Teaching

Notes on the Lesson

Example Point out to students that in the next lesson they will see an algebraic method for solving equations like $250 + 0.01x = 70 + 0.03x$. Yet, it is possible to solve some of these problems in your head. In this example, Best Printers charges 2¢ more per copy than Acme, or $1 more for 50 copies. How many copies are needed to make up for the $180 less that Best Printers charges to begin? The answer is 180 · 50, or 9,000.

Additional Example

Example You are looking at new cell phone plans. You are trying to decide between two companies. Flash Cellular charges $65 a month for the first 400 minutes and then $0.03 for each additional minute. Horizon Cellular charges $60 a month for the first 400 minutes and then $0.04 for each additional minute. Describe the break-even point, the situation for which the costs are the same.

Solution Use a table. The cost of each plan depends on the number of minutes used. To compare, you must look at prices for many situations.

1. Let x = the number of minutes used beyond the 400 minute base price. The price for x minutes from Flash Cellular = 65 + 0.03x. The price for x minutes from Horizon Cellular = 60 + 0.04x. Use your calculator to make a table showing the costs for 0, 50, 150, 250, ..., 750 minutes per month. Use the table to draw conclusions about which company's pricing plan best suits your needs.

(continued on next page)

4-3

Number of Minutes x	Flash Cellular's Price, 65 + 0.03x	Horizon Cellular's Price, 60 + 0.04x
0	65	60
50	66.5	62
150	69.5	66
250	72.5	70
350	75.5	74
450	78.5	78
550	81.5	82
650	84.5	86

2. When x ≥ __?__, Flash Cellular's price is lower. When x ≤ __?__, Horizon Cellular's price is lower. **550; 450**

3. From this table you cannot tell the exact break-even point. However, it seems to occur between __?__ minutes and __?__ minutes. **450; 550**

4. Get a closer value for number of minutes by adding the variables of x = 475 and x = 500 and x = 525 to your table. Insert new values for Flash and Horizon columns where appropriate.

5. The break-even point occurs when x = __?__ and the price is __?__. **500; $80**

6. It is important to describe the two variables for the break-even point.

   a. The x-value: How many total minutes are used when Flash and Horizon Cellular charge the same amount? __?__ **900**

   b. The y-value: What is the amount charged by each phone service when the prices are the same amount? __?__ **$80**

A graph can help you interpret the information in a chart and can help answer many questions.

Graphs, tables, and algebraic sentences each have advantages. Graphs can display a great deal of information and are useful for comparing values, but may be time-consuming to make. Tables might also be time-consuming to make. Graphing calculators and spreadsheets can make both tables and graphs, but still may not always give exact solutions. Solving equations and inequalities using algebraic properties is often preferred because they are efficient tools, and the results are precise. In the next two lessons, you will use properties to solve equations with variables on each side of the equal sign.

Questions

COVERING THE IDEAS

1. The table below lists the charges for color copies of digital photos at two different camera shops.

Number of Copies	Cost at Shop A	Cost at Shop B
1	$1.30	$1.20
2	$1.55	$1.50
3	$1.80	$1.80
4	$2.05	$2.10
5	$2.30	$2.40
6	$2.55	$2.70

1c.

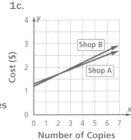

   a. For what number of copies is Shop A's cost less? **4 or more copies**
   b. For what number of copies is Shop B's cost less? **1 or 2 copies**
   c. Graph the costs of the copies. Which graph is higher for 2 copies? Which graph is higher for 7 copies? **Shop A; Shop B**
   d. If y is the cost of x copies, what are the (x, y) coordinates of the break-even point? **(3, 1.80)**

2. A bakery keeps a supply of flour and sugar. The graph at the right shows how many pounds of each are in the bakery storeroom over a period of days.

   a. Estimate when the bakery has the same amount of flour as sugar. How many pounds of each are in the storeroom? **On the 12th day, there are about 60 lb of each.**
   b. Give an example of a day for which there is more flour than sugar. **Answers vary. Sample answer: the 4th day**
   c. Use an inequality to describe when there is more sugar than flour. **x > 12**

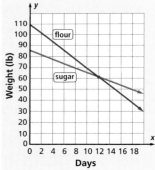

Accommodating the Learner ⬆

Have students use the Internet or published articles to research similar base cost plans for two cellular phone companies. Students should also find out how much they will be charged if they exceed the base plan. Have them write equations representing the monthly bill that represents the sum of the base plan and extended costs. Have them use tables or graphing to identify the break-even point. Identify the intervals for which one company is less expensive than the other.

3. Rental-car companies sometimes charge a set fee plus an amount for each mile that the car is driven. Suppose Extra Value Cars charges $18.32 plus $0.32 per mile and Rhodes Rental charges $26.24 plus $0.20 per mile.

a. Use the graph to approximate the point of intersection of the two lines.

b. What does the x-coordinate of the point of intersection represent in the problem? What does the y-coordinate represent?

c. Using the graph, determine which company is less expensive if 80 miles are driven. Explain how you know this from the graph. **3a–c. See margin.**

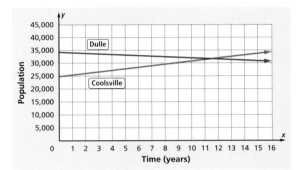

4. The population of Coolsville is currently 25,000 and is growing at a rate of 600 people per year. Across the river is the town Dulle, which currently has a population of 34,900 and is decreasing by 300 people per year. Use the graph and the table to answer the following questions. **4a–d. See margin.**

Time in Years (x)	Coolsville Population (y_1)	Dulle Population (y_2)
0	25,000	34,900
1	25,600	34,600
2	26,200	34,300
3	26,800	34,000
4	27,400	33,700
5	28,000	33,400
6	28,600	33,100
7	29,200	32,800
8	29,800	32,500
9	30,400	32,200
10	31,000	31,900
11	31,600	31,600
12	32,200	31,300
13	32,800	31,000
14	33,400	30,700
15	34,000	30,400
16	34,600	30,100

a. Write an equation for y, the population of Coolsville after x years. Write a similar equation for the population of Dulle after x years.

b. Give the approximate coordinates of the intersection or break-even point. Explain what the two coordinates of this point represent in the problem.

c. **Fill in the Blanks** Until __?__ years, __?__ had the larger population. After __?__, __?__ had the larger population. At __?__ years, Coolsville and Dulle had the same population of __?__.

d. Write an inequality that represents the values of x for which the population of Coolsville is greater, and an inequality that represents the values of x for which the population of Dulle is greater.

Using Tables and Graphs to Solve **199**

4-3

3 Assignment

Recommended Assignment
- Questions 1–16
- Question 17 (extra credit)
- Reading Lesson 4-4
- Covering the Ideas 4-4

Notes on the Questions
We suggest spending time on these questions until you are sure that students can do them.

Question 1 It is important to go over this simple question in detail, because if students do not understand it, they will have difficulty understanding the more complex situations of later questions.

Question 2 For Part c, the simplest inequality is x > 12, but if it were not so easy to tell from the graph, one would need to have equations for the lines.

Questions 3–6 Later in the year, students will learn how to solve a system of equations to determine the coordinates of the point of intersection. But in Lesson 4-4, students will equate the two values of y to find the x-coordinate of the point of intersection. Then, having determined that value, they can find y.

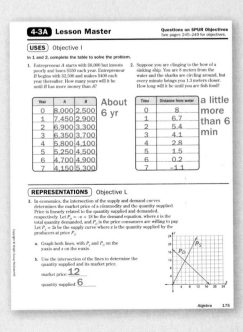

Additional Answers

3a. Answers vary. Sample answer: around (70, 40)

3b. number of miles driven for which the two costs are equal; cost of the rental

3c. Rhodes is less expensive when 80 miles are driven because at x = 80, the Rhodes' line is below the Extra Value line.

4a. for Coolsville, y = 25,000 + 600x; for Dulle, y = 34,900 − 300x

4b. (11, 31,600), which means that after 11 years the population of both towns will be 31,600

4c. 11; Dulle; 11 years; Coolsville; 11; 31,600

4d. x > 11; x < 11

Notes on the Questions

Question 17 This question shows how tables can be used to find the solution to a different type of question.

APPLYING THE MATHEMATICS

5. Theo has $30 and is *saving* at a rate of $6 per week. Michelle has $150 and is *spending* at a rate of $5 per week.

   a. Write an expression for the amount Theo has after w weeks. $30 + 6w$

   b. Write an expression for the amount Michelle has after w weeks. $150 - 5w$

   c. Make a graph. Use it to determine when Theo and Michelle will have the same amount.
   after about 11 wk

6. Alicia is offered two sales positions. With Company Q, she would earn $800 per month plus 5% commission on sales. (This means that 5% of the money her customers spend is added to her $800 salary.) With Company P, she would earn $600 per month plus a 6% commission on sales.

   a. If Alicia expects sales of about $20,000, which company would pay her more monthly? Both would pay $1,800.

   b. Complete the table at the right.

   c. Determine how much Alicia must sell to be paid more at Company P than at Company Q. more than $20,000

REVIEW

In 7 and 8, write the equation for the line pictured in the graph. (Lesson 4-2)

7. $x = 1$

8. $y = -1$

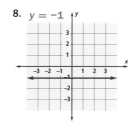

9. On a coordinate grid, graph the following three lines. (Lessons 4-2, 3-1)

   line ℓ: $y = 7$ line m: $x = 2$ line n: $y = 2x - 3$

   a. At what point do lines ℓ and m intersect? (2, 7)

   b. At what point do lines ℓ and n intersect? (5, 7)

   c. Find the area of the triangle formed by the three lines. 9 units²

10. Ms. Chang invested $8,450 in stocks. After 1 year, the value of her stocks had fallen and her investment was now worth $7,625. By what percent did her investment fall? (Lesson 4-1) about 9.8%

5c.

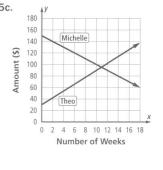

Sales (S)	Earnings at Company Q	Earnings at Company P
$12,000	$1,400	$1,320
$14,000	$1,500	$1,440
$16,000	? $1,600	? $1,560
$18,000	? $1,700	? $1,680
$20,000	? $1,800	? $1,800
$22,000	? $1,900	? $1,920
$24,000	? $2,000	? $2,040
$26,000	? $2,100	? $2,160
$28,000	$2,200	$2,280
$30,000	$2,300	$2,400

9.

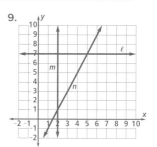

In 11 and 12, compute in your head. (Lesson 4-1)

11. What is 25% of 60? **15**   12. 110 is what percent of 100? **110%**

13. Mary has a collection of foreign coins. $\frac{5}{12}$ of her coins are from China and $\frac{1}{4}$ are from Japan. If she has 248 Japanese and Chinese coins altogether, how many coins does Mary have in all? (Lesson 3-8) **372 coins**

14. *Skill Sequence* Solve each sentence. (Lessons 3-7, 3-3)
    a. $0n = 8$ b. $8n = 0$ c. $8n > 0$ d. $-8n > 0$
    no solution $n = 0$ $n > 0$ $n < 0$

15. a. Determine whether the equations $(2x + 2)(-9) + 6x = 10$ and $2(-6x - 9) = 10$ are equivalent. **They are equivalent.**
    b. If the equations in Part a are equivalent, explain why they are equivalent. (Lesson 3-3) **See margin.**

Here are various Japanese coins, ranging in value from 1 to 500 yen.

16. Mika and June traveled from Denver, Colorado, to San Francisco, California, a distance of about 1,250 miles. Mika drove in a car, while June left later and flew by airplane. The graph shows the distance y each had traveled x hours after Mika began his trip. (Previous Course)
    a. Who arrived in San Francisco first? How can you tell?
    b. How long did June's trip take? **about 4 hr**

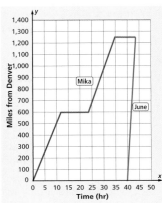

EXPLORATION

17. There are three kittens Tic, Tac, and Toe. They each have different colored fur: orange, gray, and yellow. They also live in different homes: a hotel, a condo, and a house. Using the following information, find the fur color of each kitten and where each lives.
    (1) Tic does not live in the condo.
    (2) The cat that lives in the house does not have orange fur.
    (3) Tac lives in the hotel.
    (4) Tic's favorite color is gray, but that is not her fur color.
    (5) The cat that lives in the hotel has orange fur.

(*Hint:* It can help to record what you know in a table like the one shown below. You can eliminate an incorrect pairing by placing an X in the cell. Place an O in the cell for a correct pairing.)

	Orange	Gray	Yellow	Hotel	Condo	House
Tic	?	?	?	?	?	?
Tac	?	?	?	?	?	?
Toe	?	?	?	?	?	?

16a. Mika, because he reached a distance of 1,250 mi at $x = 35$, about 9 hr before June.

17. Tic has yellow fur and lives in the house. Tac has orange fur and lives in the hotel. Toe has gray fur and lives in the condo.

Using Tables and Graphs to Solve   **201**

Additional Answers

15b. Answers vary. Sample answer:
    Distributing the left-hand side of both equations yields $-18x - 18 + 6x$, which simplifies to $-12x - 18$, in the first equation and $-12x - 18$ in the second equation. These expressions are identical.

4) Wrap-Up

Ongoing Assessment
On the overhead projector, place a table that compares two companies' charges for similar services. The table should model the ideas presented in the lesson. Present the students with an explanation of what the data represent. Call on a student to explain how to identify the appropriate domain in which the cost of the services for both companies will be the same.

Project Update
If you have not had students look over the projects on pages 240 and 241, you might want to do so now. Project 2, Hybrid Cars, and Project 3, Planning Your Trip, on page 240 relate to the content of this lesson.

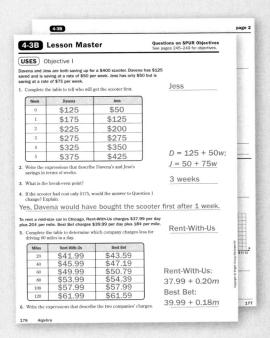

Lesson

4-4

GOAL

Solve equations of the form $ax + b = cx + d$ algebraically.

SPUR Objectives

A Solve and check equations of the form $ax + b = cx + d$.

F Apply and recognize Addition and Multiplication Properties of Equality when solving linear sentences.

H Use linear equations of the form $ax + b = cx + d$ to solve real-world problems.

Materials/Resources

· Lesson Master 4-4A or 4-4B
· Resource Masters 49 and 50
· Scientific or graphing calculator

HOMEWORK

Suggestions for Assignment
• Questions 1–30
• Question 31 (extra credit)
• Reading Lesson 4-5
• Covering the Ideas 4-5

Local Standards

---

1 Warm-Up

Begin with Equation 1 in the Activity, $3z - 4 = 5z - 23$. There are numerous options for the first step in solving the equation. Ask students what equation results from each of the following operations on both sides of the original equation. Then have them solve the equation in Question 4.

1. Add $-5z$ to both sides. $-2z - 4 = -23$
2. Add 4 to both sides. $3z = 5z - 19$
3. Subtract 4 from both sides. $3z - 8 = 5z - 27$
4. Subtract $3z$ from both sides. Solve the equation. $-4 = 2z - 23; z = 9.5$

Lesson

4-4   Solving $ax + b = cx + d$

Vocabulary

general linear equation, $ax + b = cx + d$

▶ **BIG IDEA**   An equation of the form $ax + b = cx + d$ can be solved with just one more step than solving one of the form $ax + b = c$.

Solving $ax + b = cx + d$ with a CAS

In this lesson, you will see how to solve the **general linear equation, $ax + b = cx + d$.** First we explore solving them with a CAS.

Example 1

Solve $5x - 12 = 16 + 9x$ using a CAS.

Solution

Step 1 Begin by entering the equation in a CAS.

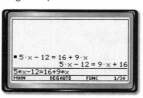

Step 2 Each side has a variable term, $5x$ on the left and $9x$ on the right. Eliminate one of these by subtracting it from each side. We choose to subtract $5x$. On some CAS, you can just type in $-5x$. On other CAS, put the equation inside parentheses and then type $-5x$.

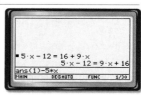

Step 3 Once you press ENTER, the CAS will subtract $5x$ from both sides of the equation. The result is $-12 = 4x + 16$. This is an equation of the type you solved in Chapter 3.

Background

At this time, we deal with linear equations that have variable terms on both sides of the equal sign. The corresponding inequalities are treated in the next lesson.

There is a significant difference in the equation-solving process that occurs when the variable appears on both sides and the one that occurs when the variable is on only one side. Equations cannot be solved by merely undoing the operations. Also, it is possible to have a variable alone on one side and still not have a solution, as in $x = 5x + 4$.

These new situations carry the potential for student errors.

This CAS activity is similar to the one in Chapter 3. Its goal is to show students what happens when various commands are carried out on both sides of an equation.

Step 4 Use the CAS to carry out the familiar steps to complete the solution. Subtract 16 from each side.

Step 5 Divide each side by 4. The equation is solved, $x = -7$.

As you can see, the methods you learned to solve simpler equations are also used to solve equations when the variable is on both sides. As before, sometimes the first step is to simplify one side of the equation. Some CAS will automatically simplify expressions. On other CAS, you must use the EXPAND command. The first step for one CAS is shown at the right. The original equation is $3z - 4 = 2 - 5(z + 5)$. The EXPAND command simplifies it to $3z - 4 = -5z - 23$. The next step would be to eliminate one of the variable terms, either $3z$ or $-5z$.

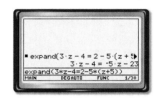

Activity

Use a CAS to solve the following equations. Remember, a CAS can help you make good decisions on the process of solving equations. Write down what you do to both sides of the equation as you go through the process.

1–8. See margin.

1. $3z - 4 = 5z - 23$
2. $21 - 6x = 22 - 8x$
3. $-p = 13p - 42$
4. $33n - 102 + 4n = -23n - 252$
5. $9(9 - k) = 6k - 1$
6. $\frac{2}{3}b - \frac{6}{7} = \frac{5}{9}b + \frac{11}{3}$
7. $\frac{3}{4}(24 - 8y) = 2(5y + 1)$
8. $12.3 - (3.4w - 4.5) = 5.6 (6.7 - 7.8w) - 8.9$
9. Write a description of the process you can use to solve $4x + 3 = 6x - 8$. See margin.
10. Use the process described in Question 9 to solve $4x + 3 = 6x - z$ for x without a CAS. Then check your solution with a CAS. $x = \frac{z + 3}{2}$
11. Solve $4x + t = 6x - z$ for x without a CAS. Then check your solution using a CAS. $x = \frac{z + t}{2}$

Solving $ax + b = cx + d$ with Algebraic Processes

An important problem-solving strategy in mathematics and other fields is to turn a problem into a simpler one that you already know how to solve. In the Activity, you saw that to solve an equation in which the unknown is on both sides, you should turn it into an equation that has the variable on just *one* side.

Additional Answers

Activity

1. $z = 9.5$; subtract $3z$; add 23; divide by 2
2. $x = -\frac{1}{14}$; add $6x$; subtract 22; divide by 14
3. $p = 3$; subtract $13p$; divide by -14
4. $n = -2.5$; combine like terms; add 102; add $23n$; divide by 60
5. $k = \frac{82}{15}$; distribute the left side; add $9k$; add 1; divide by 15
6. $b = \frac{285}{7}$; add $\frac{6}{7}$; subtract $\frac{5}{9}b$; multiply by 9
7. $y = 1$; distribute; add $6y$; subtract 2; divide by 16
8. $w = .280$; distribute both sides; combine like terms; add $43.68w$; subtract 16.8; divide by 40.28
9. add 8 to both sides; subtract $4x$ from both sides; divide both sides by 2; $x = 5.5$

---

2 Teaching

Notes on the Lesson

Example 1 The particular screen here can be found on some TI calculators. If the calculator is in Approximate Mode, then after 5x is subtracted from both sides of the equation, the result will look like $5. \cdot x - 12. = 16. + 9. \cdot x$. All the dots can be confusing and we recommend that the calculators be in Exact Mode.

Steps for solving $ax + b = cx + d$ by hand. Because the algorithm for solving $ax + b = cx + d$ has just one more step than that for solving $ax + b = c$, it is appropriate to talk about the famous Pólya problem-solving strategy: *If you cannot solve a problem, try to reduce it to one that you can solve.* Have students look at each of the four examples of this lesson and note how the equation was converted to one in a form they had seen before.

Example 2 10x was subtracted from both sides.

Example 3 The Distributive Property was used and then x was added to both sides.

Example 4 0.5w was subtracted from each side.

Additional Example
Example 1 Solve $7a + 2 = 42 - 3a$ using a CAS. $a = 4$

Notes on the Activity

Using a CAS is a good way for students to practice their equation solving skills without getting frustrated. Often students solve the equation but do so incorrectly. They don't even know their solution is incorrect until someone tells them. With the CAS, students can easily experiment with what they think are the correct steps. The CAS allows them to make changes quickly and reinforces what they already know. You should have students check their answers to all of Questions 1–8.

4-4

Notes on the Lesson

If you have not done so already, you should pick an example (perhaps Example 2) and indicate which steps you feel are necessary for students to include in their work. Our recommendation is that students include the steps that they feel they need to have. Then they can gradually reduce the number of steps, but not to the point that they make mistakes.

Whenever possible, we have tried to align equal signs vertically when solving equations. We believe that it is very helpful for students to follow this lead.

Additional Examples

Example 2 Solve $21x - 9 = 11x - 39$. -3

Example 3 Solve $-13 - (x - 2) = -3(x - 3)$. $x = 10$

Example 2

Solve $16x - 5 = 10x + 19$.

Solution Each side has a variable term, $16x$ and $10x$. Subtract one of these from each side to eliminate it. We choose to subtract $10x$.

$16x - 5 = 10x + 19$	Write the equation.
$16x - 5 - 10x = 10x + 19 - 10x$	Subtract $10x$ from each side.
$6x - 5 = 19$	Combine like terms.

The result is a simpler equation that you know how to solve.

$6x - 5 + 5 = 19 + 5$	Add 5 to each side.
$6x = 24$	Simplify.
$\frac{6x}{6} = \frac{24}{6}$	Divide each side by 6.
$x = 4$	Simplify.

Check Substitute 4 for x in the original equation.

Does $16(4) - 5 = 10(4) + 19$?
$64 - 5 = 40 + 19$
$59 = 59$ Yes.

But a question remains. In the first step, should you subtract $10x$ or $16x$ first? In solving $16x - 5 = 10x + 19$, we subtracted $10x$. We could have subtracted $16x$ instead. Either way works.

STOP QY

> **▶ QY**
>
> Solve $16x - 5 = 10x + 19$ by first subtracting $16x$ from both sides.

Equations that Require Simplifying First

Now consider an equation that is more complicated. Again, we work to turn this problem into a simpler one.

GUIDED

Example 3

Solve $7 - (x + 5) = 4(x + 11)$.

Solution First, simplify each side. On the left side rewrite the subtraction in terms of addition.

$7 + -(x + 5) = 4(x + 11)$	Rewrite the equation.
$7 + \underline{\quad ? \quad} = \underline{\quad ? \quad}$	Distributive Property to remove parentheses $-x - 5; 4x + 44$
$-x + 2 = 4x + 44$	Simplify.

Now the equation has the form $ax + b = cx + d$. It is similar to Examples 1 and 2.

Accommodating the Learner

The following problem has at least one error in its solution. Students should locate and correct each error. Have students write a brief description of the error(s) encountered.

$$-6(x - 2) - (x - 3) = (2x - 8) - 9$$

$$-6x + 12 - x + 3 = (2x - 8) - 9$$

$$-7x + 15 = 2x - 1$$

$$-9x = -16$$

$$x = \frac{16}{9}$$

Vocabulary Development

The phrase *linear equation* is probably new to the students. Students should include its definition in their notebook. They should also include a few examples with sketches. Good examples are $x = 3$, $y = 2$, and $y = 2x + 3$.

$-x + 2 + x = 4x + 44 + x$ Add x to both sides.

?	=	?	Add like terms. 2; $5x + 44$
?	=	?	Subtract 44 from each side. -42; $5x$
?	= x		Divide each side by 5. -8.4

Check

$7 - (\underline{\ ?\ } + 5) = 4 (\underline{\ ?\ } + 11)$ Substitute -8.4 for x in the original equation. -8.4; -8.4

$7 - \underline{\ ?\ } = 4(\underline{\ ?\ })$ Remember to use the order of operations. -3.4; 2.6

$10.4 = 10.4$ Yes, it checks.

Example 4

A dog breeder raises two kinds of dogs. At birth, the average puppy of breed A weighs 14.8 ounces and gains weight at a rate of 0.5 ounce per week. Breed B puppies are smaller at birth, weighing about 11.6 ounces. But they gain weight faster, at 0.9 ounce per week. How many weeks will it be before the puppies are the same weight?

Solution Let w = number of weeks that have passed. The weight of a breed A puppy will be $14.8 + 0.5w$. The weight of a breed B puppy will be $11.6 + 0.9w$. Set the expressions equal to each other to indicate that the weights are the same.

The American Kennel Club (AKC) officially recognizes more than 150 breeds of dogs.

Source: American Kennel Club

$14.8 + 0.5w = 11.6 + 0.9w$	Write the equation.
$14.8 + 0.5w - 0.5w = 11.6 + 0.9w - 0.5w$	Subtract $0.5w$ from each side.
$14.8 = 11.6 + 0.4w$	Add like terms.
$14.8 - 11.6 = 11.6 + 0.4w - 11.6$	Subtract 11.6 from each side.
$3.2 = 0.4w$	Simplify.
$\dfrac{3.2}{0.4} = \dfrac{0.4w}{0.4}$	Divide each side by 0.4.
$8 = w$	Simplify.

After 8 weeks, the weights of breed A and breed B puppies will be the same.

Check 1 Substitute 8 for w in the original equation.

Does $14.8 + 0.5(8) = 11.6 + 0.9(8)$?

$14.8 + 4.0 = 11.6 + 7.2$

$18.8 = 18.8$ Yes, it checks.

Check 2 Use a table and graph. Let x = the number of weeks that have passed, let Y_1 = weight of a breed A puppy, and Y_2 = weight of a breed B puppy. Enter `Y1=14.8+0.5x` and `Y2=11.6+0.9x`.

(continued on next page)

Notes on the Lesson
Example 4 You might want to have students solve this equation by multiplying both sides by 10 as a first step. This would clear the equation of decimals, as discussed in Lesson 3-8.

Additional Example

Example 4 The length and width of a rectangle are $x + 4$ and $x - 3$, respectively. The lengths of the three sides of a triangle are x, x, and $x + 6$. Determine the value of x for which the perimeters will be equal. Check your answer. $x = 4$; perimeter of rectangle $= 2(4 + 4) + 2(4 - 3) = 16 + 2 = 18$ and perimeter of triangle $= 4 + 4 + (4 + 6) = 18$.

Accommodating the Learner

A literal equation is an equation involving two or more variables. To solve a literal equation, you solve for one variable in terms of the others. For example, the area of a parallelogram is given by the formula $A = bh$ where A is the area of the parallelogram, b is its base, and h is its height. To solve for h in terms of A and b you would divide both sides by b to obtain $\frac{A}{b} = h$. Students should now solve for b in terms of A and h. The perimeter of a rectangle is given by the formula

$P = 2\ell + 2w$ where P is the perimeter of the rectangle, ℓ is its length, and w is its width. Students should solve this equation for ℓ in terms of P and w. $\ell = \frac{P}{2} - w$

4-4

3 Assignment

Recommended Assignment
- Questions 1–30
- Question 31 (extra credit)
- Reading Lesson 4-5
- Covering the Ideas 4-5

Notes on the Questions

Question 1 It is critical that students be able to answer questions like these. Otherwise, they cannot fully comprehend the generalizations of properties.

Question 2 The two possible answers in Part c (multiply each side by $\frac{1}{4}$; divide each side by 4) again apply the idea that $a \div b = a \cdot \frac{1}{b}$; that is, that one can "invert and multiply."

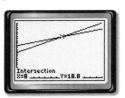

4-4A Lesson Master

Questions on SPUR Objectives
See pages 245–249 for objectives.

SKILLS Objective A

In 1–8, solve and check.

1. $24x = 16 - 8x$ $x = \frac{1}{2}$
2. $6r + 9 = 13r - 5$ $r = 2$
3. $8n + 5n - 12 = n$ $n = 1$
4. $9(a + 3) = 30a$ $a = \frac{9}{7}$
5. $3(4h + 2) = 2(h + 1)$ $h = -\frac{2}{5}$
6. $\frac{3}{5}(w + 9) = \frac{4}{5}w + 1$ $w = -\frac{45}{2}$
7. $\frac{d}{4} + 4 = \frac{4}{5} - \frac{1}{4}$ $d = -85$
8. $7 - \frac{1}{2}x = 3(x + 1)$ $x = \frac{5}{4}$

PROPERTIES Objective F

In 9, a sentence is solved. Fill in what was done.

9. $\frac{1}{4}(x - 5) = \frac{1}{3}x + 3$

$3(x - 5) = 12(\frac{1}{3}x + 3)$ Multiply both sides by 12.

$3x - 15 = 4x + 36$ Use the Distributive Property.

$-x - 15 = 36$ Add $-4x$ to each side.

$-x = 51$ Add 15 to each side.

$x = -51$ Multiply (or divide) each side by -1.

10. To solve $4x + 0.02 = 1.5x + 9$, an effective first step is to add
to both sides.   Answers vary.
Sample: $-1.5x$

USES Objective H

11. Consumer A gets a cellular telephone contract that requires monthly payments of $34.99. Consumer B's contract requires monthly payments of 39.99 but offers him a $75 rebate when he signs up.

a. After one year, who will have paid more?   Consumer A

b. After two years, who will have paid more?   Consumer B

c. After how many months will A and B have paid the same amount?   15 mo

12. Suppose the city of Atlanta, GA has a population of 471,000 people that increases by 11,000 people every year, and that Washington, DC has a population of 560,000 that decreases by 3,000 people each year. To the nearest tenth of a year, how long will it be until the two cities have about the same number of residents?   6.4 yr

178   Algebra

The row where $x = 8$ shows both breeds weigh 18.8 ounces. The INTERSECT command shows the two lines intersect at $(8, 18.8)$.

  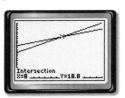

No matter how long and complex the two sides of a linear equation are to begin with, the equation can never be more complicated than $ax + b = cx + d$ after each side is simplified.

Questions   1. $a = 9.3$; $b = -4$; $c = 2$; $d = 11$

COVERING THE IDEAS

1. The equation $9.3m - 4 = 11 + 2m$ is an equation of the form $ax + b = cx + d$. What are a, b, c, and d?

2. **Fill in the Blanks** An equation is solved below. Fill in the blanks to explain the steps of the solution.
   a. $x - 4 = -3x - 7$ Add ___?___ to each side. $3x$
   b. $4x - 4 = -7$ Add ___?___ to each side.   4
   c. $4x = -3$ ___?___ each side by ___?___.   Divide; 4
   d. $x = -\frac{3}{4}$ Simplify.

3. a. To solve $10t + 5 = 4t + 7$, what can you add to both sides so t is on only one side of the equation? $-4t$ or $-10t$
   b. Solve the equation in Part a. $t = \frac{1}{3}$

4. a. Solve $3x + 18 = 5x - 22$ by first adding $-5x$ to each side. $x = 20$
   b. Solve $3x + 18 = 5x - 22$ by first adding $-3x$ to each side. $x = 20$

5. Solve $250 + 0.01n = 70 + 0.03n$ by subtracting $0.03n$ from each side. $n = 9,000$

6. a. In solving $7m - \frac{23}{4} = -5m$, what advantage does adding $-7m$ to each side of the equations have over adding $5m$?
   b. Solve $7m - \frac{23}{4} = -5m$. $m = \frac{23}{48}$

In 7–14, solve the equation and check your solution.

7. $4k + 39 = 7k + 6$
8. $9n = -6n + 5$
9. $14y + 5 = 8y - 1$
10. $46 - 8p = 19 + p$
11. $7 - m = 8 - 3m$
12. $1.55t - 2.85 = 8.4t + 10.85$
13. $3d + 4d + 5 = 6d + 7d + 8$
14. $4(x - 4) = 5(x - 3)$

206   More Linear Equations and Inequalities

6a. Adding $-7m$ puts terms with m on one side of the equation and terms without m on the other.

7. $k = 11$; $4(11) + 39 = 83$, $7(11) + 6 = 83$

8. $n = \frac{1}{3}$; $9\left(\frac{1}{3}\right) = 3$, $-6\left(\frac{1}{3}\right) + 5 = 3$

9. $y = -1$; $14(-1) + 5 = -9$, $8(-1) - 1 = -9$

10. $p = 3$; $46 - 8(3) = 22$, $19 + 3 = 22$

11. $m = \frac{1}{2}$; $7 - \frac{1}{2} = \frac{13}{2}$, $8 - 3\left(\frac{1}{2}\right) = \frac{13}{2}$

12. $t = -2$; $1.55(-2) - 2.85 = -5.95$, $8.4(-2) + 10.85 = -5.95$

13. $d = -\frac{1}{2}$; $3\left(-\frac{1}{2}\right) + 4\left(-\frac{1}{2}\right) + 5 = \frac{3}{2}$, $6\left(-\frac{1}{2}\right) + 7\left(-\frac{1}{2}\right) + 8 = \frac{3}{2}$

14. $x = -1$; $4(-1 - 4) = -20$, $5(-1 - 3) = -20$

Extension

Show students how they might go about solving the equation $-2(x + 3) - 5(x + 1) = -(-x - 5)$ using their graphing calculator. Set $Y1 = -2(x + 3) - 5(x + 1)$ and $Y2 = -(-x - 5)$. Students are to choose a window so the intersection of Y1 and Y2 appears in the window. They should find the intersection using the INTERSECT command. Have students check the solution by hand. Ask them to explain why the calculator is able to generate the correct answer. $x = -2$; $y = 3$

15. Nebraska's population had been increasing at a rate of 13,300 people per year and reached 1,711,000 in 2000. West Virginia's population had been increasing at a rate of 1,400 people per year and reached 1,808,000 in 2000. If the rates of increase do not change in the future, when will the populations be equal? about 8.15 yr after 2000 (late February 2008)

16. The 2000 population of Dallas, Texas, was 1,189,000. It has been increasing at a rate of 21,500 people each year. The 2000 population of Philadelphia, Pennsylvania, was 1,518,000 and has been decreasing at a rate of 6,500 people each year. Assuming the rates do not change in the future, when will the populations of Dallas and Philadelphia be the same?
11.75 yr after 2000 (September 2011)

APPLYING THE MATHEMATICS

17. The boxes on the balance are of equal weight. Each cylinder represents 1 ounce.

17b. First, remove 6 oz from each side. Then, remove 2W from both sides. Then, remove half the weight on each side.

a. What equation is represented by the balance? $4W + 6 = 2W + 10$
b. Describe the steps you could use to find the weight of a box using a balance.
c. What is the weight of one box? $W = 2$ oz
d. When you use a balance to represent solving $ax + b = cx + d$, why is there only one sensible choice of a variable term to eliminate from each side?

17d. because you cannot have a negative number of boxes on the balance scale

18. Five more than three times a number is three more than five times the number. What is the number? 1

19. In 2004, the women's Olympic winning time for the 100-meter freestyle in swimming was 53.84 seconds. The winning time had been decreasing at an average rate of 0.32 second per year. The men's winning time was 48.17 seconds and had been decreasing by an average of 0.18 second a year. Assume that these rates continue in the future.

a. What will the women's 100-meter winning time be x years after 2004? $53.84 - 0.32x$
b. What will the men's 100-meter winning time be x years after 2004? $48.17 - 0.18x$
c. After how many years will the winning times be the same? about 40 yr

Jodie Henry of Australia won the gold medal in the 100-meter freestyle at the 2004 Olympic Games in Athens.
Source: International Olympic Committee

Solving $ax + b = cx + d$ **207**

Notes on the Questions

Question 16 It is natural for older cities to lose population because once a city is built up, there is no place for an increase.

Question 17 Some students may find this question to be silly, but for others the balance scale remains a powerful picture of what is being done when solving an equation.

Question 19 In this problem, we are assuming that the rates of change will remain constant. This is not a bad assumption in the short term, and it enables us to make some predictions. But the quality of the prediction is only as good as the quality of the assumption, and in the long term the rates of change cannot remain constant (the record would become negative!). The probability that the winning times might become the same for the 100-meter freestyle is very low, but at longer distances it is not far-fetched. The record for swimming the English Channel has at times been held by a woman.

Notes on the Questions

Question 20 A common error is for students to think that the value of *x* is the solution to the problem.

Question 31 Students may enjoy working other puzzles by Sam Loyd, Jr. His books are still being sold, and they may be available in your school or municipal library. Many of his puzzles first appeared in newspapers and his books include discussions of readers' solutions.

20. Refer to the figures below. The perimeter of the triangle is equal to the perimeter of the square. Find the length of a side of the square. **12 units**

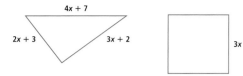

21. Lance and Chris are biking along the same road. Chris travels at a speed of 9 miles per hour, while Lance is faster and goes 13 miles per hour. Right now, Lance is next to a lake and Chris is 24 miles north of the lake.

    a. Make a table showing how far each cyclist is from the lake at hours 0, 1, 2, 3, 4, 5, and 6. **See margin.**

    b. Use the table to find how long it takes Lance to catch up with Chris. **6 hr**

    c. Solve an equation to find how long it takes Lance to catch up to Chris. $13x = 9x + 24$; $x = 6$; **6 hr**

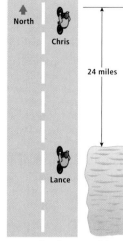

(not drawn to scale)

REVIEW

22. The table at the right shows the cost of making copies of photos from negatives at two different photo shops. **(Lesson 4-3)**

    a. For how many copies does it cost less to get photos copied at Ruby's than at Paula's? **1 or 2 copies**

    b. For how many copies does it cost less to get photos copied at Paula's than at Ruby's? **4 or 5 copies**

Number of Copies	Ruby's Photos	Paula's Prints
1	$0.75	$0.80
2	$1.25	$1.40
3	$2.00	$2.00
4	$2.75	$2.60
5	$3.50	$3.20

23. Write an equation for the line containing the points $(8, d)$, $(0, d)$, and $(-4, d)$. **(Lesson 4-2)** $y = d$

24. During the 2005–2006 National Basketball Association (NBA) season, Steve Nash scored approximately 17% of all the points that the Phoenix Suns scored, and Shawn Marion scored approximately $\frac{2}{10}$ of all the Suns' points. Nash and Marion combined to score 3,258 points that season. Approximately how many points did the team score in all? **(Lesson 3-8)** **about 8,805 points**

25. Solve $9 - \frac{5c}{8} < \frac{21}{4}$. **(Lessons 3-8, 3-7, 3-6)** $c > 6$

26. Alvin wants to spend no more than $18 at the state fair for admission and rides. If admission to the fair is $8 and each ride costs $1.25, how many rides can Alvin take? **(Lesson 3-6)** **8 rides**

208   More Linear Equations and Inequalities

Additional Answers

21a.

Hours	Chris's Distance (mi)	Lance's Distance (mi)
0	24	0
1	33	13
2	42	26
3	51	39
4	60	52
5	69	65
6	78	78

27. The reciprocal of 6 is added to the opposite of 6. What is the result? (Lessons 2-7, 2-4) $-5\frac{5}{6}$

28. Rewrite $18(3 - x)$ using each property. (Lessons 2-1, 1-2)
   a. Commutative Property of Addition $18(-x + 3)$
   b. Commutative Property of Multiplication $(3 - x)18$
   c. Distributive Property $54 - 18x$

In 29 and 30, estimate in your head to the nearest whole number. (Previous Course)

29. $\frac{9}{10} + \frac{12}{13} + \frac{8}{7}$ 3

30. $9.92 \cdot 23$ 230

EXPLORATION

31. This puzzle is from the book *Cyclopedia of Puzzles,* written by Sam Loyd, Jr. in 1914. If a bottle and a glass balance a pitcher, a bottle balances a glass and a plate, and two pitchers balance three plates, how many glasses will balance with a bottle? 5 glasses

QY ANSWER

$16x - 5 - 16x =$
$10x + 19 - 16x$

$-5 = 19 - 6x$

$-5 - 19 = 19 - 6x - 19$

$-24 = -6x$

$\frac{-24}{-6} = \frac{-6x}{-6}$

$4 = x$

Solving $ax + b = cx + d$ **209**

---

4 Wrap-Up

Ongoing Assessment

Form groups of two. Have students explain to one another how to solve the following two equations. Each student should take a turn explaining how to solve one of the equations.

$4(x - 3) + 2 = 2x$ $x = 5$

$5 - (x + 2) = -4x$ $x = -1$

4-4B Lesson Master   Questions on SPUR Objectives
See pages 245–249 for objectives.

SKILLS Objective A

In 1–16, solve and check.

1. $25x = 10 - 5x$
   $x = \frac{1}{3}$
2. $5k + 21 = 17k - 3$
   $k = 2$
3. $45m - 38 = 5m - 158$
   $m = -3$
4. $6a = 60 + 36a$
   $a = -2$
5. $15y + 5y - 6 = 17y$
   $y = 2$
6. $-3(2b - 5) = 3b$
   $b = \frac{5}{3}$
7. $7t = 13t - 5 + 4t$
   $t = \frac{1}{2}$
8. $\frac{h}{5} + \frac{2}{3} = \frac{h}{3} + \frac{2}{5}$
   $h = \frac{8}{5}$
9. $\frac{1}{4}(j - 8) = \frac{1}{2}j + 2$
   $j = -16$
10. $5(3n + 10) = 40n$
    $n = 2$
11. $4(h + 1) = 2(5h + 6)$
    $h = -\frac{4}{3}$
12. $\frac{1}{5}(s + \frac{2}{3}) - \frac{3}{10}s = \frac{-1}{5}$
    $s = \frac{10}{3}$
13. $4 - \frac{5x}{7} = x - 2$
    $x = \frac{7}{2}$
14. $5(2z + 1) = 5(z - 5)$
    $z = -6$
15. $\frac{2}{3}f + 6 = \frac{f}{4} - 2$
    $f = -\frac{96}{5}$
16. $8 + \frac{c}{9} = 2(\frac{c}{5} - 1)$
    $c = 18$

Algebra   **179**

4-4B   page 2

PROPERTIES Objective F

17. Solve $2x + 5 = 3x + 6$ ...
   a. by first adding $-2x$ to both sides. $x = -1$
   b. by first adding $-3x$ to both sides. $x = -1$
   c. Compare your answers. What does this mean?
   The answers are the same, which suggests that it doesn't matter which term you add to both sides.

18. In solving $2x + 6 = -x$, what advantage does adding $-2x$ to both sides have over adding x?
   If you add $-2x$ to both sides, you have all of your constant terms on one side, and all terms with variable x on the other.

In 19, a sentence is solved. Fill in what was done.

19. $\frac{7}{4}(y - 2) = 2y + \frac{9}{2}$
   $7(y - 2) = 8y + 18$ Multipy both sides by 4.
   $7y - 14 = 8y + 18$ Use the Distributive Property.
   $-y - 14 = 18$ Subtract 8y from both sides.
   $-y = 32$ Add 14 to both sides.
   $y = -32$ Divide both sides by –1.

USES Objective H

20. At 10 A.M. a freight train leaves Chicago for Denver traveling at an average speed of 60 miles per hour. Two hours later, a high-speed passenger train leaves Chicago for Denver traveling at an average speed of 150 miles per hour.
   a. After how many hours will the passenger train overtake the freight train? $1\frac{1}{3}$ h
   b. What will the time be?   1:20 P.M.

21. Suppose that Northwoods has a population of 33,300 people but *increases* by 4,000 people every year. Neighboring Forest Hills has a population of 52,000 but *decreases* by 2,000 every year. To the nearest tenth of a year, how long will it be until the two cities have the same number of residents?   3.1 yr

180   *Algebra*

Lesson 4-5

Lesson 4-5

Solving $ax + b < cx + d$

GOAL

Solve an inequality of the form $ax + b < cx + d$ regardless of the values of a, b, c, and d.

SPUR Objectives

B Solve and check inequalities of the form $ax + b < cx + d$.

F Apply and recognize Addition and Multiplication Properties of Equality and Inequality when solving linear sentences.

H Use linear equations and inequalities of the form $ax + b = cx + d$ or $ax + b < cx + d$ to solve real-world problems.

Materials/Resources

· Lesson Master 4-5A or 4-5B
· Resource Masters 2 and 51
· Scientific or graphing calculator

HOMEWORK

Suggestions for Assignment

• Questions 1–21
• Question 22 (extra credit)
• Reading Lesson 4-6
• Covering the Ideas 4-6

Local Standards

---

1 Warm-Up

You might write or project the following so that students can do these questions as they enter the classroom.

1. Find all solutions to the sentence.
  a. $-20x + 50 = 150$ $x = -5$
  b. $-20x + 50 < 150$ $x > -5$
  c. $-20x + 50 \geq 150$ $x \leq -5$

2. Check your answers to all three sentences from Warm-Up 1.
a. $-20(-5) + 50 = 100 + 50 = 150$
b. Pick $x = 0$, $-20(0) + 50 = 50 < 150$
c. Pick $x = -10$, $-20(-10) + 50 = 200 + 50 = 250 \geq 150$.

▶ **BIG IDEA** An inequality of the form $ax + b < cx + d$ can be solved by applying the same operations to both sides as in solving the equation $ax + b = cx + d$.

Just as an equation can have the variable on both sides of the equal sign, an inequality can have the variable on both sides of the inequality sign. The methods from the last lesson can also be used to solve linear inequalities of the form $ax + b < cx + d$.

Consider the following situation. Years ago, the Moseley family planted a 12-foot beech tree and a 4-foot maple tree. Beech trees grow at a rate of about $\frac{1}{2}$ foot per year. Maple trees grow about 1 foot per year. So t years after planting, the height of the beech tree is $12 + 0.5t$ feet and the height of the maple tree is $4 + t$ feet.

Example 1

Mrs. Moseley looked at an old photograph of the two trees. In it, the beech tree was taller than the maple tree. She wondered when the photo was taken.

Solution 1 Use an algebraic solution. Write an inequality relating the heights. The beech tree was taller than the maple tree, so the heights satisfy the inequality $12 + 0.5t > 4 + t$.

Solve this inequality as you would solve an equation.

$12 + 0.5t > 4 + t$	Write the equation.
$12 + 0.5t + (-0.5t) > 4 + t + (-0.5t)$	Add $-0.5t$ to each side.
$12 > 4 + 0.5t$	Add like terms.
$12 + (-4) > 4 + (-4) + 0.5t$	Add -4 to each side.
$8 > 0.5t$	Simplify.
$\frac{8}{0.5} > \frac{0.5t}{05}$	Divide each side by 0.5.
$16 > t$	Simplify.

So $t < 16$. The photo was taken less than 16 years after the Moseleys planted the trees.

Solution 2 Use a table as shown on the next page. You can see the beech tree was taller when $t < 16$. This verifies that the photo was taken less than 16 years after the Moseleys planted the trees.

Mental Math

a. How long is a 9-inning baseball game that averages 20 minutes per inning? 180 min or 3 hr

b. How long is a 4-quarter basketball game that averages 40 minutes per quarter?

c. How long is a 3-period hockey game that averages 50 minutes per period?
150 min or $2\frac{1}{2}$ hr

b. 160 min or $2\frac{2}{3}$ hr

National Arbor Day was founded by J. Sterling Morton in Nebraska in 1872.

Source: National Arbor Day Foundation

Background

This lesson covers the symbolic and graphical solutions of linear inequalities. Students will use the Multiplication Property of Inequality in solving these inequalities. They have already solved equations of the form $ax + b = cx + d$ and inequalities of the form $ax + b < c$. So while this lesson presents no new skills, it combines many previously encountered concepts and provides opportunities to review them.

It can be advantageous to solve $ax + b < cx + d$ by making the coefficient of the variable positive even when that isolates the unknown on the right side, as in Example 2. The issue of multiplying by a negative number can be avoided by maneuvering the terms so that the unknown has a positive coefficient. Also, since $a < b$ is equivalent to $b > a$, it is always possible to rewrite an inequality so the variable has a positive coefficient and is on the left side.

Solution 3 Use a graph. Write an equation describing each tree height. For the beech tree, $h = 12 + 0.5t$. For the maple tree, $h = 4 + t$. Graph each equation and find the point of intersection.

t	Height h (ft)	
Number of Years	Beech Tree	Maple Tree
0	12	4
4	14	8
8	16	12
12	18	16
16	20	20
20	22	24
24	24	28

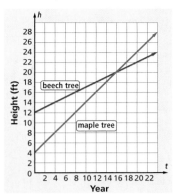

The lines intersect at the point (16, 20). So sixteen years after they were planted, the trees were both 20 feet tall. We are looking for the times when the beech tree was taller than the maple tree. So look for values of t where the beech's line is *above* that for the maple. These times lie to the left of the intersection point (16, 20). This is where $t < 16$. The photo was taken less than 16 years after the trees were planted.

The Addition and Multiplication Properties of Inequality can also be used to solve any inequality of the form $ax + b < cx + d$. In Guided Example 2, two algebraic solutions are given. Solution 2 involves dividing the inequality by a negative number. Recall that multiplying or dividing an inequality by a negative number reverses the inequality sign.

GUIDED

Example 2

Solve $7 - 11x \geq 4x + 12$.

Solution 1

$7 - 11x \geq 4x + 12$	Write the inequality.
$7 - 11x + \underline{\quad?\quad} \geq 4x + 12 + \underline{\quad?\quad}$	Add $\underline{\quad?\quad}$ to each side. **11x; 11x; 11x**
$7 \geq 15x + 12$	Add like terms.
$7 - \underline{\quad?\quad} \geq 15x + 12 - \underline{\quad?\quad}$	Subtract $\underline{\quad?\quad}$ from each side. **12; 12; 12**
$-5 \geq 15x$	Simplify.
$\underline{\quad?\quad} \geq \underline{\quad?\quad}$	$\underline{\quad?\quad}$ each side by 15. $-\frac{5}{15}$; $\frac{15x}{15}$; divide
$\underline{\quad?\quad} \geq x$	Simplify. $-\frac{1}{3}$

(continued on next page)

Solving $ax + b < cx + d$ **211**

Accommodating the Learner ⬆

Ask students to find the error in the following proof that $2 < 1$.

Let $a = -b$, $a > 0$, and $b \neq 0$.

$2a + b > a + b$	since $a + b = 0$
$2a > a$	Subtract b from both sides.
$-2b > -b$	Substitute $-b$ for a.
$\frac{-2b}{-b} < \frac{-b}{-b}$	Divide by $-b$ and change the sense.
$2 < 1$	Simplify.

2 Teaching

Notes on the Lesson

Example 1 A numerical check is not given for this example because each solution checks the other. So you might ask students how they could check that the answer $t < 16$ is correct. (First check to see that $t = 16$ makes each side of the original sentence true and then check to see that a value of t that is less than 16 satisfies the original inequality.)

Guided Example 2 You might ask students which strategy they prefer. This will reinforce the idea that there is more than one way to solve these inequalities. Do they prefer to keep the coefficient of the isolated unknown positive, as in Solution 1? Or do they prefer to isolate the unknown on the left, as in Solution 2? For many students, it makes no difference, but some students may have a definite preference.

Additional Examples

Example 1 The Bethel Company needs to ship items ordered by customers online. Quick Delivery charges a monthly service charge of $40 a month and $5 per package. On-Time Delivery charges a monthly service charge of $50 per month and $4.50 per package. Initially Quick Delivery will be the more economical carrier. Due to the large volume of packages needing to be shipped each month, at some point during the month, On-Time Delivery will become the more economical choice. When will On-Time Delivery become the more economical choice?
when the number of packages being shipped is greater than 20

Example 2 Solve $8 - 6x \leq -4x + 12$.

Solution 1

$8 - 6x + \underline{\quad?\quad} \leq -4x + 12 + \underline{\quad?\quad}$ 6x; 6x

$\qquad 8 \leq 2x + 12$

$8 - \underline{\quad?\quad} \leq 2x + 12 - \underline{\quad?\quad}$ 12; 12

$\qquad -4 \leq 2x$

$-2 \underline{\quad?\quad} \leq x$

(continued on next page)

4-5

Solution 2

$$8 - 6x + \underset{4x}{\underline{\quad?\quad}} \leq -4x + 12 + \underset{4x}{\underline{\quad?\quad}}$$

$$8 - 2x \leq 12$$

$$8 - 2x - \underline{\;?\;8\;} \leq 12 - \underline{\;?\;8\;}$$

$$-2x \leq 4$$

$$\frac{-2x}{-2} \quad\underline{\;?\;}\quad \frac{4}{-2} \quad\geq$$

$$x \quad\underline{\;?\;}\quad -2 \quad\geq$$

Notes on the Lesson

Example 3 Students often find sentences like $5n < 3n$ to be harder to solve than more complicated sentences like $5n - 40 < 3n + 6$. They think that adding $-3n$ to both sides of $5n < 3n$ results in "nothing left" on the right side—they are forgetting about 0. Furthermore, 0 does not seem to fit in inequalities. They may wonder whether to keep the sense of the inequality or change it. (Because 0 is not the coefficient of the unknown, the sense of the inequality does not come into play.) Remind students that they can do any operation with 0 except divide by it. Multiplying both sides of an inequality by 0, however, creates an equation $0 = 0$, so multiplying both sides by 0 is never a useful step.

Additional Example

Example 3 Twelve more than eight times a number n is less than four times the number. Find the number. $n < -3$

Note-Taking Tips

Students might forget to change the direction of the inequality sign when multiplying or dividing both sides of an inequality by a negative number. Have students place several examples in their notebooks which illustrate the change in direction. Also have students place several examples in their notebooks in which the inequality sign does not change direction.

Solution 2

$7 - 11x \geq 4x + 12$	Write the inequality.
$7 - 11x - \underline{\;?\;} \geq 4x + 12 - \underline{\;?\;}$	Subtract $\underline{\;?\;}$ from each side. 4x; 4x; 4x
$7 - 15x \geq 12$	Add like terms.
$7 - 15x - \underline{\;?\;} \geq 12 - \underline{\;?\;}$	Subtract $\underline{\;?\;}$ from each side. 7; 7; 7
$-15x \geq 5$	Simplify.
$\frac{-15x}{-15} \;\underline{\;?\;}\; \frac{5}{-15}$	Divide each side by -15. Be sure $\leq$ to $\underline{\;?\;}$ the inequality sign. reverse
$x \;\underline{\;?\;}\; -\frac{1}{3}$	Simplify. $\leq$

Check Recall that checking an inequality requires two steps.

Step 1 Try the boundary value of x. Check that $x = \underline{\;?\;}$ makes both sides of the original sentence equal. $-\frac{1}{3}$

$$7 - 11(\underline{\;?\;}) \geq 4(\underline{\;?\;}) + 12 \quad -\frac{1}{3}; -\frac{1}{3}$$

Step 2 Try a number that satisfies $x \leq \underline{\;?\;}$. Test to see if this number makes the original inequality true. $-\frac{1}{3}$

$$7 - 11(\underline{\;?\;}) \geq 4(\underline{\;?\;}) + 12 \quad \text{Sample answer: } -1; -1$$

Example 3

Five times a number is less than three times the same number. Find the number.

Solution It may seem that there is no such number. But let's work it out and see. Let n be such a number. Then n must be a solution to $5n < 3n$. Solve this as you would any other linear inequality.

$5n < 3n$	Write the inequality.
$5n - 3n < 3n - 3n$	Add $-3n$ to each side.
$2n < 0$	Combine like terms.
$\frac{2n}{2} < \frac{0}{2}$	Divide each side by 2.
$n < 0$	Simplify.

So n must be less than zero. Any negative number will work.

Check

Step 1 Check the boundary value. If $n = 0$, $5 \cdot 0 = 3 \cdot 0$, and $0 = 0$. It checks.

Step 2 Pick $n < 0$ to check that the inequality is true. We let $n = -4$.

$$\text{Is } 5(-4) < 3(-4)?$$
$$-20 < -12? \quad \text{Yes, it checks.}$$

5 times n will be less than 3 times n exactly when n is a negative number.

Accommodating the Learner ⬇

If students have difficulty setting up and solving inequalities, have them practice reading, setting up an inequality, and solving each inequality for the following two problems.

Once students have solved each inequality, have them check the boundary value and one other value for the variable.

a. Four less than a number is greater than negative eleven. $m - 4 > -11$, $m > -7$; boundary value is -7; for $m = 0$, $-4 > -11$

b. Negative three is greater than or equal to a number divided by negative six. $-3 \geq \frac{n}{-6}$, $n \geq 18$; boundary value is 18; for $n = 24$, $-3 \geq -4$

Questions

COVERING THE IDEAS

1. Two hot air balloons are descending from their cruising altitude at a constant rate to the ground. Both balloons begin descending at the same time, but from different elevations. The green balloon starts at 700 feet and the purple balloon starts at 550 feet as shown in the graph below.

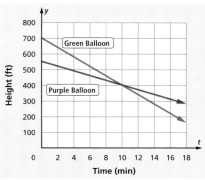

1a. Answers vary. Sample answer: 2, 4, and 9.

a. Give three values of t for which the green balloon is higher.
b. Write an inequality that describes when the green balloon is higher. $t < 10$
c. Write an inequality that describes when the purple balloon is higher. $t > 10$

2. In a typical year, a willow tree grows 3.5 feet, while a Chitalpa tree grows 2 feet. Suppose a 6-foot willow tree and a 13-foot Chitalpa tree were planted at the same time. **2c. See margin.**

a. Which tree is taller 2 years after they were planted? Chitalpa
b. Which tree is taller 10 years after they were planted? willow
c. Write an inequality to describe when the willow tree is taller.
d. Solve the inequality you wrote in Part c. $t > \frac{14}{3}$

The Chitalpa tree is a hybrid created in Uzbekistan by Nikolai Rusanov in 1964 and was first introduced into the United States in 1977.

Source: Mid-Columbia Community Forestry Council

APPLYING THE MATHEMATICS

3. a. Solve $5m + 4 > 8m + 14$ by first adding $-5m$ to each side.
   b. Solve $5m + 4 > 8m + 14$ by first adding $-8m$ to each side.
   c. Should you get the same answers for Parts a and b? Why or why not?
   d. Describe how the steps in the solutions to Parts a and b are different. **See margin.**

3a. $m < -\frac{10}{3}$
3b. $m < -\frac{10}{3}$
3c. Yes, the solutions are the same regardless of how the sentence is solved.

Solving $ax + b < cx + d$ **213**

Additional Answers

2c. Let t be the number of years since the trees were planted. The willow is taller when $6 + 3.5t > 13 + 2t$.

3d. In Part a, the second step is to subtract 14 from both sides, and the third step is to divide both sides by 3. In Part b, the second step is to subtract 4 from both sides, and the third step is to divide both sides by -3.

Recommended Assignment
- Questions 1–21
- Question 22 (extra credit)
- Reading Lesson 4-6
- Covering the Ideas 4-6

Notes on the Questions
Question 3 By working out both solutions, students should see that the processes give the same result. You might ask students which of the solution methods, if either, they felt was easier.

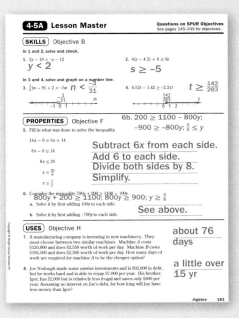

4-5

Notes on the Questions

Question 12 These skyscrapers are fictional.

Question 18 Ask what sentence could be solved to show when Delaware's population will exceed Montana's population ($840,000 + 12,000y > 935,000 + 6,700y$). Note that both this inequality and the original equation lend themselves to being divided by 1,000 as a first step in order to simplify the numbers involved.

Question 21 Students may not believe the result, so you may wish to check with pairs of values for k and m that are both positive, both negative, and one positive, one negative.

Question 22 This may look like a quadratic, but the square terms on both sides can be removed by an appropriate subtraction. Some students may solve this by graphing. It is a good question to discuss various methods.

In 4–7, a. solve the inequality, and
    b. check the inequality. 4b–7b. See margin.

4. $7a + 4 \geq 3a + 28$ $a \geq 6$

5. $-53 + 15x \leq -8 + 20x$ $x \geq -9$

6. $2y + 13 < -5y - 8$ $y < -3$

7. $14 - 4n > 29 + 6n$ $n < -\frac{3}{2}$

8. Three times a number is less than two times the same number. Find such a number. **Answers vary. Sample answer: –1**

In 9 and 10, solve the inequality.

9. $9 - 4(x + 2) < 10x$ $x > \frac{1}{14}$ 10. $-5y \geq -y + 8 + 7y$ $y \leq -\frac{8}{11}$

11. In solving the inequality $12x - 16 > 20x + 15$, you must decide which term to eliminate first, $12x$ or $20x$. Explain why this decision matters more for solving an inequality than an equation. See margin.

12. Suppose two skyscrapers are being built. The Edwards Building was already 155 feet high when work began on the King Tower. The Edwards Building is going up at an average of 24 feet per day, while the King Tower construction is progressing at an average of 29 feet per day. Let t represent the number of days since construction started on the King Tower. 12a–b. See margin.

  a. How tall will each building be when $t = 10$?

  b. Write an inequality for the following question: *When will the King Tower be taller than the Edwards Building?*

  c. Solve your inequality in Part b. $t > 31$

  d. When each building is completed, the graph of its height stops increasing and becomes horizontal. Suppose that the King Tower will be 1,230 feet tall and the Edwards Building will be taller than the King Tower. Draw a graph to show when the Edwards Tower will again be taller than the King Tower. See margin.

A typical tower crane can lift up to 18 metric tons of material at one time.

Source: howstuffworks.com

13. Angelina Wright has a Web site. She allows two music companies to advertise on it, Elevator Tunes and Sleepy Songs. Elevator Tunes pays her $5.00 plus 6¢ each time their ad gets a hit. Sleepy Songs pays her $3.50 plus 10¢ each time their ad gets a hit. (A hit is when someone clicks on the ad from Angelina's Web site.) For how many hits are the Elevator Tunes' ads more profitable than the Sleepy Songs' ads? Justify your answer.

13. Let h be the number of hits. Then, Elevator Tunes' ads are more profitable when $5.00 + 0.06h > 3.50 + 0.10h$. This occurs when there are 37 hits or fewer.

4b. Step 1: Is $7 \cdot 6 + 4 = 3 \cdot 6 + 28$? Yes, $46 = 46$.
    Step 2: Answers vary. Sample answer: For $a = 7$, is $7 \cdot 7 + 4 > 3 \cdot 7 + 28$? Yes, $53 > 49$.

5b. Step 1: Is $-53 + 15 \cdot -9 = -8 + 20 \cdot -9$? Yes, $-188 = -188$.
    Step 2: Answers vary. Sample answer: For $x = 0$, is $-53 + 15 \cdot 0 < -8 + 20 \cdot 0$? Yes, $-53 < -8$.

6b. Step 1: Is $2 \cdot -3 + 13 = -5 \cdot -3 - 8$? Yes, $7 = 7$.
    Step 2: Answers vary. Sample answer: For $n = -4$, is $2 \cdot -4 + 13 < -5 \cdot -4 - 8$? Yes, $5 < 12$.

7b. Step 1: Is $14 - 4 \cdot -\frac{3}{2} = 29 + 6 \cdot -\frac{3}{2}$? Yes, $20 = 20$.
    Step 2: Answers vary. Sample answer: For $n = -2$, is $14 - 4 \cdot -2 > 29 + 6 \cdot -2$? Yes, $22 > 17$.

11. It determines what side of the inequality x is on and could result in a negative coefficient of x, which affects the sense of the inequality.

12a. The Edwards Building will be 395 feet tall and the King Tower will be 290 feet tall.

12b. The King Tower will be taller when $29t > 155 + 24t$

12d.

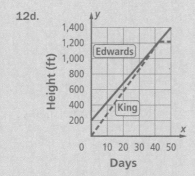

REVIEW

In 14–17, solve the equation. (Lesson 4-4)

14. $2t + 38 = 5(t + 1)$ $t = 11$

15. $\frac{7}{3} - \frac{1}{4}z = 7 + \frac{2}{5}z$ $z = -\frac{280}{39}$

16. $3(x - 6) + 12(2x + 5) = 10(2x + 7)$ $x = 4$

17. $2.83 - 0.4r = 9.02 - 4.2r$ $r = \frac{619}{380}$

18. According to the Census Bureau, in 2005, Delaware had a population of approximately 840,000, which was increasing at a rate of about 12,000 people a year. Montana had a population of approximately 935,000, increasing at a rate of about 6,700 per year. If these rates continue in the future, in how many years after 2005 will the populations be equal? (Lesson 4-4) about 18 yr

19. a. On a coordinate grid, graph $x = -5$ and $y = 9$. (Lesson 4-2) See margin.
    b. Give the coordinates of the point the two lines have in common. (Lesson 4-2) $(-5, 9)$

20. Suppose a sweater on sale costs $35 and a pair of jeans on sale costs $27. If they originally cost a total of $86, what is the percent of discount, rounded to the nearest percent? (Lesson 4-1) 28%

21. **Multiple Choice** Suppose $k > m$. What is true about $k - m$? (Lesson 3-6) B
    A $k - m$ is always negative.
    B $k - m$ is always positive.
    C $k - m$ can be either positive or negative.

EXPLORATION

22. The square of a number is less than the product of one less than the number and two greater than the number.
    a. Find one such number that makes the statement true.
    b. Find one such number that makes the statement false.
    c. Find all such numbers that make the statement true.

22a. Answers vary. Sample answer: 5, because $5^2 < 4 \cdot 7$
22b. Answers vary. Sample answer: 1, because $1^2 > 0 \cdot 3$
22c. $x^2 < (x - 1)(x + 2)$ when $x > 2$

Additional Answers

19a.

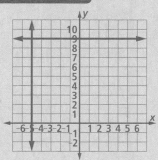

---

4 Wrap-Up

Ongoing Assessment

Provide students with the following inequalities. Ask them to verbally explain how they know the direction of the inequality changes when solving the inequality.

$2y \leq -4$ $y \leq -2$ $-\frac{1}{3}x > 7$ $x < -21$

$-18 < 0.9a$ $a > -20$ $4y - 6 \geq -22$ $y \geq -4$

Ask students to solve each inequality and check their work.

Project Update

Project 1, Growing Trees, on page 240 relates to the content of this lesson.

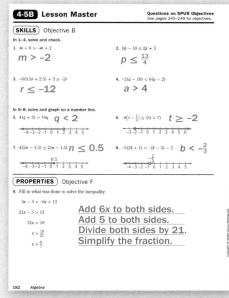

Lesson 4-6

GOAL
Determine when a problem has no solution or multiple solutions.

SPUR Objectives
G Recognize when sentences have no solution or every real number as a solution.

M Use graphs to model sentences that have no solution or every real number as a solution.

Materials/Resources
· Lesson Master 4-6A or 4-6B
· Resource Master 52
· Scientific or graphing calculator
· Quiz 2

HOMEWORK
Suggestions for Assignment
• Questions 1–18
• Question 19 (extra credit)
• Reading Lesson 4-7
• Covering the Ideas 4-7

Local Standards

1 Warm-Up

You might write or project the following so that students can do these questions as they enter the classroom.

1. **a.** Solve $4(3A + 5) \geq 3(4A + 5)$.
   Adding $-12A$ to both sides results in $20 \geq 15$, which is always true. This indicates that *any* value of A satisfies the original inequality.
   b. Check your answer to Part a by graphing $y_1 = 4(3x + 5)$ and $y_2 = 3(4x + 5)$. Explain how the graph verifies the answer.
   For any value of x, the graph of y_1 is above the graph of y_2.

Lesson 4-6 Situations That Always or Never Happen

▶ **BIG IDEA** Some linear sentences have no solution; others are true for all real numbers.

Comparing Situations
Which job would you take?

Job 1
starting salary $30,000 yearly raises of $5,000

Job 2
starting salary $28,000 yearly raises of $5,000

Of course, the answer is obvious. Job 1 will always pay more than Job 2. Looking at the pay in a table of values or on a graph supports this conclusion.

Years Worked (n)	Job 1	Job 2
0	$30,000	$28,000
1	$35,000	$33,000
2	$40,000	$38,000
3	$45,000	$43,000
4	$50,000	$48,000
5	$55,000	$53,000
6	$60,000	$58,000

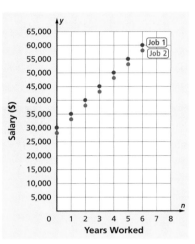

As you compare the salaries with the table, you can see that the money earned at Job 1 is always $2,000 greater than the money earned at Job 2. When the points are graphed, notice that they lie on parallel lines. For any year you pick, the pay for Job 1 is greater than for Job 2. But what happens when this is solved algebraically? Let n = number of years worked.

Mental Math
a. How many cups are in 2 pints? **4**

b. How many cups are in 3 quarts? **12**

c. How many cups are in 4 gallons? **64**

Background

A common societal picture of mathematics is that every mathematics problem has a single answer. Students using this book already know that this picture is not true, for rarely does an inequality result in a single answer. This lesson extends that idea to show that algebra can explain why certain relationships are *always true* while others are *never true*.

The two examples of the lesson show, in order, a sentence that has no solution and a sentence for which every real number is a solution.

Salary in Job 1
$30,000 + 5,000n$

Salary in Job 2
$28,000 + 5,000n$

When is the pay in Job 1 better than the pay in Job 2? You must solve
$$30,000 + 5,000n > 28,000 + 5,000n.$$

Subtract $5,000n$ from each side.

$$30,000 + 5,000n - 5,000n > 28,000 + 5,000n - 5,000n$$

Now collect like terms.

$$30,000 > 28,000$$

The variable has disappeared! Since $30,000 > 28,000$ is always true, the disappearance of n signals that n can be any real number. Job 1 will always pay a better salary than Job 2, as expected. For any equation or inequality the following generalization is true.

> **Sentences That Are Always True**
>
> When solving a sentence, if you get a sentence that is *always* true, then the original sentence is always true.

When does Job 1 pay *less* than Job 2? Looking at the table or graph on page 216, this never appears to be true. To answer this algebraically, you could solve $30,000 + 5,000n < 28,000 + 5,000n$.

$$30,000 + 5,000n < 28,000 + 5,000n$$
$$30,000 + 5,000n - 5,000n < 28,000 + 5,000n - 5,000n$$
$$30,000 < 28,000$$

It is never true that $30,000$ is less than $28,000$. So Job 1 never pays less than Job 2, something which was obvious from the pay rates. The following generalization is also true.

> **Sentences That Are Never True**
>
> When solving a sentence, if you get a sentence that is never true, then the original sentence is never true.

True and False Sentences

Suppose the sentence you are solving has only one variable and the variable disappears. The chart below summarizes the possibilities.

Solving leads to a	Possible Examples	Solutions
True statement	$0 = 0$ or $92 \leq 92$	any real number
False statement	$0 = 3$ or $-9 > 14$	no real number

Situations That Always or Never Happen **217**

4-6

2 Teaching

Notes on the Lesson

The situation that begins the lesson illustrates Examples 1 and 2. Suppose there is a third job, Job 3, with a starting salary of $30,000 and annual raises of $4,000. When will this job pay at least as well as Job 1? (Salary in Job 3: $30,000 + 4,000n$. So Job 3 pays as well as Job 1 when $30,000 + 4,000n \geq 30,000 + 5,000n$. Add $-4,000n$ to both sides to get $30,000 \geq 30,000 + 1,000n$. Then add $-30,000$ to both sides to get $0 \geq 1,000n$ and then divide both sides by 1,000 to get $0 \geq n$.

Since n is the number of years worked, it is only when $n = 0$ that Job 3 will pay at least as well as Job 1. And, from the description, it is obvious. Jobs 3 and 1 start at the same salary, but Job 1 has greater yearly raises.

Example 1 If it bothers students in Example 1 that $-20 = 6$ has no variable in it, then use the equivalent $-20 + 0 \cdot m = 6$, which is what the Distributive Property gives from the previous step. Similarly, if it bothers students in Example 2 that $0 < 6$ has no variable in it, use $0 \cdot k < 6$ as the result from the preceding line.

You might wish to show the results of Example 1 graphically. Graph $y_1 = 18x - 20 + 3x$ and $y_2 = 3(7x + 2)$. The graphs never intersect, indicating that there is no value of x that makes $y_1 = y_2$.

4-6

Notes on the Lesson

Example 2 One does not need the idea of slope to see that the lines will never intersect. Slope is introduced in Chapter 6, at which time students will have a way of determining that lines are parallel without graphing.

Additional Examples

Example 1 Solve $7x - 10 - 3x = 2(2x - 4)$. Since -10 does not equal -8, this statement is not true, so the original equation has no solution.

Example 2 Solve $7q + 1 > 60q - 4 - 53q$. Since $1 > -4$ is always true, $7q + 1 > 60q - 4 - 53q$ is true for any real number q.

The idea of a *true* or a *false* statement for an inequality may be difficult for students to understand. Provide students with a wide variety of real-world examples. For example, ask students to set up and solve an inequality for the following situation. A zoo has 5 elephants. How many monkeys does the zoo have if the total number of monkey legs is greater than the number of elephant legs? How many kangaroos does the zoo have if the total number of kangaroo legs is less than the number of elephant legs? How many snakes does the zoo have if the total number of snake legs is less (more) than the elephant legs?

Additional Answers

1a.

Year	Hamburger Heaven	Video King
0	6.90	7.50
1	7.90	8.50
2	8.90	9.50
3	9.90	10.50
4	10.90	11.50
5	11.90	12.50
6	12.90	13.50

1b. Let y be the number of years worked at either place. $6.90 + 1y < 7.50 + 1y$.

Example 1

Solve $18m - 20 + 3m = 3(7m + 2)$.

Solution

$18m - 20 + 3m = 3(7m + 2)$	Write the equation.
$21m - 20 = 21m + 6$	Simplify each side.
$21m - 21m - 20 = 21m - 21m + 6$	Subtract $21m$ from each side.
$-20 = 6$	Simplify.

Since -20 does not equal 6, this statement is not true, so the original equation has no solution.

GUIDED

Example 2

Solve $42k < 80k + 6 - 38k$.

Solution

$42k < 80k + 6 - 38k$	Write the inequality.
$42k < 42k + 6$	Combine like terms.
$\dfrac{?}{42k - 42k} < \dfrac{?}{42k + 6 - 42k}$	Subtract $42k$ from each side.
$0 < 6$	___?___ Simplify.

Since $0 < 6$ is always true, ___?___ is true for any real number k. $42k < 80k + 6 - 38k$

Check Graph both sides of the inequality, as shown at the right. The lines appear to be parallel and never intersect. The graph of $42k$ is always below the graph of $80k + 6 - 38k$. This supports the conclusion that $42k < 80k + 6 - 38k$ is true for any real number k.

1b. Let y be the number of years worked at either place. $6.90 + 1y < 7.50 + 1y$

Questions

COVERING THE IDEAS

1. Hamburger Heaven pays a starting salary of $6.90 an hour, and each year increases it by $1 an hour. Video King starts at $7.50 an hour, and also increases $1 an hour per year.
   a. Create a table for the data. **See margin.**
   b. Write an inequality to represent this situation.
   c. When does Hamburger Heaven pay more? **never**
2. Add $-12y$ to both sides of the inequality $12y + 11 > 12y - 1$.
   a. What inequality results? $11 > -1$
   b. Describe the solutions to this inequality. **Any real number is a solution to the inequality.**

218 More Linear Equations and Inequalities

In 2006, the federal minimum wage for covered, nonexempt employees was $5.15 per hour.

Source: U.S. Department of Labor

Accommodating the Learner

Students can use their graphing calculators to help them solve inequalities. Suppose students want to solve the inequality $x + 2 > 2x - 1$ using technology. Have students set $Y1 = x + 2 > 2x - 1$. The $>$ symbol can be found using the TEST command. Next have them graph Y1 in a standard window. Students should see the following:

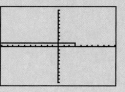

Note the solution consists of all real numbers whose y-value is 1. The endpoint, 3, must be checked by hand. Now have students solve the inequality $5x + 2 \leq 3x - 8$ using technology. $y \leq -5$

3. Add $2g$ to both sides of the equation $40 - 2g = 11 + 29 - 2g$.
   a. What equation results? $40 = 40$
   b. Describe the solution(s) to this equation.
   c. Check your solution(s) using a graph. **See margin.**

4. Check Guided Example 2 by substituting any real number for k.

In 5–8, solve the sentence.

5. $-6 + 4n > 4(n + 11)$

6. $65w = 11 + 65w$

7. $12x + 33 = 33 + 12x$

8. $-3(-9d + -2) > 30d - 3d$

9. The population of Yorkville is about 40,000 and growing at about 800 people a year. Newburgh has a population of about 200,000 and is growing at about 800 people a year.
   a. What will be the population of Yorkville in y years?
   b. What will be the population of Newburgh in y years?
   c. When will their populations be the same? **never**

3b. Any real number is a solution to the equation.

4. Answers vary. Sample answer: Let $k = 1$; $42(1) = 42 < 80(1) + 6 - 38(1) = 48$

5. no solutions

6. no solutions

7–8. Any real number is a solution.

9a. $40,000 + 800y$

9b. $200,000 + 800y$

APPLYING THE MATHEMATICS

10. Apartment A rents for $810 per month including utilities. Apartment B rents for $700 per month but the renter must pay $110 per month for utilities and a one-time $50 fee for a credit check.
    a. What sentence could you solve to find out when apartment A is cheaper? $810m < 700m + 110m + 50$
    b. Solve this inequality. **See margin.**
    c. If you wanted to rent one of these apartments for two years, which one would be cheaper? **Apartment A**

In 11 and 12, create an example of an equation different than those in this lesson with the given solution.

11. There is no real solution. **Answers vary. Sample answer: $x + 7 = x + 9$**

12. The equation is true for all real numbers. **Answers vary. Sample answer: $3(x + 9) - 27 = 3x$**

Nationally, the median rent for a one-bedroom apartment in 2003 was $550.

Source: National Multi-Housing Council

REVIEW

In 13 and 14, solve the inequality. (Lessons 4-5, 3-7)

13. $-3(5p + 2) > 24$ $p < -2$

14. $2n \geq -7 - (n + 4)$ $n \geq -\frac{11}{3}$

15. Sending a package by Wedropem shipping service costs $3.50 plus $0.25 per ounce. Brokefast Company charges $4.75 plus $0.10 per ounce. If your package weighs 16 ounces, which service is cheaper? Explain your reasoning. **(Lesson 4-5)**

15. Brokefast is cheaper, because $4.75 + 16(0.10) < 3.50 = 16(0.25)$.

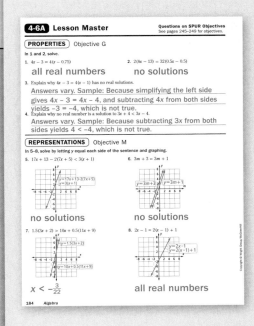

Additional Answers

3c.

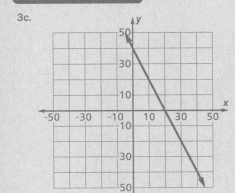

10b. $810m < 700m + 110m + 50$; $810m < 810m + 50$; $0 < 50$

4-6

4 Wrap-Up

Ongoing Assessment

Students should write a word problem that results in an inequality that is always false and one that is always true. Students should set up both inequalities and show the steps used to solve each. Students should explain in writing why the first one is false and the second one is true.

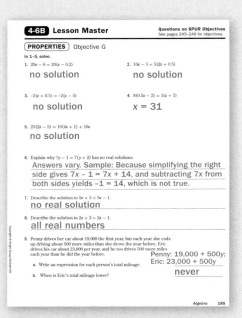

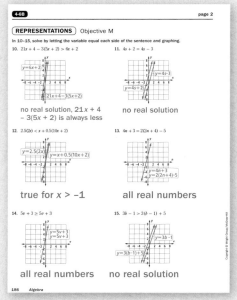

186   Algebra

16. Mama's Pizza charges $12 for a large cheese pizza and $0.90 for each additional topping. Pizza Palace charges $14 for a large cheese pizza but only $0.40 for each additional topping. **(Lessons 4-4, 4-3)**

    a. Write an equation for each pizza shop describing the cost c of a large pizza in terms of the number of toppings t.

    b. For how many toppings are the pizza prices at the two shops equal? **4 toppings**

16a. Mama's pizza:
$c = 12 + 0.90t$
dollars;
Pizza Palace:
$c = 14 + 0.40t$
dollars

17. In the 2000 United States presidential election, 105,396,641 people voted, according to the *World Almanac and Book of Facts*. In the 2004 presidential election, 122,293,332 people voted. By what percent did the number of voters in the election increase from 2000 to 2004? **(Lesson 4-1)** about 16%

18. Four instances of a general pattern are given below. **(Lesson 1-2)**

$$-(43 - 20) = 20 - 43$$
$$-(5.21 - 8.49) = 8.49 - 5.21$$
$$-\left(\frac{6}{5} - \frac{3}{7}\right) = \frac{3}{7} - \frac{6}{5}$$
$$-(w - 16) = 16 - w$$

    a. Write the pattern using the variables x and y. $-(x - y) = y - x$

    b. Is the pattern true for all real number values of x and y? Justify your answer. **yes, by the Distributive Property**

EXPLORATION

19. When solving the equation $ax + b = cx + d$ for x, there may be no solution, exactly one solution, or infinitely many solutions. What must be true about a, b, c, and d to guarantee each of the following?

    a. There is exactly one solution. $a \neq c$

    b. There are no solutions. $a = c$ and $b \neq d$

    c. There are infinitely many solutions. $a = c$ and $b = d$

Lesson 4-7 Equivalent Formulas

Vocabulary

Celsius scale

centigrade scale

Fahrenheit scale

input

output

equivalent formulas

▶ **BIG IDEA** If a formula gives a first variable in terms of a second variable, it may be possible to transform the formula to give the second variable in terms of the first.

Two different temperature scales are in common use throughout the world. The scale used wherever people use the metric system is the **Celsius scale,** named after Anders Celsius (1701–1744), a Swedish astronomer and physicist. It is also sometimes called the **centigrade scale** because of the 100-degree interval between 0°C and 100°C, the freezing and boiling points of water. The other scale is the **Fahrenheit scale,** named after the German physicist Gabriel Fahrenheit (1686–1736). In the Fahrenheit scale, which is now used only in the United States and a few other countries, water's freezing and boiling points are 32° and 212°.

People outside the United States seldom use the Fahrenheit scale. An exception is when a visitor from the U.S. asks about the weather forecast. They have to change the Celsius temperature from their forecast into Fahrenheit using the formula $F = 1.8C + 32$. This formula uses the Celsius temperature C as the **input** and produces the Fahrenheit temperature F as the **output.** We say that it gives *F in terms of C.* However, visitors to the United States have to make the reverse conversion. They must convert Fahrenheit temperatures from the U.S. forecast into Celsius. If you are going to convert from Fahrenheit to Celsius often, it is convenient to have a formula that begins with F as input and gives C as output. To find this formula, we write 1.8 as the fraction $\frac{9}{5}$.

Mental Math

Evaluate $x^2 - 2xy + y^2$ if

a. $x = 5$ and $y = 5$. 0

b. $x = -5$ and $y = 5$. 100

c. $x = 5$ and $y = -5$. 100

The lowest recorded temperature in the U.S. occurred in Prospect Creek Camp, Alaska, on January 23, 1971. The temperature fell to -80°F.

Source: *The World Almanac and Book of Facts*

GUIDED

Example 1

Solve $F = \frac{9}{5}C + 32$ for C.

Solution Solve like any linear equation. Isolate C on the right side.

$F = \frac{9}{5}C + 32$	Write the formula.
$\underline{\quad?\quad} = \underline{\quad?\quad}$	Add −32 to each side. $F - 32; \frac{9}{5}C + 32 - 32$
$\frac{5}{9}(\underline{\quad?\quad}) = \frac{5}{9}(\underline{\quad?\quad})$	Multiply each side by $\frac{5}{9}$. $F - 32; \frac{9}{5}C$
$\underline{\quad?\quad} = C$	Simplify. $\frac{5}{9}(F - 32)$

(continued on next page)

Equivalent Formulas **221**

Background

This lesson extends the concept of solving a linear equation in one variable to solving a formula for a particular variable. The variety of techniques available for solving equations is usually not available with formulas, because tables do not help one to arrive at solutions and graphs are not always possible. Consequently, for some students this kind of solving is more difficult. Thus, although these equations seldom have the unknown on both sides, we have delayed discussion until this point.

Fahrenheit-Celsius conversion formulas.
Two temperature scales are mentioned in this lesson: Fahrenheit and Celsius. The Fahrenheit scale was developed by the German physicist Gabriel Fahrenheit in 1724. A short time later, the Swedish astronomer Anders Celsius developed a scale he called the centigrade scale in which 0° was the freezing point of water and 100° was its boiling point. In 1948, the centigrade scale was renamed as the Celsius scale in his honor.

Lesson 4-7

GOAL

Solve a formula for one of the variables.

SPUR Objective

C Find equivalent forms of formulas and equations.

Materials/Resources

· Lesson Master 4-7A or 4-7B

· Resource Master 53

· Scientific or graphing calculator

HOMEWORK

Suggestions for Assignment

• Questions 1–23

• Question 24 (extra credit)

• Reading Lesson 4-8

• Covering the Ideas 4-8

Local Standards

1 Warm-Up

You might write or project the following so that students can do these questions as they enter the classroom.

1. Consider the formula $A = p + pr$, which gives the amount A (in dollars) after one year in a bank account that started with p dollars and which has an annual yield of r.

   a. Solve this formula for p. $p = \frac{A}{1 + r}$

   b. Solve this formula for r. $r = \frac{A - p}{p}$

   c. Check your answer to either Part a or b.

2. Find three formulas relating the unit cost C of an item, the number n of items purchased, and the total cost T. $T = nC; n = \frac{T}{C}; C = \frac{T}{n}$

2 Teaching

Notes on the Lesson

Guided Example 1 The classic Fahrenheit-to-Celsius conversion formula is intended to motivate the idea of equivalent formulas. Make certain students understand that pairs of numbers that work in one of the formulas must also work in the other formula.

Some people still call the Celsius scale "centigrade." As it is more commonly used than Celsius in some countries, students should learn both names.

In Example 1, we could have first multiplied both sides by 9 to clear fractions. The resulting equation is $9C = 5(F - 32)$. Now, by the Distributive Property, $9C = 5F - 160$. Solving this equation for F gives the desired equivalent formula.

You might have students graph this formula and also $F = \frac{9}{5}C + 32$ on the same axes to see how close the lines are to each other at everyday temperatures.

Additional Examples

Example 1 Solve $C = 2\pi r$ for the variable r. C is the circumference of a circle with radius r.

$$C = 2\pi r$$
$$\underline{\ ?\ } = \underline{\ ?\ } \qquad \frac{C}{2\pi r}, \frac{2\pi r}{2\pi}$$
$$\frac{C}{2\pi} = \underline{\ ?\ } \qquad r$$

Check Using 3.14 for π, substitute 31.4 for C and 5 for r.

Using $r = \frac{C}{2\pi}$: $\quad \dfrac{\ ?\ }{} = \dfrac{\ ?\ }{2\pi} \quad$ 5; 31.4

$$\underline{\ ?\ } = \underline{\ ?\ } \qquad 5;\ 5$$

Using $C = 2\pi r$: $\quad \underline{\ ?\ } = 2\pi\underline{\ ?\ } \quad$ 31.4; 5

$$31.4;\ 31.4 \quad \underline{\ ?\ } = \underline{\ ?\ }$$

The numbers $C = 31.4$ and $r = 5$ satisfy both equations.

Example 2 A formula for the area of a sphere is $A = 4\pi r^2$. Solve the formula for r. Explain what you do in each step.

$$A = 4\pi r^2$$
$$\frac{A}{4} = \pi r^2 \qquad \text{Divide each side by 4.}$$
$$\frac{A}{4\pi} = r^2 \qquad \text{Divide each side by } \pi.$$
$$\sqrt{\frac{A}{4\pi}} = r \qquad \text{Take the square root each side.}$$

Check In each formula, substitute 212 and 100 for the appropriate variables.

Using $F = 1.8C + 32$

$$\underline{\ ?\ } = 1.8 \cdot \underline{\ ?\ } + 32 \qquad 212;\ 100$$
$$\underline{\ ?\ } = \underline{\ ?\ } + 32 \qquad 212;\ 180$$
$$\underline{\ ?\ } = \underline{\ ?\ } \qquad 212;\ 212$$

Using $C = \frac{5}{9}(F - 32)$

$$\underline{\ ?\ } = \frac{5}{9}(\underline{\ ?\ } - 32) \qquad 100;\ 212$$
$$\underline{\ ?\ } = \frac{5}{9}(\underline{\ ?\ }) \qquad 100;\ 180$$
$$\underline{\ ?\ } = \underline{\ ?\ } \qquad 100;\ 100$$

The numbers $F = 212$ and $C = 100$ satisfy both equations.

The formulas $F = 1.8C + 32$ and $C = \frac{5}{9}(F - 32)$ are called **equivalent formulas** because every pair of values of F and C that satisfies one equation also satisfies the other.

GUIDED

Example 2

A formula for the volume of a cone is $V = \frac{1}{3}\pi r^2 h$, where V is the volume, r is the radius of the base, and h is the height. Octavio solved this formula for h. His work is shown below. Explain what he did to get each equation.

$$V = \frac{1}{3}\pi r^2 h$$

a. $\quad 3V = \pi r^2 h \qquad \underline{\ ?\ } \qquad$ Multiply each side by 3.

b. $\quad \dfrac{3V}{\pi} = r^2 h \qquad \underline{\ ?\ } \qquad$ Divide each side by π.

c. $\quad \dfrac{3V}{\pi r^2} = h \qquad \underline{\ ?\ } \qquad$ Divide each side by r^2.

Activity

In 1–5, use a CAS to solve for the given variable. Tell what is done to both sides in each step.

1. $-6x + 3y = 24$, for y

2. $x - y = -14$, for y

3. $S = \frac{C - 1}{3}$, for C (formula for cap size S when $C =$ circumference of the head in inches)

4. $E = \pi ab$, for b (formula for the area E of an ellipse when a is one-half the length of the major axis and b is one-half the length of the minor axis)

5. $G = \frac{s + 2d + 3t + 4h}{a}$, for h (formula for baseball slugging average G where $s =$ number of singles, $d =$ number of doubles, $t =$ number of triples, $h =$ number of home runs, and $a =$ number of at bats)

1. $y = 2x + 8$; add $6x$; divide by 3

2. $y = x + 14$. Answers vary. Sample answer: subtract x; multiply by -1

3. $C = 3S + 1$; multiply by 3; add 1

4. $b = \frac{E}{\pi a}$; divide by π; divide by a

5. $h = \frac{aG}{4} - \frac{s}{4} - \frac{d}{2} - \frac{3t}{4}$; multiply by a; subtract $(s + 2d + 3t)$; divide by 4

Accommodating the Learner

Have students consider the given diagram when answering the following questions.

Running Track

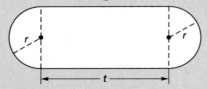

Find the perimeter P of the running track in terms of r and t. Solve for r in terms of P and t. If $P = 400$ m and $t = 100$ m, what is the value of r? Round your answer to the nearest hundredth. If $t = 115$ meters, what would the radius be? If your school has a 400 meters track, check it out. Use 3.14 for π.

$$2\pi r + 2t = P$$
$$2\pi r = P - 2t$$
$$r = \frac{P - 2t}{2\pi}$$
$$r = \frac{400 - 200}{2\pi}$$
$$r = \frac{200}{2\pi} = \frac{100}{\pi} \approx 31.85 \text{ m}$$
$$r = \frac{400 - 2(115)}{2\pi} = \frac{85}{\pi} \approx 27.07 \text{ m}$$

Whether you are working with a CAS or by hand, different people may write formulas that look quite different. However, they might be equivalent. For example, here is what Alf and Beth wrote to solve $p = 2\ell + 2w$ for w.

Alf's Solution		Beth's Solution	
$p = 2\ell + 2w$	Write the formula.	$p = 2\ell + 2w$	Write the formula.
$p - 2\ell = 2w$	Subtract 2ℓ.	$p - 2\ell = 2w$	Subtract 2ℓ.
$\frac{p - 2\ell}{2} = w$	Divide by 2.	$\frac{1}{2}(p - 2\ell) = w$	Multiply by $\frac{1}{2}$.
$w = \frac{p - 2\ell}{2}$		$w = \frac{1}{2}(p - 2\ell)$	

 QY

▶ **QY**

Explain how you know that $w = \frac{p - 2\ell}{2}$ and $w = \frac{1}{2}(p - 2\ell)$ are equivalent.

Using a Graphing Calculator

One important use of equivalent formulas arises when using graphing calculators. Often formulas that are entered must give y in terms of x.

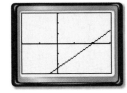

Example 3

Use a graphing calculator to graph $5x - 2y = 100$.

Solution Solve for y.

$5x - 2y = 100$	Write the equation.
$-5x + 5x - 2y = -5x + 100$	Add $-5x$ to each side.
$-2y = -5x + 100$	Combine like terms.
$\frac{-2y}{-2} = \frac{-5x + 100}{-2}$	Divide each side by -2.
$y = \frac{-5}{-2}x + \frac{100}{-2}$	Expand the fraction.
$y = 2.5x - 50$	Simplify.

Now enter the equation Y1 = 2.5x − 50 into the calculator. A window of $-20 \leq x \leq 30$ and $60 \leq y \leq 60$ is shown below.

(continued on next page)

Equivalent Formulas **223**

Notes on the Lesson

Guided Example 2 For some students, part of the difficulty in solving a formula for a particular variable is that the unknown is on the right side of the equation. This is one reason why we have included so many equations with variables on the right side in previous lessons. Remind students that it is always possible to switch sides of the equation so that the unknown is on the left side.

Additional Example

Example 3 Use a graphing calculator to graph $-7x + 3y = 18$.

Enter the equation Y1 $= \frac{7x}{3} + 6$ into the calculator. A window of $-10 \leq x \leq 10$ and $-10 \leq y \leq 10$ is appropriate.

Have students build a table to show specific values of x and y to validate the graph shown.

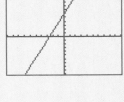

x	y
0	6
1	8.333
2	10.667
3	13
4	15.333
5	17.667
6	20

Accommodating the Learner ⬇

Students may have difficulty solving equations with more than one variable. If this is the case in your class, model the process. Have students solve each pair of equations. First have them solve the equation with one variable followed by the equation with more than one variable. Relate the process used to solve the first equation to the process used to solve the second equation. Impress students with the fact that variables represent numbers and should be treated as such.

a. $2 = x + 3$

$a = b + c$; solve for b. $x = -1$; $b = a - c$

b. $7x - 4 = 17$

$7w - x = y$; solve for w. $x = 3$; $w = \frac{x + y}{7}$

c. $\frac{x + 4}{3} = 8$

$\frac{q + r}{t} = u$; solve for q. $x = 20$; $q = tu - r$

3 Assignment

Recommended Assignment
- Questions 1–23
- Question 24 (extra credit)
- Reading Lesson 4-8
- Covering the Ideas 4-8

Notes on the Questions
Question 6 Although the distance-rate-time formula is usually given as $d = rt$, the rate unit (miles per hour) indicates that the rate is derived by dividing distance by time, so the formula given here is quite appropriate.

Question 7 S is the sum of the measures of the angles of a convex n-gon.

Question 8 F is force, m is mass, and a is acceleration.

Question 9 This is a formula for the area of a trapezoid.

Check 1 Use the TRACE feature to read the coordinates of some points on the line. Check that these satisfy the original equation. For example, our TRACE showed the point with $x \approx 10.5$, $y \approx -23.7$ on the graph.

Does $5(10.5) - 2(-23.7) = 100$?

$$99.9 \approx 100 \text{ Yes. It checks.}$$

The point $(10.5, -23.7)$ is very close to the graph of $5x - 2y = 100$.

Check 2 Compute the coordinates of a point on the line. For example, when $x = 0$, $5(0) - 2y = 100$.

$$5(0) - 2y = 100$$
$$-2y = 100$$
$$y = -50$$

The TRACE on our calculator shows that the point $(0, -50)$ is on the line.

Questions

COVERING THE IDEAS

1. There is one temperature at which Celsius and Fahrenheit thermometers give the same reading: $-40°$. Verify that $C = -40$, $F = -40$ satisfies both $F = 1.8C + 32$ and $C = \frac{5}{9}(F - 32)$.

2. A person with a head circumference of 23.5 inches wears a size $7\frac{1}{2}$ baseball cap. Verify that $C = 23.5$ and $S = 7\frac{1}{2}$ satisfy the formula $S = \frac{C-1}{3}$. $S = \frac{23.5 - 1}{3} = 7\frac{1}{2}$

3. a. Solve $p = 2\ell + 2w$ for ℓ. $\ell = \frac{p}{2} - w$
   b. **Fill in the Blanks** In Part a you are asked to find a formula for ___?___ in terms of ___?___ and ___?___. ℓ; p; w
   c. Check your solution to Part a by substituting values for ℓ, w, and p.

In 4 and 5, solve the equation for y.

4. $8x + y = 20$ $y = 20 - 8x$

5. $4x - 8y = -40$ $y = \frac{1}{2}x + 5$

In 6–9, solve the formula for the indicated variable.

6. $r = \frac{d}{t}$ for d $d = rt$

7. $S = 180n - 360$ for n $n = \frac{S}{180} + 2$

8. $F = m \cdot a$ for a $a = \frac{F}{m}$

9. $A = \frac{1}{2}(b_1 + b_2)h$ for h $h = \frac{2A}{b_1 + b_2}$

1. $1.8(-40) + 32 = -72$
   $+ 32 = -40$ and
   $\frac{5}{9}(-40 - 32) =$
   $\frac{5}{9}(-72) = -40$

3c. Answers vary.
   Sample answer: let
   $\ell = 1$, $w = 2$, and
   $p = 6$. $6 = 2(1) +$
   $2(2)$, which checks
   with $\ell = \frac{p}{2} - w$
   $= \frac{6}{2} - 2 = 3 - 2$
   $= 1$

Extension

Have students replace the ___?___ in each equation with the number or expression in a, b, and c. Then have them solve for y.

a. -4 **b.** w **c.** $a + b$

1. $3y =$ ___?___

   $3y = -12$; $y = -4$

   $3y = 3w$; $y = w$

   $3y = 3(a + b)$; $y = a + b$

2. $2x - 6 =$ ___?___

   $2x - 6 = -14$; $x = -4$

   $2x - 6 = 2w - 6$; $x = w$

   $2x - 6 = 2(a + b) - 6$; $x = a + b$

3. $\frac{x}{2} =$ ___?___

   $\frac{x}{2} = -2$; $x = -4$

   $\frac{x}{2} = \frac{w}{2}$; $x = w$

   $\frac{x}{2} = \frac{a+b}{2}$; $x = a + b$

APPLYING THE MATHEMATICS

10. The formula $S = 3F - 24$ gives the sizes of a person's shoe in terms of F, the length of a person's foot in inches.
   a. Solve this formula for F. $\;F = \dfrac{S + 24}{3}$
   b. Estimate the length of a person's foot if the person wears a size 9 shoe. **11 in.**

11. Jocelyn and Alma were asked to solve the equation $5x - 2y = 100$ for y. When solving the equation, they got the following answers.

Jocelyn	Alma
$y = \dfrac{100 - 5x}{-2}$	$y = 2.5x - 50$

   Is the work of either student correct? Explain how you know.

12. a. Solve the following equations for y. $2x + 6y = 15$ and $x = \dfrac{6y - 15}{-2}$
   b. Graph each equation and $y = 2.5 - \frac{x}{3}$ on a calculator.
   c. Which of these equations appear to be equivalent? Provide evidence to support your answer. **12b. See margin.**

13. A formula for the circumference C of a circle is $C = \pi d$, where d is the diameter.
   a. Solve this formula for π. $\;\pi = \dfrac{C}{d}$
   b. How could you use the formula to find a value of π?
   c. Use your answer to Part b to estimate π from the measurements of some circular object you have.

14. The formula $S = 2\pi r^2 + 2\pi rh$ gives the total surface area of a cylindrical solid shown below with radius r and height h.

   a. Solve this formula for h. $\;h = \dfrac{S - 2\pi r^2}{2\pi r}$ or $h = \dfrac{S}{2\pi r} - r$
   b. Find the height to the nearest hundredth if the radius is 10 centimeters and the surface area is 2,000 square centimeters.

15. Solve for y and use a graphing calculator to graph the equations $5x + 2y = 8$ and $5x + 2y = 12$. What is true about these graphs? **They are parallel.**

REVIEW

In 16 and 17, solve the sentence. (Lessons 4-6, 4-4)

16. $6(y - 4) = 2(y - 4) - 8(2 - y)\;\;y = 0$

11. Both students are correct, and their expressions are equivalent.
12a. Answers vary. Sample answer: $y = 2.5 - \dfrac{x}{3}$, $y = 2.5 - \dfrac{1}{3}x$.
12c. They are all equivalent, as shown by the identical graphs.
13b. Measure a circle's circumference and divide it by the diameter.
13c. Answers vary. Sample answer: A circle with circumference of 22 cm has a diameter of about 7 cm, meaning $\pi \approx \dfrac{22}{7} \approx 3.14$.
14b. $h \approx 21.83$ cm

Notes on the Questions
Question 13 In this question, students are revisiting the formula that is often used as the definition of π. Point out that even though π is not a variable, we can still solve for it. This is not as unusual as students might think; in future work, they might solve an equation such as $x = 2y$ for 2 and get $\dfrac{x}{y} = 2$, which is a ratio of x to y.

Question 15 Can students see without solving why the graphs cannot intersect? (If $5x + 2y = 8$, then for the same values of x and y, it cannot be that $5x + 2y = 12$, for then $8 = 12$.)

Additional Answers

12b.

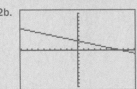

4 Wrap-Up

Ongoing Assessment

Organize students in pairs. Have each student write an equation containing at least two variables and identify the variable for which they should solve. On the back of the page, have students solve their equations for the chosen variable. Have them exchange papers with their partners. Have each student solve his or her partner's equation. Once everyone is finished, have students turn the papers over and compare their work to their partner's work. If their solutions do not match, have each pair discuss the reasons why they do not agree. Students should then find a solution upon which they both agree.

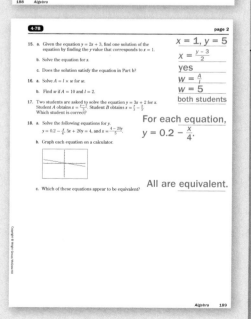

17. $52v < 22v - 7 + 30v$ **no solutions**

18. Five more than twice a number is three more than four times the number. What is the number? (**Lesson 4-4**) **1**

19. a. Write an equation for the horizontal line through $(5, -3)$.
    (**Lesson 4-2**) $y = -3$
    b. Write an equation for the vertical line through $(5, -3)$. $x = 5$

20. According to the *World Almanac and Book of Facts,* the Middle East is reported to have approximately 65% of the world's oil reserves. All together, the Middle East's crude oil reserves are estimated to total 686 billion barrels. How many barrels are estimated to be in the world's total crude oil reserves? (**Lesson 4-1**) **about 1,055 billion barrels**

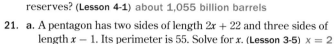

In 2004, the United States imported over 10,000,000 barrels of oil per day from foreign nations.

Source: *The World Almanac and Book of Facts*

21. a. A pentagon has two sides of length $2x + 22$ and three sides of length $x - 1$. Its perimeter is 55. Solve for x. (**Lesson 3-5**) $x = 2$
    b. Suppose the pentagon had two sides of length $x - 1$, three sides of length $2x + 22$, and still had a perimeter of 55. Why is this impossible? **It would have sides of negative length.**

In 22 and 23, write the related facts and determine the value of x for each fact triangle. (Lessons 3-5, 2-7)

22–23. See margin.

22.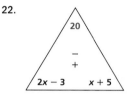

23.

EXPLORATION

24. Ask a friend or relative for a formula used in his or her job. Explain what the variables represent and show an example of how it is used. Solve the formula for one of its other variables. See margin.

Additional Answers

22. $2x - 3 + x + 5 = 20$; $x + 5 + 2x - 3 = 20$;
    $20 - (2x - 3) = x + 5$; $20 - (x + 5) =$
    $2x - 3$; $x = 6$

23. $4x - 6 + 2x + 10 = 40$;
    $2x + 10 + 4x - 6 = 40$;
    $40 - (4x - 6) = 2x + 10$;
    $40 - (2x + 10) = 4x - 6$; $x = 6$

24. Answers vary. Sample answer: $M = 220 - y$, where y is one's age in years, is the formula generally used to find one's maximum heart rate, M, in beats per minute. Solving for y gives $y = 220 - M$.

Lesson
4-8
Compound Inequalities, *And* and *Or*

Vocabulary

compound sentence

intersection

union

± notation

> ► **BIG IDEA**   Placing AND between two sentences means that you want the intersection of their solutions; placing OR between them means that you want the union of their solutions.

The Language of Compound Sentences

A car's water temperature gauge is an indicator of its engine cooling system. This gauge is marked to highlight normal temperatures as shown. Temperatures below 40°C occur when the car is warming up. Temperatures above 120°C indicate that the engine is in jeopardy of breaking down. These temperatures can be graphed. Using *t* to represent temperature, each graph can be described with a pair of inequalities.

Mental Math

a. Katie's temperature is 4 degrees away from 98.6. What are her possible temperatures? $94.6° \le t \le 102.6°$

b. Jeremy was 7 points away from getting 90 points on a test. What are his possible scores? $83 \le p \le 97$

Normal Temperatures

$t \ge 40°$ and $t \le 120°$

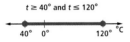

The graph is an interval.

Abnormal Temperatures

$t < 40°$ or $t > 120°$

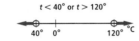

The graph is two rays without their endpoints.

A **compound sentence** is a single sentence consisting of two or more sentences linked by the words *and* or *or*. The above graphs are described by *compound inequalities*. The compound inequality at the left can be written as the *double inequality* $40° \le t \le 120°$.

Intersection and Union of Sets

The graphs of the compound inequalities above come from the *intersection* and *union* of two sets. On the left, the interval showing normal engine temperatures is the set of points shared by the graphs of the two simple inequalities. It consists of the points where the two rays $t \ge 40°$ and $t \le 120°$ overlap.

Intersection of Sets

The **intersection** of sets A and B, written A ∩ B, is the set of elements that are in both A and B.

Compound Inequalities, *And* and *Or*   **227**

Background

The material in this lesson preceding Example 3 should be review for students who have had *UCSMP Transition Mathematics*.

Intersection and union of sets. Union and intersection of sets are usually not difficult for students. Points in the *intersection* of the two streets are on one street *and* on the other. Points in the *union* of the two streets are on one street *or* on the other. The symbols for union and intersection are easy for students to remember because the union symbol looks like the letter U.

Describing the interval between two numbers. In this lesson we describe the set of numbers *from a to b* either as $a \le x \le b$ or as $m \pm 0.5L$, where *m* is the midpoint of the segment and *L* is the segment's length: $m = \frac{a+b}{2}$ and $L = b - a$. These formulas are not given in the lesson. In the next lesson, the interval $a \le x \le b$ will be described by the single inequality $|x - m| \le 0.5L$.

GOAL

Graph the union and intersection of solution sets of linear inequalities.

SPUR Objective

B Solve and check compound inequalities of the form $ax + b < cx + d$.

Materials/Resources

· Lesson Master 4-8A or 4-8B
· Resource Masters 2, 7, 54, and 55
· Scientific or graphing calculator

HOMEWORK

Suggestions for Assignment

• Questions 1–24
• Question 25 (extra credit)
• Reading Lesson 4-9
• Covering the Ideas 4-9

Local Standards

1   Warm-Up

You might write or project the following so that students can do these questions as they enter the classroom.

1. Find a number *A* that is a solution to $10 < A < 10.1$.   Answers vary. Sample answer: 10.05

2. Find a number *B* that is a solution to $B - 3 > 4$ but *not* a solution to $B - 4 > 5$.   Answers vary. Sample answer: 8

3. Find a number *C* that is a solution to $-62 \ge C \ge -64$ but *not* a solution to $-64 < C \le 64$.   −64

4-8

2 Teaching

Notes on the Lesson

Students have seen both intersections and unions many times before. An angle is the union of two rays with the same endpoint. $\triangle ABC$ is the union of the three line segments $\overline{AB}$, $\overline{BC}$, and $\overline{CA}$. That is, $\triangle ABC = \overline{AB} \cup \overline{BC} \cup \overline{CA}$. More generally, a polygon is the union of a set of line segments that satisfy certain conditions. Students are familiar with intersections of lines and curves. What is special in this lesson is that the unions and intersections take place on a single line, and the figures are described algebraically by inequalities.

You might begin by considering the possible intersections of two rays on the same line. A ray is described by an inequality of the form $x \geq k$ or $x \leq k$. If the two rays are in the same direction (e.g., $\{x: x \geq 2\} \cap \{x: x \geq 5\}$), then the intersection is a ray. If they are in opposite directions, then the intersection is either the empty set (e.g., $\{x: x \leq -3\}$ $\cap \{x: x \geq 5\}$) or a segment (e.g., $\{x: x \geq -14\} \cap \{x: x \leq -9\}$).

Next, consider unions. The possible unions of two rays are either two rays (e.g., $\{x: x \leq 0\} \cup \{x: x \geq 5\}$), the entire line (e.g., $\{x: x \geq 10\} \cup \{x: x \leq 50\}$), or a single ray (e.g., $\{x: x \geq -5\} \cup \{x: x \geq -3\}$). Describe these symbolically and with graphs. The only other thing to consider is whether the endpoints are included or excluded.

Example 1 We show three number lines because we think this helps algebra students to organize their work. However, we expect students to quickly work on one number line. Students might use pencils of different colors to differentiate the sets.

Additional Example

Example 1 Let A = the set of numbers for which $x \leq 6$. Let B = the set of numbers for which $x > -4$. Graph the set $A \cap B$. Describe the set with an *and* or an *or* statement.

This is the set "$x \leq 6$ *and* $x > -4$."

The graph of abnormal engine temperatures also begins with two rays without their endpoints, which in this case show temperatures below 40° and those above 120°. However, we do not look for the overlap. Instead, we take the union of the two rays. The meaning of *union* in mathematics is similar to its meaning in other contexts. For example, the Preamble of the Constitution of the United States of America reads:

> *We the People of the United States, in Order to form a more perfect Union, establish Justice, insure domestic Tranquility, provide for the common defense, promote the general Welfare, and secure the Blessings of Liberty to ourselves and our Posterity, do ordain and establish this Constitution for the United States of America.*

Here the word union describes a new set (the United States) formed by joining together component sets (the thirteen colonies).

Union of Sets

The **union** of sets A and B, written $A \cup B$, is the set of elements in either A or B or in both.

🛑 **QY1**

Example 1

Let A = the set of numbers for which $x > 8$.
Let B = the set of numbers for which $x \leq -3$.
Graph the set $A \cup B$. Describe the set with an *and* or an *or* statement.

Solution Draw the graph of $x > 8$. The open circle at 8 indicates that 8 is not a solution.

Draw the graph of $x \leq -3$. The closed circle at -3 shows that -3 is a solution.

Draw the graph of $x \leq -3$.

The union includes all points that satisfy either sentence or both sentences. The graph of $A \cup B$ is shown below. This is the set "$x > 8$ or $x \leq -3$."

Consider this situation: A police officer is directing traffic at the corner of Main and Oak Streets. Choose the correct word to complete each sentence.

The police officer was in the (union/intersection) of Main Street and Oak Street. This means that the officer was on Main Street (and/or) the officer was on Oak Street.
The officer was directing cars that were in the (union/intersection) of Main Street and Oak Street. This means that each car was on Main Street (and/or) on Oak Street.

Accommodating the Learner ⬆

Hooke's Law is named after the 17th-century physicist Robert Hooke. According to Hooke's Law, the force necessary to stretch a steel spring x units beyond its natural length is given by the equation $F = kx$, where x is the distance the spring is stretched, F is the restoring force exerted by the spring, and k is the force constant of the spring. Suppose $k = 2.7$ and the restoring force exerted by the spring is between 24.3 and 31.05, inclusive. What interval represents the increased length of the spring? Does your answer represent the union or intersection of two sets?

$F = kx$; $x = \frac{F}{k}$ therefore $9 \leq x \leq 11.5$; intersection

Example 2

A family purchased some neon tetras to put in their new fish tank. They looked on the Internet to determine at what temperature to set the tank water. One site wrote to keep the water temperature from 72° to 78°F. A second site wrote 68° to 74° and a third site wrote 73° to 81°. To be safe, at what temperature should the family keep the tank?

Solution Let t represent the water temperature. Appropriate temperatures for tetras are those satisfying the following.

$$72° \leq t \leq 78° \text{ according to Site 1}$$
$$68° \leq t \leq 74° \text{ according to Site 2}$$
$$73° \leq t \leq 81° \text{ according to Site 3}$$

A neon tetra can live 10 years or more with the proper conditions.

Source: animal-world.com

The family wondered if any temperatures could satisfy all three conditions. The graphs show the three intervals separately.

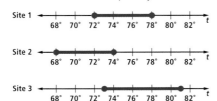

The best temperatures for the tetras are those that lie in all three intervals. This is the intersection in which the three graphs overlap. The tank should have a temperature satisfying $73° < t < 74°$.

Site 1 ∩ Site 2 ∩ Site 3

Describing the Intervals $a \leq x \leq b$

Most people would say that the average body temperature is 98.6°F. This figure was arrived at in the 19th century. Recent medical research has established that the mean temperature for healthy people is 98.2°F. However, there is some variability among healthy people. According to the new standard, the normal range varies above or below 98.2° by 1.5°. This means that the normal body temperatures t of healthy people range from $98.2 + 1.5 = 99.7$ to $98.2 - 1.5 = 96.7$. So $96.7 \leq t \leq 99.7$.

You can combine $98.2 + 1.5$ and $98.2 - 1.5$ into one expression using ± **notation.** Then the interval of normal temperatures is written $98.2°F ± 1.5°F$. The graph on the next page shows this interval and the temperatures of 129 men and women.

Notes on the Lesson

Example 2 These data are authentic. You may have students check to see if they can find Web sites that give these different temperature suggestions.

Additional Example
Example 2 Anita has three recipes for making brownies. The first recipe makes 4 servings, the second makes 8 servings, and the third makes 12 servings. Anita knows that it is not recommended to scale a recipe either up or down beyond four times its original serving size. If s represents the serving size, then the first recipe serving-size scaled interval is $1 \leq s \leq 16$, the second recipe serving-size scaled interval is $2 \leq s \leq 32$, and the third recipe serving-size scaled interval is $3 \leq s \leq 48$. Which interval satisfies all three recipes? $3 \leq s \leq 16$

Vocabulary Development

The concept of the union and intersection of two or more sets is sometimes very confusing to students. The more you can relate these ideas to real-world situations within the students' frames of reference, the more likely they will be to keep the two ideas clear. Use a Venn diagram to illustrate your examples.

Accommodating the Learner

Introduce the students to the idea of a Venn diagram by using the following example. Let $A = \{3, 4, 5, \ldots, 11\}$ and $B = \{-4, -2, 0, 2, 4, 6, 8\}$. Using the Venn diagram given, illustrate $A \cap B$ by shading the intersection. Repeat the process for $A \cup B$.

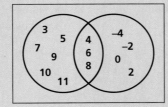

Notes on the Lesson

Example 3 This question differs from the preceding questions in that two inequalities need to be solved.

Additional Examples

Example 3 Solve and graph $-5 < 3x - 8 \leq 1$. $1 < x \leq 3$

Example 4 Solve $5z - 4 < z$ or $7z + 18 < z$.

Solve each inequality separately.

$5z - 4 < z$ or $7z + 18 < z$

$4z - 4 < \underline{\quad?\quad}$ or $6z + 18 < \underline{\quad?\quad}$
$0; 0$

$\quad 4z < \underline{\quad?\quad}$ or $6z < \underline{\quad?\quad}$ $4; -18$

$\quad z < \underline{\quad?\quad}$ or $z < \underline{\quad?\quad}$ $1; -3$

The intervals overlap and their union is described by $\underline{\quad?\quad}$. $z < 1$

Note-Taking Tips

Students should write the definitions of both *union* and *intersection* in their notebooks. Under each definition students should give a variety of examples. Examples should consist of sets, Venn diagrams, and graphs. A clear written explanation should accompany each example.

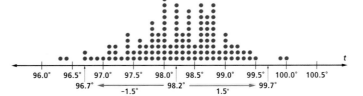

STOP QY2

▶ **QY2**

Write an expression of the form $a \pm d$ to represent the interval $40\,°C \leq t \leq 120\,°C$ for normal car engine temperatures from the beginning of this lesson.

Solving Inequalities with *And* and *Or*

If the variable is not isolated in an inequality, its solutions are not evident. The first task then is to use the Addition and Multiplication Properties of Inequality to isolate the variable.

Example 3

Solve and graph $-8 \leq 5m + 4 < 19$.

Solution 1 $-8 \leq 5m + 4 < 19$ can be rewritten as $-8 \leq 5m + 4$ and $5m + 4 < 19$. Each inequality can be solved separately and then we take the intersection of their solutions.

$$-8 \leq 5m + 4 \qquad \text{and} \qquad 5m + 4 < 19$$

$$-8 + -4 \leq 5m + 4 + -4 \qquad 5m + 4 + -4 < 19 + -4$$

$$-12 \leq 5m \qquad\qquad 5m < 15$$

$$\frac{-12}{5} \leq \frac{5m}{m} \qquad\qquad \frac{5m}{m} < \frac{15}{5}$$

$$-2.4 \leq m \qquad \text{and} \qquad m < 3$$

Now combine these two statements to describe the interval.

$$-2.4 \leq m < 3$$

Solution 2 Notice that after breaking the interval into two inequalities, the steps for solving each inequality are the same. In the future, the inequality does not need to be split apart at all. You perform the same operations to all three parts, as shown below.

$-8 \leq$	$5m + 4$	< 19	Write the equation.
$-8 + -4 \leq$	$5m + 4 + -4$	$< 19 + -4$	Add -4 to each part.
$-12 \leq$	$5m$	< 15	Simplify.
$\frac{-12}{5} \leq$	$\frac{5m}{m}$	$< \frac{15}{5}$	Divide by 5.
$-2.4 \leq$	m	< 3	Simplify.

Extension

Students can use their graphing calculators to graph the solution to a compound inequality. Suppose students want the solution to $2x + 5 > -5$ *and* $2x - 1 < 5$. First ask them to solve the compound inequality algebraically; they should find the solution to be $-5 < x < 3$. Using a graphing calculator, enter the following in Y1:

1. $2x + 5$
2. 2nd → TEST
3. Select > then enter (−5)
4. 2nd → TEST; right arrow LOGIC, select *and*
5. $2x - 1$
6. 2nd → TEST; select <; then enter 5

Graphing in a standard window yields a horizontal line segment at $y = 1$ from $-5 < x < 3$. Changing the *and* to *or* yields a horizontal line segment at $y = 1$ for all real values for x. Students must test the endpoints of the solution to see if they are part of the solution.

GUIDED

Example 4

Solve $13y + 86 > y + 2$ or $2y + 9 < 5y$.

Solution Solve each inequality separately.

$$13y + 86 > y + 2 \quad \text{or} \quad 2y + 9 < 5y$$
$$12y + 86 > \underline{\ ?\ }\ 2 \quad \text{or} \quad -3y + 9 < \underline{\ ?\ }\ 0$$
$$12y > \underline{\ ?\ }\ -84 \quad \text{or} \quad -3y < \underline{\ ?\ }\ -9$$
$$y > \underline{\ ?\ }\ -7 \quad \text{or} \quad y \underline{\ ?\ }\ \underline{\ ?\ } >; 3$$

The intervals overlap and their union is described by $y > -7$.

Questions

COVERING THE IDEAS

1. **Fill in the Blank** Fill in the blank with *and* or *or*.

   $-8.2 < x \le 4.75$ means $-8.2 < x \underline{\ ?\ } x \le 4.75$. **and**

Matching In 2–5, match the inequality with its graph.

2. $x < -2$ or $5 < x$ **d**

   a.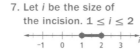

3. $-2 < x < 5$ **a**

   b.

4. $x < -2$ or $x < 5$ **c**

   c.

5. $x < -2$ and $x < 5$ **b**

   d.

6. During the summer months, Mr. and Mrs. Boller have to agree on a temperature at which to set the air conditioner. Mr. Boller prefers the room temperature to be between 68° and 72°. Mrs. Boller likes temperature between 70° and 75°. Write an inequality to show the temperatures when Mr. and Mrs. Boller will both be comfortable. **Let t be the set temperature. $70° \le t \le 72°$**

7. During thyroid surgery, doctors make a 1.5 inch ± 0.5 inch incision. Write a double inequality showing the possible lengths of the incision. Then graph the sentence.

8. A movie theater gives a discount price to children under 3 years old and to senior citizens over 65 years old.

   a. Write a compound inequality to show the ages that receive the discounted price.

   b. Graph the ages that receive this discounted price.

7. Let i be the size of the incision. $1 \le i \le 2$

8a. Let y be the age in years getting a discount.
$y < 3$ or $y > 65$

8b.

Compound Inequalities, *And* and *Or*   **231**

3 Assignment

Recommended Assignment

- Questions 1–24
- Question 25 (extra credit)
- Reading Lesson 4-9
- Covering the Ideas 4-9

Notes on the Questions

Question 6 This question can be answered without the idea of intersection, but the concept should be used in most class discussions.

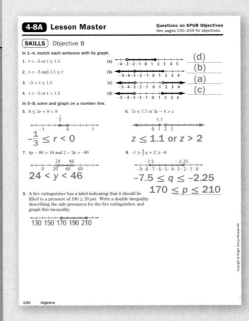

Notes on the Questions

Notes on the Questions

Questions 15 and 16 These are important for preparation for Lesson 4-9.

Question 24 This question is also given in preparation for Lesson 4-9.

Question 25 Have students tell what they found. A lively discussion may arise. It is not uncommon to use "and" in English when mathematicians would use "or." When "or" is used, the meaning is often an *exclusive or*, that is, the word does not allow both. This, too, is different from the mathematical usage.

9. Temperatures in space vary greatly. Astronauts on the International Space Station have to be able to endure outside temperatures that are $-18°C \pm 139°C$.

   a. Write an inequality to represent these temperatures in space.

   b. Graph the inequality.

In 10–13, solve the inequality and graph all solutions.

10. $2x + 9 > 17$ or $8 - 5x \leq 13$

11. $\frac{1}{4}x - 7 < -2$ and $6x + 3.8 \geq 9.2$

12. $-4 \leq 2.5x - 9 < 15$

13. $20c + 5 \geq 30c - 15$ or $9 - c > 4 - 2c$

10–13. See margin.

The International Space Station (ISS) weighs 206,043.3 kilograms and has a habitable volume of 420 cubic meters.

Source: NASA

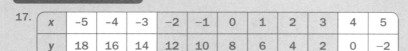

APPLYING THE MATHEMATICS

14. Marcos and Lydia want to hire a band for their wedding. The band charges a flat fee of \$950 and an additional \$275 per hour. They are willing to spend at least \$1,200 on the band, but not more than \$2,300. For how many hours can they have the band play for their wedding?

Fill in the Blanks For 15 and 16, fill in the blanks to describe the interval shown on the graph with $\pm$ notation.

15. $\underline{\ ?\ } \pm \underline{\ ?\ }$ 6.5 ± 20

    $-14 \ -7 \quad 0 \quad 7 \quad 14 \ 21 \ 28$

16. $\underline{\ ?\ } \pm \underline{\ ?\ }$ -1.05 ± 2.65

    $-3.7 \qquad\qquad 1.6$
    $-4 \ -3 \ -2 \ -1 \quad 0 \quad 1 \quad 2$

17. Make a table and graph of $y = -2x + 8$. Highlight the x-coordinates on the table and the part of the graph where $-2x + 8 > 12$ or $-2x + 8 < 1$. See margin.

18. Make a table and graph of $y = 3 + 5x$. Highlight the x-coordinates on the table and the part of the graph where $-2 \leq 3 + 5x \leq 23$. See margin.

REVIEW

19. a. Solve the formula $d = rt$ for r, where d is distance, r is rate, and t is time. $r = \frac{d}{t}$

    b. What was the average speed of a truck that traveled 245 miles in 4 hours? **(Lesson 4-7)** 61.25 mph

9a. Let t be the temperatures that astronauts can endure. $-157°C \leq t \leq 121°C$

9b.
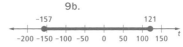

14. Let h be the number of hours for which the band will be hired. $1,200 \leq 950 + 275h \leq 2,300$, which implies $1 \leq h \leq 4$, assuming the band charges the full hourly rate for fractions of the hour.

Additional Answers

10. $x \geq -1$
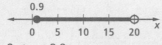

11. $0.9 \leq x < 20$

12. $2 \leq x < 9.6$

13. all real numbers
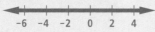

Additional Answers

17.

x	−5	−4	−3	−2	−1	0	1	2	3	4	5
y	18	16	14	12	10	8	6	4	2	0	−2

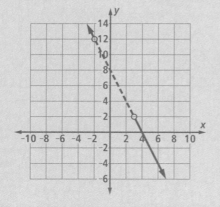

In 20 and 21, solve the sentence. (Lesson 4-6)

20. $7(k - 2) - 11 > (7k - 2) - 11$ no solutions

21. $20p - 4(p + 2) = (6p - 8) + 10p$ all real numbers

22. Solve $-5 - 2y > 14 - 6y$ and graph the set of solutions. $y > \frac{19}{4}$
(Lesson 4-5)

22.

23. Jennifer compared prices for the same pair of shoes at three different stores. The first store sold them at $75 less a discount of 15% due to a storewide sale. Jennifer had a $10 gift certificate for the second store, where the shoes cost $72. She would have to pay 8% sales tax at these two stores. The shoes at the third store cost $67 including tax. At which store can Jennifer buy the shoes for the cheapest price? (Lesson 4-1)
the second store

24. Evaluate $|-4xy + y - x|$ for each situation. (Lesson 1-6)

   a. $x = 3, y = 4$ 47

   b. $x = -1, y = 2$ 11

   c. $x = -10, y = -5$ 195

EXPLORATION

25. In mathematics, the difference between the words *and* and *or* is determined by union and intersection, but the English usage of these words is not always as clear.

   a. Consider this statement:
      In case of an emergency, women and children go first.

      Write how a mathematician would view the statement and then explain if there is a difference in what was probably meant by the statement.

   b. Find at least two other situations in which the English usage of the words *and* and *or* varies from the mathematical usage.

25a. A mathematician would view "women and children" as those people who are both women and children. To explain the English meaning to a mathematician, replace "and" with "or."

25b. Answers vary. Sample answer: Tommy's mother tells him he can have ice cream or a piece of cake for dessert (but she does not mean he can have both). Becky's math teacher told the students that all of them got As and Bs on the quiz (but you cannot get both of these grades).

QY ANSWERS

1. intersection; and; union; or
2. $80°C \pm 40°C$

Compound Inequalities, *And* and *Or*   **233**

Additional Answers

18.

x	−5	−4	−3	−2	−1	0	1	2	3	4	5
y	−22	−17	−12	−7	−2	3	8	13	18	23	28

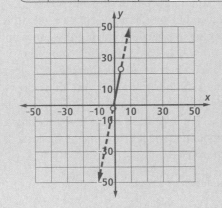

---

4 Wrap-Up

Ongoing Assessment

Instruct students to write their own definition of *compound inequality.* Students should give examples of a compound inequality using *and*, and a compound inequality using *or*. Students should graph both compound inequalities.

Project Update

Project 5, Getting Closer and Closer to Zero, on page 241 relates to the content of this lesson.

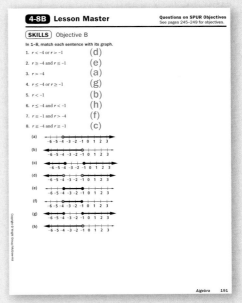

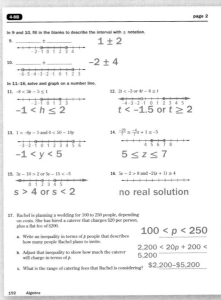

Lesson 4-9

Solving Absolute Value Equations and Inequalities

GOAL

Show a variety of ways to solve equations and inequalities using the expression $|ax + b|$.

SPUR Objectives

E Solve absolute value equations and inequalities involving linear expressions.

N Use graphs to solve absolute value inequalities of the form $|ax + b| < c$ or $|ax + b| > c$.

Materials/Resources

· Lesson Master 4-9A or 4-9B
· Resource Masters 2 and 56–58
· Scientific or graphing calculator

HOMEWORK

Suggestions for Assignment
• Questions 1–28
• Questions 29 and 30 (extra credit)
• Reading Lesson 5-1
• Covering the Ideas 5-1

Local Standards

▶ **BIG IDEA** Inequalities with $|ax + b|$ on one side and a positive number c on the other side can be solved by using the fact that $ax + b$ must equal either c or $-c$.

A school carnival had a "Guess the Number" booth featuring a jar full of pennies. Whoever guessed closest to the actual number of pennies would win a prize. Only the principal knew there were 672 pennies in the jar. When the prize was announced, the winner was off by 9 pennies. How many pennies did the winner guess?

The winning guess deviated from the actual number of pennies by 9. This does not say if the guess was too high or too low. It could have been either $672 + 9 = 681$ or $672 - 9 = 663$. These two possibilities are shown on the number line at the right.

The two numbers 663 and 681 are the solutions of $|n - 672| = 9$. The expression $|n - 672|$ is the absolute deviation of the guess n, from the actual number of pennies, 672. In this case, $|n - 672| = 9$ and the solutions to the equation are 663 and 681.

The equation $|n - 672| = 9$ is of the form $|ax + b| = c$, with $a = 1$, n in place of x, $b = -672$, and $c = 9$. All equations of this form can be solved using what you know about linear equations and compound sentences.

Mental Math

When $a > 0$, determine if the following are positive or negative.

a. $\left(-\frac{a}{2}\right)^2$ positive

b. $(-5a)^3$ negative

c. $-(-0.9a)^2$ negative

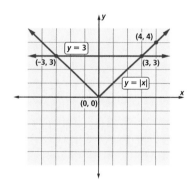

Solving $|x| = a$

Remember that $|x|$ is the distance of x from 0 on a number line. At the right is a table of some pairs of values of x and $|x|$ and the graph of $y = |x|$. Also, the line $y = 3$ is graphed.

x	$\lvert x \rvert$
−4	4
−3	3
−2	2
−1	1
0	0
1	1
2	2
3	3
4	4

Background

This lesson uses the connection between absolute value and distance on the number line in solving absolute value equations and inequalities.

The definition of absolute value provides the basic connection between absolute value and distance: $|x|$ is the distance from x to 0. From this we see the following: $|x| = |-x|$; $|0| = 0$; and $|x| = x$ if x is positive and $|-x| = x$ if x is negative. While the algebraic definition of absolute value is usually given as "$|x| = x$ if x is positive

and $|-x| = x$ if x is negative," the underlying meaning involves distance.

In Chapter 1, $|x - y|$ represented the distance between x and y. Now we take the idea one step further, solving the equation $|x - a| = b$. Because distance cannot be negative, there is no solution if $b < 0$. There is one solution, a, if $b = 0$. And there are two solutions, $a + b$ and $a - b$, if b is greater than 0. We find those solutions by solving a compound inequality of the kind discussed in Lesson 4-8.

(continued on next page)

The following conclusions about the equation $|x| = c$ can be made from the table and graph.

- $|x|$ is never negative, so there are no solutions to $|x| = -10$ or to any other equation of the form $|x| = c$ when c is negative.

- $|x| = 0$ only when $x = 0$.

- $|x| = 3$ has two solutions, 3 and –3. The two solutions can be seen in the table in the rows where $|x| = 3$. Also, the graph of the horizontal line $y = 3$ intersects $y = |x|$ in two points, where $x = 3$ and $x = -3$. Therefore, there are always two solutions to $|x| = c$ when c is positive.

Solutions to $|x| = c$

- When c is positive, then there are two solutions to $|x| = c$, namely c and $-c$.
- When c is negative, then there are no solutions to $|x| = c$.
- When c is zero, then $|x| = 0$ and there is one solution: $x = 0$.

 QY1

▶ **QY1**

Find all the solutions to each equation.
a. $|t| = 15$
b. $|u| = -88.2$
c. $|v| = 0$

Solving $|ax + b| = c$

The above ideas apply to any equation where there is an absolute value of an expression on one side and a number on the other.

GUIDED

Example 1

Consider the graph, which shows $y_1 = |6 - 2x|$ and $y_2 = 18$.
Use the graph and use algebraic properties to solve $|6 - 2x| = 18$.

Solution 1 Use the graph.   (−6, 18); (12, 18)

The points of intersection of the two graphs are ⟶?⟶ and ⟶?⟶.
The x-coordinates of these points of intersection are
⟶?⟶ and ⟶?⟶. −6; 12
The solutions to $|6 - 2x| = 18$ are ⟶?⟶ and ⟶?⟶. −6; 12

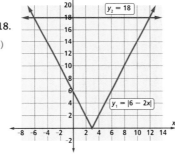

Solution 2 Use algebraic properties.

Ask yourself: What numbers have absolute value 18?
$6 - 2x = $ ⟶?⟶ or $6 - 2x = $ ⟶?⟶ 18; −18
Solve this compound sentence as you did in Lesson 4-8.

18	6	= 2x + ⟶?⟶	or	6	= 2x + ⟶?⟶	−18
⟶?⟶	= 2x	−12	or	⟶?⟶	= 2x	24
⟶?⟶	= x	−6	or	⟶?⟶	= x	12

You should have the same answers from both Solutions 1 and 2.

Solving Absolute Value Equations and Inequalities   **235**

When $b \geq 0$, $|x - a| = b$ is equivalent to $x - a = b$ or $x - a = -b$. These are equivalent to $x = b + a = a + b$ or $x = -b + a = a - b$.

For inequalities, if $b \geq 0$ then $|x| < b$ means the distance from x to 0 is less than b, so $-b < x < b$. The inequality $|x| > b$ means that the distance from x to 0 is greater than b, so either $x < -b$ or $x > b$. A number line can help illustrate these situations, for in one case the inequality sign means

an intersection of rays, and in the other it means a union of rays.

The same ideas are used in the most complex sentences of this lesson. When $c \geq 0$, $|ax + b| < c$ means the distance is constrained, and $-c < ax + b < c$. Similarly, $|ax + b| > c$ means that either $ax + b < -c$ or $ax + b > c$.

4-9

1 Warm-Up

1. Give the two numbers whose distance from 100 is equal to 43.
   57 and 143

2. The answers to Question 1 are the solutions to which of these sentences? **A**
   A $|x - 100| = 43$
   B $|x - 43| = 100$
   C $|x - 43| < 100$
   D $|x - 100| < 43$

3. A box is supposed to hold 100 clips. A store will accept one of these boxes if it holds from 100 to 104 clips.
   a. Write the acceptable number of clips n in a double inequality. $100 \leq n \leq 104$
   b. Write the acceptable number of clips in the form $a \pm b$. 102 ± 2
   c. Write the acceptable number of clips in a sentence involving absolute value. $|n - 102| \leq 2$

2 Teaching

Additional Example

Example 1 Graph $y_1 = |x + 4|$ and $y_2 = 3$. Use the graph and algebraic properties to solve $|x + 4| = 3$.

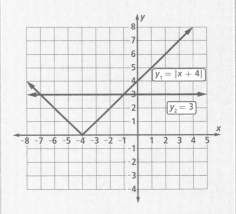

$x + 4 = 3$	or	$x + 4 = -3$
$x = 3 - 4$		$x = -3 - 4$
$x = -1$	or	$x = -7$

4-9

Notes on the Examples

Guided Example 2 This example involves inequalities of the form $|ax + b| < c$. As noted in the background for this lesson, the inequality leads to an intersection of two rays without their endpoints. Graphing provides a powerful reinforcement of the union and intersection of intervals on a number line.

Additional Example

Example 2 Solve $|3x - 6| < 21$.

Think: $|x| < a$ means $-a < x < a$.

So, $-21 < 3x - 6 < 21$.

Add -6 to all parts.

$\underline{\quad ? \quad} < 3x < \underline{\quad ? \quad}$ $-15, 27$

Divide all parts by 3.

$\underline{\quad ? \quad} < x < \underline{\quad ? \quad}$ $-5, 9$

Now decide whether the solutions occur for the values of x that are less or greater than the two values you just found. Use the table or graph to help you decide.

x	$|3x - 6|$	
−9	?	33
−5	?	21
1	?	3
7	?	15
9	?	21
11	?	27

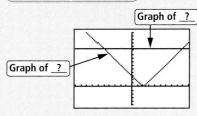

Graph of ?

Graph of ?

$y_1 = |3x - 6|$; $y_2 = 21$
So the solution to $|3x - 6| < 21$ is
_____. $-5 \le x < -9$

Solving $|x| < c$ and $|x| > c$

When c is positive, the two solutions to $|x| = c$ can be represented on a number line. They are the points at a distance c from 0.

$|x| = c$ if and only if $x = c$ or $x = -c$.

The points closer to 0 than c are the solutions to the inequality $|x| < c$. They can be described by the interval $-c < x < c$. For example, the solutions to $|x| < 3$ can be described by the double inequality $-3 < x < 3$.

$|x| < c$ if and only if $-c < x < c$.

The solutions to the inequality $|x| > 3$ are the points whose distance from 0 is greater than 3. The graph of these points has two parts and is described by the compound inequality $x < -3$ or $x > 3$.

$|x| > c$ if and only if $x < -c$ or $x > c$.

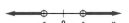

Solutions to $|x| < c$ when c is positive

$|x| < c$ if and only if $-c < x < c$.

Solutions to $|x| > c$ when c is positive

$|x| > c$ if and only if $x < -c$ or $x > c$.

STOP QY2

Solving $|ax + b| < c$, $|ax + b| > c$

To solve these inequalities, think of the simpler inequalities $|x| > c$ and $|x| < c$.

GUIDED

Example 2

Solve $|8x + 24| \le 40$.

Solution 1 Think: $|x| < a$ means $-a < x < a$.

$|8x + 24| \le 40$	Write the inequality.
$-40 \le 8x + 24 \le 40$	$|x| < a$ means $-a < x < a$.
$\underline{\;?\;} \le 8x \le \underline{\;?\;}$	Add -24 to each side. -64; 16
$\underline{\;?\;} \le x \le \underline{\;?\;}$	Divide both sides by 8. -8; 2

▶ **QY2**

Describe all solutions to $|d| > 0.9$ using a compound inequality without the absolute value symbol.

Accommodating the Learner

If students confuse absolute value inequalities involving $>$ or $\ge$ and $<$ or $\le$, present your students with the following ideas.

For all $n \ge 0$ the following are true.

1. The inequality $|x + m| < n$ means that $x + m$ is between $-n$ and n or $-n < x + m < n$.

2. The inequality $|x + m| > n$ means that $x + m$ is NOT between $-n$ and n, inclusive. This means that $x + m < -n$ or $x + m > n$.

Have students model parts 1 and 2 for $|x + m| \le n$ and $|x + m| \ge n$. Now ask students to illustrate with a concrete example.

Solution 2 Use a graph or table.

Ask yourself: When is $|8x + 24|$ below or at 40 on the graph? When is $|8x + 24|$ less than or equal to 40 in the table?

x	$|8x + 24|$
−10	? 56
−8	? 40
−6	? 24
−4	? 8
−2	? 8
0	? 24
2	? 40
4	? 56
6	? 72

$-10 \leq x \leq 10; x \text{ scl} = 1$
$0 \leq y \leq 60; y \text{ scl} = 10$

So the solution to $|8x + 24| \leq 40$ is ___?___ $\leq x \leq$ ___?___. −8; 2

Questions

COVERING THE IDEAS

1. **Multiple Choice** You are asked for the year of the Emancipation Proclamation in the United States on a test. The correct answer is 1863. You guessed g and you were off by 4 years. What equation's solution gives the possible values of g? C

   A $|1863 - 4| = g$ B $|g| = 1863 - 4$

   C $|g - 1863| = 4$ D $|g - 4| = 1863$

2. Determine whether the number is a solution to the equation $60 = |n - 90|$.

   a. 30 yes   b. −30 no   c. 150 yes   d. −150 no

In 3–6, find all solutions in your head.

3. $|A| = 6$ 4. $|B| = -600$ 5. $|C| = 0$ 6. $5|D| = 40$

7. Use the table at the right to solve each sentence.

   a. $|2x - 3| = 7$

   b. $|2x - 3| < 7$

   c. $|2x - 3| > 7$

x	$Y_1 = |2x - 3|$	$Y_2 = 7$
−5	13	7
−4	11	7
−2	7	7
0	3	7
1	1	7
2	1	7
5	7	7
6	9	7

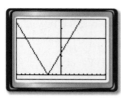

In September 1862, Abraham Lincoln called on the seceded states to return to the Union or have their slaves declared free. When no state returned, he issued the proclamation on January 1, 1863.

Source: Britannica

3. $A = 6$ or $A = -6$
4. no solutions
5. $C = 0$
6. $D = 8$ or $D = -8$
7a. $x = -2$ or $x = 5$
7b. $-2 < x < 5$
7c. $x < -2$ or $x > 5$

Solving Absolute Value Equations and Inequalities   **237**

Accommodating the Learner ⬆

Have students consider the following two ideas.

1. The graph of the inequality $|x - 6| < 4$ can be described as the set of all real numbers that are within 4 units of 6. The solution to the inequality is centered at 6 with a range of 4 units to the right and left, not inclusive.

2. The graph of the inequality $|x - 2| > 3$ can be described as the set of all real numbers that are greater than 3 units

from 2. The solution set to the inequality is centered at 2 but consists of all numbers that are at least 3 units away.

Now have students describe the solution sets to $|x + 3| < 5$ and $|x + 4| > 2$ in similar fashions.

The solution set is centered at −3 but consists of all numbers that are within 5 units of −3. The solution set is centered at −4 and includes all numbers that are at least 2 units away.

---

3 Assignment

Recommended Assignment
- Questions 1–28
- Questions 29 and 30 (extra credit)
- Reading Lesson 5-1
- Covering the Ideas 5-1

Notes on the Questions
Question 1 The Emancipation Proclamation is the presidential proclamation made by Abraham Lincoln on January 1, 1863, about slavery. It is just 661 words long. It is usually thought of as having freed all slaves, but it applied only to states that had seceded from the Union and left slavery untouched in the border states. It expressly exempted parts of the Confederacy that had already come under Northern control. Also, the freedom of slaves depended on a Union military victory. You can access the original document online at www.archives.gov/exhibits/featured_documents/emancipation_proclamation.

Question 4 The incorrect answer $B = 600$ or $B = -600$ comes from confusing this equation with $|B| = 600$.

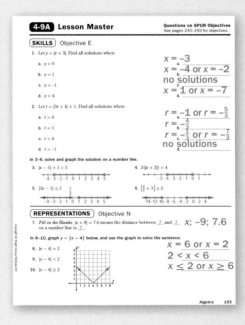

Notes on the Questions

Question 22 This question shows some of the power of graphing to find solutions. Here is an algebraic solution: Add 8 to both sides to get $|3x - 5| < x + 9$. Then use the definition of absolute value to remove the absolute value from the left side to get $3x - 5 > -(x + 9)$ and $3x - 5 < x + 9$. Now solve each inequality separately.

$$3x - 5 > -x - 9 \quad \text{and} \quad 3x - 5 < x + 9$$
$$4x > -4 \quad \text{and} \quad 2x < 14$$
$$x > -1 \quad \text{and} \quad x < 7$$

Combining the inequalities results in $-1 < x < 7$.

8. **Fill in the Blanks** The sentence $|ax + b| = 15$ is equivalent to the compound sentence ___?___ or ___?___.
   $ax + b = 15; ax + b = -15$

9. **Multiple Choice** The green portion of the graph can be used to find the solution to which of the following? C

   A $|x + 5| = 10$ B $|x + 5| \leq 10$

   C $|x + 5| \geq 10$ D $|x + 5| > 10$

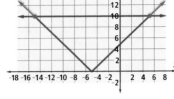

10. **Fill in the Blanks** $|x - 4| = 2.3$ means the distance between ___?___ and ___?___ on a number line is ___?___. x; 4; 2.3

In 11–16, solve the sentence.

11. $|a + 10| = 12$ $a = 2$ or $a = -22$
12. $|42 - 3b| = 45$

13. $|8 - c| < 9$ $-1 < c < 17$ 14. $|10d + 0.3| > 5.6$

15. $\frac{1}{2} \leq \left|\frac{5}{8}g + \frac{3}{4}\right|$ $g \geq -\frac{2}{5}$ or $g \leq -2$ 16. $|h + 11| - 3 \leq 0$

17. Use the graph of $y = |7 - 2x|$ at the right to solve the sentence.

   a. $|7 - 2x| = 9$ $x = -1$ or $x = 8$ b. $|7 - 2x| = 0$ $x = 3.5$

   c. $|7 - 2x| = -2$ no solutions   d. $|7 - 2x| > 5$ $x < 1$ or $x > 6$

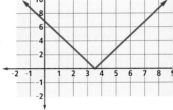

APPLYING THE MATHEMATICS

18. Let $|5x + 2| = m$. Find a value of m so that the absolute value equation has the given number of solutions.

   a. two solutions   b. one solution   c. no solutions

19. A box of Wheat-Os breakfast cereal says that it contains 24 ounces. However, because the machinery that fills the boxes cannot be exactly precise, they can be from $\frac{1}{8}$ ounce below to 1 ounce above this weight. 19a. See margin.

   a. Graph the possible number of ounces of Wheat-Os.

   b. Write an absolute value inequality to show this amount.

20. It is recommended that teenagers get 8.5 ± 0.7 hours of sleep.

   a. Write a double inequality to express the recommended amount of sleep. $7.8 \leq h \leq 9.2$

   b. Write an absolute value inequality for the recommended amount of sleep.

21. Write a single inequality for the graph below. $|x - 15.6| > 3.8$

11.8   19.4

10 11 12 13 14 15 16 17 18 19 20 21 x

12. $b = 29$ or $b = -1$
14. $d < -0.59$ or $d > 0.53$
16. $-14 \leq h \leq -8$
18a. Answers vary. Sample answer: $m = 3$
18b. $m = 0$
18c. Answers vary. Sample answer: $m = -4$
19b. Let x be the amount in the box. $|x - 24.4375| \leq 0.5625$
20b. Let h be the recommended hours of sleep for a teenager. $|h - 8.5| \leq 0.7$

Additional Answers

19a.

$23\frac{7}{8}$

22   23   24   25   26 x

22. At the right is the graph that Zoey used to solve $|3x - 5| - 8 < x + 1$. Use her graph and intersection points to give the solution. $-1 < x < 7$

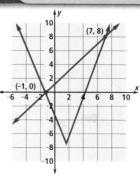

REVIEW

23. Because of traffic, Nina's drive to school takes anywhere from 12 to 20 minutes. (**Lesson 4-8**)

    a. Write an inequality expressing the time it takes Nina to get to school. Let t be the time her commute takes. $12 \le t \le 20$

    b. Write an expression of the form $a \pm d$ to represent the interval in Part a. 16 ± 4

In 24 and 25, solve the compound inequality and graph the solution. (**Lesson 4-8**)

24. $4a - 7 \le 17$ and $14 - a > -5a + 3$ $-\frac{11}{4} < a \le 6$

25. $2(m - 2) \ge 7m + 6$ or $4m - 7 > 30$ $m \le -2$ or $m > \frac{37}{4}$

26. Consider the equations $y = 5x + 9$ and $3x - y = a - 2x$. Find a value of a so that the two lines do not intersect. (**Lesson 4-7**)
Answers vary. Sample answer: $a = 0$

27. Write equations for the horizontal and vertical lines that go through the point $\left(-4.25, \frac{9}{11}\right)$. (**Lesson 4-2**)

28. Gail had $11.50 to spend on snacks for herself and her friends. She wanted to buy as many 85 cent energy bars as she could, in addition to 3 boxes of popcorn at 75 cents each and 3 juice bottles at $1.50 each. Set up an inequality and solve by clearing decimals to find the number of energy bars she can buy.
(**Lesson 3-8**) $0.85x + 3(0.75) + 3(1.50) \le 11.50$; 5 bars

EXPLORATION

29. You learned that absolute value equations can have 0, 1, or 2 solutions.

    a. Write an absolute value inequality whose solution is all real numbers.

    b. Write an absolute value inequality that has no solutions.
    Answers vary. Sample answer: $|4.7t - 867| < -3.5$

30. Solve $|x - 2| = \lceil x \rceil - 2$. $x \ge 2$

24.

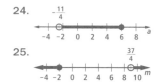

$-\frac{11}{4}$

25.

$\frac{37}{4}$

27. horizontal: $y = \frac{9}{11}$;
    vertical: $x = -4.25$

29a. Answers vary.
Sample answer:
$|3x + 1| \ge 0$

Solving Absolute Value Equations and Inequalities   **239**

4 Wrap-Up

Ongoing Assessment

Show the following four problems. Ask students to fill in the blanks using $=$, $\le$, or $\ge$, and to use concrete examples to illustrate each idea.

1. $|x| + |y| \underset{?}{\quad} |x + y| \ge$

2. $|x| \cdot |y| \underset{?}{\quad} |xy| =$

3. $\left|\frac{x}{y}\right| \underset{?}{\quad} \left|\frac{x}{y}\right|, y \ne 0 =$

4. $|x| - |y| \underset{?}{\quad} |x - y| \le$

Project Update

Project 4, Absolute Value Equations, on page 241 relates to the content of this lesson.

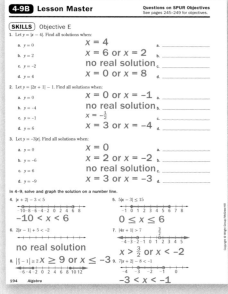

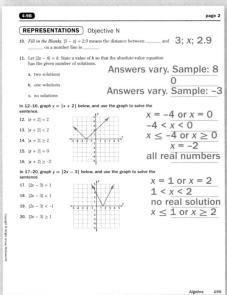

Chapter 4

The projects relate to the content of the lessons of this chapter as follows:

Project	Lesson(s)
1	4-5
2	4-3
3	4-3
4	4-9
5	4-8

1 Growing Trees

Rather than accept examples that students make up, ask students to do a little research and come up with examples that can be found in the real world. Suggest they look at newspaper or magazine articles, search the Internet, or even ask their parents to help. Certainly their parents have had the opportunity to make comparisons as consumers when trying to make a choice between competing services.

2 Hybrid Cars

Remind students they can use their graphing calculators to help solve this problem. They should set Y1 equal to the cost of owning and operating car A and set Y2 equal to the cost of owning and operating car B. The key is to choose a proper window for graphing. Tell students to consider carefully the possible range values when choosing the window. They can use the CALC command followed by the INTERSECT command to find out when the cost of operating both cars would be the same. When graphing by hand, choosing an appropriate scale for the vertical axis is very important if students expect to be able to obtain a meaningful result.

Chapter 4 Projects

1 Growing Trees

In Lesson 4-5 you read about a maple tree which, although initially smaller, grew faster than a beech tree and overtook it in height. Give three other real-world examples whose graphs would result in intersecting lines. Make sure that at least one example is meaningful for negative values of the independent variable.

2 Hybrid Cars

Suppose car A costs $20,000 and gets 25 miles per gallon of gas. Suppose a hybrid car B costs $25,000 but gets 39 miles per gallon. Suppose gas costs an average of $2.75 per gallon and you drive 12,000 miles per year.

a. Plot the cost of owning and operating each car on the same graph, with years of ownership along the x-axis.

b. Use an inequality to determine how long it will take for the cost of owning car A to overtake the cost of owning car B. Check your answer with your graph from Part a.

3 Planning Your Trip

Suppose you want to take a trip to Washington, D.C. You can either drive or fly. If you fly, the airline requires you to be at the airport two hours before your departure time and it will take you half an hour to pick up your luggage once you arrive at your destination. Let W = the distance from your home to Washington. The plane averages 500 miles per hour, and you drive at an

average speed of 60 miles per hour. Write expressions in terms of W for your travel time by car and your travel time (including waiting time) by plane. What is the farthest possible distance that you could live from Washington and still get there faster by car? Where could you live for this to be the case? Illustrate on a map similar to the one above.

Project Rubric

Advanced	Student correctly provides all of the details asked for in the project as well as additional correct independent conclusions.
Proficient	Student correctly provides all of the details asked for in the project.
Partially proficient	Student correctly provides some of the details asked for in the project or provides all details with some inaccuracies.
Not proficient	Student correctly provides few of the details asked for in the project or provides all details with many inaccuracies.
No attempt	Student makes little or no attempt to complete the project.

4 **Absolute Value Equations**

a. Solve the equation $|5x + 3| = 2x - 8$ by any method.

b. Generalize Part a by solving the equation $|mx + n| = 2x - 8$ for x.

c. Find values of m and n for which the equation of Part b has infinitely many solutions. Describe those solutions.

d. Find values of m and n for which the equation of Part b has no solution.

5 **Getting Closer and Closer to Zero**

Begin with the expression $\frac{1}{x}$. Find the value of the expression when $x = 1, 0.1, 0.01, 0.001, 0.0001,$ and 0.00001.

a. **Fill in the Blank** As x gets closer to zero, the value of the expression $\frac{1}{x}$ gets ___?___.

b. As a ray, represent the values that the expression can take when x is in the interval $0 < x \le 1$.

c. Find the value of the expression when $x = -1, -0.1, -0.01, -0.001, -0.0001,$ and -0.00001. As a pair of rays, represent the values that the expression can take when x is in the interval $-1 \le x < 0$ or $0 < x \le 1$.

3 **Planning Your Trip**

Ask students to modify this problem by figuring out how far they actually live from Washington, D.C., and how far they live from the nearest airport that flies to Washington, D.C. Students should figure out how long it would take them to drive if they averaged 60 mph and how long it would take to fly at 500 mph including the drive time to the airport at 60 mph. How many 10-hour driving days would it take for them to reach Washington, D.C., if they chose to drive?

4 **Absolute Value Equations**

Students will often assume that the values of m and n cannot be 2 and -8, respectively. This is a good time to discuss with students the idea of not excluding any possible solutions simply because there is something in the problem that makes them "think" they should not use those numbers. 2 and -8 are choices to be considered and students should not neglect them. Illustrate this idea with a second example which is different from the one found in this project.

5 **Getting Closer and Closer to Zero**

Ask students to determine the values that $\frac{1}{x}$ *cannot* take on when $-1 \le x \le 1$. They should write an inequality representing that set of numbers. Students should also explain in writing why that set of numbers is excluded.

Notes

_____   _____
_____   _____
_____   _____
_____   _____
_____   _____
_____   _____
_____   _____
_____   _____

Chapter 4

Summary and Vocabulary

Summary and Vocabulary

The Summary gives an overview of the entire chapter and provides an opportunity for students to consider the material as a whole. Thus, the Summary can be used to help students relate and unify the concepts presented in the chapter.

Terms and symbols are listed by lesson to provide a checklist of concepts that students must know. Emphasize to students that they should read the vocabulary list carefully before starting the Self-Test on the next page. If students do not understand the meaning of a term, they should refer back to the indicated lesson.

○ Equations involving percents may be written in the form $p \cdot q = r$, where p is the decimal form of the percent, q is the initial quantity, and r is the resulting quantity. The equation can then be solved as you would solve any other equation.

○ Linear sentences are equivalent to sentences of the forms $ax + b = cx + d$ and $ax + b < cx + d$. Graphs, tables, CAS, and algebraic processes all provide ways of solving these sentences. The same algebraic processes and a CAS enable you to solve many formulas for one of their variables.

○ Some sentences like $12 - 30x = -3(10x - 4)$ are true for all real numbers. When solving them, the same number appears on both sides of the equal sign. Other sentences like $2y + 5 = 2y - 3$ have no solution. When solving them, an equation with different numbers on both sides of the equal sign will result.

○ The union and intersection of sets help to describe situations with *or* and *and,* respectively. They can be used to solve compound inequalities.

○ Graphs and algebraic processes are also used to find the solution set for absolute value equations and absolute value inequalities.

○ All of this sentence-solving is for a purpose. Many real situations lead to linear equations or inequalities, and many common formulas involve linear expressions.

Vocabulary

4-1
percent

4-2
horizontal line, $y = k$
vertical line, $x = h$

4-4
general linear equation,
    $ax + b = cx + d$

4-7
Celsius scale
centigrade scale
Fahrenheit scale
input
output
equivalent formulas

4-8
compound sentence
intersection
union
± notation

Chapter 4 — Self-Test

Take this test as you would take a test in class. You will need a calculator. Then use the Selected Answers section in the back of the book to check your work.

1. Gloria found a prom dress at a local shop. The price tag said $262, but Gloria would have to pay 9% sales tax. She found the same dress for $285 online with no tax. There was no charge for shipping. Find out whether the dress costs less in the shop or online. Explain your process. **See margin.**

2. **Fill in the Blank** To solve the equation $-8t + 73 = -49 + 4t$, an effective first step is to add __?__ to each side. **See margin.**

3. By what number can each side of $\frac{7}{8}x - \frac{2}{5} = 6 - \frac{1}{8}x$ be multiplied to clear the fractions? **See margin.**

In 4–10, solve each sentence. Show your work.
4–10. See margin.

4. $-5m + 21 = 6m - 56$

5. $0.73v + 37.9 = 16 - v$

6. $\frac{x}{4} + \frac{3}{5} = \frac{x}{2}$

7. $-2(3 - d) > 3(2d - 3)$

8. $-29 < 7.5p - 44 \le 28$

9. $|2x - 3| = 21$

10. $8(4 - 2n) = -16n + 16$

11. Suppose you have graphed Y_1 and Y_2 and the result is the graph below.

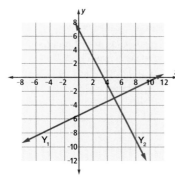

a. Estimate the x-value that is the solution to $Y_1 = Y_2$. $x \approx 5$

b. Write an inequality using x whose solutions tell when $Y_1 \ge Y_2$. $x \ge 5$

12. Silvia is offered two jobs selling air time for a local cable television station. From TurboTV she could earn a $30,000 annual salary plus 5% of the amount of her sales. Sparkle Cable offered Silvia a $25,000 annual salary plus 8% of her sales.

a. Complete the table.

Sales	Total Salary from TurboTV	Total Salary from Sparkle Cable
$25,000	$31,250	? $27,000
$50,000	? $32,500	$29,000
$75,000	? $33,750	? $31,000
$100,000	? $35,000	? $33,000
$125,000	? $36,250	? $35,000
$150,000	? $37,500	? $37,000
$175,000	$38,750	? $39,000

b. Use the table to find for what sales amount Silvia will earn more money working for Sparkle Cable. Write the answer as an inequality. $s \ge \$175,000$

c. In her current job, Silvia's sales average $83,000 per year. If this amount of sales were to continue, which job do you think Silvia should take? Explain your reasoning. **TurboTV, because she would earn more there**

13. Graph in the coordinate plane the solution to $4 - |x + 1| > -2$. **See margin.**

Additional Answers

1. The dress is cheaper online because it costs $262 + $262(0.09) = $285.58 in the store and $285 < $285.58.

2. Answers vary. Sample answer: 8t, since it would isolate the variable on one side.

3. Answers vary. Sample answer: 40

4. $21 = 11m - 56$; $77 = 11m$; $7 = m$

5. $1.73v + 37.9 = 16$; $1.73v = -21.9$; $v \approx -12.659$

6. $\frac{3}{5} = \frac{x}{4}$; $\frac{12}{5} = x = 2.4$

7. $-6 + 2d > 6d - 9$; $-6 > 4d - 9$; $3 > 4d$; $\frac{3}{4} > d$ or $d < \frac{3}{4}$

8. $15 < 7.5p \le 72$; $2 < p \le 9.6$

9. $2x - 3 = 21$ or $2x - 3 = -21$; $2x = 24$ or $2x = -18$; $x = 12$ or $x = -9$

10. $32 - 16n = -16n + 16$; $32 + 0n = 16$; $32 = -16$; no solutions

---

Self-Test

For the development of mathematical competence, feedback and correction, along with the opportunity for practice, are necessary. The Self-Test provides the opportunity for feedback and correction; the Chapter Review provides additional opportunities for practice. We cannot overemphasize the importance of these end-of-chapter materials. It is at this point that the material gels for many students, allowing them to solidify skills and understanding. In general, student performance should improve after completing these pages.

Assign the Self-Test as a one-night assignment. Worked-out solutions for all questions are in the Selected Answers section of the student book. Encourage students to take the Self-Test honestly, grade themselves, and then be prepared to discuss the test in class.

Advise students to pay special attention to those Chapter Review questions (pages 245–249) that correspond to the questions they missed on the Self-Test.

13.

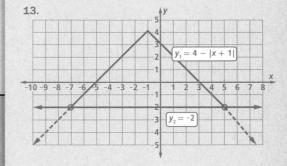

Self-Test

Additional Answers

15. $-6x = -84 - 7y; x = 14 + \frac{7}{6}y$

16. There is no solution, because the lines are parallel but not the same.

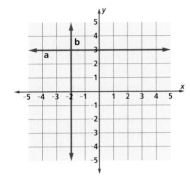

17b. 1996, which tells us that the deviation was smallest that year

17c. Answers vary. Sample answer: bad; because they would rather produce more ice cream

18a. $\frac{9}{10}e - 9 = e - 18$; $9 = \frac{1}{10}e$; $e = 90$

18b. $\frac{9}{10}e = \frac{9}{10}(90) = 81$ strokes

19a. Let n be the number of CDs produced.
$452.54 + 5.25n$

19b. $17.99n$

19c. $17.99n > 452.54 + 5.25n$; $12.74n > 452.54$; $n > 35.52$; 36 CDs or more

---

14. Give an equation for each of the lines in the graph. a. $y = 3$ b. $x = -2$

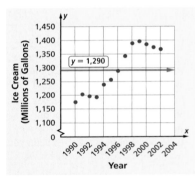

15. Solve $-6x + 7y = -84$ for x. **See margin.**

16. Use a graphing calculator to determine if there is or is not a solution to $-7.4(x - 3) = 1.2x + 8.1 - 2(4.3x - 8.05)$. Explain how the graph supports your conclusion. **See margin.**

17. The graph below gives the annual consumption of ice cream in the United States from 1990 to 2002 in millions of dollars. The horizontal line shows the mean ice cream consumption, which was approximately 1,290 million gallons.

Source: U.S. Dept. of Agriculture Economic Research Service

a. Which year had the greatest absolute deviation from the mean? **1990**

b. Which year's ice cream consumption was closest to the mean? What does that tell you about the deviation for that year? **See margin.**

c. In the last four years of the data, the consumption levels have been getting closer to the mean. Is this situation good or bad for ice cream producers? Why or why not? **See margin.**

18. At Las Sendas Golf Club, Joe's handicap is 9 while Elena's is 18. To level the playing field, the players subtract their handicaps from their stroke totals at the end of the round. Suppose Joe took $\frac{9}{10}$ as many shots as Elena but they ended up with the same score after subtracting their handicaps.

a. How many strokes did Elena take?

b. How many strokes did Joe take?

c. What were their scores with the handicaps? $e - 18 = 90 - 18 = 72$
18a–b. **See margin.**

19. Chandler has a company that produces and sells CDs. He paid $452.54 in equipment fees, and it costs him $5.25 to produce each CD. He charges customers $17.99 per CD. 19a–c. **See margin.**

a. Write an expression describing Chandler's expenditure based on the number of CDs produced.

b. Write an expression describing Chandler's revenue based on the number of CDs sold.

c. How many CDs does Chandler need to sell to make a profit?

20. 30% of what number is 7? $0.3 \cdot x = 7$; so $x = \frac{7}{0.3} = 23\frac{1}{3}$

Chapter Review

SKILLS
PROPERTIES
USES
REPRESENTATIONS

SKILLS Procedures used to get answers

OBJECTIVE A Solve and check equations of the form $ax + b = cx + d$. (Lesson 4-4)
1–8. See margin.
In 1–8, solve the equation and check your solution.

1. $14 + 8A = 4A - 10$ 2. $-5a + 9 = 5a$

3. $3n = n + 7 + 9n$ 4. $8x - 21.25 = -0.5x$

5. $4f = 2f - 7(5 - 6f)$ 6. $7(2 - y) = 3(y + 2)$

7. $\frac{1}{3}a - 1 = 3a$ 8. $\frac{x}{2} + \frac{x}{5} + 20 = x$

OBJECTIVE B Solve and check compound inequalities of the form $ax + b < cx + d$. (Lessons 4-5, 4-8)

In 9 and 10, solve and check the inequality.

9. $14w + 64 \geq 17w - 323$ $w \leq 129$

10. $4(5 + 2t) < 9(2 + t)$ $t > 2$

In 11–16, solve and graph all solutions on a number line. 11–16. See margin for graphs.

11. $\frac{7}{10}n + \frac{2}{5} > -\frac{1}{2}n - \frac{12}{5}$ $n > -\frac{7}{3}$

12. $0.42h + 3 \leq 0.6h - 0.78$ $h \geq 21$

13. $3p + 4 < 31$ and $8p - 12 \geq 7p - 11$ $1 \leq p < 9$

14. $5s - 7 > 2.5$ or $8 \leq s + 10$ $s \geq -2$

15. $-1 < 4x + 7 < 23$ $-2 < x < 4$

16. $22 \geq 2d - 40 > -55$ $-7.5 < d \leq 31$

OBJECTIVE C Find equivalent forms of formulas and equations. (Lesson 4-7)
17–22. See margin.
In 17–22, solve the equation for the stated variable.

17. $A = \frac{1}{2}ap$ for p

18. $V = \ell wh$ for h

19. $S = 2\pi r^2 + 2\pi rh$ for h

20. $k = \frac{s}{w}$ for w

21. $6x + 3y = 21$ for y

22. $5y - 7x = 25$ for y

PROPERTIES The principles behind the mathematics

OBJECTIVE D Solve percent problems. (Lesson 4-1)

23. How much tax is there on a \$32 item if the tax rate is 7.5%?   \$2.40

24. According to the Census Bureau about 2% of people in the United States are age 85 or older. In a town of 35,000, about how many people would be expected to be at least 85 years old?   700 people

25. To the nearest percent, 10 is what percent of 23?   43%

26. 47 is what percent of 30? $156\frac{2}{3}$%, or about 156.7%

27. 85% of what number is 170?   200

28. To the nearest whole number, 6.3% of what number is 7?   111

OBJECTIVE E Solve absolute value equations and inequalities involving linear expressions. (Lesson 4-9)

In 29–31, suppose $|x - 14| = n$.   29–31. See margin.

29. Find all solutions when $n = 2$.

30. Find all solutions when $n = 0$.

31. Find all solutions when $n = -5$.

In 32–34, translate the given English sentence into a mathematical sentence. Then graph the solutions on a number line.   32–34. See margin.

32. The distance between x and 4 is less than 20.

33. Liseli's dog will only go outside when the temperature is within 15 degrees of 60 degrees Fahrenheit.

34. In a math competition, Howard missed the winning score of 180 points by more than 5 points.

Chapter Review   **245**

Chapter Review

The main objectives for the chapter are organized in the Chapter Review under the four types of understanding this book promotes—Skills, Properties, Uses, and Representations.

Whereas end-of-chapter material may be considered optional in some texts, in *UCSMP Algebra* we have selected these objectives and questions with the expectation that they will be covered. Students should be able to answer these questions with about 85% accuracy after studying the chapter.

You may assign these questions over a single night to help students prepare for a test the next day, or you may assign the questions over a two-day period. If you work the questions over two days, then we recommend assigning the *evens* for homework the first night so that students get feedback in class the next day, and then assigning the *odds* the night before the test because the answers are provided to the odd-numbered questions in the Selected Answers at the back of the book.

It is effective to ask students which questions they still do not understand and use the day as a total class discussion of the material that the class finds most difficult.

Resources

• Assessment Resources: Chapter 4 Test, Forms A–D; Chapter 4 Test, Cumulative Form

30. $x = 14$

31. no solution

32. $|x - 4| < 20$

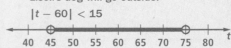

33. Let t be the temperatures at which Liseli's dog will go outside.

$|t - 60| < 15$

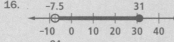

34. Let p be the number of points.

$|p - 180| > 5$

Howard did not win, so his score cannot be greater than 175.

Additional Answers

1. $A = -6$

2. $a = \frac{9}{10}$

3. $n = -1$

4. $x = 2.5$

5. $f = \frac{7}{8}$

6. $y = 0.8$

7. $a = -\frac{3}{8}$

8. $x = \frac{200}{3}$

11.

12.

13.

14.

15.

16.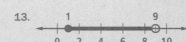

17. $p = \frac{2A}{a}$

18. $h = \frac{V}{\ell w}$

19. $h = \frac{S}{2\pi r} - r$

20. $w = \frac{s}{k}$

21. $y = 7 - 2x$

22. $y = 5 + \frac{7}{5}x$

29. $x = 12$ or $x = 16$

Chapter 4 Review

Additional Answers

37a. Multiplication Property of Equality

37b. Distributive Property

37c. Addition Property of Equality

37d. Addition Property of Equality

37e. Multiplication Property of Equality or Division Property of Equality

38a. Addition Property of Inequality

38b. Addition Property of Inequality

38c. Multiplication Property of Inequality or Division Property of Inequality

39a. She subtracted $90n$ from the left side of the equation but added $90n$ to the right side.

40. The two sides are equivalent because of the Distributive Property.

41. no solutions

42. all real numbers

43. If you subtract x from both sides, you get $5 > 6$, which is never true.

44a. After n months, Sam will have $1,850 + 25n$ dollars and Diego will have $2,000 + 20n$ dollars.

45b. It does not matter; they cost the same.

45c. at 15 mi

OBJECTIVE F Apply and recognize Addition and Multiplication Properties of Equality and Inequality when solving linear sentences. (Lessons 4-4, 4-5)

35b. $x = -5$

35. Consider the equation $3x + 2 = 5x + 12$.

   a. Solve the equation by first adding $-5x$ to each side. $x = -5$

   b. Solve by first adding $-3x$ to each side.

   c. Compare your answers to Parts a and b. They are the same.

36. Consider the inequality $2a + 3 < 5a - 6$.

   a. Solve the inequality by first adding $-5a$ to each side. 36a–b. $a > 3$

   b. Solve by first adding $-2a$ to each side.

   c. How are your answers to Parts a and b related? They are the same.

In 37 and 38, a sentence is solved. State the property that justifies each step.

37. $\frac{2}{3}x - 4 = \frac{1}{6}x + 2$ See margin.

   a. $6\left(\frac{2}{3}x - 4\right) = 6\left(\frac{1}{6}x + 2\right)$

   b. $6 \cdot \frac{2}{3}x - 6 \cdot 4 = 6 \cdot \frac{1}{6}x + 6 \cdot 2$
      $4x - 24 = x + 12$

   c. $3x - 24 = 12$

   d. $3x = 36$

   e. $x = 12$

38. $-3y + 7 \geq 8y - 5$ See margin.

   a. $-3y + 12 \geq 8y$

   b. $12 \geq 11y$

   c. $\frac{12}{11} \geq y$

39. Alexis is trying to solve the equation $100n + 10 = -90n + 4$. After the first step the resulting equation was $10n + 10 = 4$.
   39a. See margin.

   a. Identify the mistake Alexis made.

   b. Correct the mistake and solve the equation. $190n + 10 = 4$; $n = -\frac{3}{95}$

OBJECTIVE G Recognize when sentences have no solution or every real number as a solution. (Lesson 4-6)

40–43. See margin.

40. Explain why any real number is a solution to the equation $8y - 30 = 4(2y - 7.5)$.

41. Find all the solutions to the equation $t - t = 1$.

42. Find all solutions to the equation $t - t = 0$.

43. Explain why no real number is a solution to $x + 5 > x + 6$.

USES Applications of mathematics in real-world situations

OBJECTIVE H Use linear equations and inequalities of the form $ax + b = cx + d$ or $ax + b < cx + d$ to solve real-world problems. (Lessons 4-4, 4-5)

44. Sam has $1,850 in her savings account and adds $25 each month. Diego has $2,000 in his account and adds $20 each month.

   a. How much will be in each account after n months? See margin.

   b. After how many months of saving will they have the same amount in their accounts? 30 mo

45. Taxi, Inc., charges a fee of $5 for each ride and an additional $0.75 for each mile you travel. Calling Cabs charges an initial fee of $3.50 and an additional $0.85 per mile.
   45b–c. See margin.

   a. If you are going to take a cab 10 miles, which company should you use? Calling Cabs

   b. If you are going to take a cab 15 miles, which company should you use?

   c. What is the break-even point?

46. Kim has $15 and is saving $9 per week. Alberto has $100 and is spending $8 per week.

    a. Let x = the number of weeks that have passed. Write a linear inequality that can be used to find out when Kim will have more money than Alberto. See margin.

    b. Solve the inequality. $x > 5$

47. A sign-making company, Signs-R-We, charges a set-up art fee of $50 plus an additional $1.50 for each sign printed. Their competitor Sign-Me-Up waives the art fee but charges $3.50 per sign. What is the largest number of signs you could print so that Sign-Me-Up would be a better deal than Signs-R-We? 24 signs

---

OBJECTIVE I Use tables and graphs to solve real-world problems involving linear situations. (Lessons 4-2, 4-3) 48c–d. See margin.

48. Two music downloading Web sites offer music discounts. Site 1 has a $19.95 membership fee and charges $0.99 per download. Site 2 charges $14.95 to join and $1.03 per download.

    a. Copy and complete the table below.

Number of Downloads	Charges	
	Site 1	Site 2
2	? $21.93	? $17.01
4	? $23.91	? $19.07
6	? $25.89	? $21.13
8	? $27.87	? $23.19
10	? $29.85	? $25.25

    b. How many downloads must you buy for the charges of the two sites to be equal? 125 downloads

    c. When is the price of Site 1 better?

    d. When is the price of Site 2 better?

49. Sherita was investigating the number of baby carrots that came pre-packaged. She bought ten bags and recorded her data in a table.

Bag Number	Number of Carrots
1	30
2	35
3	27
4	32
5	39
6	29
7	31
8	35
9	32
10	29

    a. Make a dot plot of these data. See margin.

    b. Determine the mean amount of carrots per bag and draw the horizontal line representing the mean on your plot. mean = 31.9

    c. Which bag(s) is closest to the mean? bags 4 and 9

    d. Which bag has the greatest absolute deviation from the mean? bag 5

50. Michael is considering two different sales positions. Rent-A-Vehicle would pay a total salary of $1,100 per month plus a 6% sales commission. Borrow-Our-Car would pay a total salary of $900 plus an 8% commission.

    a. Copy and complete the table below.

Sales	Rent-A-Vehicle	Borrow-Our-Car
$0	$1,100	$900
$5,000	? $1,400	? $1,300
$10,000	? $1,700	? $1,700
$15,000	? $2,000	? $2,100
$20,000	? $2,300	? $2,500
$25,000	? $2,600	$2,900
$30,000	$2,900	? $3,300

    b. For what amounts of sales will Borrow-Our-Car pay a greater total salary? all sales over $10,000

Additional Answers

46a. Kim will have more money than Alberto when $15 + 9x > 100 - 8x$.

48c. for more than 125 downloads

48d. for less than 125 downloads

49a–b.

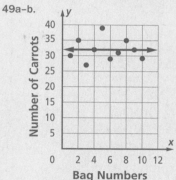

Chapter 4 Review

54.

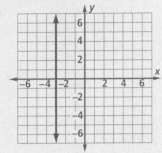

55.

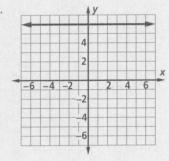

59b.

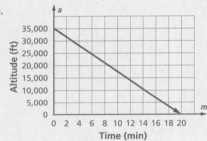

OBJECTIVE J Solve real-world problems involving percents. (Lesson 4-1)

51. According to the *World Almanac and Book of Facts,* there were approximately 217,000 women serving in the Armed Forces of the United States in 2004, accounting for about 15% of total military personnel. In all, about how many persons are serving in the Armed Forces? **1,447,000**

52. According to the *Pew Internet & American Life Project,* 17% of United States households used online banking in 2000. In 2005, 35% of U.S. households used online banking. If there were 98,000,000 U.S. households in both years, how many more households used online banking in 2005 than in 2000? **17,640,000 households**

53. After a 30% discount, a mattress sold for $896. What was its price before the discount? **$1,280**

REPRESENTATIONS Pictures, graphs, or objects that illustrate concepts

OBJECTIVE K Graph horizontal and vertical lines. (Lesson 4-2)

In 54 and 55, graph the points in the coordinate plane satisfying each equation. **54–55. See margin.**

54. $x = -3$ 55. $y = 6$

56. **True or False** The graph of all points in the coordinate plane satisfying $y = 23$ is a horizontal line. **true**

57. Write an equation for the line containing the points (5, 12), (5, –3), and (5, –15). **$x = 5$**

58. Write an equation for the line in the graph below. **$x = 3$**

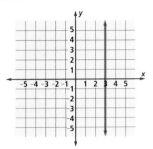

OBJECTIVE L Use graphs to solve problems involving linear equations. (Lesson 4-3)

59. An airplane is cruising at 35,000 feet when it begins its descent into an airport at 1,750 feet per minute. **59b. See margin.**

a. Write an equation that relates the plane's altitude a in feet and the time m in minutes since it started to descend.

b. Graph your equation from Part a.

c. Use the graph to determine how many minutes it will take to land. **20 min**

59a. $a = 35,000 - 1,750m$

In 60 and 61, lines ℓ, m, and n are graphed below. Line ℓ has equation $y = -\frac{8}{7}x + 8$, line m has equation $y = -5 - x$, and line n has equation $y = 2x - 5$.

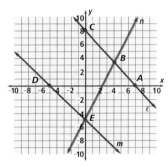

62.

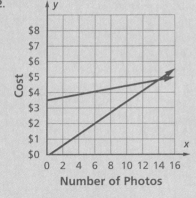

Number of Photos

For 14 photos, the cost is the same.

63c.

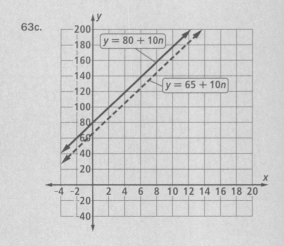

$y = 80 + 10n$

$y = 65 + 10n$

60. a. Fill in the blank, then answer the question. The solution to the equation $2x - 5 = -\frac{8}{7}x + 8$ is the __?__-coordinate of which named point? x; B

    b. Estimate a solution to the equation in Part a. $x \approx 4$

61. Suppose $E = (0, -5)$. Use this information to solve the inequality $2x - 5 \le -5 - x$.
    $x \le 0$

62. Picture Perfect will develop a roll of film for $0.35 per photo with no developing charge. You Oughta Be In Pictures charges $0.10 per photo plus a $3.50 developing charge. Make a graph to determine the break-even point.
    See margin.

OBJECTIVE M Use graphs to model sentences that have no solution or every real number as a solution. (Lesson 4-6)

63. Nate starts July with $80 and decides to mow lawns for $10 per lawn to earn money. His friend Owen starts with $65 and also decides to mow lawns for $10 per lawn. 63c. See margin.

    a. How much money will Nathan have after mowing n lawns? $80 + 10n$ dollars

    b. How much money will Owen have after mowing n lawns? $65 + 10n$ dollars

    c. Let y equal each of your expressions in Parts a and b. Graph the two equations.

    d. Using your graph, when will Owen have as much money as Nate? never

In 64–66, solve by letting y equal each side of the sentence and by using a graph. 64–66. See margin.

64. $4(h - 7) + 6h < 2(5h - 4)$

65. $-7g + 4 = 5 - 7g$

66. $2.5(4.6p - 4) \ge 10p + \frac{3}{2}(p + 20)$

OBJECTIVE N Use graphs to solve absolute value inequalities of the form $|ax + b| < c$ or $|ax + b| > c$. (Lesson 4-9)

67. The air (heat or cooling) in Peggy's house turns on when the temperature varies 5 degrees or more from 70°F.

    a. On a number line, graph the temperatures corresponding to when the air is on. See margin.

    b. Using t for temperature, write inequalities describing the temperatures graphed in Part a.
    $t \le 65$ or $t \ge 75$

68. Use the graph of $y = |2x - 7|$ and $y = 4$ below to solve each of the following.

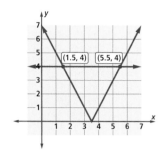

a. $|2x - 7| = 4$ $x = 1.5$ or $x = 5.5$

b. $|2x - 7| > 4$ $x < 1.5$ or $x > 5.5$

c. $|2x - 7| \le 4$ $1.5 \le x \le 5.5$

Assessment

Evaluation The *Assessment Resources* provide four forms of the Chapter 4 Test. Forms A and B present parallel versions of a short-answer format. Form C consists of four to six short-response questions that cover the SPUR objectives from Chapter 4. Form D offers performance assessment that covers a subset (or even just one) of the SPUR objectives for the chapter.

Feedback After students have taken the test for Chapter 4 and you have scored the results, return the tests to students for discussion. Class discussion on the questions that caused trouble for most students can be very effective in identifying and clarifying misunderstandings. You might want to have them note the items they missed and work either in groups or at home to correct them. It is important for students to receive feedback on every chapter test, and we recommend that students see and correct their mistakes before proceeding too far into the next chapter.

Additional Answers

66. no solution

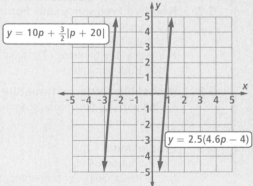

67a.

Additional Answers

64.
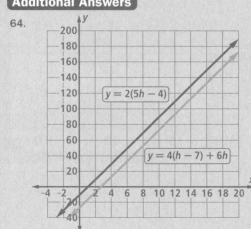

65. no solution
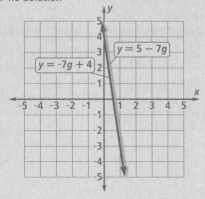

Chapter Overview

		Local Standards	Pacing (in days)		
			Average	Advanced	Block
5-1	**Multiplication of Algebraic Fractions** **A** Multiply and simplify algebraic fractions.		1	1	0.5
5-2	**Division of Algebraic Fractions** **B** Divide algebraic fractions.		1	0.5	0.5
5-3	**Rates** **B** Divide algebraic fractions. **E** Use rates in real situations.		1	1	0.5
5-4	**Multiplying and Dividing Rates** **F** Convert units and use reciprocal rates in real situations.		1	0.5	0.5
	QUIZ 1		0.5	0.5	0.25
5-5	**Ratios** **G** Use ratios to compare two quantities.		1	0.5	0.75
5-6	**Probability Distributions** **H** Calculate relative frequencies and probabilities in situations with a finite number of equally likely outcomes.		1	1	0.5
5-7	**Relative Frequency and Percentiles** **H** Calculate relative frequencies and probabilities in situations with a finite number of equally likely outcomes. **K** Interpret the meaning of percentile for benchmarks of 10th, 25th, 50th, 75th, and 90th percentiles.		1	1	0.5
5-8	**Probability Without Counting** **I** Find probabilities involving geometric regions.		1	0.5	0.5
	QUIZ 2		0.5	0.5	0.25
5-9	**Proportions** **C** Solve proportions. **D** Use the language of proportions and the Means-Extremes Property. **J** Solve problems involving proportions in real situations.		1	1	0.75
5-10	**Similar Figures** **J** Solve problems involving proportions in real situations. **L** Find lengths and ratios of similitude in similar figures.		1	1	0.5
	Self-Test		1	1	0.5
	Chapter Review		2	2	1
	Test		1	1	0.5
	TOTAL		15	13	8.0

Differentiated Options Universal Access

	Accommodating the Learner	Vocabulary Development	Ongoing Assessment	Materials
5-1	p. 253		written, p. 257	scientific or graphing calculator, Computer Algebra System (CAS)
5-2	pp. 259, 260	p. 259	group, p. 262	scientific or graphing calculator
5-3	pp. 264, 265		written, p. 268	scientific or graphing calculator
5-4	pp. 270, 272	p. 271	group, p. 273	scientific or graphing calculator
5-5	pp. 276, 277		oral, p. 279	scientific or graphing calculator; ruler, meter stick, or tape measure
5-6	pp. 282, 283	p. 281	group, p. 288	scientific or graphing calculator
5-7	pp. 291, 292	p. 290	oral, p. 295	graphing calculator
5-8	pp. 297, 298		oral, p. 300	scientific or graphing calculator; compass; colored pencils, crayons, or markers
5-9	pp. 303, 304	p. 302	written, p. 307	scientific or graphing calculator; large bowl; markers; pennies, beans, or uncooked popcorn
5-10	pp. 310, 311		written, p. 314	scientific or graphing calculator, ruler

Objectives

	Lessons	Self-Test Questions	Chapter Review Questions
Skills			
A Multiply and simplify algebraic fractions.	5-1	1, 4	1–6
B Divide algebraic fractions.	5-2, 5-3	2, 3, 19	7–12
C Solve proportions.	5-9	5–7	13–17
Properties			
D Use the language of proportions and the Means-Extremes Property.	5-9	8	18–21
Uses			
E Use rates in real situations.	5-3	9, 14	22–27
F Convert units and use reciprocal rates in real situations.	5-4	11, 15	28–32
G Use ratios to compare two quantities.	5-5	20	33–39
H Calculate relative frequencies and probabilities in situations with a finite number of equally likely outcomes.	5-6, 5-7	10, 16–18	40–44
I Find probabilities involving geometric regions.	5-8	13, 22	45–47
J Solve problems involving proportions in real situations.	5-9, 5-10	21, 23	48–51
K Interpret the meaning of percentile for benchmarks of 10th, 25th, 50th, 75th, and 90th percentiles.	5-7	24	52–55
Representations			
L Find lengths and ratios of similitude in similar figures.	5-10	12	56–59

Resource Masters Chapter 5

Resource Master 1, Graph Paper (page 2), can be used with Lessons 5-2 and 5-6.
Resource Master 2, Four-Quadrant Graph Paper (page 3), can be used with Lessons 5-7 and 5-10.
Resource Master 3, Centimeter Grid (page 4), can be used with Lesson 5-1.

Resource Master 60 Lesson 5-1
Resource Master 59 Lesson 5-1

Warm-Up
Consider the multiplication $\frac{2}{5} \cdot \frac{3}{4}$.
1. Give the product as a fraction and verify your answer using decimals.
2. Verify the product by using the areas of rectangles.
3. Write three fractions equal to $\frac{2}{5}$ and three fractions equal to $\frac{3}{4}$.

Additional Examples
1. Multiply $\frac{A}{3} \cdot \frac{B}{5}$.
2. Show that each of the following expressions equals $\frac{2y}{7}$.
   a. $\frac{2}{7}y$ b. $\frac{1}{7} \cdot 2y$ c. $2 \cdot \frac{y}{7}$
3. Simplify $\frac{108xy}{9y}$.
4. Assume $x \neq 0$ and $y \neq 0$. Multiply $\frac{6x^2}{35y}$ by $\frac{7y}{3x^2}$, and simplify the product.

Resource Masters for Lesson 5-1

Resource Master 61 Lesson 5-2

Warm-Up
Consider the division $\frac{3}{4} \div \frac{2}{5}$.
1. Find the quotient.
2. Verify your answer to Question 1 using decimals.
3. Find a fraction $\frac{a}{b}$ equal to $\frac{3}{4}$ with $a > 20$. Find a fraction $\frac{c}{d}$ equal to $\frac{2}{5}$ with $c > 20$. Calculate $\frac{a}{b} \div \frac{c}{d}$. Explain why the quotient is or is not equal to your answer to Question 1.

Additional Examples
1. Simplify $\frac{5}{9} \div \frac{7}{8}$.
2. Simplify $\dfrac{\frac{7x}{4}}{\frac{21x}{8}}$

$$\frac{\frac{7x}{4}}{\frac{21x}{8}} = \frac{7x}{4} \cdot \underline{\quad} = \frac{\underline{\quad}}{\underline{\quad} x} = \frac{x}{\underline{\quad}} = \underline{\quad}$$

Question 27

Resource Master for Lesson 5-2

Resource Master 62 Lesson 5-3

Warm-Up
1. A teacher has two algebra classes with a total of 71 students.
   a. How many students is this per class?
   b. In your answer to Part a, what is the rate unit?
2. At a rate r, a person goes a distance d in a time t. How are r, d, and t related? Give an example with specific values of the three variables, indicating their units.
3. Make up an example in which a rate is negative.

Additional Examples
1. In a job interview, Matthew has to take a typing test. In 6 minutes, Matthew types 270 words. The job is his if he can type 55 words per minute. Will he get the job? What is his average number of words per minute?
2. a. If a car accelerates from 10 to 60 miles per hour in 45 seconds, write the change in speed in miles per hour per second.
   b. If the car decelerates from 90 miles per hour to 55 miles per hour in 10 seconds, what is the change in speed in miles per hour per second?

Resource Master for Lesson 5-3

Resource Master 63 Lesson 5-3

Additional Example
3. a. For what value(s) of x is $\frac{x+2}{x-3}$ undefined?
   b. For what value(s) of x does $\frac{x+2}{x-3} = 0$?

Solutions
a. A fraction is undefined whenever its _____ is zero.
   So $\frac{x+2}{x-3}$ is undefined when _____ = 0.
   Solve the equation on the preceding line for x. $x =$ _____
   Therefore, $\frac{x+2}{x-3}$ is undefined when $x =$ _____.
b. A fraction equals zero whenever its _____ is zero.
   So $\frac{x+2}{x-3} = 0$ when _____ = 0.
   Therefore, $\frac{x+2}{x-3} = 0$ when $x =$ _____.

Question 13

x	y
−3	
−2	
−1	
0	
1	
2	
3	

Resource Master for Lesson 5-3

Resource Master 64 Lesson 5-4

Warm-Up
1. If you throw a ball into the air, it will rise until the negative acceleration of gravity counterbalances the acceleration you gave the ball, and then it returns to Earth. If an object is propelled high enough and is traveling fast enough, the decreasing power of gravity will not be enough to bring it back to earth. The speed required to propel an object out of the Earth's gravitational pull is called the *escape velocity* and is about 25,000 miles per hour. (Use the conversion: 1 kilometer ≈ 0.62 mile.)
   a. How much is that speed in miles per minute?
   b. How much is that speed in miles per second?
   c. How much is that speed in kilometers per second?
2. The escape velocity from the moon is about 2,373 meters per second. How many miles per hour is this?

Additional Examples
1. On average, Cairo gets 2 millimeters of rainfall per month. How much rainfall does Cairo get in one year?
2. Explain why a car traveling 120 $\frac{km}{hr}$ is traveling about 75 $\frac{mi}{hr}$. Use the conversion 1 mile ≈ 1.6 kilometers. The goal is to convert kilometers to _____.

Use conversion rates so that the units cancel in the numerator and denominator just like common factors.

$$\frac{120 \text{ km}}{\text{hr}} = \frac{120 \text{ km}}{1 \text{ hr}} \cdot \frac{1 \text{ mi}}{\underline{\quad} \text{ km}} = 120 \cdot \frac{1}{1 \cdot \underline{\quad} \frac{m}{hr}} = \underline{\quad} \frac{m}{hr}$$

Resource Master for Lesson 5-4

Resource Master 66 Lesson 5-5
Resource Master 65 Lesson 5-5

Warm-Up
1. Pick a relative of yours whose age is different from yours. What is the ratio of your age to the age of that relative, in lowest terms?
2. a. What will be the ratio of your age to the age of that relative next year?
   b. Will the ratio be greater or less than the ratio you found in Question 1?
   c. Five years from now, will the ratio be higher or lower than the ratio you found in Part a?

Additional Examples
1. David's foot is exactly 1 foot long, while Julene's is only 10 inches long. Write a ratio comparing Julene's foot size to David's.
2. A shirt that sells for $30 is on sale for $25. The tax on the sale price is $1.93, so the total cost with tax is $26.93.
   a. What is the discount rate?
   b. What is the tax rate?
   c. Including tax, how much would a customer save by buying the shirt on sale?
3. In your mother's punch recipe, she recommends that you use 2 parts cream soda to 3 parts pineapple-orange juice. How much of each ingredient will you need if you wish to make 15 cups of punch?

Resource Masters for Lesson 5-5

Resource Master 67 Lesson 5-6

Warm-Up

1. Suppose a drawer contains 8 white socks, 6 black socks, and 2 gray socks. If you reach in without looking, what is the probability that the sock you pick is:
   a. black?   b. not black?

2. Suppose a drawer contains w white socks, b black socks, and g gray socks. If you reach in without looking, what is the probability that the sock you pick is:
   a. gray?   b. not gray?

Additional Example

1. Given the chart of blood types below,
   a. what is the probability that a person has type A+ or O+ blood?
   b. what is the probability that a person does not have type AB− blood?
   c. what is the probability that a person who has type AB blood is AB−?

Type	Percent
O+	38.4
O−	7.7
A+	32.3
A−	6.5
B+	9.4
B−	1.7
AB+	3.2
AB−	0.7

Resource Master for Lesson 5-6

Resource Master 68 Lesson 5-6

Probability Distributions

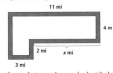

x	P(x)
2	$\frac{1}{36} = 0.02\overline{7}$
3	$\frac{2}{36} = 0.05$
4	$\frac{3}{36} = 0.08\overline{3}$
5	$\frac{4}{36} = 0.\overline{1}$
6	$\frac{5}{36} = 0.13\overline{8}$
7	$\frac{6}{36} = 0.1\overline{6}$
8	$\frac{5}{36} = 0.13\overline{8}$
9	$\frac{4}{36} = 0.\overline{1}$
10	$\frac{3}{36} = 0.08\overline{3}$
11	$\frac{2}{36} = 0.05$
12	$\frac{1}{36} = 0.02\overline{7}$

Resource Master for Lesson 5-6

Resource Master 69 Lesson 5-7

Warm-Up

1. Find the random-number generator on a calculator. Use it to randomly generate 25 numbers from 1 to 6.
2. Calculate the relative frequencies of each number occurring. Do you think the numbers are really generated at random or does there seem to be some trend?
3. Test your opinion in Part b by generating 25 more numbers from 1 to 6 using the random-number generator. Do your results change your opinion?
4. From your experiment, what would you say the probabilities are of getting a 1, 2, 3, 4, 5, and 6 using your random-number generator?

Additional Example

1. The dot plot shows the weights of 400,000 newborns in a given country over a six-year period. Every 10,000 births in a weight category are represented as a dot. The information, to the nearest 0.5 kg, is summarized in the table.

Birth Weight (kg)	Number of Births
2.5	20,000
3.0	80,000
3.5	150,000
4.0	90,000
4.5	50,000
5.0	10,000

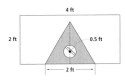

What is the relative frequency of a newborn's weight
a. being less than 3 kg?
b. being at least 3 kg?
c. being at most 3.5 kg?
d. having a weight w given by $2.5 \le w \le 4.5$?

Resource Master for Lesson 5-7

Resource Master 70 Lesson 5-7

Additional Example

2. Find the meaning of the 50th percentile in the newborn data and explain its meaning.

The Differences between Probability and Relative Frequency

Outcome	1	2	3	4	5	6
Probability	$\frac{1}{6} = 0.1\overline{6}$	$\frac{1}{6} = 0.1\overline{6}$	$\frac{1}{6} = 0.1\overline{6}$	$\frac{1}{6} = 0.1\overline{6}$	$\frac{1}{6} = 0.1\overline{6}$	$\frac{1}{6} = 0.1\overline{6}$
Relative Frequency	$\frac{24}{100} = 0.24$	$\frac{16}{100} = 0.16$	$\frac{13}{100} = 0.13$	$\frac{14}{100} = 0.14$	$\frac{16}{100} = 0.16$	$\frac{17}{100} = 0.17$

Relative Frequency	Probability
1. Calculated from data	1. Deduced from assumptions (like randomness) or assumed to be close to some relative frequency
2. The ratio of the number of times an event has occurred to the number of times it could occur	2. If outcomes are equally likely, the ratio of the number of outcomes in an event to the total number of possible outcomes
3. 0 means that an event did not occur. 1 means that the event occurred every time it could.	3. 0 means that an event is impossible. 1 means that an event is sure to happen.
4. The more often an event occurs relative to the number of times it could occur, the closer its relative frequency is to 1.	4. The more likely an event is, the closer its probability is to 1.
5. The sum of the relative frequencies of all outcomes in an experiment is 1.	5. The sum of the probabilities of all outcomes in an experiment is 1.
6. If the relative frequency of an event is r, then the relative frequency of its complement is $1 - r$.	6. If the probability of an event is p, then the probability of its complement is $1 - p$.

Resource Master for Lesson 5-7

Resource Master 71 Lesson 5-8

Warm-Up

Find the area of each figure.

1. A circle with a radius of 5 centimeters
2. A square with sides of length 1.5 inches
3. A right triangle with legs 7 centimeters and 8 centimeters
4. A circle with a diameter of 2 feet
5. A rectangle with a length of $5k$ and a width of $2k$
6. The largest circle that can be drawn inside a square with perimeter 100 units

Additional Example

1. Suppose a dart is thrown at a target consisting of three concentric circles with radii 20 centimeters, 40 centimeters, and 60 centimeters, as shown. Assuming that the dart hits the board, what is the probability that the dart will land somewhere inside the smallest circle?

Resource Master for Lesson 5-8

Resource Master 72 Lesson 5-8

Resource Master 73 Lesson 5-8

Additional Examples

2. The given figure represents a walking path. Suppose when you stand on a nearby hill, you can see only the part of the path labeled x. If your friend is walking the entire path when you reach the peak of the hill, what is the probability that she is visible to you at the moment you reach the peak?

3. Suppose you throw a dart somewhere randomly at the board shown below. Assume the height of the triangle is approximately 1.7 feet, and that the diameter of the circle is 0.5 foot. Assuming you hit the board, find the probability that your dart will land in the shaded region.

Resource Masters for Lesson 5-8

Resource Master 74 Lesson 5-9

Warm-Up

1. If you are charged $1.69 for 3 cans of peaches, how much should you expect to pay for 8 cans?
2. If in traffic it takes a bus 5 minutes to travel $\frac{3}{4}$ of a mile, how long at that rate would it take the bus to travel 6 miles?
3. Booker is reading a 300-page novel. It has taken him 2 hours to read the first 72 pages. At this rate, how many more hours will it take him to finish the novel?

Additional Examples

1. Complete the sentence, "5 is to 15 as 9 is to _____."
2. A survey of 200 high school students found that 145 of them had their own television set. Based on the results of this survey, about how many students in a school of 3,175 would have their own television set?
3. Two runners, Eric and Leslie, competed in a race. Eric's time was 0.8 minute slower than Leslie's. Their times were in the ratio of 11 to 10. What was Eric's time?

Resource Master for Lesson 5-9

Resource Master 75 Lesson 5-10

Warm-Up

Try to draw a picture of yourself on a piece of paper. Picture yourself standing. Of course, if you are not a good artist, this picture may not look very good, but you can still make the picture look reasonably good by careful work with proportions. Decide what the scale of your picture should be. A possibility is to make the picture $\frac{1}{12}$ actual size. Then one foot on you would be one inch on the picture. Or you might make the picture $\frac{1}{10}$ actual size. Then one centimeter on you would be one millimeter on the picture. How tall will the picture be? How large will the head be? How long will it be from your waist to the floor? How wide should the picture be? Find these dimensions before you begin drawing the actual picture and then fill in the details using those dimensions.

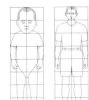

	Infant	Adult
Ratio of head length to height	$\frac{2 \text{ parts}}{8 \text{ parts}} = \frac{1}{4}$	$\frac{1 \text{ parts}}{8 \text{ parts}} = \frac{1}{8}$
Ratio of trunk length to leg length	$\frac{3 \text{ parts}}{3 \text{ parts}} = \frac{1}{1}$	$\frac{3 \text{ parts}}{4 \text{ parts}} = \frac{3}{4}$

Resource Master for Lesson 5-10

Resource Master 76 Lesson 5-10

Resource Master 77 Lesson 5-10

Additional Examples

1. A child's cup has base radius 1 inch and height 2.5 inches. An adult size cup is similar, but has a base radius of 1.5 inches. What is the height of the adult cup?
2. The two triangles below are similar, with corresponding sides parallel. Find x, the length of $\overline{AB}$.

Write the proportion: $\frac{5}{x} = \underline{\quad}$

Use the Means-Extremes Property: _____ · $x = $ _____ · _____

Solve: $x = $ _____ cm

3. Use the measurements on the diagram to find the height h of the building.

Resource Masters for Lesson 5-10

Pacing

Each lesson in this chapter is designed to be covered in one day. At the end of the chapter, you should plan to spend 1 day to review the Self-Test, 1 to 2 days for the Chapter Review, and 1 day for a test. You may wish to spend a day on projects and possibly a day is needed for quizzes. This chapter should therefore take 13 to 15 days. We strongly advise you to not spend more than 20 days on this chapter.

Using Pages 250–251

This opener describes the basic applications of division. For students who have been through previous UCSMP courses, it should be review. Emphasize that while the answer to a division problem with arithmetic expressions can usually be written as a decimal or a fraction, with algebraic expressions the answer is almost always a fraction (if the dividend is not a multiple of the divisor).

Chapter 5 Projects

At the end of each chapter, you will find projects related to the chapter. At this time you might want to have students look over the projects on pages 315 and 316. You might want to have students tentatively select a project on which to work. Then, as students read and progress through the chapter, they can finalize their project choices.

Sometimes students might work alone; at other times, you might let them collaborate with classmates for a presentation and discussion. We recommend that you allow for diversity and encourage students to use their imaginations when presenting their projects. As students work on projects throughout the year, they should see the many uses of mathematics in the real world.

Division and Proportions in Algebra

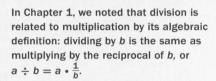

▶ Contents

In Chapter 1, we noted that division is related to multiplication by its algebraic definition: dividing by b is the same as multiplying by the reciprocal of b, or $a \div b = a \cdot \frac{1}{b}$.

In Chapter 2, you saw that division is also related to multiplication by related facts.

If a and b are not zero and $ab = c$, then $a = \frac{c}{b}$ and $b = \frac{c}{a}$.

Division is also an important operation in its own right. Three kinds of situations lead directly to division.

250

Chapter 5 Overview

Chapter 5 takes an algebraic view of a variety of important mathematical ideas: multiplication of fractions; applications of division; and proportions in statistics, algebra, and geometry. Many of the ideas of this chapter are important enough to be covered in more than one UCSMP course. Some of the applications of division and probability are review, while some of the geometric ideas are introduced here for the first time and will be reviewed in geometry.

Lessons 5-1 and 5-2 generalize the arithmetic operations of multiplication and division of fractions to their algebraic counterparts. The discussion includes the justification for "invert and multiply" when dividing fractions.

(continued on next page)

Splitting Up

If a quantity a is split into b equal parts, then each part has measure $\frac{a}{b}$. For this reason, every fraction can be viewed as a division $\left(\frac{a}{b} = a \div b\right)$.

The value of the fraction is the quotient of a and b.

Rate

If a and b are quantities with different units, then the quotient is a *rate*. For example, dividing 50 miles by 2 hours yields the rate 25 miles per hour: $\frac{50 \text{ mi}}{2 \text{ hr}} = \frac{25 \text{ mi}}{\text{hr}}$.

Ratio

If a and b have the same kind of units, then the quotient is a *ratio*. For example, if one doll weighs 36 grams and another weighs 4.5 grams, then the quotient $\frac{36 \text{ g}}{4.5 \text{ g}}$ equals 8, the ratio of the first weight to the second weight.

If two rates or ratios are equal, then the result is a *proportion*. For example, dividing 75 miles by 3 hours yields the same rate as dividing 50 miles by 2 hours. The equation $\frac{50 \text{ mi}}{2 \text{ hr}} = \frac{75 \text{ mi}}{3 \text{ hr}}$ is a proportion. In this chapter, you will study these and related topics.

251

Lessons 5-3 through 5-5 discuss rates and ratios, the basic models for division, from an algebraic standpoint. Lesson 5-3 covers rates and rate units and is likely to be review for students who have had the preceding UCSMP courses. Lesson 5-4 discusses conversion rates and reciprocal rates. The latter is likely to be new material. Lesson 5-5 moves to ratios and discusses taxes and discounts.

Lessons 5-6 through 5-8 apply ratios to the discussion of ideas from probability and statistics. Each lesson contains some review for students who have had previous UCSMP courses as well as introducing new ideas.

Lessons 5-9 and 5-10 discuss proportions. Lesson 5-9 introduces proportions and will be somewhat of a review, but includes some problems related to sampling and statistics. Lesson 5-10 discusses proportions as found in lengths of similar figures.

Lesson 5-1

GOAL

Understand the algebraic rendering of two fundamental properties that deal with fractions—the rule for multiplying fractions (here called the Multiplying Fractions Property) and the Equal Fractions Property. Be able to apply them in skill exercises and in applications, to represent them, and to see how the second of these properties follows from the first.

SPUR Objective

(The SPUR Objectives for all of Chapter 5 are found in the Chapter Review on pages 320–323.)

A Multiply and simplify algebraic fractions.

Materials/Resources

· Lesson Master 5-1A or 5-1B
· Resource Masters 3, 59, and 60
· Scientific or graphing calculator
· Computer Algebra System (CAS)

HOMEWORK

Suggestions for Assignment
• Questions 1–30
• Question 31 (extra credit)
• Reading Lesson 5-2
• Covering the Ideas 5-2

Local Standards

Lesson 5-1 Multiplication of Algebraic Fractions

Vocabulary

algebraic fraction

> ▶ **BIG IDEA** Algebraic fractions are multiplied in the same way you multiply numeric fractions.

In algebra, a division is represented by a fraction. An **algebraic fraction** is a fraction with a variable in the numerator, in the denominator, or in both. Here are some algebraic fractions.

$$\frac{7t}{2} \qquad \frac{-a}{6.4bc} \qquad \frac{3m+4}{4m+3} \qquad \frac{\frac{2}{3}+\frac{4}{5}}{x^2} \qquad \frac{x-y}{\sqrt{x^2+y^2}}$$

Multiplying Algebraic Fractions

Algebraic fractions are multiplied just as you multiply numeric fractions. Below is a way to picture the product of the fractions $\frac{a}{b}$ and $\frac{c}{d}$. First draw a unit square as shown below. Split one side into b parts and the other side into d parts, and draw lines creating bd small rectangles. Then find $\frac{a}{b}$ of one side and $\frac{c}{d}$ of an adjacent side.

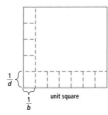 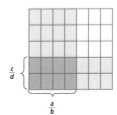

There are ac shaded rectangles out of bd small rectangles in the unit area. So the area is $\frac{ac}{bd}$. This describes the common rule for multiplying fractions, which applies to all algebraic fractions.

> **Multiplying Fractions Property**
>
> For all real numbers a, b, c, and d, with $b \neq 0$ and $d \neq 0$,
> $$\frac{a}{b} \cdot \frac{c}{d} = \frac{ac}{bd}.$$

Mental Math

Evaluate.
a. $0.5 \cdot 4$ 2
b. $5 \cdot 0.4$ 2
c. $0.5 \cdot 0.4$ 0.2

Background

Decimals and fractions are not comparable ways of representing numbers. Decimals are a *notation,* what we call base 10. In contrast, fractions represent the *operation* of division. Unlike the algorithms in arithmetic for addition, which are very much based on the decimal system, the algorithms for dealing with fractions are independent of how numbers are written.

Consequently, the two properties in this lesson are each simple generalizations of properties students have learned in dealing with arithmetic fractions. Mathematically, each property can be derived from basic properties of multiplication (associative, commutative, identity, and inverse) and the Algebraic Definition of Division.

Example 1

Multiply $\frac{L}{4} \cdot \frac{W}{3}$.

Solution Use the Multiplying Fractions Property.

$$\frac{L}{4} \cdot \frac{W}{3} = \frac{LW}{12}.$$

Check 1 Substitute values for L and W, say $L = 20$ and $W = 8$.

Does $\frac{20}{4} \cdot \frac{8}{3} = \frac{20 \cdot 8}{12}$?

Yes, the left side is $5 \cdot \frac{8}{3}$, or $\frac{40}{3}$. The right side is $\frac{160}{12}$, or $\frac{40}{3}$.

Check 2 Use an area model. Draw a rectangle with length L and width W. Divide the length into fourths and the width into thirds. Shade a smaller rectangle with dimensions $\frac{L}{4}$ and $\frac{W}{3}$. Since the L by W rectangle with area LW is divided into twelfths, the shaded rectangle has area $\frac{1}{12} \cdot LW$ or $\frac{LW}{12}$.

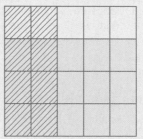

The fraction $\frac{LW}{12}$ is another way of writing $\frac{1}{12}LW$. Example 2 below shows how the Multiplying Fractions Property can be used to explain why many different expressions with algebraic fractions are equivalent.

Example 2

Show that each of the following expressions equals $\frac{5x}{3}$.

    a. $\frac{5}{3}x$ **b.** $\frac{1}{3} \cdot 5x$ **c.** $5 \cdot \frac{x}{3}$

Solutions Notice how each part below uses the property that $x = \frac{x}{1}$ and the Multiplying Fractions Property.

    a. $\frac{5}{3}x = \frac{5}{3} \cdot \frac{x}{1} = \frac{5x}{3}$

    b. $\frac{1}{3} \cdot 5x = \frac{1}{3} \cdot \frac{5x}{1} = \frac{5x}{3}$

    c. $5 \cdot \frac{x}{3} = \frac{5}{1} \cdot \frac{x}{3} = \frac{5x}{3}$

This shows that $\frac{5x}{3}$, $\frac{1}{3} \cdot 5x$, and $5 \cdot \frac{x}{3}$ are all equal to each other.

Equal Fractions

As you know, every numerical fraction is equal to many other fractions. For example, $\frac{3}{5} = \frac{30}{50}$ and $\frac{30}{50} = \frac{9}{15}$. These equalities are examples of the *Equal Fractions Property*.

Equal Fractions Property

For all real numbers a, b, and k, if $b \neq 0$ and $k \neq 0$, then $\frac{a}{b} = \frac{ak}{bk}$.

---

1   Warm-Up

Consider the multiplication $\frac{2}{5} \cdot \frac{3}{4}$.

1. Give the product as a fraction and verify your answer using decimals.
$\frac{2}{5} \cdot \frac{3}{4} = \frac{6}{20} = \frac{3}{10}$; $0.4 \cdot 0.75 = 0.3$

2. Verify the product by using the areas of rectangles. $\frac{2}{5} \cdot \frac{3}{4} = \frac{6}{20} = \frac{3}{10}$

3. Write three fractions equal to $\frac{2}{5}$ and three fractions equal to $\frac{3}{4}$. Answers vary. Sample answers: $\frac{4}{10}, \frac{6}{15}, \frac{20}{50}; \frac{30}{40}, \frac{9}{12}, \frac{-3}{-4}$

2   Teaching

Notes on the Lesson

There is always a question regarding how much to assume students know. Here, we assume that students know how to multiply arithmetic fractions and how to simplify arithmetic fractions. You might wish to go through the examples one by one with students.

There is also always a question of how many steps to include in these problems. We have tried to be realistic in the solutions we give.

Example 1 shows how the Area Model for Multiplication works also with algebraic fractions. The Multiplying Fractions Property is applied in Example 2 to show that expressions that look quite different may be equivalent. You should go through this example carefully so that students understand why the various expressions are equivalent.

Additional Examples

Example 1 Multiply $\frac{A}{3} \cdot \frac{B}{5}$. $\frac{AB}{15}$

Example 2 Show that each of the following expressions equals $\frac{2y}{7}$.

    a. $\frac{2}{7}y$ $\frac{2}{7}y = \frac{2}{7} \cdot \frac{y}{1} = \frac{2y}{7}$

    b. $\frac{1}{7} \cdot 2y$ $\frac{1}{7} \cdot 2y = \frac{1}{7} \cdot \frac{2y}{1} = \frac{2y}{7}$

    c. $2 \cdot \frac{y}{7}$ $2 \cdot \frac{y}{7} = \frac{2}{1} \cdot \frac{y}{7} = \frac{2y}{7}$

5-1

Notes on the Lesson

Equal fractions. If you begin with a fraction $\frac{ak}{bk}$ and multiply or divide both numerator and denominator by the same number, then the result is of the form $\frac{a}{b}$. Students may not realize that this is an application of the Equal Fractions Property, because they have started with the right side and ended with the left side.

Example 3 Notice the additional step between the first two lines, where you separate the expression as $\frac{7a}{7a} \cdot \frac{16b}{1}$ on the right side.

Additional Example

Example 3 Simplify $\frac{108xy}{9y}$. $12x$

Notes on the Activity

Students should try to predict what the CAS will show before they see the answer. Remind students not to use zero to check using substitution. Discuss the reasoning for this. The result may be undefined, or it may be zero, which does not allow us to check for accuracy in the answer.

The Equal Fractions Property holds for all fractions $\frac{a}{b}$ and values of k as long as the denominator is not zero. In $\frac{3}{5} = \frac{30}{50}$, $a = 3$, $b = 5$, and $k = 10$. That is, $\frac{3}{5} = \frac{3 \cdot 10}{5 \cdot 10} = \frac{30}{50}$. In $\frac{30}{50} = \frac{9}{15}$, $a = 9$, $b = 15$, and $k = \frac{10}{3}$. The Equal Fractions Property is true because of the Multiplying Fractions Property and the Multiplicative Identity Property. Here is how.

$$\frac{a}{b} = \frac{a}{b} \cdot 1 \quad \text{Multiplicative Identity Property}$$
$$= \frac{a}{b} \cdot \frac{k}{k} \quad \frac{k}{k} = 1, k \neq 0$$
$$= \frac{ak}{bk} \quad \text{Multiplying Fractions Property}$$

Algebraic fractions, like numeric fractions, can sometimes be written in simpler form. To use the Equal Fractions Property to simplify algebraic fractions, find common factors in the numerator and denominator of the fraction.

Example 3

Simplify $\frac{112ab}{7a}$.

Solution 1 $7a$ is a common factor of the numerator and denominator.

$$\frac{112ab}{7a} = \frac{7a \cdot 16b}{7a \cdot 1} \quad \text{Multiplying Fractions Property}$$
$$= \frac{16b}{1} \quad \text{Equal Fractions Property}$$
$$= 16b \quad x = \frac{x}{1} \text{ for all } x.$$

Solution 2 People often skip steps. They sometimes show division of the common factors with slashes.

$$\frac{\overset{16}{\cancel{112}}\,\overset{1}{\cancel{ab}}}{\underset{1}{\cancel{7a}}\,\underset{1}{}} = \frac{16b}{1} = 16b$$

STOP QY1

> ▶ QY1
>
> Show that $\frac{25m}{30n}$ and $\frac{5m^2}{6mn}$ equal the same algebraic expression.

Activity

Use a CAS to simplify the following algebraic fractions. Check your work with a CAS or by substitution.

1. $\frac{5ab}{10b}$ $\frac{a}{2}$
2. $\frac{27x^2}{9x^2}$ 3
3. $\frac{2y}{2yz}$ $\frac{1}{z}$
4. $\frac{48cd}{6ac}$ $\frac{8d}{a}$
5. $\frac{12m^2}{18m}$ $\frac{2m}{3}$
6. $\frac{8\pi x}{6x^2}$ $\frac{4\pi}{3x}$

Accommodating the Learner

Ask students to simplify the following expressions.

1. $\frac{x^3}{x^6}$
2. $\frac{x^3}{x^5}$
3. $\frac{x^3}{x^4}$
4. $\frac{x^3}{x^3}$

What pattern do they recognize? Discuss the basic concept to prepare students for learning the quotient rule for exponents later in this course. $\frac{1}{x^3}, \frac{1}{x^2}, \frac{1}{x^1} = \frac{1}{x}, \frac{1}{x^0} = 1$

Example 4

Assume $x \neq 0$ and $y \neq 0$. Multiply $\frac{4x}{27y}$ by $\frac{3y}{2x^2}$ and simplify the product.

Solution 1 Here we show all the major steps.

$$\frac{4x}{27y} \cdot \frac{3y}{2x^2} = \frac{4x \cdot 3y}{27y \cdot 2x^2} \qquad \text{Multiplying Fractions Property}$$

$$= \frac{12xy}{54x^2y} \qquad \text{Multiply.}$$

$$= \frac{6 \cdot 2 \cdot x \cdot y}{6 \cdot 9 \cdot x \cdot x \cdot y} \qquad \text{Factor each expression.}$$

$$= \frac{6}{6} \cdot \frac{2}{9} \cdot \frac{x}{x} \cdot \frac{1}{x} \cdot \frac{y}{y} \qquad \text{Multiplying Fractions Property}$$

$$= \frac{2}{9} \cdot \frac{1}{x} \qquad \frac{k}{k} = 1 \text{ if } k \neq 0; \text{ Identity Property}$$

$$= \frac{2}{9x} \qquad \text{Multiplying Fractions Property}$$

Solution 2 Look for common factors in the numerator and denominator.

$$\frac{4x}{27y} \cdot \frac{3y}{2x^2} = \frac{\overset{2}{\cancel{4}} \cdot \overset{1}{\cancel{x}} \cdot \overset{1}{\cancel{3}} \cdot \overset{1}{\cancel{y}}}{\underset{9}{\cancel{27}} \cdot \underset{1}{\cancel{y}} \cdot \underset{1}{\cancel{2}} \cdot \underset{1}{\cancel{x}} \cdot x} = \frac{2}{9x}$$

 QY2

▶ **READING MATH**

The Equal Fractions Property is a property related to multiplication. It does not work when the same terms are *added* to the numerator and denominator.

▶ **QY2**

Multiply $\frac{-5a^2}{12b} \cdot \frac{2b^2}{6a}$ and simplify the product.

Questions

COVERING THE IDEAS

1. State the Multiplying Fractions Property.

2. The rectangle at the right has base b and height h.
   a. If all the small rectangles have the same dimensions, what is the area of the shaded region? $\frac{bh}{2}$
   b. What product of algebraic fractions is represented by the area of the shaded region? $\frac{3h}{4} \cdot \frac{2b}{3}$

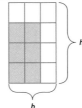

In 3 and 4, multiply the fractions.

3. $\frac{a}{7} \cdot \frac{b}{2}$ $\frac{ab}{14}$

4. $\frac{x}{30} \cdot \frac{3y}{z^2}$ $\frac{xy}{10z^2}$

5. Determine whether $\frac{1}{5}n = \frac{n}{5}$ is *always, sometimes but not always,* or *never* true. **always true**

6. Explain why $\frac{3}{8}x$ is equal to $\frac{3x}{8}$.

7. **Multiple Choice** Which expression does *not* equal the others? **D**

   A $\frac{5n}{8}$ B $\frac{5}{8}n$ C $5n \cdot \frac{1}{8}$ D $\frac{5}{n} \cdot 8$

1. For all real numbers $a, b, c,$ and d, with b and d not zero, $\frac{a}{b} \cdot \frac{c}{d} = \frac{ac}{bd}$.

6. Answers vary. Sample answer: $\frac{3}{8}x = \frac{3}{8} \cdot \frac{x}{1} = \frac{3x}{8}$

Notes on the Lesson

Example 4 We show only major steps, because to show all the steps would involve the repeated use of the Commutative and Associative Properties of Multiplication that are generally obvious to students at this point.

Caution Rewriting $\frac{a+k}{b+k}$ as $\frac{a}{b}$ is one of the most common errors of elementary algebra. We do not explicitly discuss this error because we think some students get confused by the discussion. Instead, emphasize the first sentence. The Equal Fractions Property is a property related to multiplication (and division). You know $\frac{1}{2} \neq \frac{2}{3}$. You cannot add the same nonzero number to both numerator and denominator and get an equal fraction. (See Question 16.)

Additional Example

Example 4 Assume $x \neq 0$ and $y \neq 0$. Multiply $\frac{6x^2}{35y}$ by $\frac{7y}{3x^3}$, and simplify the product. $\frac{2}{5x}$

Multiplication of Algebraic Fractions **255**

Extension

Discuss the concept of dividing by zero. Help students identify which variables cannot equal zero in an algebraic fraction.

5-1

3 Assignment

Recommended Assignment

- Questions 1–30
- Question 31 (extra credit)
- Reading Lesson 5-2
- Covering the Ideas 5-2

Notes on the Questions

Question 2 Do not be surprised if students have trouble with these questions. They seem to be more difficult for students than they appear.

Question 7 The key is to realize that 5 and n are in the numerator, while 8 is in the denominator.

Question 23 This kind of reverse given-find problem is helpful for understanding multiplication of fractions and may generate a nice class discussion.

Question 26 At this point, we expect that students will find the number and then find 12% of it. However, some students may use a proportion. You should accept any reliable method.

In 8–10, use the Equal Fractions Property to simplify the fraction.

8. $\frac{1{,}875}{225}$ $\frac{25}{3}$

9. $\frac{-4n}{24n^2}$ $\frac{-1}{6n}$

10. $\frac{10mn}{15np}$ $\frac{2m}{3p}$

In 11–14, multiply and simplify the result.

11. $\frac{1.2m}{n} \cdot \frac{1.2n}{m}$ 1.44

12. $\frac{7v}{x^2} \cdot \frac{x^2}{7v}$ 1

13. $\frac{4abc}{27c} \cdot \frac{3}{2a^2b^3}$ $\frac{2}{9ab^2}$

14. $\frac{1}{4} \cdot 2n \cdot \frac{3n}{6}$ $\frac{n^2}{4}$

15. a. One rectangle is half as wide and one-fourth as long as another rectangle. How do their areas compare?

   b. Draw a figure to illustrate your answer.

16. a. Show that $\frac{30 + x}{10 + x}$ and $\frac{30}{10}$ are *not* equivalent by letting $x = 7$.

   b. Show that $\frac{30 + x}{10 + x}$ and $\frac{3 + x}{1 + x}$ are *not* equivalent by letting $x = -4$.

   c. Why can't the Equal Fractions Property be applied in Parts a and b? Answers vary. Sample answer: The Equal Fractions Property is a property of multiplication, not addition.

17. The Brock and Pease families have rectangular vegetable gardens. The length of the Brocks' garden is $\frac{2}{3}$ the length and $\frac{3}{4}$ the width of the Peases' garden.

   a. How do the areas of the gardens compare?

   b. Check your answer by using a specific length and width for the Peases' garden. See margin.

APPLYING THE MATHEMATICS

18. *Skill Sequence* Compute in your head.

   a. $\frac{5}{3} \cdot 3b$ 5b

   b. $\frac{9}{x} \cdot xc$ 9c

   c. $\frac{a}{b} \cdot bd$ ad

   d. $n^2 \cdot \frac{a}{n^2}$ a

19. Combine and simplify $\frac{4n - 5}{n} + \frac{5}{n}$. 4

In 20–22, multiply and simplify where possible.

20. $\frac{a}{b} \cdot \frac{b}{c} \cdot \frac{c}{a}$ 1

21. $\frac{-30r^3}{7s} \cdot \frac{-28s}{120r^4}$ $\frac{1}{r}$

22. $\frac{-2y}{3} \cdot \frac{5y}{6} \cdot z$ $\frac{-5y^2z}{9}$

23. Find two *algebraic* fractions whose product is $\frac{36a^2}{5x}$.

24. **Multiple Choice** Find the fraction that is *not* equal to the other three. C

   A $\frac{110}{130}$

   B $\frac{121}{143}$

   C $\frac{121}{169}$

   D $\frac{550}{650}$

15a. One rectangle has one-eighth as much area as the other.

15b. Answers vary. Sample answer:

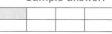

16a. $\frac{30 + 7}{10 + 7} = \frac{37}{17} \neq$

$3 = \frac{30}{10}$

16b. $\frac{30 + -4}{10 + -4} = \frac{26}{6} \neq$

$\frac{2}{6} = \frac{-1}{-3} = \frac{3 + -4}{1 + -4}$

Recent surveys show the average size of a garden is between 500 and 1,000 square feet.

Source: www.oldhouseweb.com

17a. The Brocks' garden is half the area of the Peases' garden.

23. Answers vary. Sample answer: $\frac{6a^3}{5}$ and $\frac{6}{ax}$

Additional Answers

17b. Answers vary. Sample answers: The Peases have a 12-by-12 foot garden that has 144 ft² area; the Brocks' 8-by-9 foot garden has a 72 ft² area, which is half of 144 ft².

25. a. Find the volume of the brick at the right. $\frac{L^3}{6}$ units^3

b. Check your answer by letting $L = 12$. $(12)(6)(4) = 288 = \frac{(12)^3}{6}$

c. Think of a cube with sides of length L. How many of these bricks would fit into the cube? How can you tell?
6, stack them 2 high and 3 deep

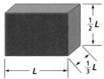

REVIEW

26. If 5% of a number is 12, what is 12% of that number? **(Lesson 4-1)**
28.8

27. Solve $150x + 200x = 14{,}000$. **(Lessons 3-4, 2-2)** $x = 40$

28. **Skill Sequence** State the reciprocal of each number. **(Lesson 2-8)**

a. $5\frac{1}{5}$ b. $\frac{1}{100}$ 100 c. $\frac{-2}{3}$ $\frac{-3}{2}$

29. A single-story house is to be built on a lot 75 feet wide by 100 feet deep. The shorter side of the lot faces the street. The house must be set back from the street at least 25 feet. It must be 20 feet from the back lot line, and 10 feet from each side lot line. What is the maximum area the house can have? **(Lesson 2-1)** 3,025 ft^2

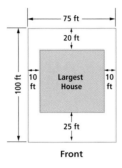

Front

30. Consider $\frac{3}{4} \div \frac{9}{32}$.

a. Rewrite the problem as the multiplication of two fractions. $\frac{3}{4} \cdot \frac{32}{9}$

b. What is the answer in lowest terms? $\frac{8}{3}$

c. What is the answer as a decimal? **(Previous Course)** $2.\overline{6}$

EXPLORATION

31. a. Calculate the products at the right. 3; 4; 5

b. Write a sentence or two describing the patterns you observed in Part a.

c. Predict the following products.

$\frac{2}{1} \cdot \frac{3}{2} \cdot \frac{4}{3} \cdot \frac{5}{4} \cdot \ldots \cdot \frac{2{,}010}{2{,}009}$ 2,010

$\frac{2}{1} \cdot \frac{3}{2} \cdot \frac{4}{3} \cdot \frac{5}{4} \cdot \ldots \cdot \frac{n+1}{n}$ $n+1$

$\frac{2}{1} \cdot \frac{3}{2}$

$\frac{2}{1} \cdot \frac{3}{2} \cdot \frac{4}{3}$

$\frac{2}{1} \cdot \frac{3}{2} \cdot \frac{4}{3} \cdot \frac{5}{4}$

31b. Answers vary.
Sample answer:
Since the numerator of each preceding fraction is the denominator of each succeeding fraction, the product simplifies to the first denominator and the last numerator.

QY ANSWERS

1. $\frac{25m}{30n} = \frac{5 \cdot 5m}{5 \cdot 6n} = \frac{5m}{6n}$

and $\frac{5m^2}{6mn} = \frac{m \cdot 5m}{m \cdot 6n} = \frac{5m}{6n}$.

2. $\frac{-5ab}{36}$

Multiplication of Algebraic Fractions   **257**

5-1B Lesson Master   Questions on SPUR Objectives
See pages 320–323 for objectives.

SKILLS Objective A
In 1–12, simplify.

1. $\frac{10x^2y}{5x}$ **2xy**

2. $\frac{36x^3y^4}{-4xy}$ **$-9x^2y$**

3. $\frac{26a^4b^2}{39a^2b}$ **$\frac{2a^2b^2}{3}$**

4. $\frac{-75c^5d^6}{30cd^2}$ **$\frac{-5c^2}{2d^4}$**

5. $\frac{7r^2s^4}{77r^4s^4t^{10}}$ **$\frac{1}{11r^2t^3}$**

6. $\frac{84p^4s^4}{16p^4s^2}$ **$\frac{21p^3}{4q^5}$**

7. $\frac{-102m^7n}{51m^{13}n^7}$ **$\frac{-2}{m^6n^6}$**

8. $\frac{27x^5w^3}{81x^6w^2}$ **$\frac{v^3w^3}{3}$**

9. $\frac{16x^6y}{56x^4y^2}$ **$\frac{2x}{7y}$**

10. $\frac{-63x^4b^2}{18x^6b^2}$ **$\frac{-7a^2}{2b^4}$**

11. $\frac{15c^4d^2}{150c^6d^4}$ **$\frac{d}{10c^3}$**

12. $\frac{48f^{-1}x^5}{12f^{-3}x^2}$ **$\frac{4f^4}{g^2}$**

13. Multiple Choice. Which fraction is equivalent to $\frac{16mnp^3}{64n^2p}$? **D**

A $\frac{2mp^2}{8n}$ B $\frac{4mnp}{16}$ C $\frac{m}{4np}$ D $\frac{mp}{4n}$

Algebra   **197**

5-1B   page 2

The width of a family room is $\frac{2}{3}$ as long as its length. Let L = the length of the family room.

14. Write an expression to find the area of the family room. **$L \cdot \frac{2}{3}L$**

15. Simplify the expression in Question 14. **$\frac{2}{3}L^2$**

A box of cereal has a length of x inches. The width is $\frac{1}{6}$ its length and its height is 3 times $\frac{1}{2}$ its length.

16. The volume of a box is found by multiplying length × width × height. Write an expression to find the volume of the cereal box. **$x \cdot \frac{x}{6} \cdot \frac{3x}{2}$**

17. Multiply and simplify the expression in Question 16. **$\frac{x^3}{4}$**

In 18–25, multiply the fractions. Simplify if possible.

18. $\frac{3x^2}{4y} \cdot \frac{8y^3}{9x}$ **$\frac{2xy}{3}$**

19. $\frac{15a^2b}{4} \cdot \frac{-12b}{5a^3}$ **$\frac{-5b^2}{a}$**

20. $\frac{26c^4d}{5d^3} \cdot \frac{d^2}{13c^2}$ **$\frac{2c^2}{3d}$**

21. $\frac{-42f^5}{70g^4} \cdot \frac{5g f^3}{6}$ **$\frac{-f^4g^2}{2}$**

22. $\frac{18m^3n^2}{9n^4} \cdot \frac{72m^2 \cdot n}{36m^3}$ **$\frac{4m^4}{n^3}$**

23. $\frac{121r^5}{24p^6} \cdot \frac{6p^3r}{33p^3}$ **$\frac{11r^4}{12}$**

24. $\frac{20u^3}{u^3} \cdot \frac{v^2}{15w^7}$ **$\frac{4v^5}{3w^2}$**

25. $\frac{54d^3f}{18d^5e^3} \cdot \frac{-45e^4}{12d^4f^4}$ **$\frac{-12}{de^4f^3}$**

198   Algebra

Lesson 5-2

GOAL

See division of algebraic fractions in the two ways that this operation is found in algebra: with fractions separated by the ÷ sign, and with fractions in which the numerator and denominator are themselves fractions.

SPUR Objective

B Divide algebraic fractions.

Materials/Resources

· Lesson Master 5-2A or 5-2B
· Resource Masters 1 and 61
· Scientific or graphing calculator

HOMEWORK

Suggestions for Assignment

- Questions 1–26
- Question 27 (extra credit)
- Reading Lesson 5-3
- Covering the Ideas 5-3

Local Standards

1 Warm-Up

Consider the division $\frac{3}{4} \div \frac{2}{5}$.

1. Find the quotient. $\frac{15}{8}$
2. Verify your answer to Question 1 using decimals. $\frac{0.75}{0.4} = 1.875 = \frac{15}{8}$
3. Find a fraction $\frac{a}{b}$ equal to $\frac{3}{4}$ with $a > 20$. Find a fraction $\frac{c}{d}$ equal to $\frac{2}{5}$ with $c > 20$. Calculate $\frac{a}{b} \div \frac{c}{d}$. Explain why the quotient is or is not equal to your answer to Question 1.

   Answers vary. Sample answer: $\frac{21}{28} \div \frac{22}{55}$ $= \frac{1,155}{616} = \frac{15}{8}$. It is equal because the fractions are equal.

Lesson 5-2 Division of Algebraic Fractions

▶ **BIG IDEA** Algebraic fractions are divided in the same way as you divide numeric fractions.

Remember that two numbers are *reciprocals* if the product of the numbers is 1. The reciprocal of the number $\frac{c}{d}$ is $\frac{d}{c}$, with $c \neq 0$ and $d \neq 0$, because $\frac{c}{d} \cdot \frac{d}{c} = \frac{c \cdot d}{d \cdot c} = 1$.

When 32 ounces of orange juice are shared equally among 5 people, each person gets $\frac{1}{5}$ of a quart. This is an example of the Algebraic Definition of Division: dividing by a number is the same as multiplying by its reciprocal.

Dividing Algebraic Fractions

Consider the division of fractions $\frac{a}{b} \div \frac{c}{d}$. Since dividing by a number is the same as multiplying by its reciprocal, dividing by $\frac{c}{d}$ gives the same result as multiplying by $\frac{d}{c}$.

Dividing Fractions Property

For all real numbers a, b, c, and d, with b, c, and $d \neq 0$,
$$\frac{a}{b} \div \frac{c}{d} = \frac{a}{b} \cdot \frac{d}{c}.$$

For example, $\frac{5}{3} \div \frac{7}{11} = \frac{5}{3} \cdot \frac{11}{7} = \frac{55}{21}$. The Dividing Fractions Property is sometimes called the "invert and multiply" rule.

Mental Math

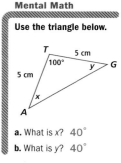

Use the triangle below.

a. What is x? 40°
b. What is y? 40°

Background

This is a relatively short and easy lesson. First we discuss the Dividing Fractions Property. Then two examples of its use are shown. The key to the lesson is to realize that $\frac{a}{b} \div \frac{c}{d}$ and $\frac{\frac{a}{b}}{\frac{c}{d}}$ are two ways to represent the same division problem.

Dividing Fractions Property. With the expression $\frac{a}{b} \div \frac{c}{d}$, we usually think to "invert and multiply." The logic is explained in the lesson preceding the statement of the Dividing Fractions Property.

Example 1

Simplify $\frac{x}{4} \div \frac{3}{5}$.

Solution Dividing by $\frac{3}{5}$ is the same as multiplying by $\frac{5}{3}$.

$$\frac{x}{4} \div \frac{3}{5} = \frac{x}{4} \cdot \frac{5}{3} = \frac{5x}{12}$$

Check Substitute some value for x. Use this number to evaluate the original expression and your answer. Suppose $x = 2$. Does $\frac{2}{4} \div \frac{3}{5} = \frac{5 \cdot 2}{12}$? To determine this, change each fraction to a decimal. Does $0.5 \div 0.6 = \frac{10}{12}$? Yes, each side equals $0.8\overline{3}$.

Simplifying Complex Fractions

Recall that a horizontal fraction bar indicates division. The division $\frac{a}{b} \div \frac{c}{d}$ can be written as $\frac{\frac{a}{b}}{\frac{c}{d}}$. Fractions of the form $\frac{\frac{a}{b}}{\frac{c}{d}}$ are called *complex fractions*. A **complex fraction** consists of three fractions; One is the numerator and the second is the denominator of a third "bigger" fraction.

$$\text{fraction in numerator} \qquad \frac{\frac{a}{b}}{\frac{c}{d}} \quad \text{"big fraction"}$$
$$\text{fraction in denominator}$$

Since a fraction is a division, one way to simplify a complex fraction is as follows: $\frac{\frac{a}{b}}{\frac{c}{d}} = \frac{a}{b} \div \frac{c}{d}$.

GUIDED

Example 2

Simplify $\frac{\frac{6x}{5}}{\frac{9x}{10}}$.

Solution Rewrite the fraction as a division.

$$\frac{\frac{6x}{5}}{\frac{9x}{10}} = \underline{\ ?\ } \div \underline{\ ?\ } \qquad \frac{6x}{5}, \frac{9x}{10}$$

$$\frac{6x}{5} \div \underline{\ ?\ } = \frac{6x}{5} \cdot \underline{\ ?\ } \quad \text{Dividing Fractions Property} \quad \frac{9x}{10}, \frac{10}{9x}$$

$$= \frac{\underline{\ ?\ } \times 60}{\underline{\ ?\ } \times 45} \quad \text{Multiply the fractions.}$$

$$= \frac{4}{3} \qquad \text{Simplify.}$$

Check Let $x = 20$. Then $\frac{6x}{5} = \underline{\ ?\ }$ and $\frac{9x}{10} = \underline{\ ?\ }$. 24; 18

Does $\frac{6x}{5} \div \frac{9x}{10} = \frac{4}{3}$? $\underline{\ ?\ }$ yes

Division of Algebraic Fractions **259**

2 Teaching

Notes on the Lesson

When do we want to divide fractions? The answer is simple: whenever we divide and the numbers are fractions. In the rest of the chapter, students will see situations that require division, and sometimes the numbers being divided are fractions.

Additional Examples

Example 1 Simplify $\frac{y}{9} \div \frac{7}{8}$. $\frac{8y}{63}$

Example 2 Simplify $\frac{\frac{7x}{4}}{\frac{21x}{8}}$.

$$\frac{\frac{7x}{4}}{\frac{21x}{8}} = \frac{7x}{4} \cdot \underline{\ ?\ } = \frac{\underline{\ ?\ } x}{\underline{\ ?\ } x} = \underline{\ ?\ }.$$

$$\frac{8}{21x}; 56; 84; \frac{2}{3}$$

Accommodating the Learner ⬇

Before moving on, check students' understanding of the Algebraic Definition of Division. Work with them on a variety of examples until they are clear on why dividing by a number is the same as multiplying by the reciprocal.

ENGLISH LEARNERS
Vocabulary Development

Students now have definitions for fractions, complex fractions, algebraic fractions, and reciprocals. Ask students if any of the categories can overlap. For example, can two complex fractions be reciprocals? Can a fraction be complex and algebraic? Ask them to give examples to support their claims.

5-2

3 Assignment

Recommended Assignment

- Questions 1–26
- Question 27 (extra credit)
- Reading Lesson 5-3
- Covering the Ideas 5-3

Notes on the Questions

Questions 5–11 Point out to students that these questions may seem to be two different types, but they are all division of fractions. If students do not see Questions 8 and 11 as division of fractions, you can write x as $\frac{x}{1}$ in Question 8, and 6π as $\frac{6\pi}{1}$ in Question 11.

When entering complex fractions into a calculator, be sure to group the numerator fraction in parentheses and the denominator fraction in parentheses. Otherwise, the calculator will follow the order of operations and the result will be incorrect.

For $\dfrac{\frac{2}{3}}{\frac{5}{12}}$, enter $(2/3)/(5/12)$. If you enter $2/3/5/12$, you will

obtain $\frac{1}{90}$, which is incorrect. The correct quotient is $\frac{8}{5}$ or 1.6.

STOP QY

▶ QY

Write $\dfrac{\frac{3}{8}}{\frac{3}{11}}$ as a decimal.

Questions

COVERING THE IDEAS

1. In this lesson, it is noted that $\frac{5}{3} \div \frac{7}{11} = \frac{55}{21}$. Check this result by approximating all three fractions by decimals.

2. State the Algebraic Definition of Division.

In 3 and 4, fill in the blanks.

3. a. $\frac{m}{n} = m \div \underline{\ ?\ }\ n$ b. $\frac{m}{n} = m \cdot \underline{\ ?\ }\ \frac{1}{n}$

4. a. $\dfrac{\frac{p}{q}}{\frac{r}{s}} = \frac{p}{q} \div \underline{\ ?\ }\ \frac{r}{s}$ b. $\frac{p}{q} \div \frac{r}{s} = \frac{p}{q} \cdot \underline{\ ?\ }\ \frac{s}{r}$

In 5–11, simplify the expression.

5. $\dfrac{\frac{4}{5}}{\frac{5}{6}}\ \frac{24}{25}$ 6. $\dfrac{\frac{4}{x}}{\frac{x}{y}}\ \frac{4y}{x^2}$ 7. $\dfrac{\frac{3a}{2}}{\frac{a}{2}}\ 3$ 8. $\frac{1}{2} \div x\ \frac{1}{2x}$

9. $\frac{m}{30} \div \frac{n}{84}\ \frac{14m}{5n}$ 10. $\frac{8v}{5} \div \frac{2v}{25}\ 20$ 11. $\dfrac{\frac{3\pi}{5}}{6\pi}\ \frac{1}{10}$

APPLYING THE MATHEMATICS

12. Cody and Troy solved $\frac{3}{8}x = 15$ using different methods. Explain why Cody and Troy got the same solution.

Cody's Method

$$\dfrac{\frac{3}{8}x}{\frac{3}{8}} = \dfrac{15}{\frac{3}{8}}$$

$$x = 15 \div \frac{3}{8}$$

$$x = 15 \cdot \frac{8}{3}$$

$$x = 40$$

Troy's Method

$$\frac{8}{3} \cdot \frac{3}{8}x = 15 \cdot \frac{8}{3}$$

$$x = 40$$

13. The area of a rectangle with side lengths of m and $\frac{4}{23}$ is 16. Find the value of m. $m = 92$

Answers (right margin):

1. $\frac{5}{3} \approx 1.67$, $\frac{7}{11} \approx 0.64$, $1.67 \div 0.64 \approx 2.61 \approx \frac{55}{21}$

2. Dividing yields the same result as multiplying by the reciprocal.

12. Dividing both sides of an equation by $\frac{3}{8}$ gives the same result as multiplying both sides by $\frac{8}{3}$.

Accommodating the Learner ⬆

Ask students to consider complex fractions

that fit the pattern $\dfrac{\frac{a}{b}}{\frac{1}{d}}$. What is the result?

Ask students to defend this result by using the Algebraic Definition of Division.

$\frac{a}{b} \cdot d = \frac{ad}{b}$; dividing by $\frac{1}{d}$ is the same as multiplying by the reciprocal, d.

5-2A Lesson Master

Questions on SPUR Objectives
See pages 320–323 for objectives.

SKILLS Objective B

In 1–4, fill in the blanks.

1. $\dfrac{\frac{2}{5}}{\frac{7}{8}} = \frac{2}{5} \div \frac{7}{8}$ 2. $\frac{1}{n} \div \frac{-48}{n} = \frac{1}{n} \cdot \frac{n}{-48}$

3. $\frac{11w}{12} = 11w \cdot \frac{1}{12}$ 4. $\dfrac{\frac{n}{d}}{\frac{n}{d}} = \frac{n}{d} \cdot \frac{n}{d}$

In 5–14, simplify.

5. $\frac{9x}{3} \div \frac{6x}{2}$ __1__   6. $\frac{64r^2}{9} \div \frac{24}{r}\ \frac{8r^3}{27}$

7. $\frac{34x}{3y} \div \frac{17x^2}{2}\ \frac{4}{3xy}$ 8. $4xt \div \frac{16t}{5t^2}\ \frac{5t^2}{4}$

9. $\frac{45ab}{2c} \div \frac{8a}{b}\ \frac{5b}{2}$ 10. $\frac{72}{r^2} \div \frac{4t}{3}\ \frac{54}{x^4}$

11. $\frac{8r}{s}\ \frac{wq}{p}$ 12. $\frac{24x}{30b}\ \frac{4a^2}{3b^2}$

13. $\frac{130h^2}{3b}\ \frac{15p^2}{4}$ 14. $\frac{144x^2}{12p^2}\ \frac{12a}{b^2}$

14. Half of a pizza was divided equally among 3 people. How much of the original pizza did each person receive? $\frac{1}{6}$

15. Le Parfum Company produces perfume in 200-ounce batches and bottles it in quarter-ounce bottles.

   a. Write a division problem that will tell you how many bottles will be filled by one batch. $200 \div \frac{1}{4}$

   b. Find the answer. 800

16. A dozen bagels are bought for a group of x people. On average, how many bagels are there per person? $\frac{12}{x}$

In 17–19, simplify the expression.

17. $b \div \frac{1}{b}$ b^2

18. $\frac{xy}{21} \div \frac{x}{47}$ $\frac{47y}{21}$

19. $\frac{\frac{12m}{5}}{\frac{mn}{20}}$ $\frac{48}{n}$

20a.i. $x \div y = 6; y \div x = \frac{1}{6}$

20. a. Evaluate $x \div y$ and $y \div x$ for each of the following.

   i. $x = 12$ and $y = 2$ ii. $x = 20$ and $y = -5$ iii. $x = \frac{2}{3}$ and $y = \frac{4}{5}$

   b. Do your answers in Part a indicate that division is commutative? Explain your answer.

   c. Describe how $x \div y$ and $y \div x$ are related in general. They are multiplicative inverses of each other.

Machines and attached tanks distill perfume in the Molinard Perfumerie in France.

20a.ii. $x \div y = -4;$

$y \div x = -\frac{1}{4}$

20a.iii. $x \div y = \frac{5}{6};$

$y \div x = \frac{6}{5}$

20b. No. $x \div y$ is not equal to $y \div x$, as indicated by Part a.

REVIEW

21. Multiply and simplify $\frac{5}{13}d \cdot \left(\frac{d}{5} \cdot \frac{5}{13}d\right)$. **(Lesson 5-1)** $\frac{5d^3}{169}$

22. The graph at the right compares the values of two computers A and B over time. **(Lesson 4-3)**

   a. Which computer is decreasing in value faster? A

   b. About how much does the value of the computer you found in Part a change each year?

   c. After about how many years do the computers have the same value? about 2.5 yr

   d. Suppose you buy these two computers and you wish to sell one of them after 3 years. For which computer will you get more money? About how much more will you get for it? for computer B, about $80 more

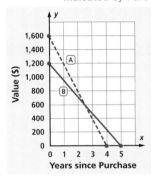

Value ($) vs *Years since Purchase*

22b. It decreases by $400 per year.

23. a. Solve $V + 0.06V - 100 = 14{,}289.16$. $V = 13{,}574.7$

   b. **Fill in the Blanks** The equation in Part a could arise from this situation. After a discount of $100 and with a ___?___ tax, the car cost ___?___. Find V, the cost of ___?___. **(Lessons 4-1, 3-5)** 6%; $14,289.16; the car before taxes or discounts

Notes on the Questions

Question 15 You might ask students to generalize this problem. Suppose Le Parfum Company produced the perfume in n-ounce batches and bottled it in quarter-ounce bottles. Then how many bottles would be filled by a batch? (4n)

Question 20 Evaluating for the fractions in (iii) is critical so that students realize that x and y do not have to be integers.

Question 27 The first thing to notice is that the area of the region is 24 square units, so each piece will have an area of 4 square units.

5-2

4 Wrap-Up

Ongoing Assessment

Ask students to simplify the following

fraction: $\dfrac{\frac{2xy}{5z}}{\frac{12x^2}{3y}}$. Students should pair up,

and as one partner does a step, the other should list the property that justifies it. $\dfrac{y^2}{10xz}$

24. Let $y =$ the depth of a point in Lake Baikal in Siberia, the deepest lake in the world. (**Lesson 3-6**)
    a. Give a reasonable domain for y.
    b. It is known that the deepest point in the Lake Baikal is 1,940 meters below the surface. What inequality does y satisfy? $-1{,}940 \le y \le 0$
    c. Graph the solution set to Part b.

25. Use the picture of the balance below. The boxes are equal in weight and the other objects are one-kilogram weights. (**Lesson 3-3**)

 $=$? $= 1$ kg

    a. Write an equation describing the situation, with B representing the weight of one box. $3B + 2 = 10$
    b. What is the weight of one box? $\frac{8}{3}$ kg

26. A circle has a radius of 1.2 meters. Find its area to the nearest tenth of a square meter. (**Previous Course**) 4.5 m^2

EXPLORATION

27. Congruent figures are figures with the same size and shape. Split this region into 6 congruent pieces. See margin.

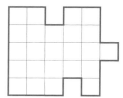

Lake Baikal is situated nearly in the center of Asia in a huge stone bowl set 445 meters above sea level.

Source: www.irkutsk.org

24a. Answers vary. Sample answer: 0 m to 11,000 m. We choose 11,000 m as the maximum reasonable depth, since the deepest point in an ocean is about 10,900 m deep and lakes are, in general, shallower than oceans.

24c.

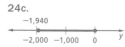

QY ANSWER

1.375

Additional Answers

27.

Lesson 5-3 Rates

Vocabulary

rate

reciprocal rates

▶ **BIG IDEA** The quotient of two measures with different units is a rate.

What Is a Rate?

In Lesson 5-2, 32 ounces of orange juice were split evenly among 5 people. By doing the division with the units left in, we see that the answer is a *rate*.

$$\frac{32 \text{ oz}}{5 \text{ people}} = \frac{6.4 \text{ oz}}{\text{person}} = 6.4 \text{ oz/person} = 6.4 \text{ ounces per person}$$

Every rate consists of a number and a *rate unit*. You may see rate units expressed using a slash "/" or a horizontal bar "——". The slash and the bar are read "per" or "for each." The rate unit $\frac{\text{oz}}{\text{person}}$ is read "ounces per person."

In general, a **rate** is the quotient of two quantities with different units.

How Are Rates Calculated?

Since rates are quotients, rates are calculated by dividing.

Example 1

Tanya and Gary drove 400 miles in 8 hours during a trip. What was their average speed?

Solution 1 Divide the distance in miles by the time in hours.

$$\frac{400 \text{ mi}}{8 \text{ hr}}$$

Separate the measurement units from the numerical parts.

$$\frac{400 \text{ mi}}{8 \text{ hr}} = \frac{400}{8} \frac{\text{mi}}{\text{hr}} = 50 \text{ miles per hour}$$

They were traveling at an average speed of 50 miles per hour.

Solution 2 You could also divide the time by the distance.

$$\frac{8 \text{ hours}}{400 \text{ miles}} = \frac{8}{400} \frac{\text{hr}}{\text{mi}} = \frac{1}{50} \text{ hour per mile}$$

This means that on the average, it took them $\frac{1}{50}$ of an hour to travel each mile.

Mental Math

Given $3x + 4 = 12$, evaluate:

a. $3x + 5$. 13

b. $3x + 12$. 20

c. $6x + 8$. 24

GOAL

Review how rates are calculated and used, and then use rates to review the division of positive and negative numbers.

SPUR Objectives

B Divide algebraic fractions.

E Use rates in real situations.

Materials/Resources

· Lesson Master 5-3A or 5-3B
· Resource Masters 62 and 63
· Scientific or graphing calculator

HOMEWORK

Suggestions for Assignment

• Questions 1–28
• Question 29 (extra credit)
• Reading Lesson 5-4
• Covering the Ideas 5-4

Local Standards

1 Warm-Up

1. A teacher has two algebra classes with a total of 71 students.
   a. How many students is this per class? 35.5
   b. In your answer to Part a, what is the rate unit? students per class

2. At a rate r, a person goes a distance d in a time t. How are r, d, and t related? Give an example with specific values of the three variables, indicating their units.
   $d = rt$; Answers vary. Sample answer: r could be 20 miles per hour, d could be 60 miles and t could be 3 hours.

3. Make up an example in which a rate is negative. Answers vary. Sample answer: 8,000 more people moved out of the city during the past three years than moved in.

Background

What is a rate? A division problem involving different units can be interpreted as a rate. Students who have had previous UCSMP courses will have seen this as a basic application of division. The Rate Model for Division says if a and b are quantities with different units, then $\frac{a}{b}$ is the amount of quantity a per quantity b.

Rate is a fundamental idea in mathematics. In the next chapter, slope is studied as a rate of change. Students have used rates in problems that involve rate-factor

multiplication, but the rates were given. Here, emphasis is on finding the rate.

The word "rate" usually conjures up the notion of "speed." However, there are other ways to utilize rates such as averages, population density, and conversion factors. We use rates in this lesson to indicate why division with negative numbers has the properties it does and why division by zero is impossible.

5-3

2 Teaching

Notes on the Lesson

How are rates calculated? Because rates are meaningless without units, you should stress that students show rate units. The unit is as important as the rate.

Rates and negative numbers. These examples may seem contrived to students, but they are not. In the next chapter, students will be calculating rates of change. Depending on the direction of the change, they may have positive or negative numbers in the numerator and denominator of the slope formula. The equality of the rate $\frac{-12 \text{ degrees}}{5 \text{ hours}}$ (found in Part b of Example 2) and $\frac{12 \text{ degrees}}{-5 \text{ hours}}$ (discussed in the paragraph after Example 2) is reflected in the choice one has for the first point of the two points in the slope formula.

Additional Examples

Example 1 In a job interview, Matthew has to take a typing test. In 6 minutes, Matthew types 270 words. The job is his if he can type 55 words per minute. Will he get the job? What is his average number of words per minute? **No, because he only types 45 words per minute.**

Example 2

a. If a car accelerates from 10 to 60 miles per hour in 45 seconds, write the change of speed in miles per hour per second. **approximately 1.11 mph increase per second**

b. If the car decelerates from 90 miles per hour to 55 miles per hour in 10 seconds, what is the change of speed in miles per hour per second? **−3.5 mph per second or a decrease of 3.5 mph per second**

In Example 1, the first solution gives the rate in *miles per hour.* The second solution gives the rate in *hours per mile,* or how long it takes to travel one mile. These are **reciprocal rates.** Notice that $\frac{1}{50}$ of an hour is $\frac{1}{50} \cdot 60$ min, or 1.2 minutes. In other words, it takes a little over a minute to go one mile. Either rate is correct. The one to use depends on the situation in which you use it.

Rates and Negative Numbers

Rates can be positive or negative quantities.

> **Example 2**
>
> **a.** If the temperature rises from 70 to 85 degrees in 2 hours, what is the change in temperature in degrees per hour?
>
> **b.** If the temperature goes down from 44 to 32 degrees in 5 hours, what is the rate of temperature change in degrees per hour?
>
> **Solutions** To find the rate, divide the number of degrees changed by the number of hours.
>
> **a.** rate of temperature change $= \dfrac{(85 - 70) \text{ degrees}}{2 \text{ hours}}$
>
> $= \dfrac{15 \text{ degrees}}{2 \text{ hours}}$
>
> = rise of 7.5 degrees per hour
>
> **b.** rate of temperature change $= \dfrac{(32 - 44) \text{ degrees}}{5 \text{ hours}}$
>
> $= \dfrac{-12 \text{ degrees}}{5 \text{ hours}}$
>
> = drop of 2.4 degrees per hour or −2.4 degrees per hour

 QY1

In Part b of Example 2, the rate −2.4 degrees per hour came from dividing a negative number (−12 degrees) by a positive one (5 hours). The same negative rate can be found by dividing 12 by −5, which would describe the 12-degree rise in temperature that would come from moving backward in time 5 hours.

So $\frac{-12}{5}$ degrees per hour $= \dfrac{-12 \text{ degrees}}{5 \text{ hr}} = \dfrac{12 \text{ degrees}}{-5 \text{ hr}}$.

> ▶ **QY1**
>
> Find the rate of change of the number of people at a restaurant if it decreased from 161 to 98 people in 45 minutes. (Pay attention to positives and negatives.)

Accommodating the Learner ⬆

In each of our examples so far, there has been only one value that is a solution to each question. Consider discussing with students some basic equations that have more than one solution. For example, ask students to consider the equation $x^2 - 4 = 0$. Students will immediately see the solution $x = 2$, but you may need to help them see that $x = -2$ is also a solution. Once they understand this, ask them to identify for what value(s) of x is $\frac{x^2 - 1}{x^2 - 4}$ undefined, and what value(s) of x make $\frac{x^2 - 1}{x^2 - 4} = 0$. **$x = 2$ and $x = -2$; $x = 1$ and $x = -1$**

Here is a way to think of this situation. If you change a numerator or denominator of a fraction to its opposite, then the value of the fraction also changes to its opposite.

Negative Fractions

In general, for all a and b, and $b \neq 0$, $-\frac{a}{b} = \frac{-a}{b} = \frac{a}{-b}$.

When *both* the numerator and denominator are changed to their opposites, the value of the fraction is unchanged.

$$\frac{-a}{-b} = \frac{-1 \cdot a}{-1 \cdot b} \quad \text{Multiplication Property of } -1$$
$$= \frac{a}{b} \quad \text{Equal Fractions Property}$$

Fractions with negative numbers are common, as you will see in the next chapter.

Division by Zero and Rates

Consider the rate $\frac{0 \text{ meters}}{10 \text{ seconds}}$, which has 0 in the numerator. This means that you do not travel at all in 10 seconds. So your rate is 0 meters per second. This reinforces that $\frac{0}{10} = 0$. In contrast, try to imagine a rate such as $\frac{10 \text{ meters}}{0 \text{ seconds}}$, which has 0 in the denominator. This would mean you travel 10 meters in 0 seconds. For this to occur, you would have to be in two places at the same time! That is impossible. Rates show that the denominator of a fraction can never be zero.

When a fraction has a variable in its denominator, then the expression is said to be *undefined* for any value of the variable that would make the denominator zero.

GUIDED

Example 3

a. For what value(s) of x is $\frac{x}{x+4}$ undefined?

b. For what value(s) of x does $\frac{x}{x+4} = 0$?

Solutions

a. A fraction is undefined whenever its __?__ is zero. denominator

So $\frac{x}{x+4}$ is undefined when __?__ = 0. $x+4$

Solve the equation on the preceding line for x. $x = $ __?__. -4

Therefore, $\frac{x}{x+4}$ is undefined when $x = $ __?__. -4

(continued on next page)

Additional Example

Example 3

a. For what value(s) of x is $\frac{x+2}{x-3}$ undefined?

b. For what value(s) of x does $\frac{x+2}{x-3} = 0$?

Solutions

a. A fraction is undefined whenever its __?__ is zero. denominator

So $\frac{x+2}{x-3}$ is undefined when

__?__ = 0. $x-3$

Solve the equation on the preceding line for x. $x = $ __?__. 3

Therefore, $\frac{x+2}{x-3}$ is undefined when $x = $ __?__. 3

b. A fraction equals zero whenever its __?__ is zero. numerator

So $\frac{x+2}{x-3} = 0$ when __?__ = 0. $x+2$

Therefore, $\frac{x+2}{x-3} = 0$ when $x = $ __?__. -2

3 Assignment

Recommended Assignment

- Questions 1–28
- Question 29 (extra credit)
- Reading Lesson 5-4
- Covering the Ideas 5-4

Notes on the Questions

Question 4 Many rates are possible, but we are thinking of the average number of hours of sleep per night.

Question 7 This question exemplifies the property $\frac{-x}{y} = \frac{x}{-y}$.

Additional Answers

1. hundreds of thousands of people per year; $40 per ticket; $150 per ticket; $20 per hour; 50 dollars per hour to park; 230 miles per hour; 354 kilometers per hour; 2.5 miles per lap

---

b. A fraction equals zero whenever its ___?___ is zero. **numerator**

So $\frac{x}{x + 4} = 0$ when ___?___ $= 0$. **x**

Therefore, $\frac{x}{x + 4} = 0$ when $x = $ ___?___ . **0**

STOP QY2

 **QY2**

a. For what values of k is $\frac{2k - 6}{k - 55}$ undefined?

b. For what values of k does $\frac{2k - 6}{k - 55} = 0$?

Questions

COVERING THE IDEAS

1. Name all of the rates (including the rate units) in the following paragraph. **See margin.**

   The Indianapolis 500 is one of the most famous auto races in the United States, with hundreds of thousands of people attending annually. Attendees in 2006 paid from $40 to $150 per ticket plus $20 to $50 per hour to park. Drivers reached speeds of more than 230 mph (354 km/hr) as they raced the 2.5-mile oval track.

2. Give an example of a rate with a rate unit that is not mentioned in the reading of this lesson.

An IRL IndyCar Series car accelerates from 0 to 100 mph in less than three seconds.

Source: www.indy500.com

In 3–5, calculate a rate suggested by the given information.

3. Danielle walked her dog 6 blocks in t minutes. $\frac{6}{t}$ **blocks per minute**

4. In the last seven days, Salali slept 6.5 hours one night, 7 hours two nights, 7.5 hours two nights, 8 hours one night, and 9.5 hours one night. **Answers vary. Sample answer:** $\frac{53}{7} \approx 7.57$ **hr/night**

5. In 2004, 2.3 billion books were sold in the United States, which had a population of about 296 million people. **about 7.77 books per person**

6. In playing a video game 4 times, Bailey scored a points, b points, c points, and d points.

   a. Give an expression for her average score. $\frac{a + b + c + d}{4}$

   b. Bailey's average is a rate. What is the rate unit? **points/game**

2. Answers vary. Sample answer: John is typing at a speed of 30 words/min.

7. Translate the change in time and temperature into positive and negative quantities. Then calculate the rate. $\frac{-5 \text{ degrees}}{8 \text{ hours}} = -\frac{5}{8}$ **degrees per hour**

   a. 8 hours ago it was 5 degrees warmer than it is now.

   b. If this rate continues, then 8 hours from now it will be 5 degrees colder. $-\frac{5}{8}$ **degrees per hour • 8 hours = –5 degrees**

8. **Multiple Choice** Which of these numbers is *not* equal to the others? **C**

   A $\frac{-153x}{82}$ **B** $-\frac{153x}{82}$ **C** $\frac{-153x}{-82}$ **D** $\frac{153x}{-82}$ **E** $\frac{-(-153)x}{-82}$

266 Division and Proportions in Algebra

Extension

Discuss the concept of averages and how it relates to the concept of rates. Describe taking the average as adding the value for each item and dividing by the number of items. Then the average is this rate: typical value per 1 item. Provide several examples to reinforce the concept. **suggested examples: test scores in algebra class, number of field goals in a basketball season**

In 9–11, an expression is given.

  a. **For what values of the variable is the expression equal to zero?**

  b. **For what value of the variable is the expression undefined?**

9. $\frac{w-12}{w+5}$ a. $w = 12$ 10. $\frac{17}{m-4}$ a. none   11. $\frac{2+y}{15}$ a. $y = -2$
               b. $w = -5$ b. $m = 4$ b. none

APPLYING THE MATHEMATICS

12. When you buy something in quantity, the cost of one item is the *unit cost*. Find the unit cost for each of the following.

  a. frozen juice at 3 cans for $5   about $1.67 per can

  b. 500 sheets of notebook paper for $2.49   about half a cent per sheet

  c. x paper clips for $0.69 $\frac{\$0.69}{x}$ per paper clip

13. Let $y = \frac{1+x}{2-x}$. Complete the table at the right.

14. A very fast runner can run a half-mile in 2 minutes. Express the average rate in each of these units.

  a. miles per minute   b. minutes per mile   c. miles per hour

15. For each state below, find the number of people per square mile to the nearest tenth. This is the state's *population density* for 2005.   15a. 1,000 people/mile^2

  a. New Jersey: population = 8.7 million; area = 8,700 square miles

  b. Montana: population = 0.9 million; area = 147,000 square miles
    about 6.1 people/mile^2

16. **Multiple Choice** In t minutes, a copy machine made n copies. At this rate, how many copies per second does the machine make?   A

  A $\frac{n}{60t}$ B $\frac{60t}{n}$ C $\frac{60n}{t}$ D $\frac{t}{60n}$

x	y	
-3	?	$-\frac{2}{5}$
-2	?	$-\frac{1}{4}$
-1	0 ?	
0	?	$\frac{1}{2}$
1	2 ?	
2	?	undefined
3	-4 ?	

14a. $\frac{1}{4}$ mi per min

14b. 4 min per mi

14c. 15 mi per hr

17. The Talkalot cell phone company sells a pay-as-you-go phone with 700 minutes for $70.

  a. What is the rate per minute? $0.10/min

  b. What is the rate per hour? $6/hr

  c. Elizabeth buys a phone and talks for m minutes. What is the value of the phone now?   70 − 0.10m dollars

REVIEW

In 18–20, simplify the expression. (Lessons 5-2, 5-1, 2-2)

18. $\frac{4xy}{-3y^2} \cdot \frac{-6y}{5x^2}$ $\frac{8}{5x}$ 19. $\frac{ab}{21} \div \frac{a}{4b}$ $\frac{4b^2}{21}$

20. a. $\frac{-8n}{3} \cdot \frac{8n}{3}$ $-\frac{64n^2}{9}$ b. $\frac{-8n}{3} + \frac{8n}{3}$ 0

21. Alice has n pounds of bologna. If she uses $\frac{1}{8}$ pound of bologna to make one bologna sandwich, how many bologna sandwiches can Alice make? (**Lesson 5-2**)   8n

Notes on the Questions

Question 12 Some books use the phrase "unit rate" as a rate when the denominator is 1 unit. We do not use this term because of the confusion with "rate unit."

Question 17 This kind of problem is found on some standardized tests.

Question 29 The debt per capita is very high. On the other hand, sometimes a rate is so near zero that the denominator is multiplied by a number in order to make it easier to understand the rate. For example, in 2002 there were 0.1136 births in the U.S. per woman aged 25–29 (the age group with the most births). This number is difficult to understand, so the rate is reported as 113.6 births per 1,000 women. Similarly there were 0.006848 deaths per infant birth in the U.S. in 2001, a number that is reported as 684.8 deaths per 100,000 infant births. While the reported numbers are easier to understand, without knowing the rate unit a person can easily be misled to believe that a rate is much greater than it actually is.

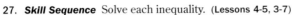

4 Wrap-Up

Ongoing Assessment

Ask students to write a summary of when a rate is undefined and when it is zero. Request that students include a justification and an example.

Project Update

If you have not had students look over the projects on pages 315–316, you might want to do so now. Project 2, Population Densities, on page 315, relates to the content of this lesson.

In 22–25, simplify the expression. (Lesson 5-2)

22. $\frac{9}{4} \frac{45}{5}$ or 11.25

23. $\frac{-6}{7} \div \frac{-6}{5}$ $\frac{5}{7}$

24. $\frac{a}{4b} \div \frac{b}{6}$ $\frac{3a}{2b^2}$

25. $\frac{2d}{3} \div 5d$ $\frac{2}{15}$

26. **a.** Draw a square with side of length x.
   b. Shade or color the diagram to show $\frac{x}{2} \cdot \frac{3x}{4}$.
   c. What is the result of the multiplication? (Lesson 5-1) $\frac{3x^2}{8}$ or $\frac{3}{8}x^2$

26a.

27. **Skill Sequence** Solve each inequality. (Lessons 4-5, 3-7)
   a. $-y > 10$ $y < -10$
   b. $-5x < 10$ $x > -2$
   c. $-2A + 3 \leq 10$ $A \geq -3.5$
   d. $-9B + 7 \geq 10 + 3B$ $B \leq -0.25$

26b.

28. **a.** How many seconds are in one day? 86,400 sec
   b. A second is what fraction of a day? (Previous Course) $\frac{1}{86,400}$

EXPLORATION

29. Use the Internet, an almanac, or some other source to find the estimated current U.S. national debt and an estimate of the U.S. population. Then calculate the average debt per capita. (The phrase *per capita* means "per person.")

   Answers vary. Sample answer: As of August 16, 2006, the national debt was about $8.463 trillion. The national population was about 299 million. The average debt per capita was about $28,300.

QY ANSWERS

1. a decrease of 1.4 people/min

2. **a.** $k = 55$
   b. $k = 3$

Lesson Master pages (5-3B)

5-3B Lesson Master

Questions on SPUR Objectives
See pages 320–323 for objectives.

SKILLS Objective B

In 1 and 2, use $\frac{6+2x}{3x}$.

1. For what value of x is the expression undefined? $x = 0$

2. For what value of x is the expression equal to zero? $x = -3$

In 3 and 4, use $\frac{a}{a-4}$.

3. For what value of a is the expression undefined? $a = 4$

4. For what value of a is the expression equal to zero? $a = 0$

In 5 and 6, use $\frac{5c}{3c-1}$.

5. For what value of c is the expression undefined? $c = \frac{1}{3}$

6. For what value of c is the expression equal to zero? $c = 0$

In 7–14, find the unit cost.

7. 24 cans of soda for $4.99 $0.21

8. 4 batteries for $5.99 $1.50

9. 48 granola bars for $7.50 $0.16

10. 36 rolls of toilet paper for $14.00 $0.39

11. x paper plates for $12 $\frac{\$12}{x}$

12. y fruit cups for $6.49 $\frac{\$6.49}{y}$

13. 12 markers for $a $\frac{\$a}{12}$

14. 10 juice boxes for $b $\frac{\$b}{10}$

Jason delivers 300 newspapers in 90 minutes.

15. How many newspapers does he deliver per minute? about 3 newspapers

16. How many newspapers does he deliver per hour? 200 newspapers

Algebra 203

5-3B page 2

USES Objective E

In 17–21, calculate the rate for the given situation.

17. Hurricane Helene traveled 480 miles in 48 hours.
   a. miles per hour 10 mi/hr
   b. miles per minute $\frac{1}{6}$ mi/min

18. Anastasia spent $42.50 on 5 movie tickets. $8.50 per ticket

19. Zanobia is paying $22,860 for her car over a period of 60 months. $381 per month

20. Ten inches of snow fell in 12 hours. $\frac{5}{6}$ inch per hour

21. The word "the" is the most used word in the English language. At what rate is it used in the following famous quote from Carl Friedrich Gauss?
   Mathematics is the queen of the sciences. 2 out of every 7 words

In 22–26, solve the problem.

22. In 2005, California's total population of 36,132,147 ranked number one in the United States. California has 155,959 square miles of land. If its population were distributed evenly throughout the state, how many people would live in each square mile of land? about 232 people

23. Printer A prints 450 pages in 15 minutes. Printer B prints 875 pages in 25 minutes. Which printer prints at a faster rate? B

24. In 2003, researchers believed that by 2008 over 90 million additional laptops and PDAs will have wireless capabilities to access the Internet. What is the yearly rate of increase for these technology tools to have wireless capabilities? 18 million per year

25. A 42-ounce carton of oatmeal costs $3.20. An 18-ounce carton costs $1.25 on sale. Which size of oatmeal is the better buy? 18-ounce

26. A 1-ounce serving of toasted chips has 130 calories of which 40 calories are from fat. A 1-ounce serving of potato chips has 150 calories of which 90 calories are from fat. Which chips have a lower rate of fat in relationship to total number of calories? toasted chips

204 Algebra

Lesson 5-4
Multiplying and Dividing Rates

Vocabulary

conversion rate

▶ **BIG IDEA** When rates are multiplied or divided, the unit of the answer follows rules of arithmetic on the units of the original rates.

Rates can be multiplied or divided by other quantities. The units are multiplied as if they were numeric fractions. Keeping the units in the calculations can help you understand the meaning.

If you bought 2.5 pounds of fish at $8.49 a pound, it would cost $2.5 \text{ lb} \cdot 8.49 \frac{\text{dollars}}{\text{lb}} = 21.225$ dollars, or $21.23.
Notice how the unit "lb" in "2.5 lb" cancels the unit "lb" in the denominator of $\frac{\text{dollars}}{\text{lb}}$, so that the result is in dollars.

Conversion Rates

A **conversion rate** is a rate determined from an equality between two quantities with different units. For example, since 1 hour = 60 minutes, dividing one unit by the other equals 1.

$$\frac{1 \text{ hour}}{60 \text{ min}} = \frac{60 \text{ min}}{1 \text{ hour}} = 1$$

Both $\frac{1 \text{ hour}}{60 \text{ min}}$ and $\frac{60 \text{ min}}{1 \text{ hour}}$ are conversion rates. Multiplying a quantity by a conversion rate does not change its value.

Example 1

On average, an adult human heart beats about 70 times per minute. At this rate, how many times does a heart beat in a 365-day year?

Solution We begin with the given information and multiply by conversion rates until one minute is converted into one year.

$$70 \frac{\text{beats}}{\text{minute}} = 70 \frac{\text{beats}}{\text{minute}} \cdot \frac{60 \text{ minutes}}{1 \text{ hour}} \cdot \frac{24 \text{ hours}}{1 \text{ day}} \cdot \frac{365 \text{ days}}{1 \text{ year}}$$

$$= 70 \cdot 60 \cdot 24 \cdot 365 \frac{\text{beats}}{\text{year}}$$

$$= 36,792,000 \frac{\text{beats}}{\text{year}}$$

The Pike Place Market in Seattle, Washington, attracts 10 million visitors per year.

Source: Pike Place Market

Mental Math

Find a pair of numbers x and y that satisfy the equation.

a. $2x + 3y = 600$
  $x = 150, y = 100$
b. $2x - 3y = 600$
  $x = 450, y = 100$
c. $20x + 30y = 600$
  $x = 15, y = 10$

Background

Units can be combined in the same way that numbers and variables are combined. Students are familiar with this in adding $3a + 2a$ just as they might add 3 apples and 2 apples. Similarly, if the sides of a rectangle are measured in a particular unit, say meters, then the area is measured in square meters. In calculating area, 3 meters is multiplied by 5 meters in the same way that $3m$ is multiplied by $5m$ to get $15m^2$. In this lesson, unit arithmetic is applied with fractions.

Conversion rates. A conversion rate may be considered as either a rate or a ratio. It is a rate when we think of the quantity as "60 minutes per hour," but it is a ratio when we realize that the quotient is 1.

Reciprocal rates. Reciprocal rates are meaningless without the rate units. "Pages per day" is not the same unit as "days per page," but "5 pages per day" is the same quantity as "$\frac{1}{5}$ day per page."

GOAL

Apply the rules for multiplying and dividing fractions to rate situations.

SPUR Objective

F Convert units and use reciprocal rates in real situations.

Materials/Resources

· Lesson Master 5-4A or 5-4B
· Resource Master 64
· Scientific or graphing calculator

HOMEWORK

Suggestions for Assignment

• Questions 1–26
• Question 27 (extra credit)
• Reading Lesson 5-5
• Covering the Ideas 5-5

Local Standards

1 Warm-Up

1. If you throw a ball into the air, it will rise until the negative acceleration of gravity counterbalances the acceleration you gave the ball, and then it returns to Earth. If an object is propelled high enough and traveling fast enough, the decreasing power of gravity will not be enough to bring it back to earth. The speed required to propel an object out of the Earth's gravitational pull is called the *escape velocity* and is about 25,000 miles per hour. (Use the conversion 1 kilometer ≈ 0.62 miles.)
   a. How much is that speed in miles per minute? **about 417**
   b. How much is that speed in miles per second? **about 6.94**
   c. How much is that speed in kilometers per second? **about 11.17**
2. The escape velocity from the moon is about 2,373 meters per second. How many miles per hour is this? **about 5,308**

2 Teaching

Notes on the Lesson

Conversion rates. Some teachers like to spread out the steps of Example 1 by multiplying by one fraction at a time.

$$70 \frac{beats}{min} = 70 \frac{beats}{min} \cdot \frac{60 \, min}{1 \, hour} = 4{,}200 \frac{beats}{hour}$$

$$4{,}200 \frac{beats}{hour} = 4{,}200 \frac{beats}{hour} \cdot 24 \frac{hours}{day} =$$

$100{,}800 \frac{beats}{day}$ and so on. You may wish to do this at the beginning to show the steps in thinking about the conversions.

Reciprocal rates. The properties of reciprocal rates are surprising to many students (and even many teachers).

Here is another possible exploration. Have students divide their weight (in pounds or kilograms) by their height (in inches or centimeters) to obtain their weight for every inch or centimeter of height. They can use this to estimate the weight of their head.

Additional Examples

Example 1 On average, Cairo gets 2 millimeters of rainfall per month. How much rainfall does Cairo get in one year? **Cairo gets approximately 24 mm of rain per year.**

Example 2 Explain why a car traveling 120 $\frac{km}{hr}$ is traveling about 75 $\frac{mi}{hr}$. Use the conversion 1 mile ≈ 1.6 kilometers.

The goal is to convert kilometers to ___?___ . **miles**

Use conversion rates so that the units cancel in the numerator and denominator just like common factors.

$$\frac{120 \, km}{hr} = \frac{120 \, km}{1 \, hr} \cdot \frac{1 \, mi}{? \, km} \quad \textbf{1.6}$$

$$= \frac{120 \cdot 1}{1 \cdot ?} \frac{mi}{hr} = \frac{?}{} \frac{mi}{hr} \quad \textbf{1.6; 75}$$

Rates are used in many formulas. One of the more important formulas is $d = rt$, which gives the distance d traveled by an object moving at a constant rate r during a time t. (r is often called the speed.)

 GUIDED

Example 2

Explain why a train traveling 68 $\frac{mi}{hr}$ is traveling about 100 $\frac{ft}{sec}$.

Solution The goal is to convert miles to $\frac{?}{feet}$ and an hour to $\frac{?}{seconds}$. Use conversion rates so that the units cancel in the numerator and denominator just like common factors.

$$\frac{68 \, mi}{hr} = \frac{68 \, mi}{hr} \cdot \frac{1 \, hr}{?} \cdot \frac{?}{60 \, sec} \cdot \frac{?}{1 \, mi} \quad \text{60 min; 1 min; 5,280 ft}$$

$$= \frac{68 \cdot ?}{60 \cdot 60} \frac{ft}{sec} \quad \frac{5{,}280}{?}$$

$$= \frac{?}{} \quad \text{about 100 } \frac{ft}{sec}$$

So 68 $\frac{mi}{hr}$ is about 100 $\frac{ft}{sec}$.

STOP QY

Using Reciprocal Rates

Sometimes a rate does not help to simplify the computation but its reciprocal does. Guided Example 2 used $\frac{1 \, hr}{60 \, min}$, while Example 1 used $\frac{60 \, min}{1 \, hr}$.

Remember the algebraic definition of division: $\frac{a}{b} = a \cdot \frac{1}{b}$. So to divide by a rate, you can multiply by its reciprocal. For example, if a book has 672 pages and Marta reads an average of 35 pages per day, you can use division.

$$\frac{672 \, pages}{\frac{35 \, pages}{day}} = 672 \, \cancel{pages} \cdot \frac{1}{35} \frac{day}{\cancel{pages}} = 19.2 \text{ days}$$

So it will take her a little more than 19 days to finish reading the book.

Not every reciprocal rate is meaningful in every situation. For example, in a school with an average of 23 $\frac{students}{class}$, the equivalent reciprocal rate of $\frac{1}{23} \frac{class}{students}$ does not have much meaning. Still, it might be useful in a computation.

There are approximately 8,000 to 10,000 professional online book dealers, selling books with an average price range of $10–$19 per book.

Source: www.bookologist.com

The International Sports Medicine Institute has a formula for daily water intake. A nonactive person should consume $\frac{1}{2}$ ounce per pound of body weight. An athletic person should consume $\frac{2}{3}$ ounce per pound of body weight. (Note: 1 cup = 8 ounces.) If a person weighs p pounds, how many cups of water should the person drink each day if he or she is:

a. nonactive?

b. athletic?

Accommodating the Learner ⬇

Work with students until you are certain they understand why the conversion rate is equal to 1. The conversion rate changes the units but not the value of the number being multiplied by it. Consider using some units they are most familiar with to understand this. For example, use 1 dozen eggs = 12 eggs.

Questions

COVERING THE IDEAS

1. **a.** If a car travels 30 minutes at an average rate of 44 miles per hour, how far will it have gone? **22 mi**

   b. If a car travels m minutes at an average rate of 44 miles per hour, how far will it have gone? $\frac{11m}{15}$ **mi**

2. Suppose ground beef is \$2.59 per pound.

   a. How much will it cost you to purchase P pounds? **\$2.59P**

   b. How many pounds can you purchase for x dollars? $\frac{x}{2.59}$ **lb**

3. One version of an English translation of the novel *War and Peace* by Leo Tolstoy has 1,370 pages. If you read 12 pages per day, show how to calculate how many months it will take you to read the entire novel. Use the conversion 1 month ≈ 30 days.

In 4 and 5, a rate is given.

   a. Write a sentence using the rate to describe a situation.

   b. Name the reciprocal rate.

   c. Write a sentence using the reciprocal rate to describe a situation.

4. 12 feet per second

5. \$4 per kilogram

In 6 and 7, give the two conversion rates that result from the given equation. 6. $\frac{1{,}000 \text{ m}}{1 \text{ km}}$; $\frac{1 \text{ km}}{1{,}000 \text{ m}}$ 7. $\frac{36 \text{ in.}}{1 \text{ yd}}$; $\frac{1 \text{ yd}}{36 \text{ in.}}$

6. 1,000 m = 1 km

7. 36 in. = 1 yd

8. A penny has a thickness of about 0.08 inch. How high, to the nearest 0.1 mile, would a stack of 1 million pennies be? **1.3 mi**

9. Convert 30 miles per hour into kilometers per hour using the conversion 1 mile ≈ 1.6 kilometers. **48 km/hr**

APPLYING THE MATHEMATICS

10. In 2005, Danica Patrick drove the fastest lap ever at the time during trials for the Indianapolis 500 auto race. In a South African newspaper, her speed for the lap was given as 360.955 km/hr.

    a. What is this speed to the nearest hundredth of a mile per hour? Use the conversion 1 mi = 1.609344 km. **224.33 mi/hr**

    b. To the nearest hundredth of a minute, how long did it take her to drive one lap of the 2.5-mile track? **0.67 min**

In 11 and 12, write a rate multiplication problem whose answer is the given quantity. **11. Answers vary. Sample answer: Annie the ant crawls one foot per minute. How far does the ant go, in inches, in 16 minutes and 40 seconds?**

11. 200 inches

12. $4.2 \frac{\text{min}}{\text{page}}$ See margin.

Multiplying and Dividing Rates   **271**

---

3. $\dfrac{\dfrac{1{,}370 \text{ pages}}{1}}{\dfrac{12 \text{ pages}}{1 \text{ day}}} \cdot \dfrac{1 \text{ mo}}{30 \text{ days}} \approx$ 3.8 months

4a. Answers vary. Sample answer: The car was moving at a speed of 12 ft/sec.

4b. $0.08\overline{3}$ sec/ft

4c. Answers vary. Sample answer: Driving at this speed, it took him $0.08\overline{3}$ sec to drive 1 ft.

5a. Answers vary. Sample answer: Those delicious tomatoes cost \$4/kg.

5b. 0.25 kg/dollar

5c. Answers vary. Sample answer: With one dollar you can buy 0.25 kg of those delicious tomatoes.

Each penny costs 1.23 cents to make, but the U.S. Mint collects only one cent for it.

Source: U.S. Department of Treasury

---

3 Assignment

Recommended Assignment
- Questions 1–26
- Question 27 (extra credit)
- Reading Lesson 5-5
- Covering the Ideas 5-5

ENGLISH LEARNERS

Vocabulary Development

Remind students that there are many methods of converting between units. Students should recognize and identify the method of converting with *conversion rates* by using the definition of rate as a ratio comparing quantities with different units.

Additional Answers

12. Answers vary. Sample answer: Billy reads 57 pages in 4 hours. What is his reading rate in minutes per page?

5-4A **Lesson Master**   Questions on SPUR Objectives
See pages 320–323 for objectives.

USES Objective F

1. The speed of light in a vacuum is 299,792,458 meters per second. In this situation, what is the meaning of the reciprocal of the given rate? **the time light takes to go 1 meter**

2. On an average day, Leo drinks 2 liters of water. Use the conversion 1 liter ≈ 0.26 gallons to calculate how many gallons of water Leo drinks, on average, every week. **3.64 gal**

3. Alexander can solve 2 long division problems in three minutes. Alexander's brother, Vladimir, is 1½ times as fast. How many long division problems can Vladimir solve in an hour? **60 problems**

4. Sophia can run 60 meters in ten seconds. What is her speed in kilometers per hour? **21.6 km/hr**

5. On average a human blinks 600 times in an hour. How many seconds, on average, pass between each blink? **6 sec**

6. The density of gold is 19,300 kilograms per cubic meter. This means that every cubic meter of gold weighs 19,300 kilograms. What is the volume of 7 kilograms of gold? **0.000363 m³**

7. Huey can complete a 35-foot obstacle course with an egg balanced on his nose in two minutes. Duey is ¾ as fast as Huey. On average, what is Duey's speed on the obstacle course? **13.125 ft/min**

8. The speedometer in Guy's car shows y miles per hour. After converting this speed into kilometers per hour, he finds that he is going z kilometers per hour. Which number is greater, y or z? **z**

9. Anna's car can be driven 44 miles per gallon of gas. If she buys gas for \$3.06 a gallon, how much will she have to pay for gas on a 500 mile trip? **approximately \$34.77**

10. A doctor instructs a patient to take p pills at regular intervals for x days. How many hours should the patient wait between each pill? $\frac{24n}{p}$ **hr**

Algebra **205**

5-4

13. Kenji can wash k dishes per minute. His sister Suna is twice as fast.
    a. How many dishes can Suna wash per minute? **$2k$ dishes per min**
    b. How many minutes does Suna spend per dish? **$\frac{1}{2k}$ min per dish**

14. Suppose Chip is baking cookies for a school bake sale. His oven bakes 36 cookies every 10 minutes. He wants to bake d dozen cookies for the sale. How long will it take him to bake all of the cookies? **$\frac{10d}{3}$ min**

15. In 2006, Gordy Savela ran 300 miles across northern Minnesota in 12 days.
    a. What distance did Gordy average each day? **25 mi per day**
    b. If a marathon is 26.2 miles, how many marathons did Gordy run during his journey? **about 11.5 marathons**

Bake sales have long been one of the most popular ways of raising funds for schools, social clubs, and other organizations.

16. People sometimes go for a walk after a big meal to burn off calories. To lose 1 pound, a person must burn 3,500 calories. Suppose a person burns about 300 calories per hour by walking.
    a. If a person walks for 2.5 hours, how many pounds will the person lose? **about 0.21 lb**
    b. If a person walks for 2.5 hours, how many ounces will the person lose? **about 3.43 oz**
    c. If a person walks for h hours, how many ounces will the person lose? **$\frac{48h}{35}$ oz**
    d. If a person walks for m minutes, how many ounces will the person lose? **$\frac{4m}{175}$ oz**

REVIEW

17. Over the past five days, Mykia has run 3.6 miles one day, 2.9 miles each of two days, 4.2 miles one day, and 1.9 miles one day. Calculate the average number of miles run per day. Write your answer as a rate. (**Lesson 5-3**) **3.1 mi per day**

18. For what value(s) of n is $\frac{19 - 2n}{19 + 2n}$ undefined? (**Lesson 5-3**) $n = -\frac{19}{2}$

19. A box is $\frac{1}{3}$ as long, $\frac{1}{3}$ as wide, and $\frac{1}{3}$ as high as a crate. How many of these boxes will fit in the crate? (**Lesson 5-1**) **27 boxes**

In 20–22, use the formula $H = \frac{M + F + 5}{2}$. It predicts the adult height H of a boy based on his mother's height M and his father's height F, where all measurements are given in inches. The formula $H = \frac{M + F - 5}{2}$ applies to the adult height of girls. (**Lesson 4-7**)

20. Solve each formula for M. $M = 2H - F - 5$; $M = 2H - F + 5$

Accommodating the Learner

Discuss the method of converting by setting the ratios equal to each other. For example, to find the number of feet that are equivalent to 30 inches, students are often taught to write $\frac{12 \text{ inches}}{1 \text{ foot}} = \frac{30 \text{ inches}}{x \text{ feet}}$. Ask students to modify this equation so that it fits the method using conversion rates. Students can multiply both sides by x feet, obtaining the equation $\frac{12 \text{ inches}}{1 \text{ foot}} \cdot x$ feet $= 30$ inches. Next, students can multiply both sides by the reciprocal rate $\frac{1 \text{ foot}}{12 \text{ inches}}$ to obtain x feet $= 30$ inches $\cdot \frac{1 \text{ foot}}{12 \text{ inches}}$, or $x = 2.5$ feet.

21. Booker's father's height is 73 inches, and his mother's height is 68 inches. How tall does the formula predict Booker will be when he is an adult? **73 in.**

22. Predict your adult height using this formula.

22. Answers vary.
Sample answer:
A mother's height of 65 in. and a father's height of 74 in. predict a height of 67 in. for a daughter.

Multiple Choice In 23–25, decide whether each equation has
  A no solution.
  B one solution.
  C more than one solution. (Lesson 4-5)

23. $\frac{x}{5} + 5 = 5$ **B**

24. $\frac{y}{4} + 4 = \frac{y}{4}$ **A**

25. $\frac{z}{3} + 3 = 3\left(\frac{z}{3} + 3\right)$ **B**

26. Solve $8(-3d - 4) \leq 13(2 - d) - (7d - 2)$. (Lessons 4-4, 2-1)
  $d \geq -15$

EXPLORATION

27. **a.** Here is a problem found in many puzzle books. If a hen and a half can lay an egg and a half in a day and a half, how long will it take 24 hens to lay 24 eggs? Explain how you got your answer.

  b. Generalize Part a. If a hen and a half can lay an egg and a half in a day and a half, how long will it take h hens to lay e eggs? $d = \frac{3e}{2h}$

27a. 1.5 days. Sample answer: 1.5 hens lay at the rate of $\frac{1.5 \text{ eggs}}{1.5 \text{ day}}$
or $1 \frac{\text{egg}}{\text{day}}$, so 3 hens lay on average $2 \frac{\text{eggs}}{\text{day}}$. 24 hens will lay
$16 \frac{\text{eggs}}{\text{day}}$, so it will take 1.5 days to lay 24 eggs.

QY ANSWERS

a. $\frac{p}{16}$ c

b. $\frac{p}{12}$ c

5-4

4   Wrap-Up

Ongoing Assessment

Organize students into groups, and provide each group with a conversion rate. Then, start a rate circulating the room. Each group is responsible for one part of the conversion. For example, to convert $\frac{3 \text{ yd}}{20 \text{ sec}}$ to $\frac{\text{in.}}{\text{hr}}$, provide each group with one of the following conversion rates: $\frac{3 \text{ ft}}{1 \text{ yd}}$, $\frac{12 \text{ in.}}{1 \text{ ft}}$, $\frac{60 \text{ sec}}{1 \text{ min}}$, and $\frac{60 \text{ min}}{1 \text{ hr}}$. The students must pass the problem to the right group to solve.

Project Update

Project 5, Converting Rates, on page 316, relates to the content of this lesson.

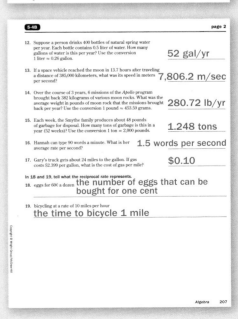

Lesson 5-5 Ratios

GOAL

Review ratios and their applications to some problems.

SPUR Objective

G Use ratios to compare two quantities.

Materials/Resources

- Lesson Master 5-5A or 5-5B
- Resource Masters 65 and 66
- Scientific or graphing calculator
- Ruler, meter stick, or tape measure

HOMEWORK

Suggestions for Assignment

- Questions 1–16
- Question 17 (extra credit)
- Reading Lesson 5-6
- Covering the Ideas 5-6

Local Standards

---

1 Warm-Up

You might use the following Warm-Up to get into the ideas of the lesson. Ask each student to answer; their answers will be different.

1. Pick a relative of yours whose age is different from yours. What is the ratio of your age to the age of that relative, in lowest terms? **Answers vary.**

2. **a.** What will be the ratio of your age to the age of that relative next year?
   Using $\frac{x}{y}$ as the original ratio, this ratio is $\frac{x+1}{y+1}$.

   b. Will the ratio be greater or less than the ratio you found in Question 1?
   It will be lower if the relative is younger, and higher if the relative is older.

   c. Five years from now, will the ratio be higher or lower than the ratio you found in Part a?
   It will still be lower or still higher.

Vocabulary

ratio
tax rate
discount rate

▶ **BIG IDEA** The quotient of two measures with the same type of units is a ratio.

What Is a ratio?

A *ratio* describes how many times larger one number is compared to another. For example, dogs come in a huge variety of shapes and sizes. Consider the three types pictured below, which are very different from each other. To compare the three dog breeds, you could use corresponding lengths on their bodies to form ratios.

Dachshund   Labrador Retriever   Greyhound

Activity

Measure the pictures to answer each question.

1. Which dog has the greatest $\frac{\text{head length}}{\text{front leg length}}$ ratio? **dachshund**

2. Which dog has the least $\frac{\text{head length}}{\text{body length}}$ ratio? **greyhound**

3. Which dog has the least $\frac{\text{front leg length}}{\text{body length}}$ ratio? **dachshund**

4. Which dog has the $\frac{\text{front leg length}}{\text{body length}}$ ratio that is closest to 1? **greyhound**

The direction of the comparison is important. The dachshund's $\frac{\text{head length}}{\text{front leg length}}$ ratio is much greater than 1 because its head is much longer than its front legs. But the reciprocal ratio $\frac{\text{front leg length}}{\text{head length}}$ is much less than 1.

Mental Math

Give the coordinates of a point on Answers vary.

a. the x-axis.
Sample answer: (1, 0)
b. the y-axis.
Sample answer: (0, 1)
c. both the x- and y-axes.
(0, 0)

Background

Ratios are comparisons using division with the same units. If $a < b$, then the ratio $\frac{a}{b}$ represents what fraction a is of b. If $a > b$, then the ratio $\frac{a}{b}$ tells how many times larger b is than a.

You may wish to point out the differences between ratio comparisons, made using division, and comparisons that are made using subtraction. Students may be surprised to realize that if numbers have a

constant difference, they may not have a constant ratio. For example, suppose a parent is 30 years old and a child is 2 years old. The parent's age is 15 times the child's age, a ratio comparison. But this ratio will change. In just two years, the parent's age will be 8 times the child's age. Nevertheless, the difference in their ages will remain constant at 28.

(continued on next page)

A **ratio** is a comparison of two quantities with the same type of units. For example, a to b is written $\frac{a}{b}$. Similarly, the ratio $\frac{b}{a}$ compares b to a. Notice the difference between a rate and a ratio. In the rate a per b, the units for a and b are different. In a ratio, the units are the same. $\frac{40 \text{ km}}{2 \text{ hr}} = 20 \frac{\text{km}}{\text{hr}}$ is a rate. $\frac{40 \text{ km}}{8 \text{ km}} = 5$ is a ratio.

Example 1

It takes Max $\frac{1}{4}$ of an hour to ride his bike to school, and it takes Riley 21 minutes to walk to school. Write a ratio comparing Max's time to Riley's time.

Solution The units of measure for 21 minutes and for $\frac{1}{4}$ of an hour are not the same, so we need to change hours to minutes. Since Max's time is to be compared to Riley's, his time is in the numerator.

$$\frac{\text{Max's Time}}{\text{Riley's Time}} = \frac{\frac{1}{4} \text{ hr}}{21 \text{ min}} = \frac{\frac{1}{4} \text{ hr} \cdot \frac{60 \text{ min}}{\text{hr}}}{21 \text{ min}} = \frac{15 \text{ min}}{21 \text{ min}} = \frac{5}{7}$$

This means that it takes Max $\frac{5}{7}$ of the time to ride his bike as it takes Riley to walk to school.

Ratios and Percents

Ratios can be expressed as fractions, decimals, or percents. In Example 1, $\frac{5}{7} \approx 0.\overline{714285}$, so you could say that it takes Max about 71% or $\frac{71}{100}$ of the time it takes Riley to go to school.

While in this book we distinguish rates from ratios, in the real world some ratios are called rates. In money matters, the **tax rate** is the ratio of the tax amount to the selling price. The **discount rate** is the ratio of the discount to the original price.

About 20 million bicycles were sold in the United States in 2005.

Source: National Bicycle Dealers Association

Example 2

A TV that normally sells for $400 is on sale for $340. The tax on the reduced price is $23.80, so the total cost with tax is $363.80.

a. What is the discount rate?

b. What is the tax rate?

c. Including tax, how much would a customer save by buying the TV on sale?

Solutions

a. discount rate $= \frac{\text{amount of discount}}{\text{original price}} = \frac{\$400 - \$340}{\$400} = \frac{\$60}{\$400} = 0.15 = 15\%$

(continued on next page)

Also, if pairs of unequal numbers have a constant ratio, the differences will vary. For example, if a person got 75% of the vote, you cannot be sure if the person got 300 of 400 votes cast (a difference of 100 votes), 3,000 of 4,000 votes cast (a difference of 1,000 votes), or some other amount that is $\frac{1}{4}$ less than the total.

2 Teaching

Notes on the Lesson

You may wish to give students more difficult problems involving situations like those in Example 2. Suppose you buy a sweater for a total cost of $83.95, which includes a 5% sales tax. What was the price of the sweater without the tax? Here is a solution using the language of ratios: Let P be the price of the sweater. The ratio of the price including tax to the price is 1.05, so $\frac{\$83.95}{P} = 1.05$, which means $\$83.95 = 1.05P$, so $P = \$79.95$. It is easy to invent similar problems.

Notes on the Activity

Encourage students to measure to the greatest possible accuracy, possibly to the nearest mm.

Additional Examples

Example 1 David's foot is exactly 1 foot long, while Julene's is only 10 inches long. Write a ratio comparing Julene's foot size to David's.

Julene's foot is $\frac{5}{6}$ of the size of David's foot.

Example 2 A shirt that sells for $30 is on sale for $25. The tax on the sale price is $1.93, so the total cost with tax is $26.93.

a. What is the discount rate? **16.7%**

b. What is the tax rate? **7.7%**

c. Including tax, how much would a customer save by buying the shirt on sale? **$5.38**

2 Teaching

Notes on the Lesson

Example 3 This type of mixture problem can be done without algebra. There are 4 parts altogether, so divide 5 gallons by 4 parts to obtain $\frac{5}{4} \frac{\text{gallons}}{\text{part}}$. Then multiply this by 3 and by 1 to find the amounts of white and red paint.

3 parts $\cdot \frac{5}{4} \frac{\text{gallons}}{\text{part}} = \frac{15}{4}$ gallons white paint, and 1 part $\cdot \frac{5}{4} \frac{\text{gallons}}{\text{part}} = \frac{5}{4}$ gallons red paint. The sum of the fractions is 5 gallons of paint, so these amounts check.

Additional Example

Example 3 In your mother's punch recipe, she recommends that you use 2 parts cream soda to 3 parts pineapple-orange juice. How much of each ingredient will you need if you wish to make 15 cups of punch?
6 cups of soda and 9 cups of juice

---

b. tax rate $= \frac{\text{amount of tax}}{\text{discounted price}} = \frac{\$23.80}{\$340} = 0.07 = 7\%$

c. Paying full price, the 7% tax is paid on $400. Recall that price + 7% of price = 1.07 • price. So at full price, the customer would pay 1.07(400) = $428. Buying the TV on sale saves the customer $428 − $363.80 = $64.20.

Using Ratios to Set Up Equations

When two numbers are in the ratio a to b, then they are also in the ratio ka to kb because $\frac{a}{b} = \frac{ka}{kb}$ for any nonzero value of k. For example, if the ratio of boys to girls in a band is $\frac{7}{6}$, the ratio is also $\frac{14}{12}$, or $\frac{21}{18}$.

If you know the original ratio, then you can multiply the numerator and denominator by the same constant and never change the value of the ratio.

Directions for mixing foods or chemicals are frequently given as ratios. You can use equations to determine actual quantities from the ratios.

Example 3

One Internet site warns painters: "Always • always • ALWAYS! make a note of the paint ratios when you mix paints." In painting a pink wall, Bethany mixed 1 part red paint with 3 parts white paint. How much of each color will be needed for a wall that will use about 5 gallons of paint in all?

Solution The red paint and white paint are in the ratio of 1 to 3. So their ratio is $\frac{1}{3}$. Now we use the fact that $\frac{1}{3} = \frac{1k}{3k}$ for any nonzero k. So let k be the number of gallons of red paint and $3k$ be the number of gallons of white paint. The total paint needed is 5 gallons, so you can set up the following equation and solve for k.

$$1k + 3k = 5$$
$$4k = 5$$
$$k = \frac{5}{4} = 1.25$$
$$\text{So } 3k = 3 \cdot 1.25 = 3.75$$

She will need 1.25 gallons of red paint and 3.75 gallons of white paint.

Check $\frac{1.25}{3.75} = \frac{1}{3}$ and 1.25 gallons + 3.75 gallons = 5 gallons. It checks.

 QY

One gallon of paint generally covers 400 square feet of wall space.

Source: Paint and Decorating Retailers Association

▶ **QY**

To paint a house light green, you want a ratio of 1 part green to 4 parts white. Find out how much of each color you must buy if you need 12 gallons of paint.

Accommodating the Learner

Discuss the sequence {1, 1, 2, 3, 5, 8, 13, 21, 34, 55, …}, also known as the Fibonacci numbers, with students. Show them the sequence and see if they can find the pattern that generates the sequence. Then, ask them to compute the ratio between consecutive pairs of numbers. Students should be careful to always find the ratio of the greater number to the smaller number, and watch for a pattern to develop as they move farther along in the sequence. Students should notice that the numbers are getting closer and closer to 1.618…,

the Golden Ratio mentioned in the Extension. Consider providing students with a brief history of the Golden Ratio or assigning students the task of discovering the history of the Golden Ratio, and its applications to art, nature, music, and architecture.

Each number is the sum of the two preceding numbers.

Changing Ratios

It is natural to ask how a ratio will change if the numerator or denominator (or both) change. For example, right now Myron is 6 years old and his little sister Ella is 2. The ratio of Myron's age to Ella's is $\frac{6 \text{ years}}{2 \text{ years}} = \frac{3}{1}$. Now, Myron is 3 times as old as his sister. But when they get 2 years older, the ratio will have changed. In two years, $\frac{6 + 2 \text{ years}}{2 + 2 \text{ years}} = \frac{8}{4} = \frac{2}{1}$, so Myron will be twice as old as Ella.

Example 4

Suppose a team has won 15 of its first 38 games. How many games must it win in a row to bring its winning percentage to at least 0.500?

Solution If the team now wins r games in a row, then the team will have played $38 + r$ games and have won $15 + r$ of them. So we want to know when $\frac{number\ of\ wins}{number\ of\ games\ played} = \frac{15 + r}{38 + r} \geq 0.500$.

To clear this inequality of fractions, multiply both sides by $38 + r$. This is a positive number so the sense of the inequality remains the same.

$15 + r \geq 0.500(38 + r)$	Multiply each side by $(38 + r)$.
$15 + r \geq 19 + 0.5r$	Distributive Property
$r \geq 4 + 0.5r$	Add -15 to both sides.
$0.5r \geq 4$	Add $-0.5r$ to both sides.
$r \geq 8$	Divide each side by 0.5.

The team must win 8 games in a row to bring its winning percentage up to at least .500.

Questions

COVERING THE IDEAS

1. Grass snakes and rattlesnakes are found in the Great Plains. Grass snakes grow up to 20 inches in length, and rattlesnakes grow to 45 inches. Express the ratio of rattlesnake length to grass snake length
   a. as a fraction. $\frac{9}{4}$
   b. as a percent. **225%**

2. An item is on sale for $16. It originally cost $28.
   a. What is the discount rate? **about 43%**
   b. If the tax on the sale price is $1.04, what is the tax rate? **6.5%**

Rattlesnakes are usually between 7 and 15 inches long at birth

Source: San Diego Zoo

Notes on the Lesson

Example 4 This is also a common type of problem, but it does not lend itself to an arithmetic solution. It is likely to be new to students, so you should go over it in some detail.

Additional Example

Example 4 During the first two quizzes of the semester, Ali got scores of 6 and 4 out of 10. On how many quizzes will Ali have to earn a 9 to bring her average up to 8? **6 more quizzes**

Accommodating the Learner ⬇

If students are struggling with writing an equation to describe the situation in Additional Example 4 provide the following instructions.

Step 1: Ask students to read the problem several times.

Step 2: Ask students to write out in words what they are looking for and call that x. (Students should consider making x the *total* number of quizzes Ali will have to take before the average reaches 8.)

Step 3: Now help them to create a table of values with the first column x and the second column showing the work the student would have to perform to find the given average. They do not need to compute the averages, but should try to recognize the pattern.

Step 4: Finally, ask students to describe the pattern in words, and then write the pattern in terms of x. Now that students have the equation, they can solve for x and then use x to answer the question.

5-5

3 Assignment

Recommended Assignment

- Questions 1–16
- Question 17 (extra credit)
- Reading Lesson 5-6
- Covering the Ideas 5-6

Notes on the Questions

Question 3 Sometimes the numbers that are given are easy, as in this problem. But what if a person wanted to make 3.5 gallons of fruit juice punch? How many quarts of each ingredient would then be needed? The general principle to stress is that students should have a powerful strategy for solving these problems regardless of the numbers.

Question 8 All circles are similar, and the results here anticipate some of the results students will see later in the chapter.

Question 17 Interested students may wish to make a project out of this question, including applications of sines, cosines, and tangents.

3. A recipe for fruit juice punch calls for 1 part tropical fruit-punch and 2 parts ginger ale. If a person wants to make 5 gallons (20 quarts) of fruit-juice punch, how many quarts of each ingredient are needed? $6\frac{2}{3}$ qt of fruit punch and $13\frac{1}{3}$ qt of ginger ale

4. A paint mixture calls for 7 parts of linseed oil, 5 parts of solvent, and 1 part of pigment. How much of each ingredient is needed to make 60 gallons of paint? $32\frac{4}{13}$ gal of oil, $23\frac{1}{13}$ gal of solvent, and $4\frac{8}{13}$ gal of pigment

5. A team has won 11 of 17 games.
   a. If the team wins its next 2 games, what will its winning percentage be? Round your answer to three decimal places. 0.684
   b. If the team loses its next n games, what will its winning percentage be? $\frac{11}{17+n}$
   c. How many games could the team lose and still have a winning percentage above .600? 1

APPLYING THE MATHEMATICS

6. At a local concert, $\frac{1}{6}$ of the attendees are teenagers and $\frac{5}{8}$ of the people are between the ages of 20 and 40. The rest of the people are older. Write the ratio (in lowest terms) of the number of people over 40 to the number of people between 20 and 40. $\frac{1}{3}$

7. The ratio of adults to children at a concert is expected to be 2 to 5. If 200 people attend, how many are expected to be children? about 143 children

8. The circles at the right have radii 2 centimeters (Circle A) and 5 centimeters (Circle B).

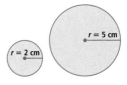

Circle A   Circle B

   a. Find the circumference and area of each circle using $C = \pi d$ and $A = \pi r^2$.
   b. Find the ratio of the diameter of Circle A to the diameter of Circle B in lowest terms. $\frac{2}{5}$
   c. Give the ratio of the area of Circle A to the area of Circle B in lowest terms. $\frac{4}{25}$

8a. Circle A has circumference 4π units and area 4π units². Circle B has circumference 10π units and area 25π units².

9. a. In 4 minutes, Liana can type 140 words. If she has an essay that is 700 words long, about how long will it take Liana to type it? 20 min
   b. In 5 minutes, Elan can type 160 words. About how many words can he type in 12 minutes? 384 words

10. Recall that two angles are called *supplementary angles* if the sum of their measures is 180°. In the diagram at the right, $\angle ABC$ and $\angle CBD$ are supplementary angles whose measures have a ratio of 7 to 3. Find the measure of each angle. $m\angle ABC = 126°$; $m\angle CBD = 54°$

278   Division and Proportions in Algebra

Extension

Extend the discussion of ratios and the human body by discussing Phi, or the Golden Ratio, with your students. Have students choose a partner, take the following measurements for one person in the pair, and find the ratios listed at right.

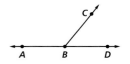

1. distance from top of head to fingertips : distance from top of head to elbow

2. distance from wrist to elbows : distance from wrist to fingertips

3. distance from top of head to floor : distance from elbow to floor

Students should find that each ratio is approximately 1.6 : 1.

REVIEW

11. An airplane is scheduled to fly from LaGuardia Airport in New York to Los Angeles International Airport in 6 hours and 18 minutes. If the distance between the two airports is 2,779 miles, what is the average speed of the airplane? **(Lesson 5-3)** approximately **441 mi/hr**

12. For what values of c is $\frac{16 - 4c}{2c + 9}$ undefined? **(Lesson 5-3)**
$c = -4.5$

13. Tell whether each fraction equals $\frac{99}{100}$. **(Lessons 5-3, 5-2)**

a. $\frac{999}{1,000}$ no   b. $-\frac{-99}{-100}$ no   c. $\frac{1}{1 - \frac{1}{100}}$ no   d. $\frac{\frac{99}{7}}{\frac{7}{100}}$ no

14. **Skill Sequence** Simplify each expression. **(Lessons 5-2, 5-1, 2-1)**

a. $\frac{x}{4} + \frac{x}{5}$ $\frac{9x}{20}$ b. $\frac{x}{4} - \frac{x}{5}$ $\frac{x}{20}$ c. $\frac{x}{4} \cdot \frac{x}{5}$ $\frac{x^2}{20}$ d. $\frac{x}{4} \div \frac{x}{5}$ $\frac{5}{4}$

15. The volume of a box is to be less than 20 cubic meters. If the base has dimensions 185 cm by 250 cm, what inequality describes possible heights of the box? **(Lesson 3-7)** $0 < h < 432$ cm

16. What fraction of a complete turn is a rotation of 75°? **(Previous Course)** $\frac{5}{24}$

Los Angeles International Airport is serviced by more than 85 major airlines and is the third largest airport in the world in terms of passenger traffic.

Source: *The New York Times*

EXPLORATION

17. The right triangle shown here has side lengths of 7, 24, and 25. One of its angles has a measure of about 74°. The lengths of the three sides can form six different ratios.

a. Write the values of all six of these ratios.

b. These ratios have special names. One of these is called the *sine*. For this triangle it is written sin 74°. Put your calculator in degree mode and compute sin 74° using the key sequence 74 $\boxed{\text{SIN}}$ or $\boxed{\text{SIN}}$ 74 (depending on your calculator), and determine which of the six ratios in Part a is the sine.

c. Another special ratio is called the *cosine*. Compute cos 74° on your calculator and determine which of the six ratios in Part a is the cosine. cos 74° $= \frac{7}{25} = 0.28$

d. A third special ratio is called the *tangent*. Compute tan 74° on your calculator and determine which of the six ratios in Part a is the tangent. tan 74° $= \frac{24}{7} \approx 3.43$

e. Which of the three ratios in Parts b, c, and d is a ratio of the other two? Tangent is the ratio of sine to cosine.

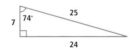

17a. $\frac{7}{25} = 0.28$;
$\frac{25}{7} \approx 3.57$;
$\frac{24}{25} = 0.96$;
$\frac{25}{24} \approx 1.04$;
$\frac{7}{24} \approx 0.29$;
$\frac{24}{7} \approx 3.43$

17b. sin 74° $= \frac{24}{25} = 0.96$

QY ANSWER

2.4 gal of green paint, 9.6 gal of white paint

Ratios **279**

Lesson 5-5 **279**

---

4 Wrap-Up

Ongoing Assessment

Ask students to give two random numbers. For each pair of numbers have them write a description of a ratio that makes sense with the pair.

Lesson 5-6

GOALS

Review probability notions, introduce function notation $P(x)$ of an event x, and discuss odds.

SPUR Objective

H Calculate relative frequencies and probabilities in situations with a finite number of equally likely outcomes.

Materials/Resources

· Lesson Master 5-6A or 5-6B
· Resource Masters 1, 67 and 68
· Scientific or graphing calculator

HOMEWORK

Suggestions for Assignment

• Questions 1–26
• Question 27 (extra credit)
• Reading Lesson 5-7
• Covering the Ideas 5-7

Local Standards

1 Warm-Up

1. Suppose a drawer contains 8 white socks, 6 black socks, and 2 gray socks. If you reach in without looking, what is the probability that the sock you pick is:

   a. black? $\frac{3}{8}$ **b.** not black? $\frac{5}{8}$

2. Suppose a drawer contains w white socks, b black socks, and g gray socks. If you reach in without looking, what is the probability that the sock you pick is:

   a. gray?   **b.** not gray?
   $\frac{g}{w+g+b}$ $\frac{w+b}{w+g+b}$

Probability Distributions

> ▶ **BIG IDEA** The distribution of the probabilities of all possible outcomes from a situation can be displayed in tables and graphs.

In a situation such as asking a question or flipping a coin, the possibilities are called **outcomes.** No two outcomes can occur at the same time. A set of outcomes is an **event.** Recall from your earlier courses that the **probability** of an event is a number from 0 to 1 that measures how likely it is that the event will happen. The sum of the probabilities of all possible outcomes must add to 1.

If an outcome or event is identified as x, then the symbol **$P(x)$** stands for the probability of the outcome or event.

How Are Probabilities Determined?

There are three common ways in which people determine probabilities.

1. Pick a probability close to the relative frequency with which the outcome or event has occurred in the past.

2. Deduce a probability from assumptions about the situation.

3. Give a best guess.

The gender of a newborn baby is a situation where there are two outcomes: B = a boy is born and G = a girl is born. Any one of the three common ways might be used to identify $P(B)$, the probability that a boy is born.

1. According to the National Center for Health Statistics, there were 4,089,950 children born in the United States in 2003. The relative frequency of boys to births is found by dividing the number of boys born by the total number of births.

$$\text{relative frequency} = \frac{\text{number of baby boys born}}{\text{total number of births}} = \frac{2{,}093{,}535}{4{,}089{,}950} \approx 0.512 = 51.2\%$$

Using relative frequency, we might say that $P(B)$ is about 51.2%.

2. However, some people would rather assume that the probabilities of a boy and a girl are equal. If the two probabilities are equal, then because the probabilities must add to 1, $P(B) = P(G) = \frac{1}{2} = 50\%$. More generally, if there are n outcomes in a situation and each has equal probability, then the probability of each is $\frac{1}{n}$.

Vocabulary

outcome
event
probability
$P(x)$
probability distribution
unbiased
fair
conditional probability
complement
odds of an event

Mental Math

Find the value of the variable.

a. The temperature T is 30° cooler than 82°. 52°

b. A book's price p is 7 times as much as a $2.25 pen. $15.75

c. A plane departs 45 minutes later than its 6:55 A.M. departure time, at d. 7:40 A.M.

The birthrate gives the number of live births per 1,000 of population. The U.S. birthrate declined from 23.7 in 1960 to a record low of 13.9 in 2002.

Source: U.S. National Center for Health Statistics

Background

We assume students have encountered both probability and relative frequency before.

How are probabilities determined? The probability of an event is obtained in one of three ways. Examples of each are found in this lesson. (1) See how often the event occurs, and from that ratio (the event's relative frequency) determine a probability. This is done with blood types, as in Example 1. (2) Make an assumption about an event, perhaps that there is an equal likelihood of something happening, or

that something occurs at random, and use that assumption to deduce the probability. This is often used with cards, coins, or dice. (3) Guess at the probability. This is often done by people who speak of odds.

(continued on next page)

3. In a family where more boys than girls have been born, some people might think that boys are much more likely than 50% or 51.2% to be born and guess that the probability that a boy will be born is much greater. But, usually we only guess when the event is a one-time event and there are no data from past experience. For example, if a new drug has been developed to cure a disease, at the start researchers may be able to only guess at the probability that the drug will actually work.

Probability Distributions

Some situations have many outcomes. A **probability distribution** is the set of ordered pairs of outcomes and their probabilities. For example, in many board games, two dice are thrown and the sum of the numbers that appear is used to make a move. Since the outcome of the game depends on landing or not landing on particular spaces, it is helpful to know the probability of obtaining each sum. The following diagram is helpful. It shows the 36 possible outcomes when two dice are thrown.

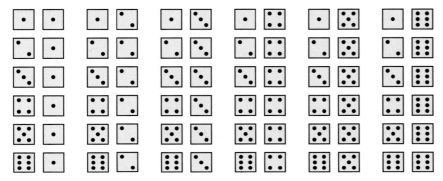

We call a situation **unbiased**, or **fair**, if each outcome has the same probability. If the dice are fair, then each of the 36 outcomes has a probability of $\frac{1}{36}$.

Let $P(x)$ = the probability of getting a sum of x. In this case, x can only be a whole number from 2 to 12. There are 36 outcomes but only 11 possible sums. For example, the event "getting a sum of 7" has 6 possible outcomes: 1 and 6, 2 and 5, 3 and 4, 4 and 3, 5 and 2, and 6 and 1. So $P(7) = 6 \cdot \frac{1}{36} = \frac{6}{36}$ or $\frac{1}{6}$. The probability distribution is shown on page 282 in the table and graph. A sum of 7 is the most likely outcome, so $P(7)$ is plotted as the highest point on the graph.

Probability Distributions **281**

2 Teaching

Notes on the Lesson
Probabilities may be expressed as fractions, decimals, or percents. It is reasonable to accept answers in any one of these forms. Students should be guided by the type of information that is given in a problem.

In many cases, fractions are the most appropriate form to use when writing and computing with probabilities. However, in some probability problems, fractions in lowest terms may not be helpful. For example, when comparing whether it is more likely that the sum will be 5 or 6 when tossing two dice, most people agree that it is easier to compare $\frac{4}{36}$ and $\frac{5}{36}$ than it is to compare $\frac{1}{9}$ and $\frac{5}{36}$.

Probability distributions. Students should realize that the sums of numbers on two dice are not equally likely, with 7 being the most likely sum.

Vocabulary Development

Probability distributions. A probability distribution is a function whose domain is a set of mutually exclusive events whose union is the sample space, and that maps each event onto its probability. Consequently, if there is a finite number of events, the sum of the values of the function is 1. This is the case with the distribution of probabilities of getting a sum of x when tossing two fair dice.

Emphasize and discuss the distinction in meaning between probability and relative frequency. Note that probability is more theoretical, and is often based on both assumptions about the situation and relative frequency over many trials or a lot of data. Relative frequency is simply a description of the specific data examined.

5-6

Notes on the Lesson

A probability distribution from relative frequencies. The table of percents of blood types in the United States is not the same as might be found in other countries. Blood types vary among people with different backgrounds. The highest frequencies of type B are found in parts of India and central Asia. The highest frequencies of type O are found in Central and South America, where they approach 100%.

Note-Taking Tips

Consider using this lesson as a practice section for teaching students how to take notes from the text. Depending on their current skill level, students may benefit from some structure. For example, consider asking students to highlight all new vocabulary in their notes, and to include with each term a definition and an example. Next, students can highlight any new notation or formulas. Help students practice summarizing the key points of the lesson.

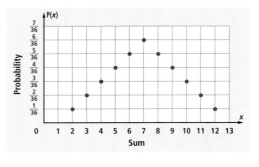

x	P(x)
2	$\frac{1}{36} = 0.02\overline{7}$
3	$\frac{2}{36} = 0.0\overline{5}$
4	$\frac{3}{36} = 0.08\overline{3}$
5	$\frac{4}{36} = 0.\overline{1}$
6	$\frac{5}{36} = 0.13\overline{8}$
7	$\frac{6}{36} = 0.1\overline{6}$
8	$\frac{5}{36} = 0.13\overline{8}$
9	$\frac{4}{36} = 0.\overline{1}$
10	$\frac{3}{36} = 0.08\overline{3}$
11	$\frac{2}{36} = 0.0\overline{5}$
12	$\frac{1}{36} = 0.02\overline{7}$

Notice that the sum of all the probabilities adds to $\frac{36}{36}$, or 1. This is because these 11 events include each outcome exactly once.

STOP **QY1**

You may have answered QY1 by adding $P(9)$, $P(10)$, $P(11)$, and $P(12)$. Another way to answer QY1 is to count the outcomes that give a sum of 9, 10, 11, and 12, and then divide that number by 36. This is because probabilities of events with equally likely outcomes satisfy the following property.

> ▶ **QY1**
>
> In tossing two fair dice, what is the probability of tossing a sum greater than 8?

Probability of an Event with Equally Likely Outcomes

If a situation has a total of n equally likely outcomes and E is an event, then $P(E) = \frac{\text{number of outcomes } E}{n}$.

A Probability Distribution from Relative Frequencies

Your blood and the blood of all humans is one of eight types: O, A, B, or AB and either positive (+) or negative (−) for each type depending on the existence of a Rh antigen. Overall in the United States, the approximate percents of people with these types are shown in the table on page 283. Note: The percents do not add to 100% due to rounding.

Blood makes up about 7% of a person's body weight.

Source: www.bloodbook.com

282   Division and Proportions in Algebra

Accommodating the Learner ⬇

Consider doing a basic coin tossing activity to help students understand the difference between a probability determined from assumptions about the situation and a probability based closely on the relative frequency. Discuss with students possible situations where the predicted probability does not match the relative frequency. For example, if you toss a coin only twice, you do not have enough information to estimate the probability.

We can take these relative frequencies as probabilities that a person at random in the United States has one of these types.

Example 1

a. What is the probability that a person in the United States has type-O blood?

b. What is the probability that a person with type-O blood is O–?

Solutions

a. A person has type-O blood if he or she is either O+ or O–.

$$P(O) = P(O+) + P(O-)$$
$$= 38.4\% + 7.7\%$$
$$= 46.1\%$$

b. Since 46.1% of the population have type-O blood, and 7.7% of the population is O–, the probability that a person with type-O blood is O– is $\frac{P(O-)}{P(O)}$, which is $\frac{7.7\%}{46.1\%} \approx 0.167$, or about 16.7%.

Type	Percent
O+	38.4
O–	7.7
A+	32.3
A–	6.5
B+	9.4
B–	1.7
AB+	3.2
AB–	0.7

Source: www.bloodbook.com

The probability calculated in Example 1b is called a **conditional probability.** It is the probability that a person has blood type O– given the condition that they are already known to be type O. You can write: P(O– given O) = 16.7%. In general, the conditional probability of event B given event A, $P(B \text{ given } A) = \frac{P(A \text{ and } B)}{P(A)}$. That is, it is the probability that both events occur divided by the probability of the first event.

Complementary Events

If the probability of a tornado occurring on a weekend is $\frac{2}{7}$, then the probability of a tornado occurring on a weekday is $\frac{5}{7}$ because there are five weekdays in a week. The events "occurring on a weekend" and "occurring on a weekday" are called *complements* of each other. Two events are **complements** if they have no elements in common and together they contain all possible outcomes.

The sum of the probability of an event and the probability of its complement is 1. The same goes for relative frequencies. Thus the probability or relative frequency of the complement of an event is found by subtracting the probability or relative frequency of the original event from 1.

The greatest incidence of tornadoes around the world is in North America.

Source: Oklahoma Climatological Survey

Probability Distributions **283**

Additional Example

Example 1 Given the chart of blood types in Example 1,

a. what is the probability that a person has type-A+ or O+ blood? **70.7%**

b. what is the probability that a person does *not* have type-AB– blood? **99.3%**

c. what is the probability that a person who has type-AB blood is AB–? **about 17.9%**

Accommodating the Learner ↑

Ask students to discuss ways that probability data can be distorted. Include examples that show false assumptions about the situation and a nonrepresentative selection of the group used to find relative frequency.

5-6

Notes on the Lesson

Odds. The following aspects of odds should be emphasized. (1) People often give the odds *against* an event when they mean the odds *favoring* the event. For example, they will say that the odds of a hole-in-one in golf are 10,000 to 1. Technically, this means the event has probability $\frac{10,000}{10,001}$. But it is understood that the statement means that the probability is $\frac{1}{10,000}$ or perhaps $\frac{1}{10,001}$. It is because of the multiple meanings of the same statement that one seldom finds the subject of odds on standardized tests. (2) Odds people give are often guesses. For example, we find on the Internet that the odds of a hole-in-one for an amateur golfer can range from 10,000 to 1 to 48,000 to 1. And, curiously, it is noted on many sites that many golfers "beat the odds." This is a misunderstanding of probability. (3) The odds in horse racing, the lottery, and other betting activities are designed so that on average the bettors will lose. This is because the purpose of these activities is for the track or the state to make money.

 QY2

The probabilities that weather forecasters use are found by using mathematical models. These models are created from a study of what happened in the past under conditions like those when the forecast is made.

Odds

Probabilities and complements of probabilities are used to compute *odds.* Odds are stated and used in different ways that are not always the same. One meaning is that the **odds of an event** occurring is the ratio of the probability that the event *will occur* to the probability that the event *will not occur.*

$$\text{odds of } E \text{ occurring} = \frac{P(E)}{P(\text{complement of } E)} = \frac{P(E)}{1 - P(E)}$$

For example, if you think that the odds of your being selected for a particular honor are 2 to 1, then you mean that you will be selected 2 out of 3 times, and that the probability of the event is $\frac{2}{3}$. This shows how to calculate a probability from odds. If the odds for the event are m to n, then the probability for the event is $\frac{m}{m+n}$ and the probability the event will not occur is $\frac{n}{m+n}$.

QY3

Questions

COVERING THE IDEAS

1. If E is an event, what does $P(E)$ stand for?
   the probability that E occurs
2. Use the data for births in the United States found on page 280.
   a. How many girls were born in the United States in 2003? 1,996,415
   b. What was the relative frequency of female births in the United States in 2003? about 48.8%
   c. Let G represent a girl being born. Using relative frequency, what is the value of $P(G)$? about 0.488
   d. Let G represent a girl being born. If a baby has an equal probability of being a boy or a girl, what is $P(G)$? 0.5
   e. Suppose someone chooses one of the children in your family at random. What is the probability that the person chosen is a girl? Answers vary. Sample answer: 100%

> **QY2**
> A weather forecaster reports that the probability of rain tomorrow is 80%. What is the probability that it does not rain tomorrow?

> **QY3**
> Cameron is managing a large project at work that is behind schedule. He estimates that there is a $\frac{1}{4}$ chance it will be completed on time. What are the odds it will be done on time?

Extension

Ask students to consider the following problem, which mimics the television show, *Let's Make a Deal.* In the problem, the contestant is shown three doors. Behind one of the doors is a car and behind the other two doors are goats. The contestant is asked to choose a door. The host then shows the contestant one of the two remaining doors, making sure to show a door with a goat behind it. Will the contestant have a better chance of winning if he stays with his original choice or if he changes to the remaining door?

He will have a $\frac{2}{3}$ chance of winning if he switches and only a $\frac{1}{3}$ chance of winning if he stays with his original choice. Consider the contestant who plans to switch. He will win if he chose a goat on the first door, which was a probability of $\frac{2}{3}$. Consider the contestant who plans to stay with his first choice. He will win only if he chose a car on his first door, which had a probability of $\frac{1}{3}$. It is inaccurate to say the odds of winning are $\frac{1}{2}$ because all three choices must be considered.

3. Suppose a multiple-choice question has 5 choices: A, B, C, D, and E. Jasmine guesses each answer randomly.
   a. What is the probability that Jasmine will get a particular question correct? **20%**
   b. What is the probability that Jasmine will miss the question? **80%**

4. Suppose you pick a number from 1 to 25 randomly out of a hat.
   a. How many outcomes are possible? **25**
   b. What is the probability that you will pick the number 17? **4%**
   c. Let E = you pick an even number. What is $P(E)$? **48%**
   d. Let D = you pick an odd number. What is $P(D)$? **52%**
   e. **Fill in the Blank** D and E are called ___?___ events.
      complementary

5. Examine the probability distribution in this lesson for the sum of the numbers on two fair dice when they are tossed.
   a. What is $P(2)$? $\frac{1}{36}$
   b. What is $P(13)$? **0**
   c. What is P(a number less than 5)? $\frac{1}{6}$

In 6 and 7, use the information on blood types in the United States found on page 283.

6. a. What blood type is the least common? **AB–**
   b. What is the most common blood type? **O+**

7. a. What is the probability that a person has type-B blood? 7a. **11.1%**
   b. What is the probability that a person with type-B blood is B+? 7b. **about 84.7%**
   c. What is the probability that a person with type-B blood is B–? 7c. **about 15.3%**
   d. **Fill in the Blank** The probability in Part c is called the ___?___ probability that a person with type-B blood is B–. **conditional**

8. When two equally matched teams play a best-of-5 series, the odds that one team will win in three games is 1 to 3. From this information, what is the probability that one team will win in three games? **25%**

9. Suppose the probability that an event will occur is $\frac{5}{12}$.
   a. What are the odds in favor of the event occurring? **5 to 7**
   b. What are the odds against the event occurring? **7 to 5**

10. **Fill in the Blank** Use *always, sometimes but not always,* or *never.* If p is the probability of an event and q is the probability of its complement, then the value of $p + q$ ___?___ equals 1.
    always

Recommended Assignment
- Questions 1–26
- Question 27 (extra credit)
- Reading Lesson 5-7
- Covering the Ideas 5-7

Probability Distributions   **285**

5-6

Notes on the Questions

Questions 13–15 These questions assume that students have a knowledge of playing cards. It is likely that some students do not, so you should go over the names of the cards and how many of each kind are in a standard deck. Although a standard deck of playing cards contains two jokers in addition to the 13 cards in each of 4 suits, generally in questions about probabilities in mathematics, jokers are ignored.

In 11 and 12, find the complement of the event.

11. A heart is chosen from a standard deck of playing cards. A standard deck has 52 cards. Each card is one of four suits (clubs ♣, diamonds ♦, hearts ♥, and spades ♠) and has one of 13 values (Ace, 2, 3, 4, 5, 6, 7, 8, 9, 10, Jack, Queen, and King).

11. A diamond, spade, or club is chosen from a standard deck of playing cards.

12. You were born on a weekday. You were born on a weekend.

APPLYING THE MATHEMATICS

In 13–15, a card is picked randomly from a standard deck of playing cards.

13. Determine the probability of selecting each card.
    a. the ace of spades
    b. a 5
    c. a 5 or a 9

13a. $\frac{1}{52}$ b. $\frac{1}{13}$ c. $\frac{2}{13}$

14. Determine the probability of selecting each card.
    a. a club
    b. a club or a heart
    c. a club or a 5 (This is a tricky one.)

14a. $\frac{1}{4}$ b. $\frac{1}{2}$ c. $\frac{4}{13}$

15. If you know the card you have selected is a face card (Jack, Queen, or King), what is the probability that it is a King? $\frac{1}{3}$

16. Detectives investigating a crime have narrowed the search for the criminal to five suspects. The table below lists each suspect's personal features.

Features	Suspect				
	1	2	3	4	5
Height	6'2"	5'8"	5'6"	6'3"	6'0"
Eye Color	Green	Blue	Green	Brown	Green
Gender	Male	Female	Female	Male	Female
Handedness	Right	Left	Right	Right	Right

a. If chosen at random, what is the probability that Suspect 3 is the criminal? $\frac{1}{5}$

b. Suppose the detectives receive evidence that the criminal is female. If this new information is true, what is the probability that Suspect 3 is the criminal? $\frac{1}{3}$

c. Suppose the detectives also receive evidence that the female criminal is between 5'5" and 5'9" tall. Given the evidence from Part b and this new information, what is the probability that Suspect 3 is the criminal? $\frac{1}{2}$

In **17** and **18**, suppose that slips of paper containing the integers from
1 to 200 are put in a hat. A number *x* is drawn.

17. Determine each probability.

   a. $x = 135$ $\frac{1}{200}$

   b. $x > 99$ $\frac{101}{200}$

   c. $x < 1$ 0

18. Determine $P(x = 135)$ given each circumstance.

   a. The number *x* is odd. $\frac{1}{100}$

   b. The ones digit of *x* is 5. $\frac{1}{20}$

   c. The hundreds digit of *x* is 1. $\frac{1}{100}$

   d. The tens digit of *x* is 8.   0

19. A person buys a raffle ticket. The person says, "The probability of winning the raffle is $\frac{1}{2}$ since either I will win or I won't." What is wrong with this argument?

19. Answers vary.
    Sample answer:
    Complementary
    events do not
    necessarily have
    equal probabilities.

REVIEW

20. A television station has scheduled *n* hours of news, *c* hours of comedy, *d* hours of drama, *s* hours of sports, and *x* hours of other programs during the week. **(Lesson 5-5)**

   a. What is the ratio of hours of news to hours of drama? $\frac{n}{d}$

   b. What is the ratio of hours of sports to total number of hours of programs during the week? $\frac{s}{n + c + d + s + x}$

21. The Jones family earned $48,735 last year on their 95-acre farm.

   a. What is their income per acre?   **$513**

   b. Is the income per acre a ratio or a rate?
      (Lessons 5-5, 5-3)   rate

22. The list price of a car is *c* dollars. Find the selling price according to the following conditions.

   a. You pay a 7% sales tax and there is no discount.   1.07c

   b. You get a 20% discount and there is no sales tax.   0.8c

   c. You pay a 7% sales tax and get a 20% discount.
      (Lessons 5-5, 4-1, Previous Course)   0.856c

In **23** and **24**, solve the equation. **(Lessons 3-5, 3-4)**

23. $D - 8.5 - 0.25D = 7.5$

   $D = \frac{64}{3}$

24. $\frac{4}{3}w + 72 = 8$

   $w = -48$

In 2004, 74 million acres
of soybeans were harvested
in the United States, a 31%
increase since 1990.

Source: U.S. Department of Agriculture

5-6

4 Wrap-Up

Ongoing Assessment

Organize students into groups and provide each group with a set of data and description of the related problem. Carefully choose problems that have an easily predicted probability, such as a coin toss. Make sure each problem also has a set of data that can be used to find relative frequency. Ask each group to first predict the probability of a given outcome, then to find the relative frequency of that outcome, and finally to compare the two. Ask students to form conclusions regarding the accuracy of the experiment based on this comparison.

Project Update

Project 1, Buffon's Needle, on page 315 relates to the content of this lesson.

25. Use the Distributive Property to compute $0.50 times 299 in your head. (**Lesson 2-1**) **$149.50**

26. Two circles with radii 6 cm and 4 cm are shown below. Let A = area of Circle 1 and B = area of Circle 2. Calculate each expression. (**Previous Course**)

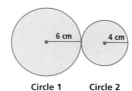

Circle 1   Circle 2

a. $A - B$ 20π b. $\dfrac{B}{A}$ $\dfrac{4}{9}$ c. $\dfrac{A - B}{A}$ $\dfrac{5}{9}$

EXPLORATION

27. a. Pick a letter of the alphabet. Estimate what percent of words used in the English language begin with that letter.
   b. Pick a reading selection that has more than 200 words. Determine the relative frequency that a word in your reading selection begins with your letter.
   c. Having done the experiment, decide whether or not you should change the probability you guessed in Part a. Explain your decision.

27a. Answers vary. Sample answer: s, 12%

27b. Answers vary. Sample answer: $\dfrac{14}{256} \approx 5.5\%$

27c. Answers vary. Sample answer: Yes, since our sample answer was relatively large, it should be nearer than the estimate to the actual probability.

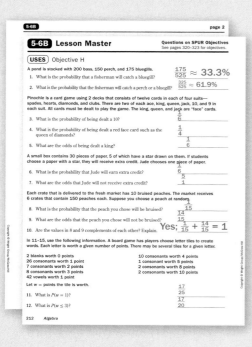

Lesson
5-7

Lesson
5-7 Relative Frequency and Percentiles

Vocabulary

relative frequency

pth percentile

▶ **BIG IDEA** The distribution of the relative frequencies of the outcomes from a situation can be displayed in tables and graphs.

Suppose a particular event has occurred with a frequency of F times in a total of T opportunities for it to happen. Then the **relative frequency** of the event is $\frac{F}{T}$. Like other ratios, relative frequencies may be written as fractions, decimals, or percents.

The Differences between Probability and Relative Frequency

There are similarities and differences between probability and relative frequency. When a single die is tossed, we often think that it is equally likely that the die will land with each side up. If we think this way, then each side will land up $\frac{1}{6}$ of the time. So $P(1) = P(2) = \dots = P(6) = \frac{1}{6}$. But in an actual experiment, it is rare that outcomes occur exactly the same number of times even if their probabilities of occurring are the same. A person simulated the random tossing of a die 100 times and recorded the results in the table below.

Outcome	1	2	3	4	5	6
Probability	$\frac{1}{6} = 0.1\overline{6}$	$\frac{1}{6} = 0.1\overline{6}$	$\frac{1}{6} = 0.1\overline{6}$	$\frac{1}{6} = 0.1\overline{6}$	$\frac{1}{6} = 0.1\overline{6}$	$\frac{1}{6} = 0.1\overline{6}$
Relative Frequency	$\frac{24}{100} = 0.24$	$\frac{16}{100} = 0.16$	$\frac{13}{100} = 0.13$	$\frac{14}{100} = 0.14$	$\frac{16}{100} = 0.16$	$\frac{17}{100} = 0.17$

Notice that the sum of the relative frequencies is 1, just as the sum of the probabilities of these events is 1. The probability of an event is what we would expect the relative frequency of the event to be close to "in the long run," after a large number of experiments.

The table on page 290 summarizes some of the important similarities and differences between relative frequencies and probabilities.

Mental Math

Use the graph to answer the questions.

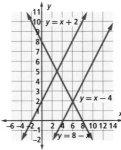

a. Where do $y = 8 - x$ and $y = x + 2$ intersect? (3, 5)

b. Where do $y = 8 - x$ and $y = x - 4$ intersect? (6, 2)

c. Where do $y = x - 4$ and $y = x + 2$ intersect? They do not intersect.

Background

The differences between probability and relative frequency. Students saw in Lesson 5-6 that the probability of an event is sometimes obtained by looking at actual data and using the data's relative frequencies.

If the data are such that there are infinitely many possible repetitions of the event (such as tossing a die or picking a card), we can repeat an experiment that involves the event and see how often the event occurs, and from that ratio determine a probability. So, for example, in the experiment described in

the above table, we would probably view the die as *fair* (unbiased) until evidence mounted that the die was not. Hypothesis testing in statistics involves hypothesizing a particular probability for an event and then running experiments to see if relative frequencies are likely with that hypothesis.

Some books use the term "experimental probability" where we use "relative frequency." Our term is favored by many statisticians.

(continued on next page)

GOALS
Compare relative frequency, a ratio that is calculated from actual data, with probability, and discuss the idea of percentiles.

SPUR Objectives

H Calculate relative frequencies and probabilities in situations with a finite number of equally likely outcomes.

K Interpret the meaning of percentile for benchmarks of 10th, 25th, 50th, 75th, and 90th percentiles.

Materials/Resources
· Lesson Master 5-7A or 5-7B
· Resource Masters 2, 69 and 70
· Graphing calculator

HOMEWORK
Suggestions for Assignment
• Questions 1–21
• Question 22 (extra credit)
• Reading Lesson 5-8
• Covering the Ideas 5-8

Local Standards

1 Warm-Up

1. Find the random-number generator on a calculator. Use it to generate 25 numbers from 1 to 6. Answers vary.

2. Calculate the relative frequencies of each number occurring. Do you think the numbers are really generated at random, or does there seem to be some trend? Answers vary.

3. Test your opinion by generating 25 more numbers from 1 to 6 using the random-number generator. Do your results change your opinion? Answers vary.

4. From your experiment, what would you say the probabilities are of getting a 1, 2, 3, 4, 5, and 6 using your random-number generator? Answers vary.

5-7

2 Teaching

Notes on the Lesson

The differences between probability and relative frequency. In these data, students can see that the numbers of times a die lands on various numbers can vary considerably. Emphasize that although we might expect the relative frequencies of the numbers 1 through 6 to be about equal, it is rare that they would ever be equal. Even if all six relative frequencies were equal at some time, one more toss would make them unequal! It is important for students to realize that the variability of relative frequencies is to be expected. The important question is what happens in the long run. Usually we think that each side of the die is equally likely to turn up, and so we say that the probability of each side turning up is $\frac{1}{6}$.

Guided Example 1 Students may ask about the heights of players in the WNBA (Women's National Basketball Association). From the 163 players on the 2006 team rosters at www.wnba.com, we obtained the following distribution.

Height in feet and inches	Frequency
5′3″	1
5′6″	6
5′7″	7
5′8″	10
5′9″	16
5′10″	10
5′11″	14
6′0″	20
6′1″	11
6′2″	24
6′3″	16
6′4″	13
6′5″	10
6′6″	2
6′7″	1
6′8″	1
7′2″	1

The median height is 6 feet 0 inches. The 10th percentile is at 5 feet 8 inches. The 75th percentile is at 6 feet 3 inches and the 90th percentile is at 6 feet 4 inches.

Relative Frequency	Probability
1. Calculated from data	1. Deduced from assumptions (like randomness) or assumed to be close to some relative frequency
2. The ratio of the number of times an event has occurred to the number of times it could occur	2. If outcomes are equally likely, the ratio of the number of outcomes in an event to the total number of possible outcomes
3. 0 means that an event did not occur. 1 means that the event occurred every time it could.	3. 0 means that an event is impossible. 1 means that an event is sure to happen.
4. The more often an event occurs relative to the number of times it could occur, the closer its relative frequency is to 1.	4. The more likely an event is, the closer its probability is to 1.
5. The sum of the relative frequencies of all outcomes in an experiment is 1.	5. The sum of the probabilities of all outcomes in an experiment is 1.
6. If the relative frequency of an event is r, then the relative frequency of its complement is $1 - r$.	6. If the probability of an event is p, then the probability of its complement is $1 - p$.

Relative Frequency Distributions

Just as there are probability distributions, there are distributions of relative frequency. Relative frequency distributions can be useful in answering questions about data when there are many possible answers. For example, how tall are professional basketball players?

GUIDED

Example 1

The dot plot on the next page shows the heights of 198 players in the National Basketball Association (NBA) during the 2005-06 season. Each player's height is represented by a dot. The information is summarized in the table at the right.

In the NBA, what is the relative frequency of a player

a. being shorter than 6 feet tall?
b. being at least 7 feet tall?
c. being at most 6 feet 7 inches tall?
d. having a height h given by $72 \leq h \leq 78$?

Height (in.)	Frequency
87	1
86	1
85	3
84	16
83	18
82	20
81	22
80	22
79	23
78	15
77	9
76	11
75	15
74	7
73	10
72	3
71	1
67	1

Source: NBA

Relative frequency distributions. Relative frequency distributions (RFDs) are the counterpart to probability distributions (PDs). RFDs are always from data, while PDs are based on assumptions. There are two RFDs described in this lesson. The first is in the table on page 289, which also has a PD. The second is in Guided Example 1. In this situation, there is no obvious corresponding PD.

ENGLISH LEARNERS
Vocabulary Development

The most essential skills for this section include understanding vocabulary, specifically the differences between probability and relative frequency and the meaning of the term percentile. Consider asking students to describe these terms and to write explanations in their own words to check for understanding.

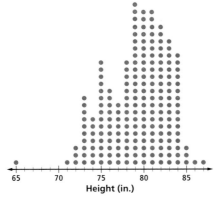

Height (in.)

Solutions

a. Two players are under 6 feet. So the relative frequency is
$\frac{2}{?} \approx 0.01 = 1\%$. **198**

b. Include all the players 7 ft or taller.

relative frequency $= \frac{?}{198} \approx 0.106 = 10.6\%$. **21**

c. Include players 6 ft 7 in. and shorter.

relative frequency $= \frac{23 + 15 + 9 + 11 + 15 + 7 + 10 + 3 + 1 + 1}{198}$

$\frac{95}{198} = \frac{?}{?} \approx \underline{?} \approx 48\%$ **0.48**

d. These heights include __?__ players. So the relative frequency is __?__%.
70; about 35%

How tall are NBA players? Part c of the Example shows that in
the NBA, almost half of the players (48%) are 6 ft 7 in. or shorter.
Since 48% is very close to 50%, we know that 6 ft 7 in. is close to the
median. Recall that the median is the middle number when a data
set is arranged in order. For the NBA heights, the median is 6 ft 8 in.
Another name for median is *50th percentile*. Fifty percent of the data
are at or below the 50th percentile.

Percentiles

Sometimes it is interesting to describe the relative position of a
person within a distribution. You have received standardized test
reports in the past that report your score as a percentile. What does
it mean if the report says you were at the 70th percentile? It means
that 70 percent of the people that took the test had scores that were
less than or equal to your score.

Percentiles. There are two different ways
to define the *p*th percentile in common use.
We define it as the smallest data value that
is greater than or equal to p percent of the
data values. Others may define it as the
smallest data value that *is greater than p*
percent of the data values. Regardless of
your view, the different definitions suggest
that the percentile of an entry as a data set
should be treated as an estimate.

Accommodating the Learner ⬆

Ask students to examine the table that
summarizes important similarities and
differences between relative frequencies
and probabilities. Ask each student to
choose the two categories that they think
describe the most significant differences,
and defend their choice either verbally or
in a journal entry.

Additional Example

Example 1 The dot plot shows the
weights of 400,000 newborns in a
given country over a six-year period.
Every 10,000 births in a weight
category are represented as a dot. The
information, to the nearest 0.5 kg, is
summarized in the table.

Birth Weight (kg)	Number of Births
2.5	20,000
3.0	80,000
3.5	150,000
4.0	90,000
4.5	50,000
5.0	10,000

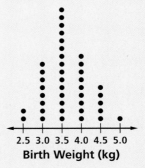

Birth Weight (kg)

What is the relative frequency of a
newborn's weight

a. being less than 3 kg?

b. being at least 3 kg?

c. being at most 3.5 kg?

d. having a weight *w* given by
$2.5 \leq w \leq 4.5$?

Solutions

a. 20,000 newborns weigh less than
3 kg. So the relative frequency is
$\frac{20,000}{?} \approx 0.05 = 5.0\%$ **400,000**

b. Include all the newborns 3 kg
or heavier. Relative frequency
$= \frac{?}{400,000} \approx 0.95 = 95\%$ **380,000**

c. Include newborns 3.5 kg and lighter.
Relative frequency
$= \frac{150,000 + 80,000 + 20,000}{400,000}$
$= \frac{?}{?} = \underline{?} = 62.5\%$

250,000; 400,000; 0.625

d. These weights include __?__
newborns. So the relative frequency
is __?__ %. **390,000; 97.5**

Additional Example

Example 2 Find the meaning of the 50th percentile in the newborn data and explain its meaning.

The 50th percentile is the least number that is greater than or equal to 50% of the data values. There are 40 values, and 50% of 40 = 20, so look at the 20th weight from the bottom of the list. This weight is 3.5 kg. So 3.5 kg is the 50th percentile of newborn weights. Thus, 50% of the newborn babies weighed less than 3.5 kg.

Percentile

The **pth percentile** of a data set is the smallest data value that is greater than or equal to *p* percent of the data values.

🛑 **QY**

Percentiles cut the data set into 100 equal-size parts. This is similar to the way data are cut into four equal-size parts by the median and quartiles.

The 25th percentile is the same as the 1st quartile.
The 50th percentile is the same as the median.
The 75th percentile is the same as the 3rd quartile.

The dot plot of the NBA heights shown below has these three percentiles marked, along with the 10th percentile and the 90th percentile. A player who is 84 in. tall (7 ft) is at the 90th percentile. About 90% of the players are 7 ft or shorter and about 10% are taller.

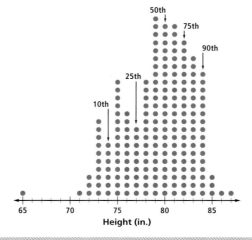

Height (in.)

Example 2

Find the 10th percentile in the NBA data and explain its meaning.

Solution The 10th percentile is the smallest data value that is greater than or equal to 10% of the data values. There are 198 values, and 10% of 198 = 19.8, so look at the 20th height from the bottom of the list. This height is 74 in. So 74 in. is at the 10th percentile of NBA heights.

▶ **QY**

Your school counselor tells you that your class rank or grade point average (GPA) is the 78th percentile. What does this mean?

Accommodating the Learner ⬇

Students often struggle with the difference between a percent and a percentile. Compare the terms and their meanings. For example, ask them to discuss what percentile you are in if 30% of people scored better than you on a standardized test.
70th percentile

Questions

COVERING THE IDEAS

1. What is the meaning of a relative frequency of 0?

2. What is the meaning of a relative frequency of 1?

3. What is the meaning when the probability of an event equals 0?

4. What is the meaning when the probability of an event equals 1?

5. A letter is picked randomly from the English alphabet.

   a. What is the probability of picking a vowel (A, E, I, O, or U)? $\frac{5}{26}$

   b. Count the number of vowels and consonants in the following sentence. **12 vowels; 24 consonants**

   > *The quick brown fox jumped over the lazy dog.*

   c. What is the relative frequency that a letter randomly picked in the sentence is a vowel? $\frac{1}{3}$

   d. Why aren't the answers to Parts a and c equal?

6. A 2006 estimate was that 116 million households in the United States would have televisions in 2007. Of these homes, 82 million were thought to have TVs with digital capability.

   a. What was the relative frequency of households with a TV having digital capability? $\frac{41}{58}$

   b. What was the relative frequency of households with a TV not having digital capability? $\frac{17}{58}$

7. What is meant by a test score that is at the 46th percentile?
   46% of tests were given this or a lower score.

In 8 and 9, refer to Example 2.

8. What height is at the 50th percentile of NBA heights? Explain how you got your answer.

9. What height is at the 80th percentile of NBA heights?

APPLYING THE MATHEMATICS

In 10 and 11, use the table which gives percentiles for weights of 3-year-old boys. Doctors use weight percentiles to see if children are growing properly.

10. 75% of the boys are heavier than Fernando. How much does he weigh? **29 lb**

11. Find possible values of a and b if 80% of the boys have weights in the interval $a \leq \text{weight} \leq b$. **$a = 28$ and $b = 37$**

Weight (lb)	Percentile
37	90th
34	75th
32	50th
29	25th
28	10th

Answer column:

1. The event did not occur in any trial.
2. The event occurred in every trial.
3. The event will never happen.
4. The event will always happen.

5d. Answers vary. Sample answer: because most words have a vowel in them

8. 80 in., since the 99th player out of 198 is 6 ft 7 in. tall

9. 82 in. About 80.3% of the NBA players in the sample answer are 82 in. tall or shorter.

---

3 Assignment

Recommended Assignment
- Questions 1–21
- Question 22 (extra credit)
- Reading Lesson 5-8
- Covering the Ideas 5-8

Notes on the Questions

Questions 1–4 These questions about relative frequency and probability can determine whether students know the difference between the two.

---

12. In 1983 the American Veterinary Medical Association surveyed 20,000 households and found that 5,680 had a cat as a pet. In 2001, a similar survey of 54,000 households found that 31.6% had a cat. Was cat ownership becoming more popular? **yes**

13. **Multiple Choice** An event occurred c times out of t possible occurrences. The relative frequency of the event was 50%. Which equation is true? **A**

    A $\frac{c}{t} = 0.5$ **B** $\frac{t}{c} = 0.5$ **C** $1 - t = 0.3$ **D** $1 - c = 0.3$

14. Of the people surveyed, $\frac{3}{5}$ thought the American League team would win the World Series. If $3n$ people were surveyed, how many thought the American League team would win?
    1.8n people

In 15 and 16, use the following data, which show the level of education of U.S. adults through 2004. The numbers in the cells are in thousands.

Education Level	Age					
	25–34	35–44	45–54	55–64	> 64	Sum
Did not complete high school	5,072	5,232	4,251	3,856	9,339	27,750
Completed high school	11,244	13,739	12,910	9,436	12,482	59,811
1–3 years of college	7,583	7,420	7,210	4,824	4,771	31,808
4 or more years of college	15,304	17,183	16,699	10,258	8,067	67,511
Sum	39,203	43,574	41,070	28,374	34,659	186,880

Source: U.S. Census Bureau

15. What is the probability that an individual older than 64 completed at least one year of college? **about 37%**

16. What is the probability that a person between the ages of 25 and 44 did not graduate from high school? **about 12.4%**

REVIEW

17. The end-of-the-year raffle at Lincoln Elementary is the school's biggest fund-raiser. Last year, the school sold 578 tickets. The grand prize was a $1,000 gift certificate to an electronics store. In addition, there were 3 prizes of computers, 5 bikes, and 10 sweatshirts with the school seal on them. (**Lesson 5-6**)

    a. Given that Rufus won a prize, what is the probability it was a computer? $\frac{3}{19}$

    b. If Randall bought one ticket, what is the probability that he won the grand prize? $\frac{1}{578}$

    c. How many times as likely is it to win a sweatshirt as a bike? **twice**

Extension

Ask students to demonstrate their knowledge of relative frequency and probability by considering the word Mississippi. First ask students to find the probability of choosing a given letter from the word Mississippi. They should find that the probabilities of i, m, p, and s are $\frac{4}{11}$ or 0.36, $\frac{1}{11}$ or 0.09, $\frac{2}{11}$ or 0.18, and $\frac{4}{11}$ or 0.36, respectively. Now, fill out 11 index cards with one letter each so they spell Mississippi, and drop them in a box. Mix them up and begin a trial, with students drawing a card and tallying the frequency as they go. Be sure to replace each card in the box and shuffle between turns. In the end, have students compare the relative frequencies with the predicted probabilities, and discuss their findings. Ask students to create a dot plot to represent the data.

18. Joanie joined a bowling league to improve her game. Her scores over 10 weeks were: 52, 65, 59, 72, 70, 92, 85, 100, 95, and 93. (Lesson 5-6)

    a. What is the relative frequency of Joanie bowling over 70? $\frac{3}{5}$

    b. What is the relative frequency of Joanie bowling 70 or under? $\frac{2}{5}$

19. In planning her trip from Toronto, Ontario, to Montreal, Quebec, Bianca looked at the legend of a map that says $\frac{3}{4}$ in. = 50 km. If the two cities are approximately 542 km apart, how far should the distance be between them on the map? (Lesson 5-4) 8.13 in.

20. Simplify each expression. (Lessons 5-3, 5-2, 5-1)

    a. $\frac{63}{34} \div \frac{9}{2}$ $\frac{7}{17}$

    b. 76 mi/hr · 2.15 hr 163.4 mi

    c. $\frac{7m^3(8n)}{4m^2n^2}$ $\frac{14m}{n}$

21. Graph $y = |6 - 3x|$ and use your graph to solve $|6 - 3x| = 15$. (Lesson 4-9)

EXPLORATION

22. a. Create an experiment in which randomness indicates certain probabilities that outcomes will occur.

    b. Conduct the experiment a large number of times. Record the appropriate data.

    c. Compare the relative frequencies you get with the probabilities predicted by randomness.

    d. Do you think the outcomes occurred randomly? Why or why not? Opinions vary.

21.

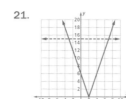

$x = -3$ or $x = 7$

22a. Answers vary. Sample answer: Flipping a coin should result in heads about 50% of the time and tails about 50% of the time if the coin is fair.

22b. Answers vary. Sample answer: 350 tosses resulted in 170 heads and 180 tails.

22c. Answers vary. Sample answer: The probabilities suggested by randomness predict the relative frequencies very well.

QY ANSWER

78 percent of students in your class have GPAs less than or equal to your GPA.

---

4 Wrap-Up

Ongoing Assessment

Create a set of problems that demonstrate relative frequency, probability, and percentile and put these on different transparencies. Check students' understanding of the different terms by showing each transparency and asking students to tell which term the problem is demonstrating.

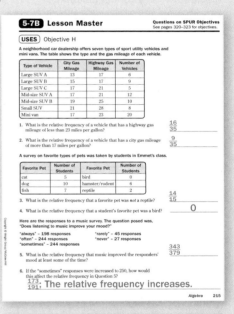

Lesson 5-8

Lesson 5-8

Probability Without Counting

GOAL

Show how probabilities can be calculated by taking ratios of lengths or areas.

SPUR Objective

I Find probabilities involving geometric regions.

Materials/Resources

· Lesson Master 5-8A or 5-8B
· Resource Masters 71–73
· Scientific or graphing calculator
· Compass
· Colored pencils, crayons, or markers

HOMEWORK

Suggestions for Assignment

• Questions 1–20
• Question 21 (extra credit)
• Reading Lesson 5-9
• Covering the Ideas 5-9

Local Standards

1 Warm-Up

Find the area of each figure.

1. A circle with a radius of 5 centimeters 25π cm^2
2. A square with sides of length 1.5 inches 2.25 in^2
3. A right triangle with legs 7 centimeters and 8 centimeters 28 cm^2
4. A circle with a diameter of 2 feet π ft^2
5. A rectangle with a length of $5k$ and a width of $2k$ 10k^2 units^2
6. The largest circle that can be drawn inside a square with perimeter 100 units 156.25π units^2

▶ **BIG IDEA** The probability that a point lands in a particular region can be calculated by taking the ratios of measures of regions.

When a situation has equally likely outcomes, the probability of an event is the ratio of the number of outcomes in the event to the total number of outcomes. But sometimes the number of outcomes is infinite and not countable. In such cases, probabilities may still be found by division.

Probabilities from Areas

Example 1

Suppose a dart is thrown at a 24-inch square board containing a target circle of radius 3 inches, as shown at the right. Assuming that the dart hits the board and that it is equally likely to land on any point on the board, what is the probability that the dart lands in the circle?

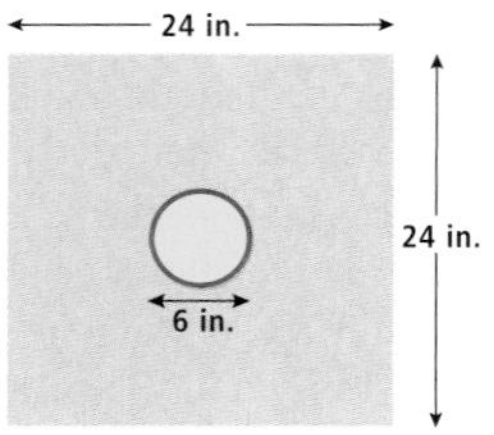

Solution Recall that the area of a circle with radius r is πr^2. Compare the area of the circle to the area of the square.

Probability the dart lands in the circle $= \frac{\text{area of circle}}{\text{area of square}}$

$$= \frac{\pi \cdot 3^2}{24 \cdot 24}$$

$$= \frac{9\pi}{576}$$

$$\approx 0.049, \text{ or about } 5\%$$

So, the probability of the dart landing in the circle is about 5%.

Example 1 illustrates the Probability Formula for Geometric Regions.

Probability Formula for Geometric Regions

Suppose points are selected at random in a region and part of that region's points represent an event E of interest. The probability P of the event is given by
$$\frac{\text{measurement of region in the event}}{\text{measure of entire region}}.$$

Mental Math

Compare using $>$, $=$, or $<$.

a. $-50 + 74$ and $-74 + 50$
$-50 + 74 > -74 + 50$
b. -5 and $(-5)^2$
$-5 < (-5)^2$
c. $y + 7$ and $y + 6$
$y + 7 > y + 6$
d. $|x|$ and -4 $|x| > -4$

Background

The geometric representation of probability gives students a model that facilitates the understanding of the probability of an event. Geometric probabilities may be ratios of lengths, angle measures, areas, or volumes.

Geometric interpretations of probability are quite important. The normal curve used in standardized tests (and discussed in later UCSMP courses) exhibits this idea. Areas of sections under the curve represent the probabilities that students will achieve scores within certain intervals.

QY1

Probabilities from Lengths

Example 2

Points *A*, *B*, *C*, *D*, and *E* below represent exits on an interstate highway.

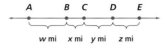

If accidents occur at random along the highway between exits *A* and *E*, what is the probability that when an accident occurs, it happens between exit *C* and exit *D*?

Solution First find the length of the entire segment.

Length of $\overline{AE} = w + x + y + z$

Probability the accident is in $\overline{CD} = \dfrac{y}{w + x + y + z}$

Traffic safety engineers might compare the probabilities in Example 2 with the actual relative frequency of accidents. If the relative frequency along one stretch of the highway is greater than predicted, then that part of the highway might be a candidate for repair or new safety features.

 QY2

Probabilities can also be determined by finding ratios of angle measures.

Activity

A basic spinner used in many games is shown here. Suppose the spinner is equally likely to point in any direction. There is a 50% probability the spinner lands in the red region. Draw a different spinner that still has a 50% probability of landing in a red region.

Sometimes the calculation of the measures needed to compute a probability requires you to do some addition or subtraction first.

> ▶ **QY1**
>
> A target consists of two concentric circles as shown below. The smaller circle (called the "bull's eye"), has a radius of 4 cm and the larger circle has a radius of 6 cm. If a point is selected at random from inside the target, what is the probability it *misses* the bull's eye?

> ▶ **QY2**
>
> What is the probability that an accident occurring between exits *A* and *E* happens between exits *C* and *E* from Example 2?

Activity:
Answers vary. Sample answer:

Accommodating the Learner ⬇

A common technique in diagram problems is to ask students to find an unlabeled part of the diagram by using the labeled parts of the diagram. Students sometimes struggle with questions such as Examples 2 and 3 and Additional Examples 2 and 3 because the numbers they will need to use to compute are not labeled on the diagram. Help students label diagrams and understand when they need to add quantities versus subtract quantities to obtain the needed result.

---

2 Teaching

Notes on the Lesson

There are two key concepts in this lesson. The first is that probabilities can be ratios of lengths, angle measures, areas, or volumes. In this lesson, Examples 1 and 3 each involve a ratio of areas and Example 2 involves a ratio of lengths. The second key idea to emphasize is that the probability is the ratio of the measure of the respective regions if the outcomes are random throughout. (If the outcomes are not random, then it may be quite difficult to calculate the probability without using calculus or some other powerful tool.)

Additional Examples

Example 1 Suppose a dart is thrown at a target consisting of three concentric circles with radii 20 centimeters, 40 centimeters, and 60 centimeters, as shown. Assuming that the dart hits the board, what is the probability that the dart will land somewhere inside the smallest circle? $\frac{1}{9}$ or 11%

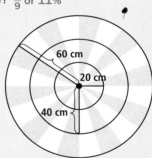

Example 2 The given figure represents a walking path. Suppose when you stand on a nearby hill, you can see only the part of the path labeled *x*. If your friend is walking the entire path when you reach the peak of the hill, what is the probability that she is visible to you at the moment you reach the peak? **23.5%**

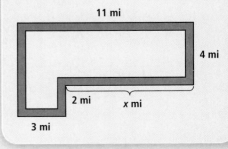

5-8

Additional Example

Example 3 Suppose you throw a dart randomly at the board shown below. Assume the height of the triangle is approximately 1.7 feet, and that the diameter of the circle is 0.5 foot. Assuming you hit the board, find the probability that your dart will land in the shaded region. **about 19%**

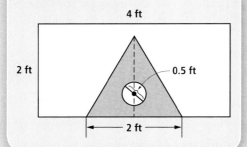

Additional Answers

2. Answers vary. Sample answers:

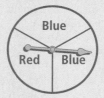

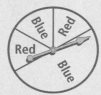

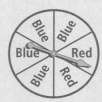

Example 3

A target consisting of three evenly spaced concentric circles is shown below. If a point is selected at random from inside the circular target, what is the probability that it lies in the red region?

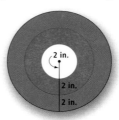

Solution Probability of a point in the red region = $\dfrac{\text{area of red region}}{\text{area of largest circle}}$

Area of the red region = the difference in the areas of the circles with radii 4 inches and 2 inches

$$\text{Area of red region} = \pi(4)^2 - \pi(2)^2$$
$$= 16\pi - 4\pi$$
$$= 12\pi \ in^2$$

The radius of the largest circle is 6 inches.

$$\text{Area of largest circle} = \pi(6)^2 = 36\pi \ in^2$$

Thus the probability of choosing a point in the red region is $\dfrac{12\pi}{36\pi} = \dfrac{1}{3}$.

Questions

COVERING THE IDEAS

1. Consider the square archery target board at the right.
   a. What is the area of the bull's eye? **0.49π ft^2**
   b. What is the area of the entire target board? **5.29 ft^2**
   c. To the nearest percent, what is the probability that an arrow shot at random that hits the board will land in the bull's eye? **29%**
   d. What is the probability that the arrow hitting the board will land on the target outside the bull's eye? **71%**

2. Draw three different spinners that have a $\frac{2}{3}$ probability of landing in a blue region. **See margin.**

3. An electric clock with a continuously-moving second hand is stopped by a power failure. What is the probability that the second hand stopped between the following two numbers?
   a. 12 and 2 $\frac{1}{6}$ b. 5 and 6 $\frac{1}{12}$ c. 7 and 11 $\frac{1}{3}$

2.3 ft

0.7 ft

2.3 ft

Accommodating the Learner ⬆

Combine the concepts of ratio and probability by showing students that even when we do not know the exact dimensions of an object, the ratios of these dimensions are often all we need to determine probability. For example, assume we have a dartboard of concentric circles with radii r and $5r$, respectively. Ask students to find the probability of a random point on the board being inside the inner circle. $\dfrac{\pi r^2}{25\pi r^2}$ $= \dfrac{1}{25} = 4\%$

In 4 and 5, use the following scenario and diagram. A student from the University of Chicago wanted to ride her bike north to Loyola University. Along the bike trek, she planned on making stops at Navy Pier and North Avenue Beach. If the student has a flat tire on the trip, what is the probability it occurs between each pair of locations?

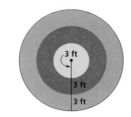

9.32 mi   2.24 mi   7.56 mi

University   Navy   North   Loyola
of Chicago   Pier Avenue University
                    Beach

4. Navy Pier and North Avenue Beach **Approximately 11.7%**

5. University of Chicago and North Avenue Beach
   approximately 60.5%

In 6–8, refer to the target at the right. Suppose a point on the target is chosen at random.

6. What is the probability that it lies inside the bull's eye? $\frac{1}{9}$

7. What is the probability that it lies in the outermost ring? $\frac{5}{9}$

8. What is the probability that it lies in the middle ring? $\frac{1}{3}$

APPLYING THE MATHEMATICS

9. The land area of Earth is about 57,510,000 square miles and the water surface area is about 139,440,000 square miles. Give the probability that a meteor hitting the surface of the earth will
   a. fall on land.   **b.** fall on water.
   approximately 29.2%   **approximately 70.8%**

10. In a rectangular yard of dimensions q by p, there is a rectangular garden of dimensions b by a. If a newspaper is thrown randomly into the yard, what is the probability that it lands on a point in the garden? $\frac{ab}{pq}$

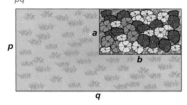

p

a

b

q

11. The table below displays the membership in the Drama Club. Design a spinner that can be used to select a representative group from the club.

Grade	Members
9	5
10	15
11	17
12	23

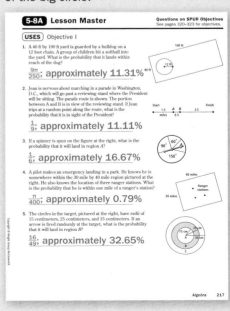

Ocean waters cover nearly 71% of Earth's surface, whereas fresh waters in lakes and rivers cover less than 1%.
Source: NASA

11. Answers vary.
    Sample answer:

11th 10th
          9th
   12th

3 Assignment

Recommended Assignment

- Questions 1–20
- Question 21 (extra credit)
- Reading Lesson 5-9
- Covering the Ideas 5-9

Notes on the Questions

Question 3 Here we are assuming that the power failure is occurring at a random time.

Questions 6–8 and 12 These questions are all related to Example 3.

Question 9 You might ask students what assumption is being made in calculating the probability. The meteor has an equal probability of landing in any region. You might note that these kinds of assumptions are not always valid. For instance, tornadoes do not occur randomly over land; they are more often spawned over flat land.

Question 12 You might ask students if an odd number n of concentric circles are in a target, equally spaced, then the area of the middle ring is always $\frac{1}{n}$ times the area of the largest circle. It is the case, but the proof requires some algebra that students have not yet encountered. Here is a proof: Suppose that the radii of the circles are 1, 2, 3, ..., $2k + 1$. ($2k + 1$ ensures that there is an odd number of circles.) The middle ring is between the circles with radii k and $k + 1$, so it has area $\pi(k + 1)^2 - \pi k^2$, which equals $\pi(2k + 1)$. The area of the largest circle is $\pi(2k + 1)^2$. So the middle ring has $\frac{1}{2k + 1}$ the area of the big circle.

4 Wrap-Up

Ongoing Assessment

Draw a Venn diagram on the board with one circle representing the probability formula for geometric regions, and the other representing previous methods of computing probability. Ask students to give ways they are different and ways they are similar, and fill in the different regions based on their responses.

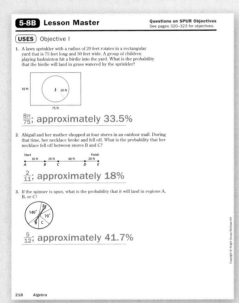

12. One student, seeing that the answer to Example 3 is $\frac{1}{3}$, said that if there were five concentric circles instead of 3, then the middle ring would have $\frac{1}{5}$ the area of the largest circle. Is the student correct? Why or why not?

13. What is the probability that a point selected from the region within the red rectangle at the right is also inside the circle? $\frac{9\pi}{160}$

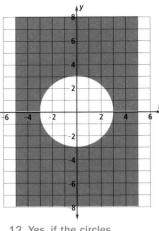

REVIEW

14. A die is tossed once. (**Lessons 5-7, 5-6**)
    a. If the die is assumed to be fair, which event is more likely, "the number showing is less than 3" or "the number showing is odd"?
    b. If a 4 showed on the die, what was the relative frequency that a 2 showed? $\frac{0}{1}$

15. A 14-foot-long metal rod is cut so that the two pieces formed have lengths in a ratio of $\frac{7}{3}$. How long is each piece? (**Lesson 5-5**)
    9.8 ft and 4.2 ft

16. Write an equation of a line that passes through the points $(1, -8)$ and $(1, 1)$. (**Lesson 4-2**) $x = 1$

17. a. If $42n = 0$, then $\frac{2n}{5} = \underline{\ ?\ }$. 0
    b. What property was used to answer Part a? (**Lesson 2-8**)
       The Zero Product Property

In 18–20, rewrite the fraction in lowest terms. (**Previous Course**)

18. $\frac{20}{25}$ $\frac{4}{5}$ 19. $\frac{42}{54}$ $\frac{7}{9}$ 20. $\frac{112}{28}$ 4

EXPLORATION

21. a. A circle with radius of 10 units is drawn inside a square with sides of 20 units, as shown below. What part of the area inside the square is outside the circle? $\frac{400 - 100\pi}{400} \approx 21.46\%$

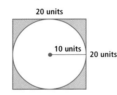   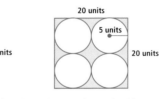

20 units   20 units

10 units   20 units   5 units   20 units

    b. Four circles with radii of 5 units are drawn inside a square with sides of 20 units, as shown at the right. What part of the area inside of the square lies outside the four circles? $\frac{400 - 4 \cdot 25\pi}{400} \approx 21.46\%$
    c. Generalize Parts a and b. Explain why you believe your generalization to be true. See margin.

12. Yes, if the circles had radii of 2, 4, 6, 8, 10, the area of the middle ring would be 20π and the area of the largest circle would be 100π.

14a. The number showing is odd; An odd number occurs with probability $\frac{1}{2}$, while a number less than 3 occurs with probability $\frac{1}{3}$.

QY ANSWERS

1. $0.5\overline{5}$ or about 56%

2. $\frac{y + z}{w + x + y + z}$

Additional Answers

21c. Answers vary. Sample answer: A circle enclosed by a square fills the same percent of the square as four circles, each with half the original radius, enclosed by the same square. The generalization is true, since $\pi r^2 = 4\pi\left(\frac{r}{2}\right)^2$.

Lesson 5-9 Proportions

▶ **BIG IDEA** Proportions can be solved algebraically using the Means-Extremes Property.

In his 1859 autobiography, Abraham Lincoln wrote about his childhood in Indiana. "There were some schools, so called; but no qualification was ever required of a teacher beyond 'readin, writin, and cipherin' to the Rule of Three. . . . Of course when I came of age I did not know much. Still somehow, I could read, write, and cipher to the Rule of Three; but that was all." After his short stint at school, Lincoln went on to teach himself algebra and geometry from books.

The "Rule of Three" refers to a method of solving a *proportion*, a sentence such as "4 is to 6 as 3 is to __?__." It is equivalent to solving $\frac{4}{6} = \frac{3}{x}$. In a simple proportion such as this, whenever you know three out of the four numbers, you can determine the fourth. The Rule of Three is a method that dates from ancient times and is not usually taught today. Today we use algebra, and so are able to solve this and more complicated proportions.

Solving Proportions

A **proportion** is a statement that two ratios are equal. Thus any equation of the form $\frac{a}{b} = \frac{c}{d}$ is a proportion. This equation is sometimes written $a : b = c : d$. Because a and d are at the two ends of this statement, a and d are called the **extremes.** Because b and c are in the middle, b and c are called the **means.**

Example 1

Complete the sentence; "4 is to 6 as 3 is to __?__."

Solution Let x be the unknown number.

$\frac{4}{6} = \frac{3}{x}$ Write the sentence as a proportion.

$\frac{4}{6} \cdot 6x = \frac{3}{x} \cdot 6x$ Multiply each side of the equation by 6x.

$\frac{4}{6} \cdot 6x = \frac{3}{x} \cdot 6x$ Simplify each side.

$4x = 18$ Simplify.

$x = \frac{18}{4} = 4.5$ Divide each side by 4 and simplify.

(continued on next page)

Vocabulary

proportion
extremes
means
population
sample
randomly
capture-recapture method

Mental Math

Write in lowest terms.

a. $\frac{35}{7,000}$ $\frac{1}{200}$

b. $-\frac{27}{72}$ $-\frac{3}{8}$

c. $\frac{18}{-78}$ $-\frac{3}{13}$

The Rail Splitter, a painting by J. L. G. Ferris of a young Abraham Lincoln splitting logs

Proportions   **301**

Lesson 5-9

GOAL

Justify and use the Means-Extremes Property in solving proportions.

SPUR Objectives

C Solve proportions.

D Use the language of proportions and the Means-Extremes Property.

J Solve problems involving proportions in real situations.

Materials/Resources

· Lesson Master 5-9A or 5-9B
· Resource Master 74
· Scientific or graphing calculator
· Large bowl
· Markers
· Pennies, beans, or uncooked popcorn

HOMEWORK

Suggestions for Assignment

• Questions 1–27
• Question 28 (extra credit)
• Reading Lesson 5-10
• Covering the Ideas 5-10

Local Standards

1   Warm-Up

1. If you are charged $1.69 for 3 cans of peaches, how much should you expect to pay for 8 cans? **$4.51**

2. If in traffic it takes a bus 5 minutes to travel $\frac{3}{4}$ of a mile, how long at that rate would it take the bus to travel 6 miles? **40 min**

3. Booker is reading a 300-page novel. It has taken him 2 hours to read the first 72 pages. At this rate, how many more hours will it take him to finish the novel? **8.33 hours to read 300 pages, so 6.33 hours more**

Background

Solving proportions. The first part of this lesson is likely to be review for students. We include this review because proportions are important content and we want to ensure that students new to UCSMP materials are familiar with the language that we use.

The Means-Extremes Property. The text exhibits a proof of the Means-Extremes Property. Thus, the Means-Extremes Property is a theorem, and you could call it the Means-Extremes Theorem.

Proportions and statistics. The capture-recapture method discussed in the Activity is used in some wildlife surveys. When this method is used in actual practice, a major question that arises is how accurate the estimate is. For example, if in the Activity your handful has 2 tagged pieces out of 10, then the estimate is 150 pieces in the bowl. But if your handful has 3 tagged pieces out of 10, then the estimate is 100 pieces in the bowl. So it is clear that you need to draw out more than just 10 pieces to get an accurate estimate of the number of pieces.

5-9

2 Teaching

Notes on the Lesson

Proportions arise from equal rates or equal ratios. They are important because they appear so often in applications. The standard method of solving a proportion, using the Means-Extremes Property, is unique to proportions. But its application is so simple that some students will want to use it when it does not apply, such as to solve equations like $\frac{2x}{3} = \frac{x}{2} + 1$.

In this equation they will multiply means and extremes in the fractions to get a new equation, $4x = 3x + 1$. Emphasize that the equation must have *only* equal fractions in order for the Means-Extremes Property to apply.

Point out that if there is one proportion in a situation, then many other proportions are also possible. This is an advantage when solving problems that lead to proportions, but it may confuse students.

Watch out for student use of proportions where they are not called for. You might wish to mix the proportion questions with others than look like proportions but are not. For example, if 3 people take 5 hours to complete a task, how long will it take 6 people to complete the same task? (The quantities are inversely, not directly related.) If a solid cube with side 2 inches weighs 6 pounds, what will a solid cube of the same material with side 3 inches weigh? (Volume is proportional to the cube of an edge.)

Additional Example

Example 1 Complete the sentence; "5 is to 15 as 9 is to ___?___." **27**

Check Substitute 4.5 for x in the proportion $\frac{4}{6} = \frac{3}{x}$. Does $\frac{4}{6} = \frac{3}{4.5}$? Yes, in lowest terms the left side equals $\frac{2}{3}$, and the right side equals $\frac{30}{45}$ or, in lowest terms, $\frac{2}{3}$.

The Means-Extremes Property

Look at Step 4 in the solution to Example 1. The left side, $4x$, is the product of the extremes, 4 and x of the original proportion. The right side, 18, is the product of the means 6 and 3. The general pattern is that the product of the means is equal to the product of the extremes. Algebra explains why this is true. Consider any proportion $\frac{a}{b} = \frac{c}{d}$.

$\frac{a}{b} \cdot bd = \frac{c}{d} \cdot bd$ Multiply both sides of the equation by bd to clear the fractions.

$\frac{a}{\cancel{b}} \cdot \cancel{b}d = \frac{c}{\cancel{d}} \cdot b\cancel{d}$ Simplify both sides of the equation.

$ad = bc$ Simplify.

> **Means-Extremes Property**
>
> For all real numbers a, b, c, and d (with b and d not zero), if $\frac{a}{b} = \frac{c}{d}$ then $ad = bc$.

Proportions and Statistics

In statistics, the set of individuals or objects you want to study is called the **population** for that study. If you cannot collect data from the entire population, the part studied is called a **sample.** When samples are taken **randomly,** every member of the population has an equal chance of being chosen. Therefore, data from the sample can be used to estimate information about the population.

> **Activity**
>
> **Step 1** Fill a large bowl with pennies, beans, popcorn kernels, or something similar. Do not count how many there are.
>
> **Step 2** Take out at least 30 pieces. Mark or tag them and then return the pieces to the bowl.
>
> **Step 3** Mix the contents of the bowl. Draw out a handful of the pieces. Be sure to get at least one tagged piece. Answers vary.
>
> How many pieces are there in your handful? __?__
>
> How many pieces are tagged? __?__

302   Division and Proportions in Algebra

ENGLISH LEARNERS

Vocabulary Development

Discuss the vocabulary words *sample* and *population* in greater detail. Consider expanding the terminology to include *representative sample,* or when a sample is an accurate representation of a population. Use this to start a discussion on when statistics can be misleading due to a biased sample.

Step 4 Set up a proportion to estimate how many pieces are in the bowl and solve it.

Step 5 Return all pieces to the bowl and repeat Steps 3 and 4 at least two more times.

Step 6 Compare and contrast your totals. Based on your random samples, do you believe you have a good estimate of how many pieces are in the bowl? Explain why or why not.

Steps 4 and 5. Answers vary.
Step 6. Answers vary.
Sample answer: If you tag 30 pennies and have 13 in a handful, 5 of which are tagged, you should have about 78 total. Because there were actually 90 total, you do not have a very accurate estimate.

In this activity, the method you used to find the total pieces in the bowl is called the **capture-recapture method.** This method has been used to estimate the number of fish in a lake or deer in a forest. In Step 2, you captured pieces and tagged them. Step 3 is where you recaptured the pieces. If the sample in the recapture is chosen randomly, the ratio of tagged pieces to the number of pieces is nearly the same as the percentage of tagged pieces in the entire bowl.

Surveys give information about a part of a population. Proportions are used to extend that information to a larger group. When we do this, we assume that the ratios are the same for the survey group and the larger population.

A biologist uses a computer while colleagues capture spring-summer Chinook salmon smolts for counting and tagging on the Idaho Salmon River.

Example 2

A survey of 454 undergraduates at the University of Texas in 2003 found that 409 of them used their own computers at home. The actual number of undergraduates at the school was 37,409. Based on the survey, how many undergraduates were expected to use computers at home?

Solution 1 Let x be the number of 2003 undergraduates using a personal computer. Set up a proportion with equal ratios that compares undergraduates with computers to the total number of undergraduates.

$$\frac{\text{number of undergraduates with computers in survey}}{\text{total number of undergraduates surveyed}} = \frac{\text{number of total undergraduates with computers}}{\text{total number of undergraduates}}$$

$$\frac{409}{454} = \frac{x}{37,409}$$

$454x = 409 \cdot 37,409$ Means-Extremes Property

$454x = 15,300,281$ Simplify.

$x \approx 33,701$ Multiply each side by $\frac{1}{454}$.

About 33,701 undergraduates would be expected to have computers at home in 2003.

(continued on next page)

Proportions   **303**

Notes on the Activity

Students may not be sure how to determine whether their estimate is correct without counting the pieces in the bowl. Have all students write their proportions and estimates on the board, and then create a frequency table to show a pattern. Use intervals on the frequency table to help group the various answers together. Be prepared to discuss why certain results are far off from the mean.

Additional Example

Example 2 A survey of 200 high school students found that 145 of them had their own television set. Based on the results of this survey, about how many students in a school of 3,175 would have their own television set? **about 2,302 students**

Accommodating the Learner

Students sometimes become confused as to when the Means-Extremes Property can be applied. For instance, they may accidentally simplify $\frac{a}{b} \cdot \frac{c}{d}$ to $ad \cdot bc$ or $ad = bc$. To prevent this confusion, emphasize the reasoning behind the pattern, and that it is only used to solve a proportion.

5-9

Solution 2 Let x be the number of 2003 undergraduates using their own computer. Use ratios that compare undergraduates with computers to the total number of undergraduates.

$$\frac{\text{number of undergraduates with computers in survey}}{\text{total number of undergraduates with computers}} = \frac{\text{total undergraduates surveyed}}{\text{total number of undergraduates}}$$

$$\frac{409}{x} = \frac{454}{37,409}$$

$409 \cdot 37,409 = 454x$	Means-Extremes Property
$15,300,281 = 454x$	Simplify.
$33,701 \approx x$	Multiply each side by $\frac{1}{454}$.

About 33,701 undergraduates were expected to have computers at home in 2003.

The equations that were written for the two solutions are different. But notice that when the Means-Extremes Property is used, the resulting equations are the same.

STOP QY

Some proportions contain algebraic expressions.

Example 3

Two candidates, A and B, ran in a village election. Candidate A received 450 more votes than Candidate B. Their vote counts were in the ratio of 8 to 3. How many votes did each candidate get?

Solution Let $x =$ number of votes Candidate B received. Because Candidate A received 450 more votes than Candidate B, the expression $x + 450$ is the number of votes Candidate A received.

$$\frac{\text{number of votes for A}}{\text{number of votes for B}} = \frac{x + 450}{x} = \frac{8}{3}$$

$3(x + 450) = x \cdot 8$	Means-Extremes Property
$3x + 1,350 = 8x$	Distribute.
$1,350 = 5x$	Add $-3x$ to both sides.
$270 = x$	Divide both sides by 5.

Because $x = 270$, Candidate B got 270 votes. Candidate A got $x + 450$, or $270 + 450 = 720$ votes.

Check Is the ratio of A's votes to B's votes equal to $\frac{8}{3}$?

Is $\frac{720}{270} = \frac{8}{3}$?

$\frac{8}{3} = \frac{8}{3}$ Yes, it checks.

▶ **QY**

Emilio knows he can do 11 pushups in 15 seconds.
a. If his wrestling coach times him for a minute, at this rate how many pushups could he do?
b. At this rate, how long will it take Emilio to do 74 pushups?
c. Why is the answer to Part b likely an underestimate?

Accommodating the Learner ⬆

Ask students to create a proportion in which the Means-Extremes Property takes longer than another method. For example, for $\frac{x}{5} = \frac{9}{15}$, one faster method includes multiplying both sides of the equation by 15 and then simplifying. Another faster method is recognizing that $\frac{x}{5} \cdot \frac{3}{3} = \frac{9}{15}$, so $x = 3$.

Questions

COVERING THE IDEAS

In **1** and **2**, complete the sentence.

1. 4 is to 12 as 18 is to __?__. **54**   2. 5 is to 13 as 17 is to __?__. $\frac{221}{5}$

3. What is a proportion? **a statement that two ratios are equal**

In **4** and **5**, a proportion is given.

    a. Use the Means-Extremes Property to solve the proportion.

    b. Check your work.

4. $\frac{n}{4} = \frac{20}{48}$ 4a. $n = \frac{5}{3}$ 5. $\frac{-28}{21} = \frac{64}{p}$ 5a. $p = -48$

4b. $\frac{\frac{5}{3}}{4} = \frac{5}{3} \cdot \frac{1}{4} = \frac{5}{12}$, $\frac{20}{48} = \frac{5}{12}$

5b. $\frac{64}{-48} = \frac{-4}{3}$; $\frac{-28}{21} = \frac{-4}{3}$

6. On a map of Spain, 3 centimeters represents 200 kilometers.

    a. Seville and Madrid are approximately 417 kilometers apart. How far apart would they be on the map? **6.255 cm**

    b. If Barcelona and Madrid are 9.4 centimeters apart on a map, about how many kilometers apart are they? **627 km**

7. After soccer's World Cup was held in Germany in 2006, the national tourist board surveyed about 1,300 foreign visitors who attended. Of them, approximately 1,200 responded that the World Cup had been a great event.

    a. Based on the survey, about how many of the 2 million foreign visitors felt the World Cup was a great event?

    b. How many foreign visitors felt the World Cup was *not* a great event? **about 150,000**

8. In a capture-recapture study, suppose 60 deer in a forest are tagged. On the recapture, 52 deer are caught, of which 10 are found to have been tagged. Estimate the number of deer in the forest. **312 deer**

9. In 1995, scientists began restoring gray wolves to Yellowstone National Park. The recovery plan called for introducing 10 breeding pairs of gray wolves each year for three years. Suppose that in 2000, the scientists recaptured 14 wolves and 3 had tags. What was the estimated population of gray wolves in Yellowstone in 2000? **280 wolves**

10. Two numbers are in the ratio of 9 : 5. One number is 76 greater than the other. What are the numbers? **95 and 171**

In **11** and **12**, solve the proportion.

11. $\frac{4m - 1}{7} = \frac{m + 2}{2}$ $m = 16$

12. $\frac{5}{12} = \frac{2p - 3}{3p + 5}$ $p = \frac{61}{9}$

France and South Korea square off in group play during the 2006 World Cup in Berlin, Germany.

7a. about 1.85 million people

Proportions   **305**

3 Assignment

Recommended Assignment

- Questions 1–27
- Question 28 (extra credit)
- Reading Lesson 5-10
- Covering the Ideas 5-10

Notes on the Questions

Questions 16–19 Students should get to the point where solving these kinds of problems is automatic.

Question 27b This question may be difficult, as it involves algebra that has not yet been discussed (though it is within students' ability).

APPLYING THE MATHEMATICS

In 13–15, solve the proportion for the indicated variable. No variables equal 0.

13. $\frac{2}{3} = \frac{b}{c}$ for c $c = \frac{3b}{2}$ 14. $\frac{4x}{w} = \frac{3}{m}$ for w 15. $\frac{a}{b} = \frac{x}{y}$ for a $a = \frac{bx}{y}$ 14. $w = \frac{4xm}{3}$

16. A baseball team plays 2 innings in 25 minutes. At this rate, how many minutes will a 9-inning game take? 112.5 min

17. During the first 7 days of November, Gabby used her cell phone for 133 minutes. At this rate, how many minutes will she talk during the entire month? 570 min

18. Kauai, Hawaii, is considered the rainiest place on Earth. In an average week, 9.1 inches of rain falls on the island. If you are on Kauai for 2 days, how much rain would you expect to fall during your stay? 2.6 in.

19. The target heart rates for 22-year-old females exercising in the "fitness zone" is 122–143 beats per minute. Annie, a 22-year-old female, regularly checks her pulse rate while exercising. She found that her heart beats 19 times in 10 seconds.

    a. At this rate, how many times does Annie's heart beat in 60 seconds? 114 bpm

    b. Is Annie in her target heart rate zone? no

20. The Havalot family bought a 26-inch and a 50-inch plasma TV. The total cost of the two televisions was $4,600. If the ratio of the prices was 6 : 17, how much did each TV cost? $1,200 and $3,400

21. A useful baseball statistic is a pitcher's earned run average (ERA), which is a measure of the average number of runs a pitcher allows during 9 innings. Suppose a pitcher has an ERA of 3.33 and has pitched 150 innings. How many earned runs has he allowed during those innings? 56 earned runs

Mt. Waialeale on the island of Kauai in Hawaii (3,000 feet high) is the wettest spot on Earth, averaging about 460 inches of rain per year.

Source: www.infoplease.com

REVIEW

22. A raft that is a rectangle 8 feet by 12 feet is in a circular pool that is 40 feet in diameter. If a watch is at the bottom of the pool, what is the probability it is under the raft? (**Lesson 5-8**) about 7.6%

23. Consider the following situation. A bowl contains 8 green beads, 4 red beads, 11 blue beads, and 6 black beads. One bead from the bowl is then chosen at random. (**Lesson 5-6**)

    a. Find the probability of choosing a red bead. $\frac{4}{29}$

    b. Find the probability of choosing a black or blue bead. $\frac{17}{29}$

    c. Find the probability of choosing a bead that is *not* green. $\frac{21}{29}$

306   Division and Proportions in Algebra

24. Square I has sides of length a and Square II has sides of length $3a$, as shown at the right. **(Lesson 5-5)**

   Square I **Square II**

   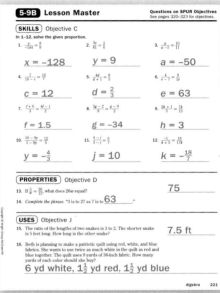

   a. Find the ratio of a side of Square II to a side of Square I. 3

   b. Find the areas of Square I and Square II. a^2; $9a^2$

   c. Find the ratio of the area of Square II to the area of Square I. 9

25. A formula to find the sum S of the measures of the interior angles of a polygon is $S = 180(n - 2)$, where n is the number of sides of the polygon. **(Lesson 4-7)**

   a. Solve this formula for n. $n = \frac{S}{180} + 2$

   b. If the sum of the measures of the interior angles of a polygon is $1{,}260°$, find the number of sides of the polygon. 9 sides

26. **Skill Sequence** Find each reciprocal. **(Lesson 2-8)**

   a. $\frac{5}{9}$ $\frac{9}{5}$ b. $\frac{5x}{9}$ $\frac{9}{5x}$ c. $\frac{-5x}{9}$ $\frac{-9}{5x}$

27. a. The following number puzzle deals with your seven-digit phone number, not including the area code.

   27a. your seven-digit phone number

   Step 1 Write down the first 3 digits of your phone number.

   Step 2 Multiply this by 80.

   Step 3 Add 1.

   Step 4 Multiply this by 250.

   Step 5 Add the last four digits of your phone number.

   Step 6 Add the last four digits of your phone number again.

   Step 7 Subtract 250.

   Step 8 Divide by 2.

   What is your result?

   b. Use algebra to explain your answer to Part a.
      (Lesson 2-3) See margin.

EXPLORATION

28. The tallest person ever measured was Robert Wadlow, who was 8 feet 11.1 inches tall. At 13 years of age, he was 7 feet 4 inches tall. Because schools are constructed for a much shorter person, many things were too small for him. Assume that schools are designed for a person who is up to 6 feet tall. Measure the dimensions of five things that you see in school every day. How big would these objects be if they were made proportionally to fit Robert Wadlow when he was 13 years old? See margin.

Additional Answers

27b. If we let x be the first three digits of your phone number and y be the last four, then your phone number can be written as $10{,}000x + y$. We can also write the result of the puzzle as an algebraic expression involving x and y: $\frac{(80x + 1) \cdot 250 + y + y - 250}{2} = 10{,}000x + y$, which is the same as the expression for your phone number.

28. Answers vary. Sample answer:
   calculator — actual height 7.3 inches, proportional height for Wadlow 9.9 inches; textbook — actual height 11 inches, proportional height for Wadlow 14.9 inches; water fountain — actual height 2 feet, 11 inches, proportional height for Wadlow 3 feet, 11 inches; computer screen — actual height 17 inches, for Wadlow 23 inches; chair height — actual height 2 feet, 6 inches, for Wadlow 3 feet, 5 inches

---

4 Wrap-Up

Ongoing Assessment

Ask students to write a proportion with one variable and use the Means-Extremes Property to solve. Remind students to use substitution to check their answer. If a student encounters difficulties, discuss their proportion as a class.

Project Update

Project 4, Calculating Density, on page 316 relates to the content of this lesson.

5-9B **Lesson Master** Questions on SPUR Objectives
See pages 320–323 for objectives.

SKILLS Objective C

In 1–12, solve the given proportion.

1. $\frac{-t}{-144} = \frac{8}{9}$ $x = -128$

2. $\frac{3y}{81} = \frac{2}{6}$ $y = 9$

3. $\frac{a}{a-5} = \frac{10}{11}$ $a = -50$

4. $\frac{7}{19-c} = \frac{12}{7}$ $c = 12$

5. $\frac{4d}{d+1} = \frac{8}{5}$ $d = \frac{2}{3}$

6. $\frac{4}{e-7} = \frac{9}{2e}$ $e = 63$

7. $\frac{t+6}{3} = \frac{4t-1}{2}$ $f = 1.5$

8. $\frac{3g-2}{8} = \frac{g-9}{2}$ $g = -34$

9. $\frac{2h+1}{5} = \frac{7h}{15}$ $h = 3$

10. $\frac{16-9y}{1-8y} = \frac{12}{5}$ $y = -\frac{4}{3}$

11. $\frac{4-j}{3-j} = \frac{6}{7}$ $j = 10$

12. $\frac{-1}{k+5} = \frac{18}{17k}$ $k = -\frac{18}{7}$

PROPERTIES Objective D

13. If $\frac{5}{6} = \frac{20}{18}$, what does $26w$ equal? 75

14. *Complete the phrase.* "3 is to 27 as 7 is to 63 ."

USES Objective J

15. The ratio of the lengths of two snakes is 3 to 2. The shorter snake is 5 feet long. How long is the other snake? 7.5 ft

16. Beth is planning to make a patriotic quilt using red, white, and blue fabrics. She wants to use twice as much white in the quilt as red and blue together. The quilt uses 9 yards of 36-inch fabric. How many yards of each color should she buy? 6 yd white, $1\frac{1}{2}$ yd red, $1\frac{1}{2}$ yd blue

Algebra **221**

5-9B page 2

17. Bianca mixes 5 parts nuts to 2.5 parts dried apricots to make an afternoon snack. If she has 3 cups of apricots, how many cups of nuts does she need to make her snack? 6 c

18. A liquid treatment for the prevention of rose diseases is mixed with water at a rate of 1:64. If 8 cups of water are poured into a watering can, how many cups of the treatment should be added? $\frac{1}{8}$ c

19. Pierce and Fabian have collected autographed baseballs. Pierce has 3 more than twice the number of baseballs Fabian has. The ratio of the number of baseballs that Fabian has collected to the number of baseballs Pierce has collected is 3 : 7. How many autographed baseballs does each have? Fabian has collected 9 baseballs and Pierce has collected 21 baseballs.

20. The state Department of Natural Resources uses a capture/recapture program to check the number of fish of various types in Long Lake. One year, 50 large-mouth bass were tagged. Two years later, of 20 large-mouth bass that were netted, 2 were tagged. Estimate the total number of large-mouth bass in Long Lake. 500

A landscaping company is hired to plant maple, ash, and locust trees along the streets of a new subdivision. The landscapers plant 3 times as many ash trees as maple trees and 20 more locust trees than ash trees. The ratio of the number of ash trees to the number of locust trees is 3 : 4.

21. How many of each type of tree is planted? 20 maple trees, 60 ash trees, 80 locust trees

22. What percent of the trees planted are maple trees? 12.5%

222 Algebra

Lesson 5-10

Lesson 5-10   Similar Figures

Lesson 5-10   Similar Figures

Vocabulary

ratio of similitude

GOAL

Use proportions to find the lengths of sides in similar figures.

SPUR Objectives

J Solve problems involving proportions in real situations.

L Find lengths and ratios of similitude in similar figures.

Materials/Resources

· Lesson Master 5-10A or 5-10B
· Resource Masters 2 and 75–77
· Scientific or graphing calculator
· Ruler

HOMEWORK

Suggestions for Assignment
• Questions 1–24
• Question 25 (extra credit)
• Reading Lesson 6-1
• Covering the Ideas 6-1

Local Standards

1   Warm-Up

Try to draw a picture of yourself on a piece of paper. Picture yourself standing. Of course, if you are not a good artist, this picture may not look very good, but you can still make the picture look reasonably good by careful work with proportions. Decide what the scale of your picture should be. A possibility is to make the picture $\frac{1}{12}$ actual size. Then, one foot on you is one inch on the picture. Or you might make the picture $\frac{1}{10}$ actual size. Then, one centimeter on you is one millimeter on the picture. How tall will the picture be? How large will the head be? How long will it be from your waist to the floor? How wide should the picture be? Find these dimensions before you begin drawing the actual picture and then fill in the details using those dimensions.
Answers vary.

▶ **BIG IDEA**   Ratios of lengths of similar geometric figures are equal, giving rise to many applications of proportions.

Model airplanes, architect's drawings, models of buildings, and photographs are all pictures of objects that have the same shape as the originals but not necessarily the same size. Mathematically, the original object and the model are *similar*. Blow-ups of photographs are also similar.

In some species of animals, babies are shaped much like their parents, like the elephants shown below. However, for humans this is not the case. Infants have very different shapes than adults. This drawing shows a baby and an adult, with each one's height divided into 8 equal parts. The divisions allow us to form ratios to compare the shapes of the infant and adult.

Mental Math

If you can bike to a friend's house in 15 minutes, averaging 10 miles an hour, how long will it take if you average 20 miles an hour? **7.5 min**

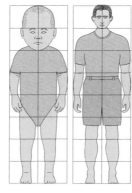

The largest land animal is the African bush elephant, standing 13 feet high and weighing 8 tons.

Source: *The World Almanac for Kids*

	Infant	Adult
Ratio of head length to height	$\frac{2 \text{ parts}}{8 \text{ parts}} = \frac{1}{4}$	$\frac{1 \text{ part}}{8 \text{ parts}} = \frac{1}{8}$
Ratio of trunk length to leg length	$\frac{3 \text{ parts}}{3 \text{ parts}} = \frac{1}{1}$	$\frac{3 \text{ parts}}{4 \text{ parts}} = \frac{3}{4}$

Notice that the ratios in an infant's body are quite different from an adult's body. An infant is not a scaled-down version of an adult.

Background

The importance of proportional thinking and similar figures in mathematics makes this lesson an important one. Though its context is geometric, the work is algebraic. This lesson is typically not difficult and will help students greatly in their study of geometry.

Activity. The goal of this activity is to provide a hands-on example of the fact that in similar figures corresponding lengths are in the same ratio (they are proportional).

When two similar figures are presented simultaneously, then there are two ratios of similitude, and they are reciprocals of each other. But when there is a figure and its image, the ratio of similitude is the ratio of the length on the image to a corresponding length on the preimage.

(continued on next page)

Activity

Pictured at the right is a coffeemaker that is 12.5 inches tall and 5.625 inches wide.

Step 1 Measure AB and CD to find the height and width of the coffeemaker in the picture. Height: $2\frac{1}{2}$ in.; Width: $1\frac{1}{8}$ in.

Step 2 Calculate these ratios to the nearest tenth.

  a. $\dfrac{AB}{\text{actual height of coffeemaker}}$ 0.2

  b. $\dfrac{CD}{\text{actual width of coffeemaker}}$ 0.2

  You should find that these ratios are about equal.

Step 3 Measure EF, the height of the coffeepot. $\frac{13}{16}$ in.

Step 4 Solve a proportion to find the height of the actual coffeepot. $4\frac{1}{16}$ in.

You also should have found that the dimensions of the picture are $\frac{1}{5}$ of the length of the corresponding dimensions of the coffeemaker. This illustrates a basic property of similar figures.

> **Fundamental Property of Similar Figures**
>
> If two polygons are similar, then ratios of corresponding lengths are equal and corresponding angles have the same measure.

The ratio of the lengths of corresponding sides of two similar figures is called a **ratio of similitude.** In the activity the ratio of similitude is $\frac{1}{5}$ because $\dfrac{AB}{\text{actual height}} = \dfrac{CD}{\text{actual width}} = \frac{1}{5}$.

Finding Lengths in Similar Figures

When two figures are similar, a true proportion can be written using corresponding lengths. If three of the four lengths in the proportion are known, the fourth can be found by solving an equation.

2 Teaching

Notes on the Lesson

Finding lengths in similar figures. In this lesson, the corresponding sides in the similar figures are always parallel. Using colored chalk or pens or fonts to indicate corresponding sides can help students see the pairs of corresponding sides. The emphasis here is on writing and solving proportions, not on recognizing when two figures are similar. However, do point out that in similar figures, corresponding sides do not have to be parallel. That is why we must state in Example 2 and Questions 3–5 and 12 that the corresponding sides are parallel.

You might also note that even when corresponding sides of a figure are parallel, the figures might not be similar. For instance, a rectangle that is not a square is never similar to a square.

Finding lengths in similar figures. The similar figures in the lesson originate in three different ways. In Example 1, the assumption is made that a baby elephant is similar in shape to an adult. (While for some species this is a poor assumption, it is reasonable with elephants.) In Guided Example 2, the figures are given as similar and students are told which sides correspond. In Example 3, the situation (using lengths of shadows to find heights of objects) causes similar figures to be created.

5-10

Additional Examples

Example 1 A child's cup has base radius 1 inch and height 2.5 inches. An adult-size cup is similar, but has a base radius of 1.5 inches. What is the height of the adult cup? $\frac{1}{1.5} = \frac{2.5}{h}$; $h =$ 3.75 in.

Example 2 The two triangles below are similar, with corresponding sides parallel. Find x, the length of $\overline{AB}$.

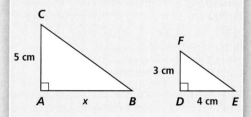

Write the proportion: $\frac{5}{3} = \frac{?}{?}$ $\frac{x}{4}$

Use the Means-Extremes Property: $\underline{\;?\;} \cdot x = \underline{\;?\;} \cdot \underline{\;?\;}$. 4, 3, 5

Solve: $x = \underline{\;?\;}$ cm $\frac{20}{3} \approx 6.7$

Example 1

An adult African elephant can be 30 feet long and 11 feet high at the shoulder. Estimate the length of a baby elephant that is 3 feet high at the shoulder.

Solution Compare lengths on the adult with the corresponding lengths on the baby. Set up a proportion by forming two equal ratios. Let x be the length of the baby. Since the elephants are similar, the ratios are equal.

$$\frac{\text{height of adult}}{\text{height of baby}} = \frac{\text{length of adult}}{\text{length of baby}}$$

$$\frac{11}{3} = \frac{30}{x}$$

$$11x = 90$$

$$x = \frac{90}{11} \approx 8.2$$

We estimate that the baby elephant is slightly over 8 feet long.

GUIDED

Example 2

The two quadrilaterals at the right are similar, with corresponding sides parallel. Find x, the length of $\overline{CD}$.

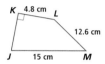

Solution The side corresponding to the unknown length $\overline{CD}$ is $\underline{\;?\;}$. There is a pair of corresponding sides whose lengths are both known. These are $\underline{\;?\;}$ and $\underline{\;?\;}$. Because the figures are similar, the ratios of lengths of these corresponding sides are equal. $\overline{LM}$; $\overline{BC}$; $\overline{KL}$

$$\frac{CD}{LM} \; \frac{?}{?} = \frac{?}{?} \; \frac{BC}{KL} \qquad \text{Write the proportion.}$$

$$\frac{x}{12.6} \; \frac{?}{?} = \frac{?}{?} \; \frac{3}{4.8} \qquad \text{Substitute the known lengths.}$$

$$\underline{\;?\;} \cdot x = \underline{\;?\;} \cdot \underline{\;?\;} \qquad \text{Means-Extremes Property} \quad 4.8; 3; 12.6$$

$$x = \underline{\;?\;} \text{ cm} \qquad \text{Divide by } \underline{\;?\;} \text{ and simplify.} \quad 7.875; 4.8$$

Using Similar Figures to Find Lengths without Measuring

Similar figures have many uses. For example, you can use similar triangles to find the height of an object you cannot measure easily. Suppose you want to find the height h of a flagpole. Here is how you can do it. Holding a yardstick parallel to the flagpole, measure the length of the yardstick's shadow. Then measure the length of the shadow of the flagpole. The picture on the next page illustrates one possible set of measurements.

Accommodating the Learner

Students who are weak on solving proportions may need additional examples that require them to write and solve proportions. Allow time for extra questions on this topic.

Example 3

Use the measurements at the right to find the height h of the flagpole.

Solution Two similar right triangles are formed. Now, use ratios of corresponding sides to find h.

$$\frac{3}{h} = \frac{5}{72}$$

$$5h = 72 \cdot 3$$

$$5h = 216$$

$$h = 43.2$$

The flagpole is about 43 feet tall.

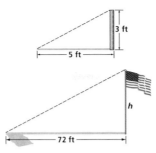
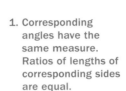
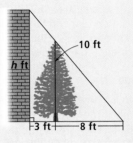

Questions

COVERING THE IDEAS

1. What is the fundamental property of similar figures?

2. An adult male African elephant is about 11 feet tall, with ears that measure 5 feet from top to bottom. If a baby elephant is 3 feet tall, find out how big its ears are. **about 1.36 ft**

In 3–5, refer to the two similar triangles below. Corresponding sides are parallel.

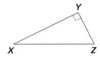

3. Which side of $\triangle XYZ$ corresponds to the given side of $\triangle ABC$?

   a. $\overline{AC}$ $\overline{XZ}$ b. $\overline{BC}$ $\overline{YZ}$ c. $\overline{AB}$ $\overline{XY}$

4. Find two ratios equal to $\frac{XY}{AB}$. $\frac{YZ}{BC}, \frac{XZ}{AC}$

5. Suppose $AB = 12$, $BC = 5$, $AC = 13$, and $XY = 18$. Find

   a. YZ. **7.5** b. XZ. **19.5**

6. The quadrilaterals shown below are similar.

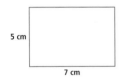

   a. Find x. **$x = 2.94$**

   b. Write two possible ratios of similitude.

1. Corresponding angles have the same measure. Ratios of lengths of corresponding sides are equal.

6b. Answers vary. Sample answer: $\frac{2.1}{5}$ and $\frac{5}{2.1}$

Notes on the Lesson

Example 3 Students need to take it on faith that the triangles are similar. Mathematically, they are similar because they have congruent angles (what is known as AA Triangle Similarity).

Additional Example

Example 3 Use the measurements on the diagram to find the height h of the building. **$h = 13.75$ ft**

Note-Taking Tips

Because this chapter includes many new and easily confused terms, encourage students to summarize the new vocabulary and concepts in a review sheet. Ask students to include a clear definition of the term and give an example. Students should describe new concepts and formulas in their own words.

Accommodating the Learner

Diagrams of similar figures are often misleading when used to portray changes in quantities. For example, suppose an investment earns $1,000 the first year and $2,000 the second year. The bank decides to create diagrams to represent the two years. They use a cube with side length 1 inch for the first year and a cube with side length 2 inches for the second year. Their diagrams imply that the volumes of the cubes represent the amount of money. Write a ratio of the money earned and a ratio of the volumes of the figures. Compare the ratios. How are the cubes misleading? **The ratio of money amounts is $\frac{2}{1}$. The ratio of cube volumes is $\frac{2^3}{1^3} = \frac{8}{1}$.**

5-10

3 Assignment

Recommended Assignment

- Questions 1–24
- Question 25 (extra credit)
- Reading Lesson 6-1
- Covering the Ideas 6-1

Notes on the Questions

Question 6 We assume here that corresponding sides are parallel. In theory, it is possible that the drawing is not accurate and that the side of length x cm could correspond to the side of length 5 centimeters. But that is not what is meant in Part b when students are asked for the two possible ratios of similitude.

Question 11 Rectangles are similar if and only if they have the same ratio of length to width. So a student could determine x here using the proportion $\frac{x}{x+6} = \frac{14}{18}$, that is, equating ratios of lengths within the rectangles rather than between them. Notice that because $x + 6$ is larger than x, there is no question which sides must correspond. This proportion can be solved in a variety of ways. One way is to consider the reciprocal of each side. $\frac{x+6}{x} = \frac{18}{14}$. Now expand the fraction on each side: $1 + \frac{6}{x} = 1 + \frac{4}{14} = 1 + \frac{2}{7}$, so $\frac{6}{x} = \frac{2}{7}$, which can be solved in one's head.

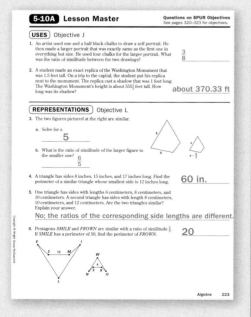

7. A bookcase is pictured at the right. The actual bookcase is 36 in. wide.
   a. Measure the width of the bookcase in the picture. **1.5 in.**
   b. What is the ratio of the similitude comparing the picture's width to the actual width? $\frac{1}{24}$
   c. Measure the height of the bookcase in the picture. **1 in.**
   d. Use your answers to Parts b and c to determine the height of the actual bookcase. **24 in.**

8. Suppose a 3-foot yardstick casts a 4-foot shadow. A nearby building casts a shadow of 56 feet at the same time. What is the height of the building? **42 ft**

APPLYING THE MATHEMATICS

9. A person who is 160 cm tall is photographed. On the photo, the image of the person is 12 cm tall. What is the ratio of similitude? $\frac{40}{3}$

10. The Crazy Horse Memorial in the Black Hills of South Dakota will be the world's largest mountain carving. From the chin to the top of the head is 87.5 feet. Use the picture, a ruler, and your knowledge of similar figures to approximate the length of the outstretched arm in the carving. **about 292 ft**

11. The two rectangles below are similar.

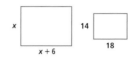

   a. Use a proportion to find the value of x. **$x = 21$**
   b. Find the perimeter of the larger rectangle. **96**

12. The quadrilaterals at the right are similar. Corresponding sides are parallel.
   a. Write a true proportion involving $\frac{s}{a}$.
   b. **Fill in the Blank** Complete $\frac{k}{w} = \frac{?}{t}$ and solve for k. **p; $k = \frac{pw}{t}$**

13. At a certain time on a sunny day, Shadrack, who is 6 feet tall, casts a shadow that is 9 feet long. A nearby building that is t feet tall casts a shadow that is 24 feet long. **13a. See margin.**
   a. Draw a diagram of this situation and label the lengths.
   b. Write a proportion that describes the situation. $\frac{6}{9} = \frac{t}{24}$
   c. How tall is the building? **16 ft**

When completed, the Crazy Horse mountain carving (shown in the background) will be 641 feet long by 563 feet high. Crazy Horse's completed head is 87 feet 6 inches high. The horse's head, currently the focus of work on the mountain, is 219 feet, or 22 stories high.

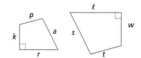

12a. $\frac{s}{a} = \frac{t}{p}$, $\frac{s}{a} = \frac{w}{k}$, or $\frac{s}{a} = \frac{\ell}{r}$

Additional Answers

13a.

14. For this question, you need to use a ruler and properties of similar figures. A scale drawing of a house, as seen from its front, is shown below. The actual width (across the front, not including the roof) of the house is 12 meters.

a. Write a ratio comparing the width of the house in the drawing to the actual width of the house.
b. Write a proportion you could use to find the actual distance from the ground to the peak of the roof.
c. Solve the proportion in Part b. $d \approx 9.2$ m

14a. $\frac{9.4}{1,200}$

14b. Answers vary.
Sample answer:
$\frac{7.2 \text{ cm}}{d} = \frac{9.4 \text{ cm}}{12 \text{ m}}$

REVIEW

In 15 and 16, solve the proportion. (Lesson 5-9)

15. $\frac{64}{3} = \frac{4x}{9}$ $x = 48$

16. $\frac{2}{1-a} = \frac{4}{a-3}$ $a = \frac{5}{3}$

In 17 and 18, use the fact that a *karat* is a measure of fineness used for gold and other precious materials. Pure gold is 24 karats. Gold of 18-karat fineness is 18 parts pure gold and 6 parts other metals, giving 24 parts in all. (Lessons 5-9, 4-1)

17. A ring is 18-karat gold. What percent gold is this? 75%

18. A necklace weighing 6 ounces is 14-karat gold. How many ounces of pure gold are in the necklace? 3.5 oz

Central banks of nations hold an estimated 32,000 tons of gold as official stock, and about 96,000 tons is privately held in bullion, coin, and jewelry.

Notes on the Questions
Question 14 The drawing conveys only a small hint of the complexity that one sees in blueprints of buildings. Although this drawing may seem complicated, the problem is not difficult.

Similar Figures **313**

5-10

4 Wrap-Up

Ongoing Assessment

Ask students to create a sketch that one could use the following proportion to solve: $\frac{4}{5} = \frac{7}{x}$. Share these sketches as a class.

Project Update

Project 3, Copy Machine Puzzle, on page 316 relates to the content of this lesson.

Additional Answers

22a.

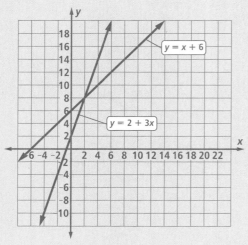

19. In a 3-ounce serving of beef, there are about 26 grams of protein. About how many grams of protein are in an 8-ounce steak? (Lesson 5-9) about 69.3 g

20. The scale of a map for Yellowstone National Park is 1.75 in. = 10 miles. If the distance between Old Faithful and Mammoth Hot Springs on the map is about 8.5 inches, what is the approximate distance between these two places in miles? (Lesson 5-9) about 48.6 mi

21. When rolling two 6-sided dice and recording their sum, there are two ways to get a 3—rolling a 1 on the first die and a 2 on the second die, or rolling a 2 on the first die and a 1 on the second die. (Lesson 5-6)
   a. How many ways are there to roll a 4? 3
   b. Find the probability of rolling 4 if the dice are fair. $\frac{1}{12}$
   c. When rolling two 6-sided fair dice, a sum of seven is the most likely outcome. Explain why this is true. 22a. See margin.

22. a. Graph $y = 6 + x$ and $y = 2 + 3x$ on the same set of axes.
   b. According to the graph, for what value(s) of x is $6 + x = 2 + 3x$? (Lesson 4-3) $x = 2$

In 23 and 24, consider the table at the right that shows the land area of three of the five largest countries in the world in area. (Lessons 4-1, 3-4)

Country	Square Miles
Russia	6,592,735
Canada	?
United States	3,717,792
China	?
Brazil	3,286,470

Source: infoplease.com

23. If the land area of Russia is 399,121 square miles less than the sum of the areas of China and Brazil, find the land area of China.

24. If the area of Canada is 3.6% larger than the area of the United States, estimate the area of Canada.

EXPLORATION

25. Find the highest point of a tree, a building, or some other object, using the shadow method described in this lesson. Draw a diagram to illustrate your method.

An eruption of Old Faithful lasts anywhere from $1\frac{1}{2}$ to 5 minutes, spraying 3,700 to 8,400 gallons of boiling water into the air.
Source: National Park Service

21c. There are 6 ways to achieve a sum of 7, and each other sum has fewer than 6 ways in which it can be obtained.

23. 3,705,386 mi²
24. 3,851,633 mi²

25. See margin for diagram. Answers vary. Sample answer: A yardstick made a shadow of 6 ft, while a tree made a shadow of 45 ft. So, the tree was 22.5 ft tall.

25.

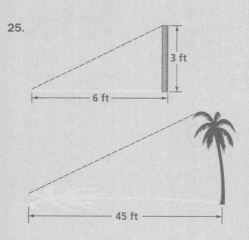

Chapter 5 Projects

1 Buffon's Needle

The French naturalist George Buffon (1707–1788) discovered the following method of approximating π.

Step 1 Measure the length of a needle.

Step 2 On a piece of paper, draw many horizontal lines, where the distance between the lines is the same as the length of the needle.

Step 3 Drop the needle randomly on the paper, and check if it crossed any of the lines. Repeat this process at least twenty times. Keep a tally of the number of times you dropped the needle and the number of times it crossed one of the lines.

Step 4 As you repeat the process in Step 3, the relative frequency of the times the needle crosses one of the horizontal lines should get closer and closer to $\frac{2}{\pi}$.

a. Calculate the relative frequency of the number of times that the needle crossed one of the lines to the number of times that you dropped the needle. Calculate the reciprocal of this relative frequency, and multiply it by 2. The number you get should be close to π.

b. Suppose Trevor performed this experiment 50 times, and the needle crossed a horizontal line every time. Does this mean that $\frac{2}{\pi} = 1$? Explain how your answer shows the difference between probability and relative frequency.

2 Population Densities

A *population density* is a type of rate, defined as the number of people living in a region divided by the area of that region.

a. Find the most dense and least dense countries in the world.

b. The area of the United States is 5,984,685 square miles. What would the population of the United States be if it had the same population density as the most dense country in the world? What would the population of the United States be if it had the same population density as the least dense country in the world?

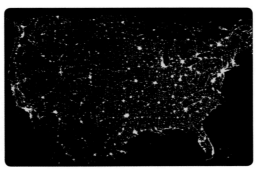

c. Which would you expect to have a higher population density: the United States or Singapore? Explain your answer. Give some examples of geographic and cultural features that affect a country's population density.

d. Suppose a country has population density d. What is the meaning of the number $\frac{1}{d}$?

The projects relate to the content of the lessons of this chapter as follows:

Project	Lesson(s)
1	5-6
2	5-3
3	5-10
4	5-9
5	5-4

1 Buffon's Needle

It is simplest to draw the lines so that they cut across the entire paper. Suggest that students create a table with the following column headings to organize their work: number of times dropped, number of times crossed a line, relative frequency, and 2 times the reciprocal of the relative frequency.

2 Population Densities

Students should be careful to use accurate information to find the current population and geographic area information. A reputable online source is the CIA Factbook. Students can extend their project to focus on population densities of different states or regions of the United States. This might help them answer Part c.

Project Rubric

Advanced	Student correctly provides all of the details asked for in the project as well as additional correct independent conclusions.
Proficient	Student correctly provides all of the details asked for in the project.
Partially proficient	Student correctly provides some of the details asked for in the project or provides all details with some inaccuracies.
Not proficient	Student correctly provides few of the details asked for in the project or provides all details with many inaccuracies.
No attempt	Student makes little or no attempt to complete the project.

Chapter 5 Projects

3 Copy Machine Puzzle

Recommend that students make the enlargement from the original small picture. Otherwise, it may be confusing as to how much the image was enlarged. To justify why 141% is used, encourage students to measure the figure and consider the proportion they would use to find the measure of a side of the larger figure, given a side of the smaller figure.

4 Calculating Density

Remind students that to calculate the amount of water spilled, they can simply find how much water is left in the container and the original volume of the container. Students may realize that this method of measuring volume will only work with an object that has greater density than water, otherwise the object will simply float. Encourage students to write a proportion to describe the situation.

5 Converting Rates

Recommend to students that if they are struggling, they can work the problem out by hand first so they can create the program and explain how it works. Also, encourage students to create a table of values with x representing the rate in $\frac{feet}{second}$ and y representing the rate in $\frac{kilometers}{hour}$.

---

3 Copy Machine Puzzle

Most copy machines have an enlargement feature that creates a figure similar to the one being copied.

a. Use the enlarge feature on a copy machine to enlarge the figure below on the left so that the copy is exactly the same size as the figure below on the right. You may have to enlarge more than once. Record how much you enlarged the figure each time.

b. Many copiers can copy in a range of sizes that goes from 100% to 141%. Why is 141% used in this case?

---

4 Calculating Density

In science, the *density* of an object is determined by dividing the mass of the object (weight in grams) by its volume (in cubic centimeters). For example, the density of cool tap water is one gram per cubic centimeter. You already know how to measure the weight of an object. But how do you measure its volume? The Greek mathematician Archimedes (287 BCE–212 BCE) discovered that when an object is placed in a full container of water, the volume of the water that spills out is equal to the volume of the object that was placed in the water.

a. Use Archimedes' discovery and the density of water to explain how you could calculate the volume of an object.

b. Explain how you could use the result from Part a to calculate the density of an object.

c. Look up the story of Archimedes' discovery. How was density used in this story?

5 Converting Rates

Write a computer or calculator program that converts measurements in $\frac{ft}{sec}$ to measurements in $\frac{km}{hr}$. Write a short paragraph explaining how your program works.

Notes

Chapter 5 — Summary and Vocabulary

Fractions in algebra are generalizations of fractions in arithmetic. Every fraction can be treated as a division, and division by 0 is undefined (the denominator cannot be 0). For all real numbers a and b and $b \neq 0$, $\frac{a}{b} = a \div b = a \cdot \frac{1}{b}$.

Algebraic fractions are multiplied and divided just like fractions in arithmetic. For all real numbers a, b, c, and d, with b, c, and $d \neq 0$,

$$\frac{a}{b} \cdot \frac{c}{d} = \frac{ac}{bd} \text{ and } \frac{a}{b} \div \frac{c}{d} = \frac{\frac{a}{b}}{\frac{c}{d}} = \frac{a}{b} \cdot \frac{d}{c} = \frac{ad}{bc}.$$

Because fractions represent division, all the applications of division in arithmetic lead to applications of fractions in algebra. When quantities with different units are divided, the result is a rate. Rates are often signaled by the word "per" as in students per class, miles per hour, and people per square mile. Rates have rate units, and these units are multiplied and divided just as if they were fractions. Rate units are useful for converting from one unit to another.

When quantities with the same type of units are divided, the result is a ratio, a number without a unit. Ratios may be represented as fractions, percents, or decimals. The relative frequency of an event is the ratio of the number of times an event has occurred to the number of times it could have occurred. A probability is a number that is the expectation of what the relative frequency ratio would be in the long run. Both relative frequencies and probabilities are numbers from 0 to 1.

When two fractions, rates, or ratios are equal, the result is a proportion, an equation of the form $\frac{a}{b} = \frac{c}{d}$. So proportions are found wherever there are fractions. Proportions can be solved by applying the Multiplication Property of Equality or by using the Means-Extremes Property. In similar figures, the ratios of corresponding lengths are equal to a ratio of similitude k. Proportions are everywhere when there are similar figures.

Theorems and Properties

Multiplying Fractions Property p. 252
Equal Fractions Property p. 253
Dividing Fractions Property p. 258
Means-Extremes Property p. 302
Fundamental Property of Similar Figures p. 309

Vocabulary

5-1 algebraic fraction
5-2 complex fraction
5-3 rate, reciprocal rates
5-4 conversion rate
5-5 ratio, tax rate, discount rate
5-6 outcome, event, probability, $P(x)$, probability distribution, unbiased, fair, conditional probability, complement, odds of an event
5-7 relative frequency, pth percentile
5-9 proportion, extremes, means, population, sample, randomly, capture-recapture method
5-10 ratio of similitude

Self-Test

For the development of mathematical competence, feedback and correction, along with the opportunity for practice, are necessary. The Self-Test provides the opportunity for feedback and correction; the Chapter Review provides additional opportunities for practice. We cannot overemphasize the importance of these end-of-chapter materials. It is at this point that the material gels for many students, allowing them to solidify skills and understanding. In general, student performance should improve after completing these pages.

Assign the Self-Test as a one-night assignment. Worked-out solutions for all questions are in the Selected Answers section of the student book. Encourage students to take the Self-Test honestly, grade themselves, and then be prepared to discuss the test in class.

Advise students to pay special attention to those Chapter Review questions (pages 320–323) that correspond to the questions they missed on the Self-Test.

Chapter

5 Self-Test

Take this test as you would take a test in class. You will need a calculator. Then use the Selected Answers section in the back of the book to check your work.

In 1–3, simplify the expression. 1–3. See margin.

1. $\frac{75c}{8p} \cdot \frac{2}{15c}$ 2. $\frac{5}{a} \div \frac{9}{3a^2}$ 3. $\frac{\frac{2x}{5}}{\frac{x}{5}}$

4. **Multiple Choice** Which of the following is *not* equal to $\frac{a}{b}$? B

A $\frac{1}{b} \cdot \frac{a}{1}$ B $6 \div \frac{6a}{b}$

C $\frac{a}{b} \cdot \frac{c}{c}$ D $\frac{1}{2b} \div \frac{1}{2a}$

5–7. See margin.
In 5–7, solve the proportion. Show your work.

5. $\frac{h}{17} = \frac{6}{101}$ 6. $\frac{9}{5} = \frac{4u}{3}$ 7. $\frac{x}{8} = \frac{2x-3}{24}$

8. Suppose $\frac{7}{x} = \frac{8}{15}$.
   a. What does the Means-Extremes Property tell you? $8x = 105$
   b. Solve for x. $x = \frac{105}{8} = 13.125$

9. Mrs. Wright bought six boxes of pencils, with each box containing 10 pencils to be split among her four children. Writing your answer as a rate, find how many pencils each child received. See margin.

10. The Colorado Department of Public Health and Environment reported that for the years 2001–2005, 1,563 bats were examined for rabies. Of that number, 221 actually had rabies. Use this information to estimate the probability that if you see a bat in Colorado, it has rabies.

11. Teresa can run one mile in seven and a half minutes. Using the approximation 1.6 km ≈ 1 mi, how many seconds does it take her to run one kilometer? See margin.

10. $\frac{221}{1,563} \approx 0.141 = 14.1\%$

12. The two rectangles below are similar with corresponding sides parallel. Solve for x. See margin.

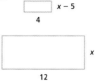

13. If the electricity goes out and a clock stops, what is the probability that the second hand stops between 3 and 4? See margin.

14. A DVD costs $18 after a discount of $4.50. What is the percent of discount? See margin.

15. In 2003, Markus Riese set a world record by bicycling backwards a distance of 50 kilometers in 1 hour and 47 minutes.
   a. To the nearest kilometer, what was his speed in kilometers per hour? See margin.
   b. Write the reciprocal rate to your answer from Part a. about 0.036 hr/km

In 16–18, consider the table below that displays the results of a survey of 50 people asked about their types of allergies.

Allergy	Number of People
Only Peanuts	7
Only Bees	16
Both Peanuts and Bees	2

16. 18%, because 7 + 2 = 9 people out of 50.
16. What is the relative frequency of people who are allergic to peanuts?

17. What is the relative frequency of people who are allergic to neither peanuts nor bees? See margin.

Additional Answers

1. $\frac{75c}{8p} \cdot \frac{2}{15c} = \frac{5}{4p} \cdot \frac{1}{1} = \frac{5}{4p}$

2. $\frac{5}{a} \div \frac{9}{3a^2} = \frac{5}{a} \cdot \frac{3a^2}{9} = \frac{5}{1} \cdot \frac{a}{3} = \frac{5a}{3}$

3. $\frac{2x}{5} \div \frac{x}{5} = \frac{2x}{5} \cdot \frac{5}{x} = \frac{2}{1} \cdot \frac{1}{1} = 2$

5. $h = \frac{6}{101} \cdot 17 = \frac{102}{101}$

6. $4u = \frac{9}{5} \cdot 3$; $u = \frac{27}{5} \cdot \frac{1}{4} = \frac{27}{20}$

7. $24\left(\frac{x}{8}\right) = 24\left(\frac{2x-3}{24}\right)$; $3x = 2x - 3$; $x = -3$

9. $\left(6 \text{ boxes} \cdot \frac{10 \text{ pencils}}{\text{box}}\right) \div 4 \text{ children}$
   $= 60 \text{ pencils} \div 4 \text{ children} = 15 \frac{\text{pencils}}{\text{child}}$

11. $\frac{7.5 \text{ min}}{1 \text{ mi}} \cdot \frac{1 \text{ mi}}{1.6 \text{ km}} \cdot \frac{60 \text{ sec}}{1 \text{ min}} = 281.25 \frac{\text{sec}}{\text{km}}$;
   281.25 sec

12. $\frac{x}{x-5} = \frac{12}{4}$; $4x = 12(x - 5)$;
    $4x = 12x - 60$; $60 = x$; $x = \frac{60}{8} = 7.5$

13. The sector between 3 and 4 represents $\frac{1}{12}$ of the clock, so the probability is $\frac{1}{12}$.

14. The discount is $4.50 off $22.50, so
    $4.50 ÷ $22.50 = .2, or 20%.

15a. $\frac{50 \text{ km}}{(1\frac{47}{60} \text{ hr})} \approx 28$ km/hr

17. 50%, because 50 − 7 − 16 − 2 = 25 people out of 50.

18. What is the relative frequency of people who are allergic to either peanuts or bees, but not both? **46%, because 7 + 16 = 23 people out of 50.**

19. In the expression $\frac{12k}{k-2}$, k cannot be what value? Explain. **See margin.**

20. A pet store has f goldfish, s snakes, c cats, and d dogs. What is the ratio of the number of cats to the total number of these animals? $\frac{c}{f+s+c+d}$

21. If a bus travels 350 miles on 20 gallons of gas, about how far can it travel on 35 gallons of gas? **See margin.**

22. A circle with radius 21 inches is contained inside a rectangle that is 4 feet by 7 feet. If a point within the rectangle is chosen at random, what is the probability that it lies inside the circle? **See margin.**

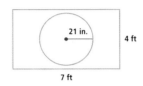

21 in.

4 ft

7 ft

23. The Canadian National (CN) Tower in Toronto is one of the tallest towers in the world. Suppose the tower casts a shadow that is 1,210 feet long, and at the same time a 6-foot-tall man standing next to the tower casts a shadow that is 4 feet long. About how tall is the CN tower?

24. Suppose an 8th grade gym class recorded the amount of sit-ups each student could do in 1 minute. Janice was in the 75th percentile and only 6 students did more sit-ups than she did. How many people are in the gym class? **24; The 75th percentile implies 25% performed better.** $\frac{6}{x} = \frac{1}{4}$; $x = 24$

23. $\frac{1,210}{x} = \frac{4}{6}$; $x = 1,815$ ft

19. k cannot be 2, because then the denominator would be 0, and division by zero is undefined.

21. Let m be the number of miles. Then $\frac{350}{20} = \frac{m}{35}$. $20m = 12,250$. $m = 612.5$ mi.

22. Area of rectangle = 4 ft · 7 ft = 28 ft². Area of circle = $\pi \cdot \left(21 \text{ in.}/ 12 \frac{\text{in.}}{\text{ft}}\right)^2$ ≈ 9.62 square feet. So the probability is about $\frac{9.62}{28}$ ≈ 34%.

Chapter Review

The main objectives for the chapter are organized in the Chapter Review under the four types of understanding this book promotes—Skills, Properties, Uses, and Representations.

Whereas end-of-chapter material may be considered optional in some texts, in *UCSMP Algebra* we have selected these objectives and questions with the expectation that they will be covered. Students should be able to answer these questions with about 85% accuracy after studying the chapter.

You may assign these questions over a single night to help students prepare for a test the next day, or you may assign the questions over a two-day period. If you work the questions over two days, then we recommend assigning the *evens* for homework the first night so that students get feedback in class the next day, and then assigning the *odds* the night before the test because the answers are provided to the odd-numbered questions in the Selected Answers at the back of the book.

It is effective to ask students which questions they still do not understand and use the day as a total class discussion of the material that the class finds most difficult.

Resources

- Assessment Resources: Chapter 5 Test, Forms A–D; Chapter 5 Test, Cumulative Form

---

Chapter 5 Chapter Review

SKILLS
PROPERTIES
USES
REPRESENTATIONS

SKILLS Procedures used to get answers

OBJECTIVE A Multiply and simplify algebraic fractions. (Lesson 5-1)

In 1–4, multiply the fractions. Simplify if possible.

1. $\frac{7a}{2} \cdot \frac{4}{5}$ $\frac{14a}{5}$

2. $\frac{12}{5x} \cdot \frac{2x}{3}$ $\frac{8}{5}$

3. $\frac{6}{5p} \cdot 10$ $\frac{12}{p}$

4. $\frac{2ax}{3} \cdot \frac{9x}{a}$ $6x^2$

In 5 and 6, simplify the fraction.

5. $\frac{121bcd}{11cd}$ $11b$

6. $\frac{-24x^3y}{32x^2y^2}$ $-\frac{3x}{4y}$

OBJECTIVE B Divide algebraic fractions. (Lessons 5-2, 5-3)

In 7–10, find the quotient.

7. $\frac{c}{6} \div \frac{9}{2}$ $\frac{c}{27}$

8. $\frac{x}{y} \div \frac{x}{z}$ $\frac{z}{y}$

9. $\frac{\frac{4a}{15}}{\frac{20a}{9}}$ $-\frac{3}{25}$

10. $\frac{-625x}{\frac{50x}{8}}$ -100

In 11 and 12, what value(s) can the variable *not* have?

11. $\frac{10+x}{8+x}$ -8

12. $\frac{28v}{4v-2.4}$ 0.6

OBJECTIVE C Solve proportions. (Lesson 5-9)

In 13–16, solve the equation.

13. $-\frac{28k}{5} = \frac{14}{3}$ $k = -\frac{5}{6}$

14. $\frac{6}{y-4} = \frac{2}{5}$ $y = 19$

15. $\frac{3(t-5)}{4} = \frac{9t}{2}$ $t = -1$

16. $\frac{a+12}{a-3} = 4$ $a = 8$

17. **Fill in the Blank** 6 is to 54 as 54 is to ___?___. 486

PROPERTIES Principles behind the mathematics

OBJECTIVE D Use the language of proportions and the Means-Extremes Property. (Lesson 5-9)

18. Consider the proportion $\frac{7}{8} = \frac{28}{32}$.

   a. Which numbers are the means? 8, 28

   b. Which numbers are the extremes? 7, 32

19. If $\frac{6}{15} = \frac{x}{8}$, what does $\frac{8}{x}$ equal? $\frac{15}{6}$

20. **Fill in the Blanks** If $\frac{a}{b} = \frac{x}{y}$, then by the Means-Extremes Property ___?___ = ___?___. *ay; bx*

21. **Fill in the Blank** If $\frac{m}{n} = \frac{u}{v}$, then $\frac{v}{n} = $ ___?___. $\frac{u}{m}$

USES Applications of mathematics in real-world situations

OBJECTIVE E Use rates in real situations. (Lesson 5-3)

22. Suppose a 225-mile train ride took 3 hours. 22a. 75 mi/hr   22b. $\frac{1}{75}$ hr/mi

   a. What was the rate in miles per hour?

   b. What was the rate in hours per mile?

23. A 16-oz box of pasta costs $1.20 and a 32-oz box of pasta costs $1.80.

   a. Find the unit cost (cost per ounce) for the 16-oz box. $0.075 per oz

   b. Find the unit cost of the larger box of pasta. $0.05625 per oz

   c. Which is the better buy? the 32-oz box

24. It took Jamila 45 minutes to answer 32 questions on her Algebra test. On average, how much time did it take her to answer 1 question? $\frac{45}{32}$ or about 1.4 min per question

25. Which is faster, typing w words in $2m$ minutes or typing $4w$ words in $6m$ minutes? Explain your answer. $4w$ words in $6m$ min, since $\frac{4w}{6m} = \frac{2w}{3m} > \frac{w}{2m}$

26–27. See margin.
In 26 and 27, calculate a rate for the given situation.

26. In 22 almonds there are about 160 calories.

27. The red oak tree grew 12 feet in 8 years.

OBJECTIVE F Convert units and use reciprocal rates in real situations. (Lesson 5-4)

28. During a meteor shower, some meteors approach Earth's atmosphere at speeds of 95 kilometers per second. Using the fact that 1 mile ≈ 1.6 km, convert this rate into miles per hour. about 213,750 mi/hr

29. The average human adult at rest takes 16 breaths per minute.

a. At this rate, how many breaths would a human take in a week? 161,280 breaths

b. If a cat takes 1,500 breaths per hour, does the cat or human breathe at a faster rate? Explain your answer. See margin.

30. Sliced turkey costs $6.50 per pound and there are 20 slices per pound. How many slices of turkey can you buy for $2.60? 8 slices

31. It takes Clara 1 min to stuff $4n$ envelopes with letters. Melanie is half as fast.

a. How many envelopes can Melanie stuff per minute? $2n$ envelopes

b. How many minutes does Melanie spend per envelope? $\frac{1}{2n}$ min

32. A more efficient halogen bulb can be used exactly six hours per day for a year before burning out. How many hours can the halogen bulb be used? 2,190 hr

OBJECTIVE G Use ratios to compare two quantities. (Lesson 5-5)

33. **Multiple Choice** Which of the following is *not* equal to the ratio of 12 to 7? D

A $\frac{12x}{7x}$ B 60 : 35   C $\frac{24\text{ ft}}{14\text{ ft}}$ D 700 to 1,200

In 34 and 35, consider the table below that lists the types and number of televisions in stock at Eli's Electronic Store.

Type of TV	Number of TVs
High-Definition (HD)	12
Flat-Screen	36
Projection	8
Cathode-Ray Tube (CRT)	64

34. What is the ratio of HD televisions to all televisions? $\frac{1}{10}$

35. What is the ratio of CRT televisions to projection televisions? 8

36. A pair of shoes that originally cost $53 is on sale for $42.40.

a. What is the discount rate? 20%

b. Find the total amount saved, including tax, if the tax rate is 6.25%. $11.27

37. To make a certain shade of green paint, a painter mixes 5 parts blue paint with 3 parts yellow paint. If he needs 20 gallons of green paint, how many gallons of each paint color are needed in the mixture? See margin.

In 38 and 39, consider the following information. A baseball player's batting average can be viewed as the ratio of total number of hits divided by total number of at-bats. In 2005, Vladimir Guerrero got 20 hits in his first 57 at-bats for a batting average of .351.

38. If Guerrero got only 2 hits in his next 10 at-bats, what would have been his new batting average? .328

39. How many hits in a row would Guerrero have needed to raise his batting average to at least .400? 5 hits

Additional Answers

26. Answers vary. Sample answer: $\frac{80}{11} \approx 7.3$ calories per almond.

27. Answers vary. Sample answer: 1.5 ft per year.

29b. The cat breathes at a faster rate, because humans take $16 \cdot 60 = 960$ breaths per hour.

37. 12.5 gal of blue paint, 7.5 gal of yellow paint

Chapter 5 Review

OBJECTIVE H Calculate relative frequencies and probabilities in situations with a finite number of equally likely outcomes.
(Lessons 5-6, 5-7)

40. A number is selected randomly from the integers {−1, 0, 1, ..., 8}. What is the probability that the number is greater than 1? $\frac{7}{10}$

41. A fair die is thrown once. Find the probability of getting an even number greater than 2. $\frac{1}{3}$

42. If the probability of winning a raffle is $\frac{1}{25,000}$, what is the probability of *not* winning? $\frac{24,999}{25,000}$

43. A study shows that the relative frequency of people who eat cold cereal for breakfast in the United States is 31%. What is the relative frequency of people in the United States who do *not* eat cold cereal for breakfast? 69%

44. Event *X* has a probability of 42%, event *B* has a probability of $\frac{5}{12}$, and event *C* has a probability of 0.45.

    a. Which event is most likely to happen? C
    b. Which event is least likely to happen? B

OBJECTIVE I Find probabilities involving geometric regions. (Lesson 5-8)

45. A 5-cm square inside a 6-cm square is shown below. If a point is selected at random from the figure, what is the probability that it lies in the shaded region? $\frac{11}{36}$

5 cm

6 cm

46. Tate drives to work every morning and follows the same route each day. The map below shows his path. One morning Tate runs out of gas while on the way to work. If each point on the map is equally likely, what is the probability that Tate ran out of gas on the highway? 72%

18 mi of Highway

4 mi   3 mi

Home

Work

47. A target consists of a set of 4 concentric circles with radii of 4 inches, 8 inches, 12 inches, and 16 inches. The largest circle is inscribed in a square. A person with a bow and arrow randomly shoots at the target so that all points inside the square are equally likely to be hit. The arrow hits somewhere inside the square.

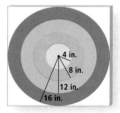

4 in.
8 in.
12 in.
16 in.

    a. What is the probability that the arrow hits the bull's eye? $\frac{\pi}{64}$
    b. What is the probability that the arrow hits within one of the two middle rings (but not within the bull's eye)? $\frac{\pi}{8}$

OBJECTIVE J Solve problems involving proportions in real situations.
(Lessons 5-9, 5-10)

48. If $\frac{1}{2}$ cup of brown sugar equals 24 teaspoons of brown sugar, how many teaspoons are there in $2\frac{1}{3}$ cups of brown sugar? 112 tsp

49. A school donating money to a charity decides that for every student donation of $5, the school will donate $12. If the total student donation amount is $490, how much money will the school donate? **$1,176**

50. On September 27, 2005, you could buy 10.89 pesos (the currency in Mexico) for one U.S. dollar. If a sombrero cost 290 pesos then, what was its cost in U.S. dollars, rounded to the nearest cent? **$26.63**

51. Suppose a ranger caught, tagged, and released 28 moose in a state park. Two months later, the ranger caught 20 moose, and 14 of these had tags. Based on these findings, estimate the total number of moose in the park. **40 moose**

OBJECTIVE K Interpret the meaning of percentile for benchmarks of 10th, 25th, 50th, 75th, and 90th percentiles. (Lesson 5-7)

In 52–55, a class of 20 students at O'Sullivan High School received the following SAT scores.

2330	2200	1900	1870	2050
1680	1790	1950	2110	2020
1880	1790	2230	2000	1970
2050	1680	1550	1780	1910

52. What is the median of the students' scores? **1930**

53. Nolan scored a 1790. At what percentile is he in his class? **25th**

54. Tia hopes that her score is at least at the 90th percentile of her classmates. What score must she have for this to be true? **at least 2200**

55. How many scores are in each of the following percentiles?

   a. 10th **3**   **b.** 25th **6**   **c.** 75th **16**

REPRESENTATIONS Pictures, graphs, or objects that illustrate concepts

OBJECTIVE L Find lengths and ratios of similitude in similar figures. (Lesson 5-10)

56. One rectangular field has dimensions 900 m by 1,200 m; another rectangular field has dimensions 800 m by 1,100 m. Are the fields similar in shape? Explain your reasoning. **no, $\frac{8}{9} \neq \frac{11}{12}$**

57. The quadrilaterals below are similar. Corresponding sides are parallel.
57a. Answers vary. Sample answer: $\frac{x}{6}, \frac{y}{4}$

57b. $y = \frac{128}{9}$

   a. Give the two possible ratios of similitude.

   b. Solve for y.   **c.** Solve for x. $x = \frac{27}{16}$

58. A building casts a shadow that is 480 feet long. A yardstick casts a shadow n feet long at the same time. How tall is the building?

   a. Draw a sketch of the situation. See margin.
   b. Show how a proportion can be used to solve the problem. $\frac{x}{3} = \frac{480}{n}; x = \frac{1,440}{n}$

59. Pentagons $PQRST$ and $VWXYZ$ are similar with ratio of similitude $\frac{4}{5}$. If $VWXYZ$ has area 60 square units, what is the area of $PQRST$? **93.75 units^2**

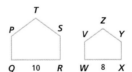

Assessment

Evaluation The *Assessment Resources* provide four forms of the Chapter 5 Test. Forms A and B present parallel versions of a short-answer format. Form C consists of four to six short-response questions that cover the SPUR objectives from Chapter 5. Form D offers performance assessment that covers a subset (or even just one) of the SPUR objectives for the chapter.

Feedback After students have taken the test for Chapter 5 and you have scored the results, return the tests to students for discussion. Class discussion on the questions that caused trouble for most students can be very effective in identifying and clarifying misunderstandings. You might want to have them note the items they missed and work either in groups or at home to correct them. It is important for students to receive feedback on every chapter test, and we recommend that students see and correct their mistakes before proceeding too far into the next chapter.

Additional Answers

58a.

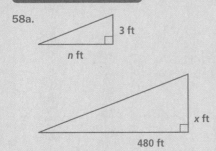

6 Slopes and Lines

Chapter Overview

		Local Standards	Pacing (in days)		
			Average	Advanced	Block
6-1	**Rate of Change** E Calculate rates of change from real data and describe their real-world meanings.		1	1	0.5
6-2	**The Slope of a Line** A Find the slope of the line through two given points. D Use the definition and properties of slope.		1	1	0.5
6-3	**Properties of Slope** D Use the definition and properties of slope. E Calculate rates of change from real data and describe their real-world meanings. H Graph a line given its equation, or given a point and its slope.		1	0.5	0.75
	QUIZ 1		0.5	0.5	0.25
6-4	**Slope-Intercept Equations for Lines** B Find an equation for a line given either its slope and any point or two points on it. C Write an equation for a line in standard form or slope-intercept form, and using either form, find its slope and y-intercept. F Use equations for lines to describe real situations. H Graph a line given its equation, or given a point and its slope.		1	1	0.5
6-5	**Equations for Lines with a Given Point and Slope** B Find an equation for a line given either its slope and any point or two points on it. F Use equations for lines to describe real situations.		1	0.5	0.5
6-6	**Equations for Lines through Two Points** B Find an equation for a line given either its slope and any point or two points on it. F Use equations for lines to describe real situations.		1	1	0.75
	QUIZ 2		0.5	0.5	0.25
6-7	**Fitting a Line to Data** G Given data whose graph is approximately linear, find a linear equation to fit the graph and make predictions about data values.		1	0.5	0.5
6-8	**Standard Form of the Equation of a Line** C Write an equation for a line in standard form or slope-intercept form, and using either form, find its slope and y-intercept. F Use equations for lines to describe real situations. H Graph a line given its equation, or given a point and its slope.		1	1	0.5
6-9	**Graphing Linear Inequalties** I Graph linear inequalities.		1	0.5	0.5
	Self-Test		1	1	0.5
	Chapter Review		2	2	1
	Test		1	1	0.5
	TOTAL		14	12	7.5

Differentiated Options Universal Access

	Accommodating the Learner	Vocabulary Development	Ongoing Assessment	Materials
6-1	pp. 328, 329		group, p. 332	
6-2	pp. 335, 336	p. 334	written, p. 340	
6-3	pp. 343, 344	p. 343	oral, p. 347	
6-4	pp. 351, 352		group, p. 355	dynamic graphing software
6-5	pp. 358, 359		group, p. 360	
6-6	pp. 362, 363		oral, p. 367	
6-7	pp. 370–372	p. 372	oral, p. 373	graphing calculator
6-8	pp. 376, 377		group, p. 380	
6-9	pp. 383, 384		written, p. 386	

Objectives

		Lessons	Self-Test Questions	Chapter Review Questions
⑤kills				
A	Find the slope of the line through two given points.	6-2	1, 2	1–6
B	Find an equation for a line given either its slope and any point or two points on it.	6-4, 6-5, 6-6	15	7–16
C	Write an equation for a line in standard form or slope-intercept form, and using either form, find its slope and y-intercept.	6-4, 6-8	3, 6, 8	17–24
Ⓟroperties				
D	Use the definition and properties of slope.	6-2, 6-3	5, 7, 18, 19	25–31
Ⓤses				
E	Calculate rates of change from real data and describe their real-world meanings.	6-1, 6-3	10, 11	32–39
F	Use equations for lines to describe real situations.	6-4, 6-5, 6-6, 6-8	4, 14, 21	40–47
G	Given data whose graph is approximately linear, find a linear equation to fit the graph and make predictions about data values.	6-7	16, 17	48, 49
Ⓡepresentations				
H	Graph a line given its equation, or given a point and its slope.	6-3, 6-4, 6-8	12	50–57
I	Graph linear inequalities.	6-9	9, 13, 20	58–65

Resource Masters Chapter 6

Resource Master 1, Graph Paper (page 2), can be used with all Lessons. **Resource Master 2, Four-Quadrant Graph Paper** (page 3), can be used with all Lessons, **Resource Master 4, Graphing Equations** (page 5), can be used with Lessons 6-2, 6-3, and 6-7.

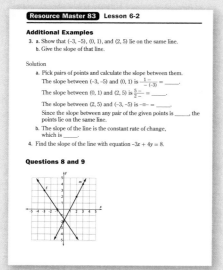

Resource Master 79 Lesson 6-1

Resource Master 78 Lesson 6-1

Warm-Up
Refer to the graph to answer the questions.

1. How fast (in people per year) did the population change from 1850 to 1900?

2. Did the population increase at a faster rate from 1850 to 1900, or from 1900 to 1950?

3. How fast (in people per year) did the population change from 1950 to 2000?

Population of Chicago 1830–2000

Resource Masters for Lesson 6-1

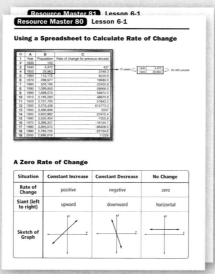

Resource Master 81 Lesson 6-1

Resource Master 80 Lesson 6-1

Using a Spreadsheet to Calculate Rate of Change

A Zero Rate of Change

Situation	Constant Increase	Constant Decrease	No Change
Rate of Change	positive	negative	zero
Slant (left to right)	upward	downward	horizontal
Sketch of Graph			

Resource Masters for Lesson 6-1

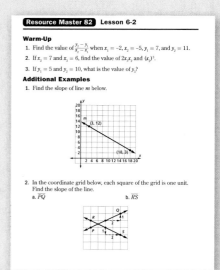

Resource Master 82 Lesson 6-2

Warm-Up

1. Find the value of $\frac{y_2 - y_1}{x_2 - x_1}$ when $x_1 = -2$, $x_2 = -5$, $y_1 = 7$, and $y_2 = 11$.

2. If $x_2 = 7$ and $x_3 = 6$, find the value of $2x_2x_3$ and $(x_2)^3$.

3. If $y_1 = 5$ and $y_2 = 10$, what is the value of y_3?

Additional Examples

1. Find the slope of line m below.

2. In the coordinate grid below, each square of the grid is one unit. Find the slope of the line.
   a. $\overline{PQ}$ b. $\overline{RS}$

Resource Master for Lesson 6-2

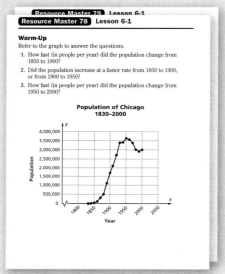

Resource Master 83 Lesson 6-2

Additional Examples

3. a. Show that (-3, -5), (0, 1), and (2, 5) lie on the same line.
   b. Give the slope of that line.

Solution
   a. Pick pairs of points and calculate the slope between them.
   The slope between (-3, -5) and (0, 1) is $\frac{1 - \_\_}{\_ - (-3)} = \_\_\_\_$.

   The slope between (0, 1) and (2, 5) is $\frac{5 - \_\_}{2 - \_\_} = \_\_\_\_$.

   The slope between (2, 5) and (-3, -5) is $\frac{-\_}{-\_} = \_\_\_\_$.

   Since the slope between any pair of the given points is _____, the points lie on the same line.
   b. The slope of the line is the constant rate of change, which is _____.

4. Find the slope of the line with equation $-3x + 4y = 8$.

Questions 8 and 9

Resource Master for Lesson 6-2

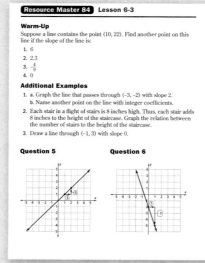

Resource Master 84 Lesson 6-3

Warm-Up
Suppose a line contains the point (10, 22). Find another point on this line if the slope of the line is:

1. 6
2. 2.3
3. $-\frac{4}{9}$
4. 0

Additional Examples

1. a. Graph the line that passes through (-3, -2) with slope 2.
   b. Name another point on the line with integer coefficients.

2. Each stair in a flight of stairs is 8 inches high. Thus, each stair adds 8 inches to the height of the staircase. Graph the relation between the number of stairs to the height of the staircase.

3. Draw a line through (-1, 3) with slope 0.

Question 5   **Question 6**

Resource Master for Lesson 6-3

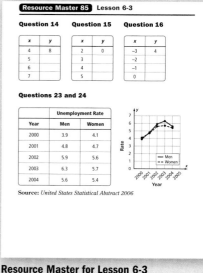

Resource Master 85 Lesson 6-3

Question 14		Question 15		Question 16	
x	y	x	y	x	y
4	8	2	0	-3	4
5		3		-2	
6		4		-1	
7		5		0	

Questions 23 and 24

	Unemployment Rate	
Year	Men	Women
2000	3.9	4.1
2001	4.8	4.7
2002	5.9	5.6
2003	6.3	5.7
2004	5.6	5.4

Source: *United States Statistical Abstract 2006*

Resource Master for Lesson 6-3

Resource Master 86 — Lesson 6-4

Warm-Up

A line has equation $y = 9 - 5x$.

1. What is its slope?
2. Where does the line cross the y-intercept?
3. Where does the line cross the x-intercept?
4. What is an equation of the line whose graph is parallel to and 1 unit above this line?

Additional Examples

1. Write the equation $-2x - 4y = 12$ in slope-intercept form. Give the slope and y-intercept of the graph.
2. Find the equation of the line graphed below.

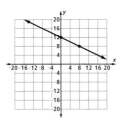

Resource Master for Lesson 6-4

Resource Master 87 — Lesson 6-4
Resource Master 88 — Lesson 6-4

Additional Examples

3. A mountain climber begins the second day of a climb at an elevation of 2,100 feet and climbs at a rate of 170 feet per hour.
   a. Find a slope-intercept equation for her height h after t hours.
   b. How high is the climber after 8 hours?

Accommodating the Learner

Make an observation about the slope and y-intercept of each line in relation to the equation of the line.

Equation of Line	Two Points on Line	Slope	y-intercept
$y = -2x + 3$	(1, 1) and (-1, 5)	$\frac{5-1}{-1-1} = \frac{4}{-2} = -2$	$y = -2(0) + 3 = 3$
$y = \frac{2}{3}x - 1$			
$y = 0.5x + 4$			

Accommodating the Learner

The circumference of a circle C varies directly with the circle's diameter d. The equation is modeled by the direct variation $C = kd$ where k is the constant of variation. The table below gives the circumference C and diameter d of several circles. Find the constant of variation. Identify by name the number which represents the constant of variation. Write the equation that relates C and d.

	C	d	k
Circle 1	3.454	1.1	
Circle 2	6.4056	2.04	
Circle 3	1.57	0.5	

Resource Masters for Lesson 6-4

Resource Master 89 — Lesson 6-5

Warm-Up

1. Give equations for four different lines containing the point (7, 11).
2. For each line in Problem 1, give its slope.

Additional Examples

1. Normally the depth of the river is 12 feet. After a torrential downpour the water is rising at a rate of 1.5 feet per hour. Assuming this rate remains steady, find an equation relating the depth of the river d to the time t.

2. A line has slope 4, and its x-intercept is -13. Find an equation for the line in point-slope form.

   Because the x-intercept is -13, the point (-13, 0) is on the line. Because the slope is 4, $m = 4$. Use the point-slope form
   $y - \underline{\quad} = m(x - \underline{\quad})$.
   Substitute for m, x, and k.
   $y - \underline{\quad} = \underline{\quad}(x - \underline{\quad})$

Resource Master for Lesson 6-5

Resource Master 90 — Lesson 6-6

Warm-Up

Example 1 of Lesson 6-6 asks for an equation for the line that passes through the points (10, -4) and (18, 20).

1. Without finding an equation for the line, find the y-coordinates of points on the line with x-coordinates 2, 26, and 14.
2. Without finding an equation for the line, try to find the y-intercept of the line.

Additional Example

1. Find an equation for the line that passes through (7, -2) and (-5, 4).

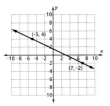

Resource Master for Lesson 6-6

Resource Master 91 — Lesson 6-6

Additional Examples

2. Two inches from the top, a drop d of thick syrup drips down the side of a container at the rate of 0.25 inch per second t. After 2 seconds it is 2.5 inches from the top of the container, and after 5 seconds it is 3.25 inches from the top. This information is graphed below.
   a. Find an equation for the line through the two points.
   b. How far from the top was the drop after 8 seconds?

3. Suppose a hot air balloon is resting on a platform above the ground. As it begins its ascent, it is 175 feet above the ground after 3 minutes and is 275 feet above the ground after 5 minutes. Assume a constant rate of ascent.
   a. Express the given information as two ordered pairs (minutes, feet).
   b. Find an equation that expresses the height y of the balloon in terms of x, the length of ascent in minutes.
   c. What does the y-intercept b represent in this situation?
   d. What does the slope m represent in this situation?
   e. How long does it take for the balloon to reach an altitude of 1,125 feet?

Resource Master for Lesson 6-6

Resource Master 92 — Lesson 6-7
Resource Master 93 — Lesson 6-7

Warm-Up

Graph the three points (1, 5), (2, 9), and (4, 12).

1. Eyeball two points on a line that is close to these points and find its equation.

Additional Example

The table below shows the number of U.S. cell phone subscribers in millions from 2000 to 2006.

Year	Year since 2000	Subscribers (millions)
2000	0	97.0
2001	1	118.4
2002	2	134.6
2003	3	148.1
2004	4	169.5
2005	5	194.5
2006	6	219.4

a. Using a graphing calculator, create a scatterplot of the points (Year since 2000, Total Subscribers).
b. Use a calculator to find an equation for the line of best fit. Graph the line in the same window as the scatterplot.
c. In this situation what is the meaning of $x = -4$ and $x = 10$?
d. Use the equation of the line to predict the number of cell phone subscribers in 1996. The actual number was 38.2 million. Did the line of best fit over or under predict the number of 1990 subscribers?
e. Use the equation to predict the number of subscribers in 2010. Do you expect the equation to over predict or under predict the number of 2010 subscribers? Explain why.

Resource Masters for Lesson 6-7

Resource Master 94 — Lesson 6-8
Resource Master 95 — Lesson 6-8

Warm-Up

Examine the linear combination situation on pages 374 and 375, where Lourdes spent $24 on 30 neon bouncing balls and 12 glow-in-the-dark necklaces.

1. If a neon ball cost $0.30, then how much did a necklace cost?
2. What is the most a necklace could have cost? What is the cost of one neon ball?
3. What is the most a neon ball could have cost?

Additional Examples

1. Graph $5x + 2y = 10$.
2. Rewrite $y = -\frac{3}{2}x - \frac{1}{2}$ in standard form with integer coefficients. Tell the values of A, B, and C.
3. Rewrite $y = -0.8x$ in standard form with integer values of A, B, and C.

Resource Masters for Lesson 6-8

Resource Master 96 — Lesson 6-9

Warm-Up

Consider the three sentences below:
a. $7x - 3y > 10$
b. $7x - 3y = 10$
c. $7x - 3y < 10$

Which sentence does each of these points satisfy?

1. (1, 1)
2. (0, 0)
3. (5, 4)
4. (-3, -7)
5. (-2, -8)
6. (200, 100)
7. (-200, -100)
8. (40.328, 6.897)

Additional Examples

1. Graph $x \leq -2$ on the coordinate plane.
2. Write an inequality that describes the set of points in the shaded region.

Resource Master for Lesson 6-9

Resource Master 97 — Lesson 6-9

Additional Examples

3. Draw the graph of $y > 3x - 3$.
4. Graph $-3x + 5y < -15$.
5. You have $20 to spend on party decorations. Ribbon costs $1.50 a roll and balloons cost $2.00 per package. How many rolls of ribbon and packages of balloons can you buy?

Question 16

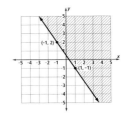

Resource Master for Lesson 6-9

Pacing

Each lesson in this chapter is designed to be covered in one day. At the end of the chapter, you should plan to spend 1 day to review the Self-Test, 1 to 2 days for the Chapter Review, and 1 day for a test. You may wish to spend a day on projects and possibly a day is needed for quizzes. This chapter should therefore take 12 to 15 days. We strongly advise you to not spend more than 16 days on this chapter; there is ample opportunity to review ideas in later chapters.

Chapter 6 Projects

At the end of each chapter, you will find projects related to the chapter. At this time you might want to have students look over the projects on pages 387 and 388. You might want to have students tentatively select a project on which to work. Then, as students read and progress through the chapter, they can finalize their project choices.

Sometimes students might work alone; at other times, you might let them collaborate with classmates for a presentation and discussion. We recommend that you allow for diversity and encourage students to use their imaginations when presenting their projects. As students work on projects throughout the year, they should see the many uses of mathematics in the real world.

▶ Contents

On the next page is a table of the population of Chicago from 1830 to 2000 according to the United States census. The ordered pairs (year, population that year) are also graphed.

The slopes of the line segments connecting the points indicate how fast the population increased or decreased in each decade. In this chapter, you will study many examples of lines and slopes.

324

Chapter 6 Overview

Students need a good understanding of the relationship between equations and their graphs. The graphing capabilities of calculators and computers have greatly increased the utilization of graphs over the years. Graphing lines from a table of values was covered in earlier chapters. The emphasis in this chapter is finding and analyzing equations of lines, which are tied in with the applications that use them and with the geometry of the plane.

The goal of this chapter is to have students interpret the slope of a line as a special kind of rate of change. Lesson 6-2 shows a line as a graph of a situation involving constant rate of change. These two lessons build on the work students did with rates in Chapter 5. Students study the properties of slope in Lesson 6-3. Lesson 6-4 presents the slope-intercept form, $y = mx + b$, for writing equations of lines or for graphing.

(continued on next page)

Year	Population
1830	100
1840	4,470
1850	29,963
1860	112,172
1870	298,977
1880	503,185
1890	1,099,850
1900	1,698,575
1910	2,185,283
1920	2,701,705
1930	3,376,438
1940	3,396,808
1950	3,620,962
1960	3,550,404
1970	3,369,357
1980	3,005,072
1990	2,783,726
2000	2,896,016

Source: U.S. Census Bureau

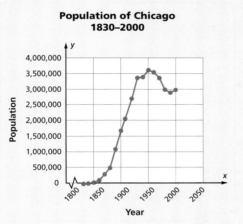

Population of Chicago 1830–2000

325

Lesson 6-5 deals with situations in which a data point and the rate of change are known and introduce the point-slope form for equations of lines $y - k = m(x - h)$. In Lesson 6-6, two data points are known. Lesson 6-7 discusses situations in which more than two data points are known, and they tend to lie on a line, so the problem is to approximate the data with a line.

Lesson 6-8 discusses the standard form for equations of lines, $Ax + By = C$. Both the standard form and the slope-intercept form are applied to graphing linear inequalities in Lesson 6-9.

Encourage your students to use their graphing calculators to save time and to increase accuracy. Use graph paper to aid understanding. For instance, slope is illustrated better when students can accurately count squares to move between two points on the graph, and the geometry of lines is easier to understand from accurate drawings.

Lesson 6-1

Rate of Change

GOAL

Introduce the formula for rate of change between two points, and show this idea graphically.

SPUR Objective

(The SPUR Objectives for all of Chapter 6 are found in the Chapter Review on pages 392–395.)

E Calculate rates of change from real data and describe their real-world meanings.

Materials/Resources

· Lesson Masters 6-1A and 6-1B
· Resource Masters 1, 2, and 78–81

HOMEWORK

Suggestions for Assignment
• Questions 1–18
• Question 19 (extra credit)
• Reading Lesson 6-2
• Covering the Ideas 6-2

Local Standards

1 Warm-Up

Refer to the graph of the population of Chicago on page 325.

1. How fast (in people per year) did the population change from 1850 to 1900? about 33,400 people/yr

2. Did the population increase at a faster rate from 1850 to 1900, or from 1900 to 1950? from 1900 to 1950

3. How fast (in people per year) did the population change from 1950 to 2000? about –14,500 people/yr

---

▶ **BIG IDEA** The rate at which a quantity changes can be determined either by computation or by looking at a graph.

What Is a Rate of Change?

Mr. and Mrs. Overjoyed had a healthy baby girl named Joy who weighed 7.5 pounds at birth. At the end of 4 months, the baby weighed 13.5 pounds. How fast did her weight change from birth to 4 months? To answer this question, we calculate the *rate of change* of Joy's weight, that is, how much she gained per month.

From 0 to 4 months

$$\frac{\text{change in weight}}{\text{change in age}} = \frac{13.5 \text{ lb} - 7.5 \text{ lb}}{4 \text{ mo} - 0 \text{ mo}} = \frac{6 \text{ lb}}{4 \text{ mo}} = 1.5 \ \frac{\text{lb}}{\text{mo}}$$

At age 6 months, Joy weighed 15.75 pounds. How fast did she grow from 4 months to 6 months? Use the same method to calculate the rate of change in her weight per month, from 4 months to 6 months.

From 4 to 6 months

$$\frac{\text{change in weight}}{\text{change in age}} = \frac{15.75 \text{ lb} - 13.5 \text{ lb}}{6 \text{ mo} - 4 \text{ mo}} = \frac{2.25 \text{ lb}}{2 \text{ mo}} = 1.125 \ \frac{\text{lb}}{\text{mo}}$$

Because 1.5 > 1.125, Joy gained weight at a faster rate from 0 to 4 months than from 4 to 6 months.

These data points have been plotted at the right and connected to make a *line graph*. The **rate of change** measures how fast the graph goes up or down when reading from left to right. Since Joy's rate of change was greater for the 0 to 4 month period than for the 4 to 6 month period, the line segment connecting (0, 7.5) to (4, 13.5) is steeper than the line segment connecting (4, 13.5) to (6, 15.75).

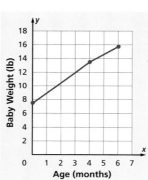

A square chessboard has 64 squares, alternating black and white.

a. How many black squares are there? 32

b. How many white squares are there? 32

c. How many squares are on the edge of the board? 32

In 2003, there were 4,089,950 births in the United States.

Source: National Center for Health Statistics

Background

In this lesson, we use situations and graphs in which quantities change over time. The problems in this lesson result in line graphs (unions of line segments), and we talk about the rate of change between pairs of points. In the next lesson we look at lines and introduce the term *slope*.

One reason to start with rate of change rather than slope is that no lines are needed, just two points. This is intuitively easier. Also, the subtraction and division in the formula come from change and rate, so the name *rate of change* is easily associated with the operations in the formula. Specifically, $y_2 - y_1$ and $x_2 - x_1$ are changes, so $\frac{y_2 - y_1}{x_2 - x_1}$ is a rate of change. This makes the formula easier to understand.

This application approach helps students make sense of positive, negative, and zero rates of change. It is easy to picture

(continued on next page)

Negative Rates of Change

Joy was gaining weight, so the rate of change was positive. But a rate of change can be negative.

Example 1

The population of Chicago from 1830 to 2000 is shown in the table and graph on page 325. Find the rate of change of the population of Chicago (in people per year) during the given time period, and describe how the rate is pictured on the graph.

a. 1890 to 1900   b. 1970 to 1980

Solutions

a. the rate of change, in people per year, from 1890 to 1900:

$$\frac{\text{change in population}}{\text{change in years}} = \frac{1{,}698{,}575 - 1{,}099{,}850}{1900 - 1890}$$

$$= \frac{598{,}725 \text{ people}}{10 \text{ yr}}$$

$$= 59{,}872.5 \; \frac{\text{people}}{\text{yr}}$$

Between 1890 and 1900 the population increased, so the rate of change is positive. The graph slants upward as you read the graph from left to right.

b. the rate of change between 1970 and 1980:

$$\frac{\text{change in population}}{\text{change in years}} = \frac{3{,}005{,}072 - 3{,}369{,}357}{1980 - 1970}$$

$$= \frac{-364{,}285 \text{ people}}{10 \text{ yr}}$$

$$= -36{,}428.5 \; \frac{\text{people}}{\text{yr}}$$

Between 1970 and 1980 the population decreased, so the rate of change is negative. In that interval, the graph slants downward as you read the graph from left to right.

When you read graphs in algebra, read them from left to right just as you would read a line in a book. A *positive rate of change* indicates that the graph slants *upward*. A *negative rate of change* indicates that the graph slants *downward*.

In both Joy's weight and Chicago's population, the *changes* are found by subtraction. The *rates* are found by division. So, you can calculate the rate of change between two points by dividing the difference in the y-coordinates by the difference in the x-coordinates. We use the subscripts $_1$ and $_2$ to identify the coordinates of the two points. For example, x_1 is read "x one" or "x sub one." The point (x_1, y_1) simply means the *first point*, while (x_2, y_2) means the *second point*.

population or height increasing, decreasing, or remaining constant.

The lesson begins with a familiar situation, the change in weight over time. Most students do not need a formula to determine how fast someone's weight has changed. Example 1 follows the chapter opener and illustrates both positive and negative rates of change. The generalization is then made to obtain a formula for rate of change. Example 2 shows a situation in which there is a zero rate of change.

2 Teaching

Notes on the Lesson

What is a rate of change? When discussing the graph of the population of Chicago, distinguish *rate* of change from *amount* of change. Point out that the faster the rate of change, the steeper the incline of the segment. This is seen in the Overjoyed family's baby's rate of weight gain, which was faster between ages 0 and 4 months than between 4 months and 6 months.

Students should label their answers with units of rate. The rate unit in the weight example at the beginning of the lesson is *pounds per month*.

Additional Example

Example 1 The table below shows the home attendance figures for one baseball team during the years 1998–2005. Find the rate of change in attendance (in people per year) during the given time and tell how the rate is pictured on the graph.

Year	Attendance (in millions)
1998	1.4
1999	1.3
2000	1.9
2001	1.8
2002	1.7
2003	1.9
2004	1.93
2005	2.34

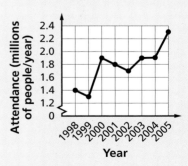

a. 1999 to 2000 600,000 people per year; the graph slants upward

b. 2001 to 2002 –100,000 people per year; the graph slants downward

6-1

Notes on the Lesson

Using a spreadsheet to calculate rate of change. You may have to remind students that in the rate of change formula, x_1 stands for the "first x-value" and x_2 stands for the "second x-value", and this is similar for y_1 and y_2. Some students may still want to think of the 2 as being multiplied by x or as an exponent. It may be useful to point out that for some calculators and computer programs, x_1 and x_2 would be typed as X1 and X2, and in that sense they are like locations in a column of a spreadsheet.

The table at the top of page 330 should be discussed in class and learned by students.

If students seem to have a solid understanding of rate of change and percent, you may wish to compare rate of change with percent of change. (If the students' understanding seems tentative, the comparison may be too confusing.) When populations are small, the rate of change will generally be small, but the percent of change will be large. When populations are large, the rate of change may be large, but the percent will be less.

Here is the general formula.

> ### Rate of Change
> The rate of change between points (x_1, y_1) and (x_2, y_2) is $\frac{y_2 - y_1}{x_2 - x_1}$.

Because every rate of change comes from division, the unit of a rate of change is a **rate unit.** In Example 1, a number of people is divided by a number of years. So, the unit of the rate of change is *people per year*, written as $\frac{people}{year}$ or people/year.

Using a Spreadsheet to Calculate Rate of Change

Spreadsheets and other table generators can be used to calculate rates of change. The spreadsheet below shows the years from 1830 to 2000 in column A, the population of Chicago in column B, and the rate of change of population for the previous decade in column C.

	A	B	C
			Rate of change for previous decade
1	Year	Population	
2	1830	100	
3	1840	4,470	437
4	1850	29,963	2549.3
5	1860	112,172	8220.9
6	1870	298,977	18680.5
7	1880	503,185	20420.8
8	1890	1,099,850	59666.5
9	1900	1,698,575	59872.5
10	1910	2,185,283	48670.8
11	1920	2,701,705	51642.2
12	1930	3,376,438	674773.3
13	1940	3,396,808	2037
14	1950	3,620,962	22415.4
15	1960	3,550,404	-7055.8
16	1970	3,369,357	-18104.7
17	1980	3,005,072	-36428.5
18	1990	2,783,726	-22134.6
19	2000	2,896,016	11229

→ 10 years

1840	4,470
1850	29,963

25,493 peop

Accommodating the Learner ⬆

Have students go online and find the total yearly attendance figures for their favorite professional sports team for the last 10 years. Students should build a table and a line graph. Students should identify the interval where the attendance increased, decreased, and stayed the same. Next, have students find their team's number of victories per year over this same time period. Again students should build a table and a line graph. Students should identify the interval where the victories increased, decreased, and stayed the same. Have students compare the attendance intervals to the victory intervals. What, if anything, can they conclude?

Each rate of change is calculated using years and populations from two rows of the spreadsheet. Each formula in column C involves two subtractions, one to find the change in population and one to find the change in years. Then the population change is divided by the change in years. For example, C4 describes the change from 1840 to 1850.

The rate of change is $\frac{25{,}493 \text{ people}}{10 \text{ yr}} = 2{,}549.3 \frac{\text{people}}{\text{yr}}$. The formula to calculate this for C4 is $= (\text{B4}-\text{B3}) / (\text{A4}-\text{A3})$. Notice that cell C2 is empty because there is no population previous to 1830 in column B.

 QY

A Zero Rate of Change

Sometimes quantities do not change over a certain interval. Then the rate of change is zero.

> **▸ QY**
>
> Chicago's population in 2005 was 2,842,518.
>
> **a.** Find the rate of change of Chicago's population from 2000 to 2005.
>
> **b.** The answer to Part a is negative. Explain what that means in the context of the problem.

Example 2

The table below shows estimated attendance by the hour at a professional baseball game that went into extra innings.

a. During what time interval did the attendance not change?

b. Find the rate of change of attendance during that time.

Time	1 P.M.	2 P.M.	3 P.M.	4 P.M.	5 P.M.	6 P.M.	7 P.M.
Attendance	1,200	18,400	23,200	23,200	23,200	20,100	2,000

Fans watch the first pitch at the first regular season game at Pacific Bell Park in San Francisco in 2000.

Solutions

a. From 3:00 pm to 5:00 pm the attendance did **not** change. Notice this is associated with a horizontal line segment on the graph at the right.

b. Use the coordinates (3, 23,200) and (5, 23,200) to calculate the rate of change.

$$\text{rate of change} = \frac{23{,}200 - 23{,}200}{5 - 3} =$$

$$\frac{0 \text{ people}}{2 \text{ hours}} = 0 \frac{\text{people}}{\text{hour}}$$

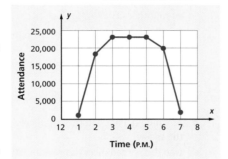

In general, a rate of change of 0 corresponds to a horizontal segment on the graph. The table on page 330 summarizes the relationship between rate of change and the graph.

Rate of Change **329**

Note-Taking Tips

Rate of change foreshadows the idea of slope of a line. Students often quickly lose or never really see the relationship between the slope of a line and the rate of change. In their notebooks, have students write several examples of situations where the rate of change is positive, negative, and zero. As the chapter progresses, have students review these notes to constantly reinforce this relationship.

Additional Example

Example 2 The table below shows the daily gross sales at an auto dealership for one week.

Days of the Week	Sales
Monday	$86,000
Tuesday	$123,000
Wednesday	$117,000
Thursday	$99,000
Friday	$99,000
Saturday	$147,000

a. On which two consecutive days did the gross sales not change? **From Thursday through Friday, the gross sales did not change.**

b. Find the rate of change in gross sales during that time. **0**

Accommodating the Learner

Have students make a list of places in their lives where rate of change plays a role. For each idea, have students give an example of how rate of change comes into play. These examples should model increasing, decreasing, and remaining constant. Have them describe why the rate of change increases, decreases, or remains the same for each example.

6-1

3 Assignment

Recommended Assignment
- Questions 1–18
- Question 19 (extra credit)
- Reading Lesson 6-2
- Covering the Ideas 6-2

Notes on the Questions
For most classes, answer Questions 1–9 in order. This will ensure that the basic ideas of the lesson are clear to students.

Questions 2b and 2c Emphasize the connection between steepness and rate of change. The steeper the segment, the greater the rate of change.

Question 3d The key is that the *same* formula gives rise to both positive and negative answers.

Situation	Constant Increase	Constant Decrease	No Change
Rate of Change	positive	negative	zero
Slant (left to right)	upward	downward	horizontal
Sketch of Graph			

Questions

COVERING THE IDEAS

1. **Fill in the Blanks** A rate of change is given in dollars per hour. It is found by dividing change in ___?___ by change in ___?___.
   (dollars / hours)

2. The table at the right shows Jack's weight from birth to age 2.
   a. Make a line graph for this data.
   b. Which is steeper, the segment joining $(0, 8)$ to $(4, 15)$ or the segment joining $(6, 19)$ to $(12, 24)$? the segment joining $(0, 8)$ to $(4, 15)$
   c. Which has the greater rate of change, the segment joining $(0, 8)$ to $(4, 15)$ or the segment joining $(6, 19)$ to $(12, 24)$?
   d. Explain why we would not expect the rate of change of Jack's weight to be negative during his childhood.
   e. Was the rate of change in his weight greater from ages 6 to 12 months or from 12 to 18 months? 6 to 12 months
   f. What is the rate of change in his weight from birth to 24 months? $0.875 \frac{lb}{mo}$

Age	Weight (lb)
birth	8
4 mo	15
6 mo	19
12 mo	24
18 mo	27
24 mo	29

3. Refer to the graph and table of the population of Chicago on page 325.
   a. In which decade did Chicago's population grow the fastest? 1920s
   b. In which 20-year period did the population of Chicago grow the fastest? 1910–1930
   c. In which decade did the population of Chicago decline the most? 1970s
   d. Use the spreadsheet of the population of Chicago on page 328 to find the formula that created cell C10. (B10−B9)/(A10−A9)

2a.
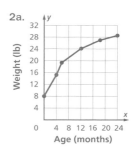

2c. the segment joining $(0, 8)$ to $(4, 15)$

2d. Answers vary. Sample answer: Young people generally gain weight rather than lose weight.

6-1A Lesson Master

Questions on SPUR Objectives
See pages 392–395 for objectives.

USES Objective E

In 1–4, use the chart below, showing the weight of Anthony's golden retriever, Leo.

Age (weeks)	8	12	16	20	24
Weight (lb)	10	16	27	39	45

1. Make a line graph for Leo's weight on the grid at the right.

2. In which time period did Leo have a greater rate of growth, from week 16 to week 20 or from week 20 to week 24?
   From week 16 to week 20

3. What was the rate of change of Leo's weight from 8 weeks to 12 weeks? $\frac{3}{2}$

4. Was the rate of change ever negative? Explain.
   No; the weight does not decrease over time.

In 5–7, use the table below. It shows the number of bushels of corn, in thousands, produced by three states: Illinois, Iowa, and Kansas.

State	Number of Bushels (in thousands)		
	2002	2003	2004
Iowa	1,931,550	1,868,300	2,244,400
Illinois	1,471,500	1,812,200	2,088,000
Kansas	301,600	300,000	432,000

5. Find the rate of change in corn production for Iowa from 2002 to 2004.
   156,425 thousands of bushels per year

6. Which state had the greatest rate of change in production from 2002 to 2004?
   Illinois

7. Which states had a negative rate of change in production from 2002 to 2003?
   Iowa and Kansas

226   Algebra

---

330   **Chapter 6**

In 4–8, refer to the graph at the right of attendance at a football game.

4. Identify all one-hour time periods where the rate of change is negative. **See margin.**

5. Did attendance increase or decrease between 2:00 P.M. and 3:00 P.M.? **increase**

6. Calculate the rate of change in attendance from 5:00 P.M. to 6:00 P.M. $0 \frac{\text{people}}{\text{hr}}$

7. Did the attendance increase, decrease, or stay the same from 6:00 P.M. to 7:00 P.M.? **decrease**

8. When do you think the game started and ended? Explain your answer. **See margin.**

9. Evaluate the expression $\frac{y_2 - y_1}{x_2 - x_1}$ for the points $(-6, 9)$ and $(-3, 7)$. $-\frac{2}{3}$

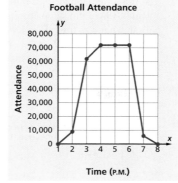

Football Attendance

Time (P.M.)

Notes on the Questions
Question 9 There will be many opportunities in the next lesson for substitution into this formula. It should be discussed here to ensure that students know what to do.

Question 14 This is an important question to discuss in some detail. Ask students what is being graphed on each axis (time on the x-axis, distance between the bulldozer and a point on the highway on the y-axis). Students may be confused because there seems to be no scale, but point out that the answers to the questions do not depend on the scale.

APPLYING THE MATHEMATICS

10. Find the rate of change from point A to point B on the graph at the right. $\frac{4}{3}$

11. Refer to the table below. a. $\frac{7}{60} \frac{\text{m}}{\text{hr}}$

Hours After Midnight	Height of Tide Above Sea Level (m)
0	0.9
6	0.6
12	−0.2
18	0.5
24	0.9

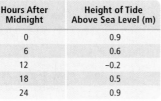

a. Calculate the rate of change from 12 hours to 18 hours after midnight.

b. Is the rate of change between 6 and 12 hours after midnight positive, negative, or zero? **negative**

12. Refer to the table at the right of the population of Hong Kong, one of the most densely populated places in the world.

a. In which time period was the rate of population growth per year the greatest? **1991 to 1999**

b. Hong Kong has an area of about 425 square miles. In 1999, Hong Kong had about how many people per square mile? **about 16,095 $\frac{\text{people}}{\text{mi}^2}$**

Year	Population
2006	6,940,432
1999	6,840,600
1991	5,647,114
1986	5,395,997
1981	4,986,560
1976	4,439,250

Source: Advertising Age

Rate of Change **331**

Additional Answers

4. 6:00 P.M. to 7:00 P.M., 7:00 P.M. to 8:00 P.M.

8. Answers vary. Sample answer: The game started between 3 and 4 P.M. and ended between 6 and 7 P.M. because the attendance was clustered between 4 and 6.

6-1

4 Wrap-Up

Ongoing Assessment

Form groups of two students. Have one student name a situation in which rate of change plays a role. The second student should describe a situation where the rate of change would be positive, negative, or remain the same. Repeat the process with the students exchanging roles.

Additional Answers

16a.

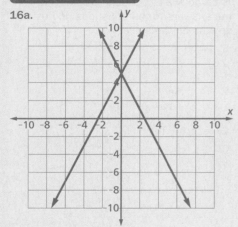

13. The Beier family had $2,324 in a checking account on December 1st and $490 in the same account two weeks later. In this time period, what was the rate of change of the amount of money in their account per day? **–$131 per day**

14. A bulldozer is working on a highway. The graph at the right shows the distance between the bulldozer and a fixed point on the highway measured over time. Use the graph to complete the table.

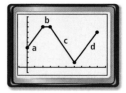

Section of Graph	Rate of Change (positive, negative, or zero)	Bulldozer's Movement (towards point, away from point, standing still)
a	positive ?	away from point
b	zero ?	? standing still
c	negative ?	? towards point
d	positive	? away from point

REVIEW

15. **True or False** The rate *9 apple pies for 15 people* is equal to the rate $\frac{3}{5}$ *apple pie for 1 person*. Explain your answer. (**Lesson 5-1**)

16. **a.** Graph $y = 2x + 5$ and $y = -2x + 5$ on the same set of axes.
    b. Where do the two lines intersect? (**Lessons 4-3, 3-1**) (0, 5)
    16a. See margin.

17. A numismatist (coin collector) has a collection of 850 coins. If the collection grows at 48 coins per year, how many coins will the numismatist have in *x* years? (**Lesson 1-2**) **850 + 48x coins**

18. Suppose $2x + 5y = 10$. (**Lesson 1-1**)
    a. Find the value of *y* when $x = 0$. **2**
    b. Find the value of *y* when $x = 3$. **0.8**
    c. Find the value of *x* when $y = 0$. **5**
    d. Find the value of *x* when $y = -4$. **15**

EXPLORATION

19. Find the population of the town you live in for the years 1940, 1950, 1960, 1970, 1980, 1990, and 2000. Put this information into a spreadsheet and calculate the rate of change of population for each decade. **19a–b. See margin.**
    a. In which 10-year period was the rate of growth greatest?
    b. In which decades was there negative growth? Positive growth? Zero growth?
    c. In which 20-year period was the rate of growth greatest? **1940 to 1960**

15. True; $\frac{9}{15} = \frac{\frac{3}{5}}{1}$

The collecting of coins is one of the oldest hobbies in the world.

Source: *Encyclopædia Britannica*

QY ANSWERS

a. $-10{,}699.6 \frac{\text{people}}{\text{yr}}$

b. Chicago's population decreased from 2000 to 2005.

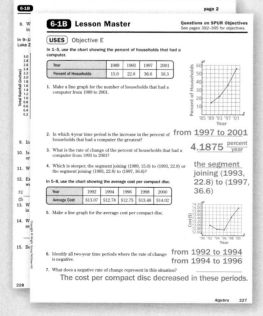

6-1B Lesson Master

Questions on SPUR Objectives
See pages 392–395 for objectives.

USES Objective E

In 1–5, use the chart showing the percent of households that had a computer.

Year	1989	1993	1997	2001
Percent of Households	15.0	22.8	36.6	56.3

1. Make a line graph for the number of households that had a computer from 1989 to 2001.

2. In which 4-year time period is the increase in the percent of households that had a computer the greatest? from **1997 to 2001**

3. What is the rate of change of the percent of households that had a computer from 1993 to 2001? **4.1875** $\frac{\text{percent}}{\text{year}}$

4. Which is steeper, the segment joining (1989, 15.0) to (1993, 22.8) or the segment joining (1993, 22.8) to (1997, 36.6)? **the segment joining (1993, 22.8) to (1997, 36.6)**

In 5–8, use the chart showing the average cost per compact disc.

Year	1992	1994	1996	1998	2000
Average Cost	$13.07	$12.78	$12.75	$13.48	$14.02

5. Make a line graph for the average cost per compact disc.

6. Identify all two-year time periods where the rate of change is negative. from **1992 to 1994** from **1994 to 1996**

7. What does a negative rate of change represent in this situation? **The cost per compact disc decreased in these periods.**

Algebra 227

Additional Answers

19a. Answers vary. Sample answer: The population for Denver appears in the table at the right. The growth rate was the fastest from 1940 to 1950.

19b. There was a negative growth rate in the 70s and 80s, and a positive growth rate in the 40s, 50s, 60s, and 90s.

Year	Population
1940	322,412
1950	415,786
1960	493,887
1970	514,678
1980	492,365
1990	467,610
2000	554,636

Lesson 6-2 The Slope of a Line

▶ **BIG IDEA** A line has a constant slope equal to the rate of change between any two of its points.

Constant-Decrease Situation

During a fire drill in a skyscraper with 50 floors, people were asked to move swiftly down the stairwell. To see how much time it would take to empty the building in a real emergency, the evacuation of the people on the top floor was monitored closely. They walked down the stairs at a rate of 5 floors every 2 minutes, or down $2\frac{1}{2}$ floors each minute.

This is a constant-decrease situation. The floor number decreases at a rate of $2\frac{1}{2}$ floors per minute. You can see the constant decrease by graphing the floor of the people after 0, 1, 2, 3, 4, ... minutes of walking. Below is a table of ordered pairs (time, floor) charting their progress.

Time (min)	Floor
0	50
1	$47\frac{1}{2}$
2	45
3	$42\frac{1}{2}$
4	40
5	$37\frac{1}{2}$
6	35
7	$32\frac{1}{2}$

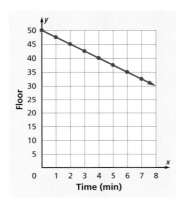

Pick any two points on this line, say (4, 40) and (6, 35). The rate of change between them is shown below.

$$\frac{\text{change in floor}}{\text{change in time}} = \frac{35\text{th floor} - 40\text{th floor}}{6\text{ min} - 4\text{ min}} = \frac{-5\text{ floors}}{2\text{ min}} = -2\frac{1}{2}\frac{\text{floors}}{\text{min}}$$

 QY

▶ **QY**

Pick two other nonconsecutive points on the line and calculate the rate of change of the floor.

Background

A constant-decrease situation. The lesson begins with a constant-decrease situation, people exiting a skyscraper during a fire drill. The rate of change between different points is constant. For this reason, the points lie on the same line.

Two methods are given here for finding the slope of a line through two points. First is the familiar formula $\frac{y_2 - y_1}{x_2 - x_1}$. The second is to examine the graph and find the rate of change from that graph.

If the algebra of slope is considered outside of applications, students often wonder why slope is defined as $\frac{y_2 - y_1}{x_2 - x_1}$ rather than $\frac{x_2 - x_1}{y_2 - y_1}$. The approach in this lesson should make this clear.

Expect that some students will prefer to count units on graphs rather than use the formula. They need to understand that there are cases in which counting spaces is impractical or inaccurate, such as in the case of noninteger coordinates. Then, the formula will be the more efficient method.

GOAL

Find the slope of a line through two given points.

SPUR Objectives

A Find the slope of the line through two given points.

D Use the definition and properties of slope.

Materials/Resources

- Lesson Masters 6-2A and 6-2B
- Resource Masters 1, 2, 4, 82, and 83

HOMEWORK

Suggestions for Assignment

- Questions 1–24
- Question 25 (extra credit)
- Reading Lesson 6-3
- Covering the Ideas 6-3

Local Standards

1 Warm-Up

The purpose of this Warm-Up is to help students understand that the subscripts in the slope formula are numbers used only as identification.

1. Find the value of $\frac{y_2 - y_1}{x_2 - x_1}$ when $x_1 = -2, x_2 = -5, y_1 = 7,$ and $y_2 = 11.$ $-\frac{4}{3}$

2. If $x_2 = 7$ and $x_3 = 6$, find the value of $2x_3x_2$ and $(x_2)^3$. 84; 343

3. If $y_1 = 5$ and $y_2 = 10$, what is the value of y_3? There is not enough information to tell.

Notes on the Lesson

There are quite a few points to make in this lesson. You might wish to split the lesson into six parts: the introductory situation, the definition of slope, and the four examples.

In the introductory situation, the rate going down the floors is given in two ways:

$-2.5 \frac{\text{floors}}{\text{minute}}$ and $-2\frac{1}{2} \frac{\text{floors}}{\text{minute}}$

Be sure that students realize that these are the same.

The definition of slope. In the previous lesson, there was no issue of which point was labeled (x_1, y_1) and which was labeled (x_2, y_2) because their assignment was naturally based on the order of occurrence. However, in this lesson, many of the problems are abstract and there is no natural order. Show your students why it is possible to interchange the points when calculating slope, first with any specific example (for example with Example 1), then in general. In general:

$\frac{y_2 - y_1}{x_2 - x_1} = \frac{-1(y_2 - y_1)}{-1(x_2 - x_1)} = \frac{-y_2 - -y_1}{-x_2 - -x_1} = \frac{y_1 - y_2}{x_1 - x_2}$,

so the points can be interchanged.

Additional Example

Example 1 Find the slope of line m below. $-\frac{3}{5}$

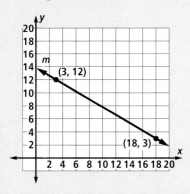

The Constant Slope of a Line

Notice that all the points on the graph on page 333 lie on the same line. In *any* situation in which there is a constant rate of change between points, the points lie on the same line. This constant rate of change is called the **slope** of the line.

> **Slope**
>
> The slope of the line through (x_1, y_1) and (x_2, y_2) is $\frac{y_2 - y_1}{x_2 - x_1}$.

In contrast, consider the graph at the right. On this graph, no three points lie on the same line, and the rate of change between each pair of the points is different. This was also the case for the graph of the population of Chicago on page 325.

slope of $a = \frac{-3}{1} = -3$ slope of $b = \frac{-1}{1} = -1$

slope of $c = \frac{2}{1} = 2$ slope of $d = \frac{0}{1} = 0$

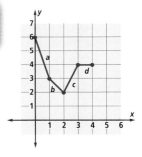

Example 1

Find the slope of line ℓ below.

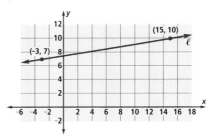

Solution 1 You can choose either point to be (x_1, y_1). The other will be (x_2, y_2). We pick $(x_1, y_1) = (-3, 7)$, and so $(x_2, y_2) = (15, 10)$. Apply the formula for slope.

$$\text{slope} = \frac{y_2 - y_1}{x_2 - x_1} = \frac{10 - 7}{15 - -3} = \frac{3}{18} = \frac{1}{6}$$

Solution 2 Instead, let $(x_1, y_1) = (15, 10)$ and $(x_2, y_2) = (-3, 7)$. Apply the formula for slope.

$$\text{slope} = \frac{y_2 - y_1}{x_2 - x_1} = \frac{7 - 10}{-3 - 15} = \frac{-3}{-18} = \frac{1}{6}$$

Check Because the line is going up to the right, the graph is expected to have a positive slope.

Vocabulary Development

It is important to link the idea of a line with positive slope to the idea of a line moving upward from left to right. It is equally important to link the idea of a line with negative slope to the idea of a line moving downward from left to right. Likewise a line with zero slope is horizontal. Reinforce these ideas at every opportunity.

Example 1 shows that when you calculate a slope, it does not matter which of the two points you consider as (x_1, y_1) and which as (x_2, y_2). The slope is the same.

Calculating Slope from a Graph

The subtractions in the slope formula allow you to find the vertical and horizontal change between any two points. This can also be done from a graph simply by counting the units of change in each direction.

Example 2

In the coordinate grid below, each square of the grid is one unit. Find the slope of the line.

a. $\overleftrightarrow{AC}$

b. $\overleftrightarrow{DF}$

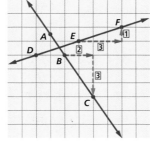

Solutions

a. Pick two points on $\overleftrightarrow{AC}$. We pick points B and C. The change in x-coordinates reading from left to right (B to C) is 2 units. The change in the y-coordinates is −3 units.

$$\text{slope of } \overleftrightarrow{AC} = \frac{-3}{2} = -\frac{3}{2}$$

b. We pick points E and F. The change in the x-coordinates reading from left to right (E to F) is 3 units. The change in the corresponding y-coordinates is 1 unit.

$$\text{slope of } \overleftrightarrow{DF} = \frac{1}{3}$$

Lines with negative slopes, such as $\overleftrightarrow{AC}$ in Example 2, go downward as they move to the right. Lines with positive slopes, such as $\overleftrightarrow{DF}$ in Example 2, go upward as they move to the right. If a line is horizontal, it is neither increasing or decreasing, and likewise the slope is zero.

If the rate of change, or slope, is the same for a set of points, then all the points lie on the same line. If the rate of change is different for different parts of a graph, then the graph is *not* a line.

The Slope of a Line   **335**

Notes on the Lesson

Example 2 shows how to calculate the slope given a graph of a line. Emphasize that the scale must be the same on the two axes in order for this method to work without knowing the coordinates. This is particularly important to emphasize when you are working with graphing utilities.

Note-Taking Tips

Students will often find the slope between two points incorrectly. For example, given points (−4, 2) and (1, 7), students will try to find the correct slope with a ratio similar to $\frac{7 - 2}{-4 - 1}$. Reinforce that given points (x_1, y_1) and (x_2, y_2), the ratio must always be $\frac{y_2 - y_1}{x_2 - x_1}$.

Additional Example

Example 2 In the coordinate grid below, each square of the grid is one unit. Find the slope of the line.

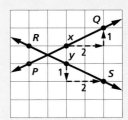

a. $\overline{PQ} = \frac{1}{2}$

b. $\overline{RS} = -\frac{1}{2}$

Using the points (−3, −5), (0, 1), and (2, 5), have the students find the slope between successive points in two ways. First let $(x_1, y_1) = (-3, -5)$ and let $(x_2, y_2) = (0, 1)$ and find the rate of change. Repeat the process with $(x_1, y_1) = (0, 1)$ and $(x_2, y_2) = (-3, -5)$. Have students do the same thing for points (0, 1) and (2, 5), as well as for points (2, 5) and (−3, −5). Ask students what they observe.

$\frac{1 - -5}{0 - -3} = \frac{6}{3} = 2$; $\frac{-5 - 1}{-3 - 0} = \frac{-6}{-3} = 2$

$\frac{5 - 1}{2 - 0} = \frac{4}{2} = 2$; $\frac{1 - 5}{0 - 2} = \frac{-4}{-2} = 2$

$\frac{-5 - 5}{-3 - 2} = \frac{-10}{-5} = 2$; $\frac{5 - -5}{2 - -3} = \frac{10}{5} = 2$

6-2

Notes on the Lesson

The statement "*If three or more points are on the same line, then the slope determined by any two of them is constant,*" allows us to define the slope of a line to be that constant. The converse of the statement (which is true) is used in Example 3: *If the slopes determined by three or more points are the same, then the points lie on the same line.*

Example 4 uses the standard form of the equation of a line. Stress that although we let $x = 0$ and $y = 0$ to find points on the line, any values for x or for y could have been chosen. Zero is picked only because calculations using zero are usually easier. Again note that the graph given by a graphing calculator will show only a geometric slope consistent with the numerical value if the scales on the axes are the same. However, changing the scales will never change a positive slope into a negative one, or vice versa.

Additional Examples

Example 3

a. Show that $(-3, -5)$, $(0, 1)$, and $(2, 5)$ lie on the same line.

b. Give the slope of that line.

Solution

a. Pick pairs of points and calculate the slope between them.

The slope between $(-3, -5)$ and $(0, 1)$ is $\frac{1 - ?}{? - (-3)} = \underline{\quad?\quad}$. $-5; 0; 2$

The slope between $(0, 1)$ and $(2, 5)$ is $\frac{5 - ?}{2 - ?} = \underline{\quad?\quad}$. $1; 0; 2$

The slope between $(2, 5)$ and $(-3, -5)$ is $\frac{? - ?}{? - ?} = \underline{\quad?\quad}$. $-5; 5; -3; 2; 2$

Since the slope between any pair of the given points is $\underline{\quad?\quad}$, the points lie on the same line. 2

b. The slope of the line is the constant rate of change, which is $\underline{\quad?\quad}$. 2

Example 4 Find the slope of the line with equation $-3x + 4y = 8$. $\frac{3}{4}$

GUIDED

Example 3

a. Show that $(-2, 5)$, $(2, 3)$, and $(-10, 9)$ lie on the same line.

b. Give the slope of that line.

Solutions

a. Pick pairs of points and calculate the slope between them.

The slope between $(-2, 5)$ and $(2, 3)$ is $\frac{? - 5}{2 - ?} = \underline{\quad?\quad}$. $3; -2; -\frac{1}{2}$

The slope between $(2, 3)$ and $(-10, 9)$ is $\frac{9 - ?}{-10 - ?} = \underline{\quad?\quad}$. $3; 2; -\frac{1}{2}$

The slope between $(-10, 9)$ and $(-2, 5)$ is $\frac{? - ?}{? - ?} = \underline{\quad?\quad}$. $\frac{9 - 5}{-10 - -2}; -\frac{1}{2}$

Because the slope between any pair of the given points is $\underline{\quad?\quad}$, the points lie on the same line. $-\frac{1}{2}$

b. The slope of the line is the constant rate of change, which is $\underline{\quad?\quad}$. $-\frac{1}{2}$

Finding the Slope of a Line from an Equation for the Line

You can find the slope of any line given its equation. Use the equation to find two points on the line and calculate the rate of change between them.

Example 4

Find the slope of the line with equation $2x - 5y = 4$.

Solution First, find two points that satisfy the equation. Pick a value for x or y and then substitute it into $2x - 5y = 4$ to find the value of the other variable. To make the calculations easier, we let $x = 0$ for the first point and $y = 0$ for the second point.

Let $x = 0$.

$2 \cdot 0 - 5y = 4$
$0 - 5y = 4$
$\frac{-5y}{-5} = \frac{4}{-5}$
$y = -\frac{4}{5}$

The point $(0, -\frac{4}{5})$ is on the line.

Let $y = 0$.

$2x - 5 \cdot 0 = 4$
$2x - 0 = 4$
$\frac{2x}{2} = \frac{4}{2}$
$x = 2$

The point $(2, 0)$ is on the line.

Use the points $(0, -\frac{4}{5})$ and $(2, 0)$ in the slope formula.

$$\text{slope} = \frac{0 - \left(-\frac{4}{5}\right)}{2 - 0} = \frac{\frac{4}{5}}{2} = \frac{4}{5} \cdot \frac{1}{2} = \frac{2}{5}$$

Accommodating the Learner ⬆

Have students find the slope of the line which contains the points $(-3, -5)$ and $(-1, -3)$. Repeat the process for the line containing the points $(4, 7)$ and $(6, -1)$ and for the line containing the points $(4, -6)$ and $(2, 2)$. What do they observe? Ask the students to plot each pair of points and draw the line passing through the points. Once students draw all three lines, ask them to make a conjecture about what they observe.

$\frac{-3 - -5}{-1 - -3} = \frac{-8}{2} = -4; \frac{-1 - 7}{6 - 4} = \frac{-8}{2} = -4;$
$\frac{2 - -6}{2} - 4 = \frac{8}{-2} = -4$

The three lines have the same slope; they are parallel.

Check Find a third point on the line $2x - 5y = 4$. For example, we let $y = 2$ and find that $x = 7$. Thus the point $(7, 2)$ is on the line, as shown on the graph at the right. Now calculate the slope determined by $(7, 2)$ and one of the points you used to find the original slope, say $(2, 0)$. This gives $\frac{2 - 0}{7 - 2}$, which equals $\frac{2}{5}$. So all three points give the same slope. It checks.

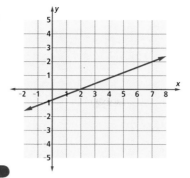

Questions

COVERING THE IDEAS

1. **Fill in the Blank** In a constant-increase or constant-decrease situation, all the points lie on the same ___?___. line

2. What is the constant rate of change between any two points on a line called? slope

3. The table at the right lists the height of a burning birthday candle in centimeters based on time in seconds. The table shows the ordered pairs (time, height), and the relationship is linear.

Time (sec)	Height (cm)
0	5.7
1	5.4
2	5.1
3	4.8
4	4.5
5	4.2

   a. Find two more ordered pairs.
   b. Find the rate of change between any two points in the table.
   c. Explain the real-world meaning of your answer to Part b. 0.3 cm of the candle burns every second.

3a. Answers vary. Sample answer: (6, 3.9) and (8, 3.3)

3b. Answers vary. Sample answer: $\frac{5.4 - 5.7}{1 - 0} = -0.3$

4. The table at the right gives coordinates of points on a line.

x	y
6	23
8	29
10	35
12	41
14	47
16 ?	53 ?

   a. If the pattern in the table is continued, what ordered pair should be entered in the next row?
   b. What is the slope of the line? 3

In 5 and 6, calculate the slope of the line through the given pair of points.

5. $(0, 4)$ and $(3, 19)$ 5

6. $(4, 3)$ and $(-6, 8)$ $-\frac{1}{2}$

7. a. Calculate the slope of the line through $(2, 1)$ and $(5, 11)$.
   b. Calculate the slope of the line through $(5, 11)$ and $(-4, -18)$.
   c. Do the points $(2, 1)$, $(5, 11)$, and $(-4, -18)$ lie on the same line? How can you tell?

7a. $\frac{10}{3}$
7b. $\frac{29}{9}$
7c. No, because the line connecting the first two points has a different slope than the line connecting the next two.

The Slope of a Line   337

Extension

Using their graphing calculator and the STAT and LIST commands, have students enter the points $(-1, -4)$ and $(2, 5)$ into L1 and L2, where L1 contains the x-values and L2 contains the y-values. Graph the points in an appropriate window using the STAT PLOT command. Ask students to determine graphically which of the following three lines contain the two given points: $y = 3x - 1$, $2y + x = 6$, and $y + 2x = 1$. Students should solve each

equation for y in terms of x and enter them into their calculator using the Y= command with the first equation equal to Y1, the second equal to Y2, and the third equal to Y3. Now have students use the GRAPH command to graph the three lines in the same graphing window as the two points to answer the question. Ask them to repeat the process for the following two sets of points: $(-1, 3)$, $(0, 1)$ and $(-2, 4)$, $(4, 1)$.

$y = 3, x = 3; y + 2x = 1$

Recommended Assignment

- Questions 1–24
- Question 25 (extra credit)
- Reading Lesson 6-3
- Covering the Ideas 6-3

Notes on the Questions

Questions 1–11 These questions should be discussed in order, as they are carefully sequenced.

Question 7 These three points are close to being on the same line. $(-4, -19)$ (not $(-4, -18)$) lies on the same line as $(2, 1)$ and $(5, 11)$.

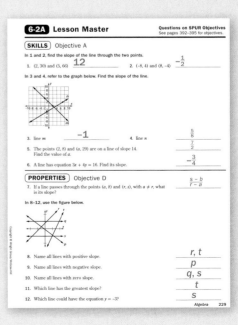

In 8 and 9, refer to the graph below. Find the slope of the line.

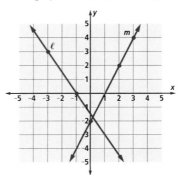

8. line ℓ $-\frac{3}{2}$

9. line m 2

In 10 and 11, an equation for a line is given.

a. Find two points on the line.
b. Find the slope of the line.
c. Check your work by graphing the line.

10. $y = -\frac{4}{3}x + 4$ 10b. $-\frac{4}{3}$

11. $6x - 5y = 30$ 11b. $\frac{6}{5}$

10a. Answers vary.
Sample answer:
(0, 4) and (3, 0)

10c.

In 12 and 13, a graph is given.

a. Find the slope of the line.
b. Describe its real-world meaning.

12.
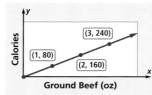

12a. 80
12b. Each ounce of
ground beef has
80 calories.

11a. Answers vary.
Sample answer:
(0, −6) and (5, 0)

13.
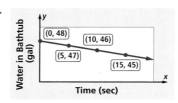

13a. $-\frac{1}{5}$
13b. Water is removed
from the bathtub
at a rate of one
gallon every five
seconds.

11c.

APPLYING THE MATHEMATICS

14. When the fire drill described on page 333 was over, the people returned to the top floor of the building, but this time via the elevator. From the 26th floor, the elevator went up 1 floor every 3 seconds. (Notice the elevator's time is given in seconds, not minutes as with the fire drill.)

   a. Make a table and graph the people's progress for the first 6 seconds of the elevator ride from the 26th floor up using ordered pairs (seconds ridden, floor number). **See margin.**

   b. Find the rate of change between any two points on the graph.

   c. How many seconds will it take for them to reach the 50th floor after leaving the 26th floor? **72 sec**

   14b. $\frac{1 \text{ floor}}{3 \text{ sec}}$

15. Suppose you graphed the data below.

Time (x)	Temperature (y)
8 A.M.	62°F
9 A.M.	63°F
10 A.M.	67°F
11 A.M.	71°F
12 P.M.	73°F

   a. What is the unit of the rate of change? **degrees per hour**

   b. Describe the real-world meaning of the rate of change.

   15b. The rate of change describes the variations in temperature over time.

16. Use the figure at the right. Which line could have the indicated slope?

   a. slope $\frac{3}{5}$ *m*

   b. slope $-\frac{3}{5}$ *l*

   c. slope 0 *n*

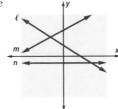

17. The points $(5, 7)$ and $(4, y)$ are on a line with slope -4. Find the value of y. $y = 11$

18. Coordinates of points are given in columns A and B in the spreadsheet at the right with a blank column for the rate of change between consecutive points.

   a. Complete the rate of change column, leaving C2 blank. **See margin.**

   b. Do the points lie on a line? Explain how you know. **Yes, because the rate of change between them is the same.**

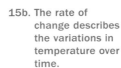

◇	A	B	C
1	x	y	rate of change
2	-4	22	
3	0	10	$\frac{10-22}{0-4} = \frac{-12}{4} = -3$
4	5	-5	
5	11	-23	

The Slope of a Line   **339**

Notes on the Questions
Question 14 Encourage students to do questions like these that have a lot of reading. Point out that it may take a little longer to read through the question slowly, but if the question is understood from the beginning, then it will take a shorter amount of time to do the question. You might also mention that the most recent college entrance tests put much more emphasis on reading longer passages.

Question 16 You might ask students if it makes a difference where the axes are located. It does not make a difference, as long as they are horizontal and vertical as in the question.

Question 19 Here slope is connected with an idea in Chapter 1. This connection can make it easy to determine an equation for the *n*th term. The constant difference is the slope.

Additional Answers

14a.

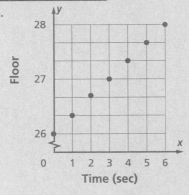

Time (sec)	Floor
0	26
3	27
6	28
9	29
12	30
15	31
18	32

Additional Answers

18a.

	A	B	C
1	x	y	rate of change
2	-4	22	
3	0	10	$\frac{10-22}{0-(-4)} = \frac{-12}{4} = -3$
4	5	-5	$\frac{-5-10}{5-0} = \frac{-15}{5} = -3$
5	11	-23	$\frac{-23-(-5)}{11-5} = \frac{-18}{6} = -3$

6-2

4 Wrap-Up

Ongoing Assessment

Write two points on the board or on the overhead. Students should find the slope of the line containing the two points. Students should then find two points such that the slope of a line passing through them is the same as the slope of the line passing through the two given points. Repeat this process several times using slopes that are negative, positive, and zero.

340   Chapter 6

---

19. In Lesson 1-4, the following sequence of toothpick designs was examined. A graph of ordered pairs (term number, number of toothpicks) is shown at the right.

   1st   2nd   3rd   4th

a. What is the rate of change of the line through these points? (Remember to include the rate unit.)   3 toothpicks per term

b. Let n be the term number and T be the number of toothpicks needed. Then $T = 1 + 3n$. Verify that the slope of the line with equation $T = 1 + 3n$ is the same as your answer to Part a.
19b–c. See margin.

c. What does the slope mean in this situation?

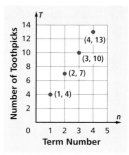

REVIEW

20. A high-rise building was built at a constant rate. The builders completed the 18th floor on the 24th day of construction, and they finished the 81st floor on the 108th day of construction. Calculate the rate of construction in terms of floors per day. (**Lesson 5-3**) $\frac{3}{4}$ floors per day

21. Solve $-5 + 8p < 3(2p - 2) + 2p$. (**Lesson 4-5**)   no solution

22. Compute in your head. (**Lesson 4-1**)
a. 16 is what percent of 64?   b. 75% of 80 is what number?
   25%   60

23. **Fill in the Blank** If $5a = \frac{1}{2}b$, then $20a = \underline{\ ?\ }$. (**Lesson 2-8**) $2b$

24. Determine whether $(x + y)(x + y)(x + y) = x^3 + y^3$ is *always*, *sometimes but not always*, or *never* true. Explain. (**Lesson 1-3**)
sometimes but not always; true for $x = y = 0$, but not true for $x = y = 1$

EXPLORATION

25. Find a record of your height at some time over a year ago. Compare it with your height now. How fast (in inches or centimeters per year) has your height been changing from then until now? Answers vary. Sample answer: 14 months ago: 68 in.; today: 68 in.; the rate of change for my height is 0.

A woman measures her daughter's height.

Additional Answers

19b. Answers vary. Sample answer: Note that $(0, 1)$ and $(1, 4)$ lie on the line and $\frac{4 - 1}{1 - 0} = 3$.

19c. It is the rate at which the number of toothpicks increases from one design to the next.

24. sometimes but not always; true for $x = y = 0$, but not true for $x = y = 1$

Lesson 6-3

Properties of Slope

▶ **BIG IDEA** The slope of a line can be determined by examining the graph; only one line through a point has a particular slope.

Most houses have slanted, or pitched roofs. The *pitch* of a roof is its slope. In the United States, the pitch is usually measured in 12ths. Why are 12ths used? Because there are 12 inches in a foot. The number of 12ths tells you the number of inches the roof rises for each foot that the roof goes across. In areas where there is a lot of snow, roofs often have higher pitches. The steepest roof a carpenter can safely walk on without the aid of ropes has a pitch of $\frac{8}{12}$.

Mental Math

Consider the data set {3, 5, 9, 1, 7, 10, 16, 25, 24, 3, 18}. Find the

a. range. 24

b. mode. 3

c. median. 9

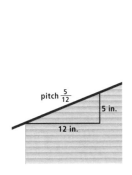
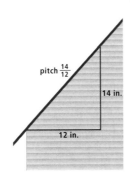

A roof with a pitch of $\frac{5}{12}$ goes up 5 inches for each 12 inches the roof goes across. But this ratio can also be expressed a different way. If the two inch measurements are converted to feet, the result is shown below.

$$\frac{5 \text{ in.}}{12 \text{ in.}} = \frac{5 \text{ in.} \cdot \frac{1 \text{ ft}}{12 \text{ in.}}}{12 \text{ in.} \cdot \frac{1 \text{ ft}}{12 \text{ in.}}} = \frac{\frac{5}{12} \text{ ft}}{1 \text{ ft}} = \frac{5 \text{ in.}}{1 \text{ ft}}$$

So a roof with a pitch of $\frac{5}{12}$ goes up 5 inches ($\frac{5}{12}$ of a foot) for every foot the roof goes across.

The situation with roofs illustrates an important property of the slope of a line. The slope of a line is the amount of change in the height of the line for every change of one unit to the right.

Properties of Slope **341**

GOAL
Apply properties of slope.

SPUR Objectives

D Use the definition and properties of slope.

E Calculate rates of change from real data and their real-world meanings.

H Graph a line given its equation, or given a point and its slope.

Materials/Resources
· Lesson Masters 6-3A and 6-3B
· Resource Masters 1, 2, 4, 84 and 85

HOMEWORK

Suggestions for Assignment
• Questions 1–26
• Questions 27–28 (extra credit)
• Reading Lesson 6-4
• Covering the Ideas 6-4

Local Standards

1 Warm-Up

Suppose a line contains the point (10, 22). Find another point on this line if the slope of the line is:

1. 6 Answers vary.
   Sample answer: (11, 28)

2. 2.3 Answers vary.
   Sample answer: (11, 24.3)

3. $-\frac{4}{9}$ Answers vary.
   Sample answer: $\left(11, 21\frac{5}{9}\right)$

4. 0 Answers vary.
   Sample answer: (11, 22)

Background

We have often asked teachers the meaning of a slope of $\frac{1}{4}$. The most common response is that it means the line goes up 1 for every 4 it goes over. If a student has this view of slope, then how is the student supposed to know the meaning of a slope of 6.372 or π? The point of this lesson is that slope is a *single number*, not a pair of numbers. For decades we have used this approach with success. There are several advantages to this interpretation.

First, by stating that slope *always* measures the change in *height*, we eliminate one of the most common errors in calculating slope, reversing the horizontal and vertical changes.

A second advantage is that it is easier to compare slopes, because it is easier to compare single numbers than quotients of numbers.

(continued on next page)

6-3

2 Teaching

Notes on the Lesson

This is a lesson that you might cover by presenting each example, assessing student understanding, and then giving comparable examples for further reinforcement.

Additional Example
Example 1

a. Graph the line that passes through (–3, –2) with slope 2.

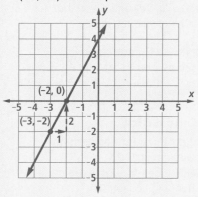

b. Name another point on the line with integer coefficients. **Answers vary.**
Sample answer: (–1, 2)

For example, if a line has slope 2, as you move one unit to the right, the line goes up 2 units. So, if the line contains the point (a, b), it will also contain the point $(a + 1, b + 2)$.

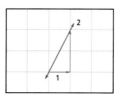

If the slope is $-\frac{2}{3}$, for every change of 1 unit to the right, the line goes down $\frac{2}{3}$ of a unit. So, if the line contains the point (a, b), it will contain the point $(a + 1, b - \frac{2}{3})$.

STOP QY1

Graphing a Line by Using Its Slope

If you know one point on a line, you can find a second point using its slope. With the two points, you can graph the line.

> **Example 1**
> a. Graph the line through (–3, 1) with slope $\frac{1}{4}$.
> b. Name another point on the line with integer coefficients.
>
> **Solutions**
>
> a. Plot (–3, 1), then move right 1 unit and up $\frac{1}{4}$ unit. Plot the resulting point $(-2, 1\frac{1}{4})$, and draw the line through the two points.
>
> b. One point with integer coordinates (–3, 1) is given. Continue plotting points by moving right 1 unit and up $\frac{1}{4}$ unit until you reach another point with integer coordinates. As shown on the graph, the point (1, 2) is also on the line.

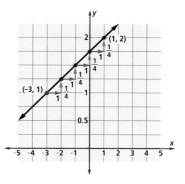

STOP QY2

▶ QY1

Find another point on the line through (20, 80) that has a slope of $\frac{3}{4}$.

▶ QY2

Find another point with integer coordinates on the line that contains (2, 6) and has a slope of $\frac{1}{2}$.

Third, it is easier to make sense of positive, negative, and zero slopes. Because we always move to the right, negative slope means to go down. Zero slope means that you don't change the height. Also, the fact that a vertical line has no slope is almost obvious. You can't measure change as you go to the right if you can't move to the right on the line.

Fourth, in the slope-intercept equation for a line, an increase of 1 in x means an increase of m in y. Thus, thinking of increasing x by 1 offers a firm interpretation of this important parameter in the slope-intercept equation. This may be the most important reason.

The idea of Examples 1 and 2 helps in drawing graphs of constant-increase or constant-decrease situations.

Example 2

A certain stacking chair is 31 inches tall. In a stack, each chair adds 4 inches to the height of the stack. Graph the relationship of the number of chairs to the height of the stack.

Solution The first point is (1, 31). Because the height increases 4 inches for each chair stacked, the slope is 4 inches per chair. The points are on a line because the situation is a constant-increase situation.

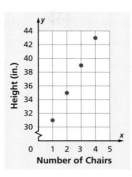

An equation for the height h of n stacking chairs is $h = 31 + 4(n - 1)$. This is an equation for the line that contains the points graphed in Example 2. Notice that the given numbers 31 and 4 both appear in this equation. In the next lesson, you will learn how the slope can be easily determined from an equation of a line.

Zero Slope and Undefined Slopes

Lines with slope 0 can be drawn using the method of the previous two examples.

Example 3

Draw a line through (2, 4) with slope 0.

Solution Plot the point (2, 4). From this point move one unit right and 0 units up. Place a point there and draw a line through the points. You should get a horizontal line.

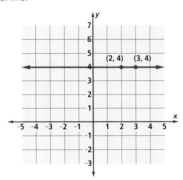

Properties of Slope **343**

Notes on the Lesson

Zero slope and undefined slopes. Some teachers use "no slope" as a synonym for "undefined slope." If you do so, make sure students understand the distinction between "0 slope" and "no slope." You may want to have students make up their own examples of each of these ideas, and show they understand the distinction. Because "no slope" in popular terminology means that ground is flat, we very much prefer using the term "slope is undefined" for vertical lines.

Additional Examples

Example 2 Each stair in a flight of stairs is 8 inches high. Thus each stair adds 8 inches to the height of the staircase. Graph the relation between the number of stairs to the height of the staircase.

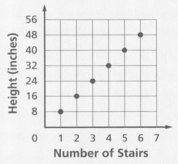

Example 3 Draw a line through (–1, 3) with slope 0.

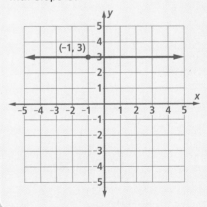

Accommodating the Learner

Ask students to explain whether a road can have more than one grade. If they believe a road can have different grades, ask them to explain their reasoning. Ask students if a road can have a zero grade. If they believe a road can have a zero grade, ask them to explain their reasoning. Ask students to think about why the grade of a road is never negative. Ask them to explain their reasoning.

Vocabulary Development

Students will invariably confuse lines with zero slope and lines with undefined slope. Associate zero slope with horizontal lines that model the horizon. Associate undefined slope with vertical lines or a path that would be nearly impossible to climb.

6-3

3 Assignment

Recommended Assignment
- Questions 1–26
- Questions 27–28 (extra credit)
- Reading Lesson 6-4
- Covering the Ideas 6-4

Notes on the Questions
Questions 1–3 Higher-pitched roofs are more common the further north one travels because snow accumulates on lower-pitched roofs and can be so heavy that the roof will collapse. You might inform students that measuring the pitch of roofs in twelfths is a U.S. practice due to changing feet to inches, and is not found in countries that are on the metric system.

There is one type of line for which the methods used in Examples 1–3 do not work. If you have points on a vertical line, you cannot move one unit to the right and stay on the line. Also, if you try to calculate the slope using the formula $\frac{y_2 - y_1}{x_2 - x_1}$, the denominator will be 0. For example, the slope of a line through (3, 4) and (3, 6) would be $\frac{6 - 4}{3 - 3} = \frac{2}{0}$, which is not defined. Thus the slope of a vertical line is *undefined*.

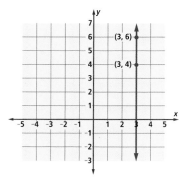

Notice the important difference between slopes of horizontal and vertical lines.

Slope of Horizontal and Vertical Lines

1. The slope of every horizontal line is 0.
2. The slope of every vertical line is undefined.

Questions

COVERING THE IDEAS

1. Suppose the pitch of a roof is $\frac{9}{12}$.
   a. Draw such a roof.
   b. Is this roof safe for a roofer to walk on without ropes? Why or why not?
   c. What is the slope of this roof? **0.75**

In 2 and 3, a roof pitch is given. If the pitch is possible, draw the roof. If it is not possible, explain why.

2. pitch $\frac{0}{12}$ **The roof is flat.**

3. pitch $\frac{12}{0}$ **Not possible because $\frac{12}{0}$ is undefined.**

4. **Fill in the Blanks** The slope of a line is the amount of change in the ___?___ of the line for every change of ___?___ to the right.
   height / **one unit**

344   Slopes and Lines

1a.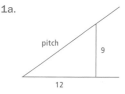

pitch   9

12

1b. No, because $\frac{9}{12} > \frac{8}{12}$, and $\frac{8}{12}$ is considered the limit for the pitch of a safe roof.

Accommodating the Learner ⬆

There are many other places where grade is important: for instance, a wheel chair ramp. Ask students why they think the grade of the ramp is important. Hopefully they will quickly see that the grade must be small. Tell them that the accepted grade is 8.3%. Ask them to figure out how long a wheel chair ramp must be if it must rise 3 feet. Students should show their work and justify that they are correct. Students should round their answer to the nearest hundredth of a foot.

$\frac{3}{x} = 0.083; x = 36.14$ ft

In 5 and 6, find the slope of the line.

5. 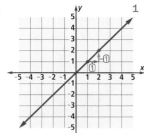 1

6. 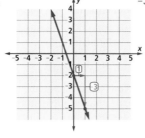 −3

In 7 and 8, a line's slope and a point on it are given.

a. Graph the line.

b. Find one other point on this line.

c. Check that your second point is on the line using the slope formula.

7. point $(2, 2)$, slope 4

8. point $(4, -2)$, slope $-\frac{2}{3}$

In 9 and 10, find another point on the line with the given slope and containing the given point.

9. point $(-3, 4)$, slope -3

10. point $(4, 1)$, slope 0

11. Explain why the slope of a vertical line is not defined, by referring to a specific example that is not in this lesson.

12. Graph the line through $(-1, 4)$ with an undefined slope.
    See margin.

13. A small plastic bathroom drinking cup is about 5.70 cm tall. These cups stack tightly and each cup adds only about 0.28 cm to the stack. Graph the relationship between the number of cups and the height of the stack. See margin.

APPLYING THE MATHEMATICS

In 14–16, the slope of a line is given as are some coordinates of points on the line. Complete the remaining entries in the table.

14. slope $\frac{1}{5}$

x	y
4	8
5	? 8.2
6	? 8.4
7	? 8.6

15. slope -4

x	y
2	0
3	? −4
4	? −8
5	? −12

16. Slope is undefined.

x	y
−3	4
−2	?
−1	?
0	?

Properties of Slope **345**

7a, 8a. See margin.

7b. Answers vary.
    Sample answer:
    (3,6)

7c. $\frac{6 - 2}{3 - 2} = \frac{4}{1} = 4$

8b. Answers vary.
    Sample answer:
    (1, 0)

8c. $\frac{0 - -2}{1 - 4} = \frac{2}{-3} = -\frac{2}{3}$

9. Answers vary.
   Sample answer:
   (0, −5)

10. Answers vary.
    Sample answer:
    $(\pi, 1)$

11. Answers vary.
    Sample answer: A vertical line is one that passes through points with the same x-coordinate, such as (1, 4) and (1, 2). If we calculate the slope of the line using the formula $\frac{y_2 - y_1}{x_2 - x_1}$, the denominator is $1 - 1 = 0$. Division by zero is undefined.

16. There are no y values corresponding to any x values, other than (−3, 4). The table cannot be completed to show the slope is undefined.

Notes on the Questions
Question 13 Students should see the similarity between this question and Example 2. The numbers in both situations were taken from actual data. You might ask students if they have similar examples and can invent a question like this with their own real data.

Additional Answers

8a.
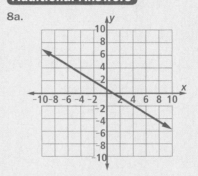

12.
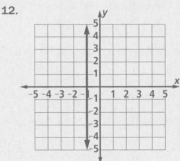

13.
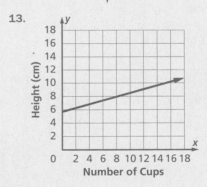

Extension

The grade of a highway is a measure of a road's steepness (slope) along its path. The grade of a road is usually expressed as a percent. For example, a road grade of 4% means that for every run of 25 feet the road rises 1 foot. To calculate the road grade simply divide the rise by the run and change the result to a decimal. (For example: $1 \div 25 = 0.04$, which equals 4%.) Ask students to find the road grade as a percent for a road rising 3 feet for every 50 feet of run. How long does a road have to be for a car to climb 240 feet?
$\frac{3}{50} = \frac{6}{100} = 6\%; \frac{3}{50} = \frac{240}{x}; x = 4{,}000$ ft

Additional Answers

7a.
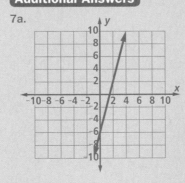

6-3

Notes on the Questions

Question 17 With roads and ramps, slopes are often given as percents. When this is done, it is probably easiest to think of the percent as indicating how much the road or ramp rises or falls in 100 feet, as is done here.

Question 18 Baldwin Street is often called the steepest street in the world.

Additional Answers

19.

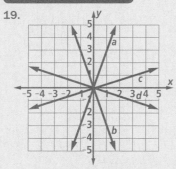

20. When the diving officer begins to zero the dive out he is trying to make the slope of the submarine equal to zero, so the sub is no longer going down but is horizontal.

22b.

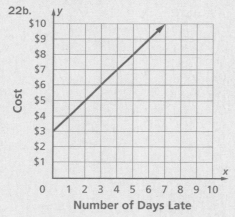

In **17** and **18**, the question relates to the slope of a road. In the United States, the slope of a road is often called its *grade*. The grade is often given in percent. In the British Commonwealth, the word for slope is *gradient*.

17. The grade of Canton Avenue in Pittsburgh, Pennsylvania between Coast and Hampshire Streets is 37%. How much does that street rise for every 100 feet horizontally? **37 ft**

18. Baldwin Street in Dunedin, New Zealand has a maximum gradient of 1 in 2.86. This means that for every horizontal change of 2.86 units, the road goes 1 unit up. What is the slope of Baldwin Street? (*Caution:* The slope is not 2.86.) $\frac{50}{143}$

19. On a piece of graph paper, plot the point (0, 0). Draw the lines through (0, 0) with the following slopes on the same coordinate grid. **See margin for graph.**

    line *a*: slope 3   line *b*: slope –3
    line *c*: slope $\frac{1}{3}$ line *d*: slope $-\frac{1}{3}$

    a. Which line(s) are slanted upward as you read from left to right? **Lines *a* and *c***
    b. Which line(s) are slanted downward as you read from left to right? **Lines *b* and *d***
    c. Can you relate the slant of the line to the sign of the slope?
    d. Which line(s) are steepest? **lines *a* and *b***
    e. Give the value of a slope that is steeper than the slope of any of the four lines on the graph. **Answers vary. Sample answer: 4**

20. In Tom Clancy's best selling fiction novel, *The Hunt for Red October,* the American attack submarine *Dallas* is chasing the renegade Russian submarine *Red October*. The captain of the *Dallas* gave orders to descend to 1,200 feet below sea level. Engineer Butler "watched the depth gauge go below 600 feet. The diving officer would wait until they got to 900 feet before starting to level off, the object being to *zero the dive* out at exactly 1,200 feet". Explain, in terms of slope, what is meant by the italicized phrase. **See margin.**

REVIEW

21. Find the slope of the line with equation $12x - 8y = 4$. (**Lesson 6-2**) **1.5**
22. The cost to rent a movie from Marcus's Movies is $2.99 for two nights with a late fee of $0.99 per day late. After *x* days late, the total cost will be *y* dollars. (**Lessons 6-2, 3-1, 1-2**)
    a. Write an equation relating *x* and *y*. **y = 0.99x + 2.99**
    b. Graph the line. **See margin.**
    c. Find the rate of change between any two points on the graph. **$0.99/day**

A house sits on the steepest residential street in the world in Dunedin, New Zealand.

19c. The lines with positive slope are slanted up to the right; the lines with negative slope are slanted down to the right.

Operators of a submarine control its buoyancy, allowing it to sink and surface at will.

Source: science.howstuffworks.com

In 23 and 24, use the table and graph below. They show the unemployment rate, the percent of the United States labor force that was unemployed, for men and women. (Lesson 6-1)

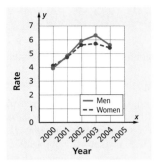

Unemployment Rate		
Year	Men	Women
2000	3.9	4.1
2001	4.8	4.7
2002	5.9	5.6
2003	6.3	5.7
2004	5.6	5.4

Source: Statistical Abstract of the United States

23. Between which two years was there the greatest increase in unemployment rate for
   a. men? **2001 and 2002**   b. women? **2001 and 2002**

24. What was the rate of change from 2001 to 2003 for
   a. men? **0.75% per yr increase** b. women? **0.5% per yr increase**

25. Find b if $y = mx + b$, $y = -10$, $m = \frac{3}{4}$, and $x = 5$.
   (Lessons 4-7, 1-1) $b = -13.75$

26. If the quadrilateral at the right has perimeter 70, what is n?
   (Lessons 3-4, 2-2) $n = 8$

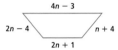

EXPLORATION

27. Canton Avenue and Baldwin Street, the roads in Questions 17 and 18, are among the steepest streets in the world. Search the Internet to find the grades of two other steep streets. Then make an accurate drawing indicating steepness of these roads.
See margin.

28. Sam Saw wants to build a shed with a $\frac{5}{12}$ roof and the base of the roof being 12 feet long. To support the roof he needs to place a vertical support every 16 inches along the base. One way to do this is to climb the ladder, measure the length needed, go down the ladder and cut the board, then go back up the ladder to nail the board in place. Use your knowledge of slope to calculate the length of all the vertical supports so Sam does not need to go up and down the ladder constantly. **6.67", 13.33", 20", 26.67", 33.33", 40", 46.67", 53.33", 60"**

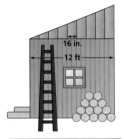

QY ANSWERS

1. Answers vary.
Sample answer: $(21, 80\frac{3}{4})$

2. Answers vary.
Sample answer: (4, 7)

Properties of Slope   **347**

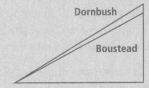
6-3

4 Wrap-Up

Ongoing Assessment

Call upon a student to describe a line with zero slope. Ask the student to give a realistic example of something that has zero slope. Call upon a second student to describe a line that has undefined slope. Ask the student to give a concrete example of something that has undefined slope.

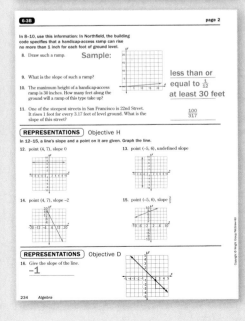

Lesson 6-4

Lesson 6-4

Slope-Intercept Equations for Lines

GOAL

Write an equation for a line in slope-intercept form.

SPUR Objectives

B Find an equation for a line given either its slope and any point or two points on it.

C Write an equation for a line in standard form or slope-intercept form, and using either form, find its slope and y-intercept.

F Use equations for lines to describe real situations.

H Graph a line given its equation, or given a point and its slope.

Materials/Resources

· Lesson Masters 6-4A and 6-4B
· Resource Masters 1, 2, and 86–88
· Dynamic graphing software

HOMEWORK

Suggestions for Assignment

• Questions 1–24
• Question 25 (extra credit)
• Reading Lesson 6-5
• Covering the Ideas 6-5

Local Standards

▶ **BIG IDEA**   The line that contains the point $(0, b)$ and slope m has equation $y = mx + b$.

You have already worked with equations whose graphs are lines. In the following activity, you will use *dynamic graphing software* to experiment with equations. As you change the equation, watch how its graph changes in response. In many software applications, *sliders* allow you to change values in an equation. A slider consists of a portion of a number line that is used to control numeric values for a specific variable. As you drag a point along a slider, the value of a corresponding variable changes automatically.

Mental Math

Express as a mixed number.

a. 175 cm in meters

b. 35 ounces in cups

c. 5 feet, 7 inches in feet

a. $1\frac{3}{4}$ m

b. $4\frac{3}{8}$ c

c. $5\frac{7}{12}$ ft

Activity

Step 1   Create a slider for the variable m. Set the software so that m can vary in the interval $-5 \le m \le 5$. Move the slider so that $m = 2$.

Step 2   Enter the equation $y = mx$. Since $m = 2$, you have created the graph of $y = 2x$.

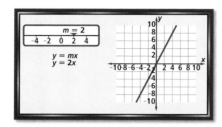

Step 3   Slowly move the slider to increase the value of m. What happens to the graph as m increases?   The line becomes steeper.

Step 4   Now move the slider so $m = 0$. What is the graph like when $m = 0$? Write an equation for this line.   The line is the horizontal line $y = 0$.

Step 5   Move the m slider to the left of zero (into the negatives). What happens to the graph when m is negative?   The line slopes down from left to right. What happens to the graph as m moves more and more to the left ("farther" into the negative values)?   It becomes steeper.

---

1 Warm-Up

A line has equation $y = 9 - 5x$.

1. What is its slope? –5

2. Where does the line cross the y-axis? 9

3. Where does the line cross the x-axis? 1.8

4. What is an equation of the line whose graph is parallel to and 1 unit above this line? $y = 10 - 5x$

Background

Activity. The goal of this activity is to use a slider to provide hands-on examples of what happens to the slope of a line whose equation is of the form $y = mx + b$ when parameter m or b is changed and the other is kept constant. As m increases, the line rotates counterclockwise until it becomes closer to the y-axis. As b increases, the line moves up the y-axis.

The two most common forms for equations of lines. Equations for lines are generally found in either of two common forms: the

slope-intercept form $y = mx + b$ or the standard form $Ax + By = C$. The slope-intercept form allows students to quickly graph equations knowing the y-intercept and then finding another point using the slope. The standard form allows students to quickly graph by finding x- and y-intercepts.

Other forms for equations of lines. Two other forms of equations for lines are the point-slope form, $y - y_1 = m(x - x_1)$, and the intercept form $\frac{x}{a} + \frac{y}{b} = 1$.

(continued on next page)

What appears to be true about the line when m is

   a. positive? The line slopes up to the right.

   b. negative? The line slopes down to the right.

   c. zero (which is neither positive nor negative)? The line is a horizontal line.

Step 6 Move the slider so that $m = 2$. Enter the equation $y = mx + b$ and create a second slider for the variable b, using the interval $-5 \leq m \leq 5$. Move this slider so $b = 1$. Also, graph the point $(0, b)$.

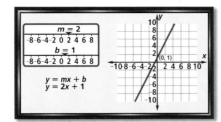

Step 7 Slowly move the b slider to the right (toward greater values of b).

   What happens to the graph as b increases? The line shifts up to the right.

Step 8 Now move the b slider so $b = 0$. Describe the graph when $b = 0$ and write the equation for this line. The line is shifted so that it passes through the origin. $y = 2x$

Step 9 Slide the b slider to the left of zero (into the negatives). What happens to the graph when b is negative? What happens to the graph as b moves farther to the left? What appears to be true about the line when b is

   a. positive? The line is shifted up above the origin.

   b. negative? The line is shifted down below the origin.

   c. zero (which is neither positive nor negative)?

Step 9. The line is below the origin. It crosses the y-axis farther down. The more negative b is, the lower it crosses the y-axis.

Step 9c. The line passes through the origin.

Step 10 Refer to the graphs below. Move both sliders until you have a graph that resembles the line pictured. Give the values of m and b. Write the equation for the line that is shown by using your slider values.

Step 10a–d. Answers vary. Sample answers are given.

a.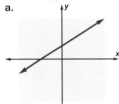

b.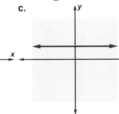

c.

d.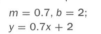

$m = 0.7, b = 2$; $m = -1, b = -1$; $m = 0, b = 2$; $m = -5, b = 0$;
$y = 0.7x + 2$ $y = -1x - 1$ $y = 2$ $y = -5x$

Slope-Intercept Equations for Lines   **349**

In this text, we call the *value* of b in the equation $y = mx + b$ the y-intercept. Some people call the *point* $(0, b)$, where the line crosses the y-axis, the y-intercept. Our definition is more common.

2 **Teaching**

Notes on the Lesson

Activity. If you do not have the appropriate software, you should modify the activity by having students choose several values for both m and b and draw the lines with those equations with graphing calculators or by hand. If possible, demonstrate the changes to the class with a view screen.

In QY1 and QY2, some people speak of *reading* the slope and y-intercept from the equation, because they can be found without any computation.

Notes on the Activity

It may help some students to write down their ideas about what they see as they increase the value of m in Steps 1–5. Likewise, it may help students to write down their ideas about what they see as they decrease the value of m in Steps 1–5. Once they have experimented with changing the values of m, students should summarize what they believe happens when the value of m is changed. Repeat this process when students experiment in Steps 6–9.

6-4

In the Activity, you should have seen that the graph of a line whose equation is of the form $y = mx + b$ is determined by the values of m and b. In Steps 1–5, as you changed the value of m, the slope of the line changed.

When $m = 2$ and you varied the value of b in Steps 6–10, the line shifted and the point at which it crossed the y-axis changed. That number is the *y-intercept* of the line. In general, when a graph intersects the y-axis at the point $(0, b)$, the number b is a **y-intercept** for the graph. Each line at the right has slope $\frac{1}{2}$, but the y-intercepts are different.

$b = -6$

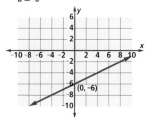

So the equation $y = mx + b$ shows the slope of the line and its y-intercept. For this reason, $y = mx + b$ is called the **slope-intercept form** for an equation for a line.

$b = -2$

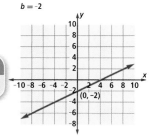

> ### Slope-Intercept Equation of a Line
>
> The line with equation $y = mx + b$ has slope m and y-intercept b.

STOP QY1

Using the Slope-Intercept Form of the Equation of a Line

Slopes and y-intercepts can be seen in equations of real-world situations. Suppose Jody is going on a vacation to Istanbul. The airfare is $940 and she expects to spend $300 per day for hotel and expenses. Then after x days, the total cost y of her trip is given by $y = 940 + 300x$. With the Commutative Property of Addition, $y = 940 + 300x$ becomes $y = 300x + 940$, which fits the slope-intercept form $y = mx + b$.

$b = 8$

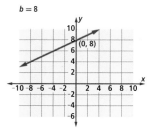

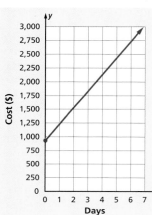

Notice how the two key numbers in Jody's expenses appear in the equation. Her starting cost of $940 is the y-intercept. Her $300 cost per day is the slope.

> ▶ **QY1**
>
> a. Find the slope and y-intercept of $y = \frac{1}{4}x + 11$.
> b. Write an equation in slope-intercept form for the line with slope 3 and y-intercept of −7.

Extension

Do the perimeters of similar rectangles form a direct variation? Ask students to explore this possibility. For instance, consider a rectangle with length ℓ of 4 centimeters and width w of 2 centimeters. Its perimeter p is given by the equation $p = 2\ell + 2w = 2(4) + 2(2) = 12$ centimeters. Now consider a rectangle similar to the first one. For example, consider a rectangle whose length is 12 centimeters and whose width is 6 centimeters. Show that that the perimeters of the two rectangles vary directly, that is $P_1 = kP_2$. Find the constant of variation k. Do the lengths and widths vary directly? Students should explain their reasoning.

The same line can have many equations. For example, $3x + y = 7$, $30x + 10y = 70$, and $y = -3x + 7$ are all equations for the same line.

 QY2

Slope-intercept equations allow us to get information about a line quickly. For this reason, it is often helpful to convert other equations for lines into slope-intercept form.

> ▶ **QY2**
>
> Give the slope and y-intercept of $y = -2 - 6x$.

Example 1

Write the equation $3x + 7y = 9$ in slope-intercept form. Give the slope and y-intercept of the graph.

Solution Solve $3x + 7y = 9$ for y.

$$3x + 7y = 9$$
$$7y = -3x + 9$$
$$\frac{7y}{7} = \frac{-3x + 9}{7}$$
$$y = -\frac{3}{7}x + \frac{9}{7}$$

The slope is $-\frac{3}{7}$. The y-intercept is $\frac{9}{7}$ or $1\frac{2}{7}$.

Recall that every vertical line has an equation of the form $x = h$, where h is a fixed number. Equations of this form clearly cannot be solved for y. Thus, equations of vertical lines cannot be written in slope-intercept form (and they cannot be graphed on many graphing calculators). This confirms that the slope of vertical lines cannot be defined.

Writing an Equation for a Line from Its Graph

The graph of a line gives information that can be used to write its equation.

Example 2

Find the equation of the line graphed at the right.

Solution The graph crosses the y-axis at −25, so −25 is the y-intercept. The line contains (0, −25) and (10, −10). Its slope is found below.

$$m = \frac{-25 - -10}{0 - 10} = \frac{-15}{-10} = 1.5$$

The slope-intercept equation of the line is $y = 1.5x - 25$.

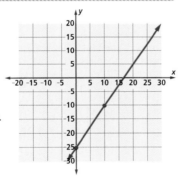

(continued on next page)

Slope-Intercept Equations for Lines **351**

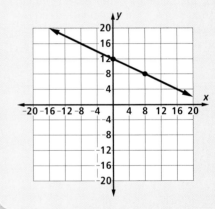

6-4

Additional Example

Example 3 A mountain climber begins the second day of a climb at an elevation of 2,100 feet and climbs at a rate of 170 feet per hour.

a. Find a slope-intercept equation for her height h after t hours.
$h = 170t + 2,100$

b. How high is the climber after 8 hours? 3,460 feet

Note-Taking Tips

Besides the definition of direct variation, the students should place several examples of equations that model a direct variation in their notebook. Included with these examples should be examples of equations that are not direct variations. Next to each example that is not a direct variation, students should write a brief explanation as to why the equation is not a direct variation. Students might also include examples of real-world applications of a direct variation such as $d = r \cdot t$.

Check Do the coordinates of the two known points $(0, -25)$ and $(10, -10)$ satisfy the equation?

Does $-25 = 1.5(0) - 25$?   Does $-10 = 1.5(10) - 25$?
$-25 = 0 - 25$ $-10 = 15 - 25$
Yes, both points check.

Every constant-increase or constant-decrease situation can be described by an equation whose graph is a line. The y-intercept of that line can be interpreted as the starting amount. The slope of that line is the amount of increase or decrease per unit.

Example 3

Assume that a skydiver opens a parachute and falls at a speed of 10 feet per second from 5,000 feet above the ground.

a. Find a slope-intercept equation for the height h of the skydiver after x seconds.

b. How high is the skydiver after 5 minutes (300 seconds)?

Solutions

a. The skydiver falls at 10 feet per second, so the slope is -10. The y-intercept is the starting height, 5,000 feet.
$y = 5,000 - 10x$ Write the equation.
$y = -10x + 5,000$ Rewrite in slope-intercept form.

b. Use the equation and substitute 300 for x because 5 minutes equals 300 seconds.
$y = 5,000 - 10(300)$
$y = 2,000$
After 5 minutes, the height of the skydiver is 2,000 feet.

Direct Variation

A special case of a linear equation occurs when the y-intercept is at the origin. Then the y-intercept is 0 and $y = mx + 0$ becomes $y = mx$. This means that y is a constant multiple of x, as shown below.

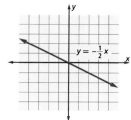

x	y
-4	2
0	0
1	$-\frac{1}{2}$
10	-5

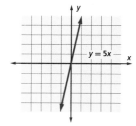

x	y
-2	-10
0	0
3	15
7	35

Accommodating the Learner ⬆

The circumference of a circle C varies directly with the circle's diameter d. The equation is modeled by the direct variation $C = kd$ where k is the constant of variation. The table below gives the circumference C and diameter d of several circles. Ask students if they can find the constant of variation. Ask them to identify by name the number which represents the constant of variation. Students should write the equation that relates C and d.
$C = 3.14d = \pi d$

	C	d	k
Circle 1	3.454	1.1	3.14
Circle 2	6.4056	2.04	3.14
Circle 3	1.57	0.5	3.14

When y is a constant multiple of x, it is said that y varies directly as x. This situation is called **direct variation.** The amount you multiply each x by to get y is the slope, also called the *constant of variation.* Direct variation equations arise in large numbers of real-world situations. For example, the distance driven at a constant speed varies directly as the time driven. The circumference of a circle varies directly as the circle's radius.

STOP QY3

Questions

COVERING THE IDEAS

1. **Fill in the Blanks** The set of ordered pairs (x, y) that satisfy $y = mx + b$ is a line with slope __?__ and y-intercept __?__. **m; b**

2. A family is taking a car trip. They expect to pay \$150 for someone to look after their pet dog while they are gone. Then they think it will cost \$200 per day for a room and meals and \$80 per day for other expenses. **2a. y = 280x + 150**
   a. What is the expected cost y for x days of the trip?
   b. If the equation in Part a is graphed, what are the slope and y-intercept of the graph? **m = 280; b = 150**

In 3 and 4, an equation of a line in slope-intercept form is given.
a. Determine the slope.
b. Determine the y-intercept.
c. Graph the line. **3c, 4c. See margin.**

3. $y = 2x + 3$ **3a. 2; 3b. 3**   4. $y = \frac{1}{4}x - 2$ **4a. $\frac{1}{4}$; 4b. -2**

In 5 and 6, an equation of a line is given.
a. Rewrite the equation in slope-intercept form.
b. Determine the slope of the line. **5a. y = -1.3x + 5.6; 5b. -1.3**
c. Determine the y-intercept of the line.

5. $y = 5.6 - 1.3x$ **5c. 5.6**   6. $x + 5y = 7$ **6c. $\frac{7}{5}$**

7. A hot air balloon begins 3 feet above the ground. It then climbs at a constant rate of 2 feet per second. **7a. h = 2t + 3**
   a. Determine an equation for the height h of the balloon at time t.
   b. Draw a graph of the equation in Part a. **See margin.**
   c. What are the slope and y-intercept of the graph in Part b?
   d. How high is the balloon after 60 seconds? **123 ft**

8. a. Find the equation in slope-intercept form using the data in the table at the right. **y = 4.5x + 2**
   b. Is this an example of direct variation? Explain. **no, $b \neq 0$**

▶ QY3

Determine which equation is an example of direct variation and give its constant of variation.

a. $y = -4x + 1$

b. $y = \frac{3}{4}x$

c. $y = 8$

Hot air balloons were invented in France in 1783.

Source: www.hotairballoons.com

6a. $y = -\frac{1}{5}x + \frac{7}{5}$;
6b. $-\frac{1}{5}$
7c. $m = 2; b = 3$

x	y
1	6.5
2	11
3	15.5
4	20
5	24.5

Slope-Intercept Equations for Lines   **353**

3 Assignment

Recommended Assignment
- Questions 1–24
- Question 25 (extra credit)
- Reading Lesson 6-5
- Covering the Ideas 6-5

Notes on the Questions
Question 7 Notice how easy it is to determine an equation in slope-intercept form from the given information. You might contrast this balloon situation with the cup or chair situations from Lesson 6-3. Here the domain of the independent variable is the set of nonnegative real numbers. The domain in the other situations was the set of nonnegative integers.

7b.
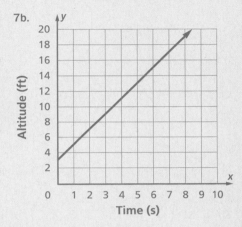
Time (s)

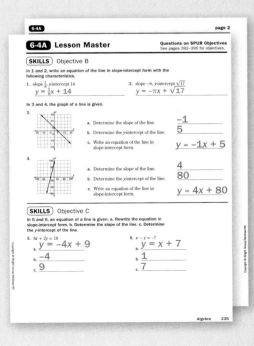

Additional Answers

3c.
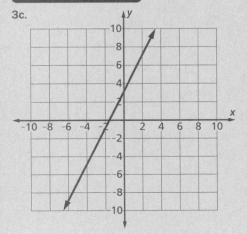

4c.
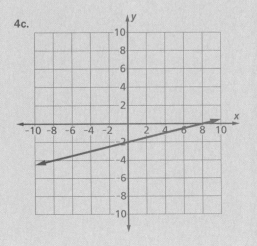

Notes on the Questions

Question 22 You might compare solving this equation by first multiplying both sides by 3 with solving by first separating the fraction on the left side of the equation into two parts.

Question 25 In general, if a line ℓ has nonzero slope m, then any line perpendicular to ℓ has slope $-\frac{1}{m}$.

Additional Answers

12. $m = \frac{1}{2}$; $b = 2$; Answers vary. Sample answer: In the graph, the line intersects the y-axis at (0, 2) and slopes up to the right. In the table, 2 is the y-intercept and, for every unit change in x, y changes 0.5 unit.

In 9 and 10, write an equation of a line in slope-intercept form with the following characteristics. 9. $y = 4x + 3$ 10. $y = 0x - 2$

9. slope 4, y-intercept 3

10. slope 0, y-intercept –2

11. Write the equation of the line graphed at the right in slope-intercept form. $y = 2x - 5$

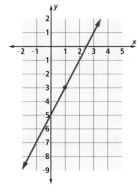

APPLYING THE MATHEMATICS

12. The equation $y = \frac{1}{2}x + 2$ was used to make the following table and graph. Find the slope and y-intercept. Explain how they are seen in the table and in the graph. **See margin.**

 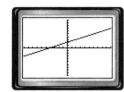

In 13–15, match the equation and graph with the situation.

Situation

13. Spencer has $80 in the bank and is spending $6 per week. **c; i**

14. Owen borrowed $80 from his uncle and is paying him back $6 per week. **a; iii**

15. Savina has $80 in the bank and is adding $6 per week to the account. **b; ii**

Equation

a. $y = 6x - 80$

b. $y = 6x + 80$

c. $y = -6x + 80$

Graph

i.
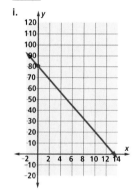

ii.
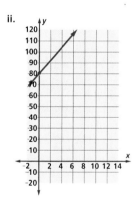

iii.
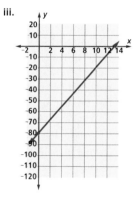

16. Consider the line through the points (3, 4) and (3, 7).
    a. Why does this line *not* have an equation in $y = mx + b$ form?
    b. What is an equation for this line? $x = 3$

16a. Its slope is undefined.

17. a. Graph the equation $y = 3x + 4$ on a piece of graph paper.
    b. Draw a line through (2, 2) that is parallel to $y = 3x + 4$.
    c. Write an equation of the parallel line in slope-intercept form.
    d. How are the two equations the same?

17a–b. See margin.

17c. $y = 3x - 4$

17d. They have the same slope.

18. A line has the equation $y = -3x + b$. For what value of b does the line pass through exactly 2 quadrants? (The axes are not considered to be in any quadrant.) 0

20. never true; Vertical lines have an undefined slope.

REVIEW

19. The Mount Washington Cog Railway in New Hampshire is one of the steepest mountain-climbing trains in the world with a gradient of 1 in 2.7. Find the slope of the path made as the train goes up the incline. (**Lesson 6-3**) $\frac{10}{27} \approx 0.37$

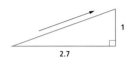

20. Determine if the following statement is *always, sometimes but not always,* or *never true* and explain your reasoning. *Vertical lines have a slope of zero.* (**Lesson 6-3**)

In 21 and 22, solve the equation. (**Lesson 5-9**)

21. $\frac{6x - 4}{3 + 2x} = \frac{5}{6}$ $x = \frac{3}{2}$

22. $\frac{w + 3}{3} = 3w - 1$

23. The sum of two consecutive integers is 8 less than three times the difference of the two numbers. Find the two numbers. (**Lesson 4-4**) -3 and -2

24. What is the area of the rectangle formed by the lines $y = 6$, $y = 2$, $x = -3$, and $x = 4$? (**Lesson 4-2**) 28 units^2

EXPLORATION

25. A line t has slope 4 and y-intercept 3.
    a. What is an equation for line t? $y = 4x + 3$
    b. By experimenting with a graphing calculator, find an equation for the line that has y-intercept 3 and seems to be perpendicular to line t. $y = -\frac{1}{4}x + 3$

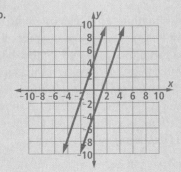

The Mount Washington Cog Railway is the world's first mountain-climbing cog railway.

Source: Mount Washington Cog Railway

22. $w = \frac{3}{4}$

QY ANSWERS

1a. slope $= \frac{1}{4}$, y-intercept $= 11$

b. $y = 3x - 7$

2. slope $= -6$, y-intercept $= -2$

3. b.; $\frac{3}{4}$

Wrap-Up

Ongoing Assessment

Form groups of three students. Each student should write the equation of a line in any form on a piece of paper and then pass the paper counterclockwise. Have the next student rewrite the equation in slope-intercept form if it is not in slope-intercept form. Pass the papers again counterclockwise and have the next students write down the slope and y-intercept of the line. Pass the papers back to the original owner and have him or her check the work.

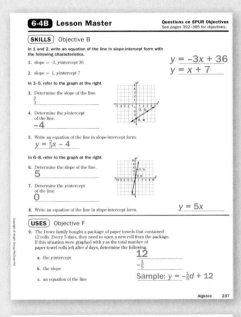

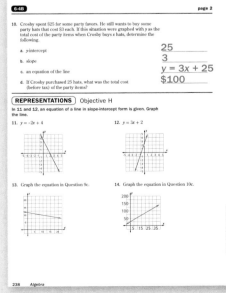

Additional Answers

17a.

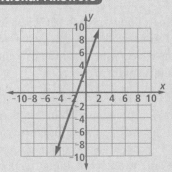

17b.

Lesson
6-5

Equations for Lines with a Given Point and Slope

GOAL

Find the equation of a line given its slope and a point on it.

SPUR Objectives

B Find an equation for a line given either its slope and any point or two points on it.

F Use equations to describe real situations.

Materials/Resources

· Lesson Masters 6-5A and 6-5B
· Resource Masters 1, 2, and 89

HOMEWORK

Suggestions for Assignment
• Questions 1–24
• Question 25 (extra credit)
• Reading Lesson 6-6
• Covering the Ideas 6-6

Local Standards

1 Warm-Up

1. Give equations for four different lines containing the point (7, 11).
   Answers vary. Sample answer:
   $11x - 7y = 0$; $y = 2x - 3$; $y = 5x - 24$;
   $y = -x + 18$.

2. For each line in Question 1, find the slope. $\frac{11}{7}$; 2; 5; –1

▶ **BIG IDEA** An equation for the line through any given point with any given slope can be determined with the slope-intercept form for the equation.

In Lesson 6-4, you saw that it is easy to find an equation of a line if you know its slope m and y-intercept b. This means that if you know the line's slope and the point $(0, b)$ where the line intersects the y-axis, then you can write an equation for the line. But what if you know the slope and some other point on the line, not necessarily the y-intercept? This is often the situation, as shown in Example 1.

Mental Math

Evaluate.
a. $3 \cdot 2\frac{2}{7}$ $6\frac{6}{7}$
b. $\frac{15}{6} \cdot \frac{4}{5}$ 2
c. $-1\frac{2}{3} \cdot 5$ $-8\frac{1}{3}$

Example 1

In 2006, the population of Alaska was 664,000. It was increasing by 7,800 people each year. Assuming this rate of increase remains steady, find an equation relating the population of Alaska y to the year x.

Solution 1 This is a constant-increase situation, so it can be described by a line with equation in the form $y = mx + b$. The rate 7,800 people/year is the slope, so $m = 7,800$. The population of 664,000 in 2006 is described by the point (2006, 664,000). You now have the slope and one point $(x, y) = (2006, 664,000)$. Follow these three steps.

Step 1 Substitute for $m, x,$ and y. $664,000 = 7,800 \cdot 2006 + b$

Step 2 Solve for b. $664,000 = 15,646,800 + b$

$-14,982,800 = b$

Step 3 Substitute the values for m and b in $y = mx + b$.

$y = 7,800x - 14,982,800$

Check After 3 years, the population should have increased by $7,800 + 7,800 + 7,800 = 23,400$ people to be 687,400.

When $x = 2009$, does $y = 687,400$?

Does $7,800 \cdot 2009 - 14,982,800 = 687,400$?

Yes, so it checks.

The solution to Example 1 begins with the slope-intercept form $y = mx + b$. Another method begins with the definition of slope.

Alaska's commercial fishing industry is the number one private sector employer in Alaska, providing more jobs than oil, gas, timber, and tourism.

Source: Alaska Department of Fish and Game

Background

Slowly the situations are becoming more general. In Lesson 6-4, an equation for a line was found given the slope and y-intercept. That is equivalent to being given the slope and the particular point $(0, b)$. In this lesson, the procedure is generalized and an equation is found for the line with a given slope and containing any given point.

Notice that we ask here for "an equation" for a line rather than "the equation" for a line. This is because every line has many equations. Distinguish between getting *an*

equation for a line (which is sufficient in many situations) and the extra step or steps that are often necessary to find *the* equation in slope-intercept form.

If you feel that your students are comfortable with distinguishing between variables, constants, and parameters, you may wish to prove that an equation for the line with slope m and containing the point (x_1, y_1) is $y - y_1 = m(x - x_1)$. Here is a proof.

(continued on next page)

Solution 2 This is a constant-increase situation. The amount of increase in a unit time, $7{,}800 \frac{people}{year}$, is the slope, so $m = 7{,}800$. The given information means that the point $(2006, 664{,}000)$ is on the line. Now picture the graph of the line, as shown at the right. If (x, y) is any point on the line, then

$$\frac{y - 664{,}000}{x - 2006} = 7{,}800.$$

Multiplying both sides by $x - 2006$, we obtain

$$y - 664{,}000 = 7{,}800(x - 2006).$$

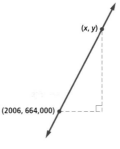

The equation found for the line using the method of the second solution has the advantage of showing all the given information. It displays the slope and the given point on the line. The general form is called the **point-slope form** of an equation of a line.

> ### Point-Slope Equation of a Line
>
> The line through the point (h, k) with slope m has equation
> $y - k = m(x - h)$.

Either the slope-intercept method or the point-slope method of solving a problem like Example 1 enables you to find an equation for any nonvertical line if you know its slope and the coordinates of one point on it.

In Example 2, we use the point-slope equation method to find an equation for a line whose slope and *x-intercept* are known. An **x-intercept** of a graph is the *x*-coordinate of a point where the graph intersects the *x*-axis.

GUIDED

Example 2
A line has slope -5, and its *x*-intercept is 22. Find an equation for the line.

Solution Because the *x*-intercept is 22, the point $(22, 0)$ is on the line. So $(h, k) = (22, 0)$. Since the slope is -5, $m = -5$. Use the point-slope form $y - \underline{} = m(x - \underline{})$.   *k; h*

Substitute for *m, h* and *k*. $y - \underline{} = \underline{}(x - \underline{})$.   *0; -5; 22*

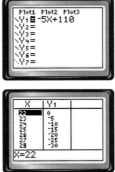

When you find the equation of a line from a point and a slope, you can use a graphing calculator to check your answer. In Example 2, the slope of –5 and the point $(22, 0)$ are indicated by the problem. Enter the equation you found into your [Y=] menu. To see if the point $(22, 0)$ lies on the line, set up a table whose first *x*-coordinate is 22. The table shows that indeed the line passes through the point.

Equations for Lines with a Given Point and Slope   **357**

---

1. Given: A line contains the fixed point (x_1, y_1) and slope m; x_1 and y_1 are constants and m is a parameter.

2. By the definition of slope and because all points on a line determine the same slope, (x, y) is another point on the line if and only if $m = \frac{y - y_1}{x - x_1}$. (*x* and *y* are variables.)

3. Multiplying both sides of the slope formula by $x - x_1$ gives the point-slope form $y - y_1 = m(x - x_1)$.

4. That equation is satisfied by every point on the line other than (x_1, y_1) because of the slope formula. And it is also satisfied by (x_1, y_1), because $y_1 - y_1 = m(x_1 - x_1)$ (both sides equal 0). So $y - y_1 = m(x - x_1)$ is an equation for the line.

Students may wonder if there is a form for an equation of a line using the *x*-intercept and some notion of slope. The answer can be found by looking for the line with slope m and containing $(a, 0)$. This line has an equation $y = m(x - a)$.

---

2 Teaching

Notes on the Lesson

Example 1 The linear model assumes that the population of Alaska over time was a linear relationship, which is not true in the long term. However, this model can be used to describe short-term events. Some lively discussion can arise on this issue, paving the way for Lesson 6-7, which discusses fitting a line to data.

Algorithm for finding an equation of a nonvertical line given one point and the slope. This algorithm is applied in the examples and summarized on page 357. It is important to emphasize the steps because in the next lesson an additional step is added to the procedure.

Example 2 Students appreciate the ease of writing equations in point-slope form, but many graphing utilities require equations in slope-intercept form. Have students rewrite $y - 0 = \frac{1}{2}(x - 22)$ in the equivalent form $y = \frac{1}{2}x - 11$, and then discuss the advantages each form has for sketching graphs.

Additional Examples

Example 1 Normally the depth of the river is 12 feet. After a torrential downpour the water is rising at a rate of 1.5 feet per hour. Assuming this rate remains steady, find an equation relating the depth of the river d to the time t. $h = 1.5t + 12$

Example 2 A line has slope 4, and its *x*-intercept is –13. Find an equation for the line in point-slope form.

Because the *x*-intercept is –13, the point $(-13, 0)$ is on the line. So $(h, k) = (-13, 0)$. Because the slope is 4, $m = 4$. Use the point-slope form $y - \underline{} = \underline{}(x - \underline{})$.   *k; m; h*

Substitute for *m, h,* and *k*.
$y - \underline{} = \underline{}(x - \underline{})$ *0; 4; –13*

3 Assignment

Recommended Assignment
- Questions 1–24
- Question 25 (extra credit)
- Reading Lesson 6-6
- Covering the Ideas 6-6

Notes on the Questions
Question 1 Vancouver, Washington, is a suburb of Portland, Oregon, and is not to be confused with the more well-known Vancouver, British Columbia, Canada, a much larger city with over a half-million inhabitants.

Questions

COVERING THE IDEAS

1. In 2000, Vancouver, Washington, had a population of 143,560 and was growing at a rate of about 9,700 people per year. Suppose that this rate of increase stays steady.

   a. Find an equation relating y, the population of Vancouver, to the year x, where x is the number of years since 2000.

   b. Predict the population of Vancouver in the year 2015.

   c. Predict which year the population of Vancouver will exceed 400,000. **2027**

1a. $y = 9,700x + 143,560$

1b. 289,060 people

In 2–5, find an equation of the line given the slope and one point on the line. 2. $y - k = m(x - h)$ 3. $y - 6 = -2(x + 8)$

2. point (h, k); slope m

3. point $(-8, 6)$; slope -2

4. point $(-2, 0)$; slope $\frac{1}{3}$

5. point $(5, -\frac{1}{2})$; slope 0 $y = -\frac{1}{2}$

4. $y = \frac{1}{3}(x + 2)$

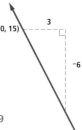

6. The slope of a line is -5 and the x-intercept is 4. Find an equation for the line. $y = -5(x - 4)$

7. Write the equation of the line graphed at the right.
   $y - 15 = -2(x - 20)$

8. What is an equation of the horizontal line through the point $(3, 9)$? $y = 9$

9. What is an equation for the line with slope -4.3 that contains the point $(6.8, -3.0)$? $y + 3 = -4.3(x - 6.8)$

APPLYING THE MATHEMATICS

10. A mountain climber leaves his camp and hikes up the side of a mountain. His altitude increases at an average rate of 200 feet per hour. After 3 hours his altitude is 4,100 feet. Write an equation to find his altitude y after he has been hiking for x hours. $y - 4,100 = 200(x - 3)$

11. A newborn koala (age 0 months) is 2 cm long. Until maturity, it grows at an average rate of 1.5 cm per month. Koalas mature at about 4 years of age.

    a. From the given information, find an equation estimating the length y of a koala at age x months. $y = 1.5x + 2$

    b. About how long are mature koalas? **74 cm**

12. The slopes of two lines are reciprocals.

    a. An equation of one of the lines is $y = -8x - 9$. What is the slope of the second line? $-\frac{1}{8}$

    b. Find the equation of the second line if it passes through the point $(4, 6)$. $y - 6 = -\frac{1}{8}(x - 4)$

Koala bears are not bears. They are marsupials, like kangaroos. Baby koalas, called joeys, are the size of a jellybean at birth. A joey remains in the mother's pouch for about 22 weeks before emerging.

Source: *National Geographic*

Accommodating the Learner ⬆

This would be a good time to begin a discussion with your students about domain and range as they relate to the problem. For instance, when a problem talks about the distance a hiker has gone over a period of time or the amount of money in a savings account if $10 is added every month, the domain in each case would consist of nonnegative numbers. In fact the second example would model a discreet situation. While you need not dwell on this point, it is worthwhile to get the students thinking about domain and range, especially when they are doing the homework problems found in the section titled "Applying the Mathematics."

13. Suppose a 5-week-old baby weighs 12 pounds and is gaining weight at the rate of 0.3 pound per week. **13b.** $y - 12 = 0.3(x - 5)$

   a. The given information represents the slope m, age x, and weight y. Find the values of m, x, and y. **$m = 0.3; x = 5; y = 12$**

   b. Determine an equation for the baby's weight y at age x weeks.

   c. Determine the baby's weight at 12 weeks. **14.1 lb**

14. The following sequence, seen in Lesson 1-3, is made up of yellow and green hexagonal tiles. Find a formula for the number of tiles y in terms of n, and the term of the sequence. **$y = 2 + 5n$**

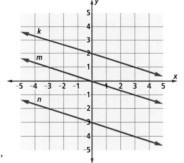

    1st   **2nd**   **3rd**

15. Determine an equation for the line that contains $(0, 3)$ and is parallel to the line with equation $y = 4x - 9.89$. **$y = 4x + 3$**

In 16 and 17, some information is given.
a. Write the slope and an ordered pair described by the information.
b. Write an equation relating x and y.

16. Kathy is on vacation and is spending $75 per day. After 4 days she has $320 left. **a. $m = -75; (4, 320)$; b. $y - 320 = -75(x - 4)$**

17. To buy a pass for the city bus system, you must pay an initial fee and then pay $1.75 per ride. Dante paid $29.25 for 15 rides. **a. $m = 1.75; (15, 29.25)$; b. $y - 29.25 = 1.75(x - 15)$**

REVIEW

18. Match each of the lines k, m, and n at the right with its equation. **(Lesson 6-4)**

   a. $y = -\frac{1}{3}x$ **m**

   b. $y = -\frac{1}{3}x - 3$ **n**

   c. $y = 2 - \frac{1}{3}x$ **k**

19. Graph the line with equation $y = -x$.
   (Lesson 6-4)

20. Do the points $(-4, 3)$, $(0, 2)$, and $(4, -7)$ lie on the same line? Justify your answer.
   (Lesson 6-2)

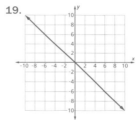

19.

20. No, since the rate of change between $(-4, 3)$ and $(0, 2)$ is $-\frac{1}{4}$, while the rate of change between $(0, 2)$ and $(4, -7)$ is $-\frac{9}{4}$.

Equations for Lines with a Given Point and Slope   **359**

Accommodating the Learner ⬇

Ask students to find an equation of a line with a slope of -6 and an x-intercept of -1. Once the students have found a correct equation, ask them to put it in slope-intercept form. Students should then write down two other equations which represent lines parallel to the equation of the line just found. Ask students how they know their lines are parallel to the first one. Ask them to find the x-intercepts and y-intercepts of their lines. Graph all three lines, labeling both the x- and y-intercepts. Now have

students check their work by graphing all three lines using their graphing calculators.
$y = -6(x - -1); y = -6x - 6; y = -6x + 3;$
$y = -6x$

6-5

4 Wrap-Up

Ongoing Assessment

Form groups of two students. Have each student write a word problem that models the ideas found in this lesson. Students should exchange papers. Each student should solve his or her partner's problem. Students should define their variables, set up an equation, and solve it. When both students are done, each student should explain the solution to the other student.

Project Update

If you have not had students look over the projects on pages 387 and 388, you might want to do so now. Project 3, The Diagonal Game, on page 388, relates to the content of this lesson.

---

21. The following two points give information about prices of corn: (4 bushels, $9.24), (12 bushels, $27.72). Calculate the rate of change and describe what it stands for. (**Lesson 6-1**)

21. $2.31 per bushel; the price of each bushel

22. Which section(s) of the graph below shows the
   a. fastest increase? C
   b. slowest decrease? (**Lesson 6-1**) F

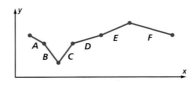

23. **Skill Sequence** Simplify each expression. (**Lesson 5-2**)
   a. $\frac{12}{5} \div \frac{12}{6} \cdot \frac{6}{5}$ b. $\frac{x}{5} \div \frac{x}{6} \cdot \frac{6}{5}$ c. $\frac{x}{y} \div \frac{x}{z} \cdot \frac{z}{y}$

24. Phone Company A charges $4.99 per month for a special 7¢ per minute rate. Company B charges 10¢ per minute with no monthly fee. Suppose you talk for T minutes in a particular month.
   a. What will it cost you if you have signed up with Company A?
   b. What will it cost you if you have signed up with Company B?
   c. How many minutes must you talk before you pay less with Company A's rate than with Company B's rate? (**Lessons 4-5, 3-4, 1-2**) 167 min

24a. $0.07T + 4.99$

24b. $0.10T$

> **EXPLORATION**

25. Use the Internet or another resource to find the population at the last census of the state where you live.
   a. Find how much your state population has changed since the previous census. Assume the rate of change is constant and that it continues.
   b. Using your estimate, find an equation relating the population y to the year x.
   c. Use this equation to estimate what the population of your state will be when you are 50 years old.

25a. Answers vary. Sample answer: The population of Hawaii was 1,211,537 in 2000 and was estimated to be 1,275,194 in 2005.

   b. Answers vary. Sample answer: $y = 12{,}731.4x + 1{,}211{,}537$

   c. Answers vary. Sample answer: 1,657,136

360   Slopes and Lines

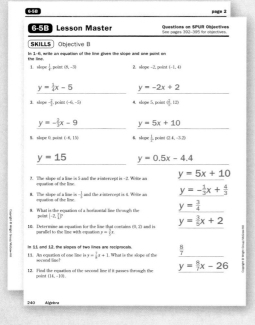

360   Chapter 6

Extension

Have students consider the following problem. Juanita's portfolio is currently worth 1.2 million dollars but is losing value at a rate of $100,000 per year. Let y be the value of Juanita's portfolio in x years. Ask students to write an equation representing this situation. Students should then graph the equation, labeling both the x- and y-intercepts. Ask students to explain what the x- and y-intercepts mean in the context of the problem. Have them identify the slope and explain its meaning.

$y = -100{,}000x + 1{,}200{,}000$; y-intercept: 1,200,000; x-intercept: 12; The y-intercept shows that the portfolio's value starts at $1,200,000; the x-intercept tells when the value of the portfolio will be zero. The slope is –100,000, indicating that the portfolio bases $100,000 each year.

Lesson
6-6
Equations for Lines through Two Points

> ▶ **BIG IDEA** An equation for the line through any two given points can be determined by first calculating the slope of the line.

A powerful approach to problem solving is to change the problem you are given into a simpler problem that you know how to solve. In Lesson 6-5, you learned how to find an equation of a line if you know its slope and one point on it. Now, consider a different problem. You are given two points and want to find the equation of the line that passes through them. With just a little work, you can turn this problem into a problem like one in the last lesson.

Mental Math

Find the measure of the angle between spokes if the spokes are equally spaced around the circle and there are:

a. 3 spokes. **120°**

b. 10 spokes (pictured) **36°**

c. 15 spokes **24°**

d. n spokes $\dfrac{360°}{n}$

Example 1

Find an equation for the line that passes through (10, −4) and (18, 20).

Solution Use the coordinates of the given points to find the slope.

$$m = \frac{20 - {-4}}{18 - 10} = \frac{24}{8} = 3$$

Now you have more information than you need. You know two points and need to use only one of them to find an equation. Either point can be used. We choose to use (18, 20). Follow the algorithm from Lesson 6-5.

$y - k = m(x - h)$ Write the equation.
$y - 20 = 3(x - 18)$ Substitute $h = 18$, $k = 20$, and $m = 3$.

An equation of the line is $y - 20 = 3(x - 18)$.

Check Substitute the coordinates of the two points in the equation $y - 20 = 3(x - 18)$ to check if they produce true statements.

Using (10, −4), does $-4 - 20 = 3(10 - 18)$?
$-24 = 30 - 54$ Yes, the equation checks.

Using (18, 20), does $20 - 20 = 3(18 - 18)$?
$0 = 3 \cdot 0$ Yes, the equation checks.

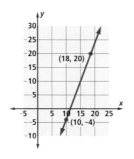

Equations for Lines through Two Points   **361**

Background

This lesson discusses the last in a three-problem sequence on finding equations of lines. Each problem requires one more step for its solution than the previous one.

1. given slope and y-intercept (just substitute into $y = mx + b$)

2. given slope and one point (substitute into $y - k = m(x - h)$)

3. given two points (reduce to type 2 by calculating slope)

When working with applications, there is always a question of the naming of

variables. If cost depends on time, as in Example 3, should we name the variables c and t, so that the reference is clear, or should we name them x and y? In solving sentences in previous lessons and chapters, we have usually opted for the first letters of the attribute being measured, such as in this case c and t. Here we usually use x and y. Though the resulting equations are not quite as easy to relate to the application, these variables make it easier to think about intercepts and slopes.

Lesson
6-6

GOAL
Find the equation of a line through two points.

SPUR Objectives

B Find an equation for a line given either its slope and any point or two points on it.

F Use equations for lines to describe real situations.

Materials/Resources
· Lesson Masters 6-6A and 6-6B
· Resource Masters 1, 2, 90, and 91
· Quiz 2

HOMEWORK

Suggestions for Assignment
- Questions 1–21
- Question 22 (extra credit)
- Reading Lesson 6-7
- Covering the Ideas 6-7

Local Standards

1 Warm-Up

Example 1 of Lesson 6-6 asks for an equation for the line that passes through the points (10, −4) and (18, 20).

1. Without finding an equation for the line, find the y-coordinates of points on the line with x-coordinates 2, 26, and 14. **−28, 44, 8**

2. Without finding an equation for the line, try to find the y-intercept of the line. **−34**

6-6

2 Teaching

Notes on the Lesson

Example 1 Some students may be uncomfortable with the number of choices they must make when solving these problems. They can reverse their choice of points in computing slope and still get the right answer. They can use either given point for substitution in the equation and still get the right answer.

Example 2 Some problems work naturally with the variables assigned in either order. Our solution has been stated with chirps per minute as the independent variable x and temperature as the dependent variable y.

Additional Examples

Example 1 Find an equation for the line that passes through $(7, -2)$ and $(-5, 4)$. $y - 4 = \frac{-1}{2}(x + 5)$ or $y + 2 = -\frac{1}{2}(x - 7)$

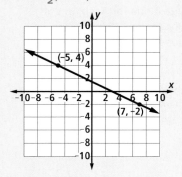

Example 2 Two inches from the top, a drop d of thick syrup drips down the side of a container at the rate of 0.25 inch per second t. After 2 seconds it is 2.5 inches from the top of the container, and after 5 seconds it is 3.25 inches from the top. This information is graphed below.

a. Find an equation for the line through the two points. $d = 0.25t + 2$

b. How far from the top was the drop after 8 seconds? **6 in.**

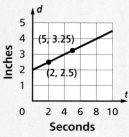

Relationships that can be described by an equation of a line occur in many places. Here is a relationship that may surprise you.

Example 2

Biologists have found that the number of chirps field crickets make per minute is related to the outdoor temperature. The relationship is very close to being linear. When field crickets chirp 124 times per minute, it is about 68°F. When they chirp 172 times per minute, it is about 80°F. Below is a graph of this situation.

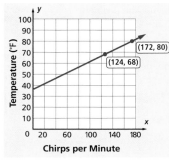

Field crickets are the crickets everyone sees and hears in late summer and fall.

a. Find an equation for the line through the two points.

b. About how warm is it if an instrument records 150 chirps in a minute?

Solutions

a. Find the slope using the points (124, 68) and (172, 80).

$$\text{slope} = \frac{80 - 68}{172 - 124} = \frac{12}{48} = \frac{1}{4}$$

Substitute $\frac{1}{4}$ and the coordinates of (124, 68) into $y = mx + b$.

$$68 = \frac{1}{4}(124) + b$$

Solve for b.

$$68 = 31 + b$$
$$37 = b$$

Substitute for m and b.

An equation is $y = \frac{1}{4}x + 37$.

b. Substitute 150 for x in the equation $y = \frac{1}{4}x + 37$.

$$y = \frac{1}{4} \cdot 150 + 37$$
$$= 37.5 + 37$$
$$= 74.5$$

It is about 75°F when you hear 150 chirps in one minute.

STOP QY

▶ **QY**

Check Example 2 by showing that (124, 68) is on the line with equation $y = \frac{1}{4}x + 37$.

Accommodating the Learner ⬆

Have students form groups of three. Each student is to write the ordered pairs for two points on a piece of paper. Rotate the papers counterclockwise. Using the two points given to them, each student is to calculate the slope of the line containing the two points. Rotate the papers a second time counterclockwise. Using the slope and one of the two points, each student should find the equation of the line in slope-intercept form. Rotate the papers counterclockwise for the last time. Each student should have

his or her original paper back. Now have students graph and label the original two points and draw the line containing the two points. Next have them graph the line using the equations found on their pieces of paper. If the two lines are not the same, have the members of the group find the error.

The equation in Example 2 enables the temperature to be found for any number of chirps. By solving for x in terms of y, you could get a formula for the number of chirps expected at a given temperature. Formulas like these seldom work for values far from the data points. Field crickets tend not to chirp at all below 50°F, yet the formula $y = \frac{1}{4}x + 37$ predicts about 50 chirps per minute at 50°F.

GUIDED

Example 3

Suppose when using a calling card to call Iceland, you were charged $2.23 for a 10-minute call and $4.12 for a 20-minute call. Assume that this is a constant-increase situation.

a. Express the given information as two ordered pairs (minutes, cost).

b. Find an equation that expresses the cost y of the call in terms of x, the length of the call in minutes.

c. What does the y-intercept b represent in this situation?

d. What does the slope m represent in this situation?

e. How long could you talk for $25?

Solutions

a. Two points the line passes through are (? , ?) and (? , ?). **(10, 2.23)   (20, 4.12)**

b. First, find the ____?____, m. **slope**

$m = \frac{?-?}{?-?} = 0.189$ $\frac{4.12 - 2.23}{20 - 10}$

Substitute 0.189 and the coordinates of one of the points into $y = mx + b$.

__?__ = 0.189(__?__) + b **2.23; 10 (or 4.12; 20)**

Solve for b. **$b = 0.34$**

Substitute the values found for m and b into the equation $y = mx + b$.

$y = $ __?__ $x +$ __?__ **0.189; 0.34**

c. The y-intercept represents the cost of calling for __?__ minutes. This is usually a charge that is automatic no matter how long the call lasts. In this case, the automatic charge is $0.34. **0**

d. The slope represents the ____?____. **cost per minute**

e. Substitute $25 for __?__ in the equation $y = 0.189x + 0.34$ and solve for __?__. Solving this equation shows that you could talk __?__ minutes for $25. **$y$; x; about 130**

The equation $y = 0.189x + 0.34$ in Example 3 gives the cost for talking any number of minutes. If the equation were solved for x in terms of y, the result would be a formula for the number of minutes you could talk at a given cost.

Equations for Lines through Two Points   363

Accommodating the Learner ⬇

Write an equation in slope-intercept form similar to $y = \frac{3}{4}x + 2$ on the board or overhead. Ask students to identify the slope of the line. Next have students find two points on the line. Students should not use the y-intercept. Using these two points, ask students to find the slope of the line containing them. Students should verify that the slope identified in the equation of the line is the same as the slope found using the two points. Ask students to find two more points on the line and repeat the

process. Ask them what they think will be true concerning the slope for each pair of points on the line.

Notes on the Lesson

Example 3 In an application problem there is often a choice about which quantity will be represented by the independent variable x and which by the dependent variable y. Sometimes a problem will naturally lend itself toward one choice. In this example, it makes sense to view the cost of the call as a function of its duration. But if you are wondering how long you can call for a certain amount, then the duration becomes a function of the cost.

Note-Taking Tips

This is the time to go back and reinforce what the students learned in Lesson 6-2. Students will still make mistakes finding the slope of a line given two points on the line. They will either find the run over the rise or they will interchange the position of the two points when calculating the slope. Remind students that the ratio is change in y divided by the change in x. Also remind them that slope is found by dividing the difference of the y's by the difference of the x's, but they must start both differences with the same point.

Additional Example

Example 3 Suppose a hot air balloon is resting on a platform above the ground. It ascends 175 feet in 3 minutes, and is 275 feet above the ground after 5 minutes. Assume a constant rate of ascent.

a. Express the given information as two ordered pairs (minutes, feet).

b. Find an equation that expresses the height y of the balloon in terms of x, the length of ascent in minutes.

c. What does the y-intercept b represent in this situation?

d. What does the slope m represent in this situation?

e. How long does it take for the balloon to reach an altitude of 1,125 feet?

Solution on page 365.

6-6

3 Assignment

Recommended Assignment
- Questions 1–21
- Question 22 (extra credit)
- Reading Lesson 6-7
- Covering the Ideas 6-7

Notes on the Questions
Questions 1–6 Reassure students who used different choices of points that the intermediate work shown in class might be different from theirs, but the slope-intercept equation of the line will be the same. It may be informative to have students present different strategies for solving at least one of these problems to the class.

Questions

COVERING THE IDEAS

1. A katydid, or long-horned grasshopper, chirps about 70 times per minute at 70°F and 124 times per minute at 95°F.
   a. Find an equation relating x, the number of chirps per minute and y, the temperature in degrees Fahrenheit. $y = \frac{25}{54}x + \frac{1,015}{27}$
   b. Use your equation from Part a to estimate the temperature when a katydid cricket is chirping 90 times a minute. **about 79°F**

2. Suppose a 15-minute call costs $5.26, and a 30-minute call costs $10.24. Find a formula relating time (in minutes) and cost (in dollars). **Let c be cost and t be time, c = 0.332t + 0.28.**

3. Find an equation for the line shown at the right. $y = -1.5x + 7$

In 4 and 5, find an equation for the line through the two given points. Check your answer.

4. $(3, 0), (7, 16)$ $y - 16 = 4(x - 7)$ 5. $(4, 11), (10, 5)$ $y - 11 = -(x - 4)$

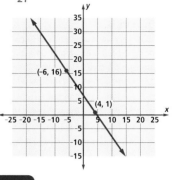

APPLYING THE MATHEMATICS

6. Raini ran a marathon, which is 26.2 miles long. It took him 2 hours and 6 minutes to reach mile 13 on the race course and he crossed the finish line in 4 hours and 18 minutes. Raini tends to run at a constant speed.
   a. Express the given information as two ordered pairs (time, distance). **(126, 13) and (258, 26.2), where time is in minutes**
   b. Write an equation to find the distance Raini ran in terms of the time. $d = 0.1t + 0.4$, **where d is distance and t is time**
   c. What does the slope represent in this situation? **Raini's speed**
   d. How long did it take Raini to reach mile 7? **66 min**

7. Write an equation for the line that produced the table of values shown below. $y - 27 = 0.5(x - 30)$

8. Find an equation for the line with x-intercept 7 and y-intercept 3. $y = -\frac{3}{7}x + 3$

---

9. Penicillin was discovered in 1928. However, the medicine was not mass produced until the 1940s. In 1943, the price of a dose of penicillin was $20. By 1946, the price per dose was $0.55.

   a. Assuming the price of a dose of penicillin decreased at a constant rate, find an equation relating the year and price.

   b. According to the equation, what was the 1957 price of a dose of penicillin? **about –$70.77**

   c. Do you believe this equation gives good estimates for the price of penicillin? Why or why not?

10. a. Use the graph at the right to estimate the Italian shoe size that corresponds to a women's size 9 in the United States. **39.5**

   b. Write an equation to relate women's shoe size in Italy to women's shoe size in the United States.

   c. Use your equation from Part b to find the Italian shoe size of a women's size 9 in the United States.

11. Old Faithful is a geyser in Yellowstone National Park that erupts often. The National Park Service has studied the length of the eruption and the amount of time between eruptions for many years. They have found that the relationship between how long an eruption lasts x and the amount of time until the next eruption y is approximately linear. One eruption lasted 2.1 minutes and the time before the next eruption was 59.24 minutes. Another eruption lasted 3.7 minutes and the time before the following eruption was 70.08 minutes. **11a. (2.1, 59.24) and (3.7, 70.08)**

   a. Write the data as two ordered pairs.

   b. Find the slope of this linear relationship. **6.775**

   c. Explain what the slope represents in this situation.

   d. Find an equation for y in terms of x.

   e. If the park rangers posted a sign at the end of an eruption that said 94 minutes until the next eruption of Old Faithful, approximately how long had the previous eruption lasted? **7.23 min**

10b. $i = \frac{4}{3}a + \frac{83}{3}$, where

   i is the Italian shoe size and a is the U.S. shoe size

10c. $i = \frac{119}{3} \approx 40$

11c. The slope represents how much longer you will have to wait for the next eruption for every minute of an eruption.

11d. $y = 6.775x + 45.0125$

9a. $y = -\frac{389}{60}x + \frac{757{,}027}{60}$
   where x is the year
   and y is the price

9c. Answers vary.
   Sample answer:
   No, since the price
   of penicillin should
   never be negative.

An eruption at Old Faithful expels between 3,700 and 8,400 gallons of boiling water.

Source: National Park Service

Italian Women's Shoe Size (y-axis)
U.S. Women's Shoe Size (x-axis)
(10, 41)
(7, 37)

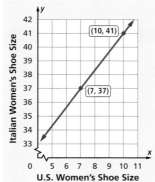

Example 3 Solution

a. Two points the line passes through are (__?__, __?__) and (__?__, __?__). **3; 175; 5; 275**

b. First find the __?__, m. **slope**

   $m = \frac{? - ?}{? - ?} = 50$. **275; 175; 5; 3**

   Substitute 50 and the coordinates of one of the points into $y = mx + b$.

   $\underline{\quad?\quad} = 50(\underline{\quad?\quad}) + b$
   175; 3 or 275; 5

   Solve for b. **$b = 25$**

   Substitute the values found for m and b into the equation $y = mx + b$.

   $y = \underline{\;?\;}x + \underline{\;?\;}$ **50; 25**

c. The y-intercept represents height of the balloon when $x = \underline{\;?\;}$. This is the height of the platform. **0**

d. The slope represents the __?__.
   rate of ascent of the balloon

e. Substitute 1,125 feet for __?__ in the equation $y = 50x + 25$ and solve for __?__. **y; x**

   Solving shows that it took __?__ minutes to reach a height of 1,125 feet. **22**

Notes on the Questions

Question 9 The history of the cost of penicillin is much like the costs of many other mass-produced items. When the items were produced in small numbers, each item cost quite a bit because the start-up cost (b) was so high. But when they are mass-produced, the slope (m) becomes more important than the start-up cost, and the cost per item becomes closer to the slope. The same type of scenario occurred with calculators in the 1970s and early 1980s, with personal computers in the 1980s and 1990s, and with digital cameras in the 2000s.

6-6

Notes on the Questions

Question 12 This context, one we use quite often, is tailor-made for this lesson because the freezing points and boiling points on the two scales are often the only things people remember about them. Yet from these two points the entire relationship between the temperatures can be derived. Here we have arbitrarily selected the Fahrenheit temperature as *x* and the Celsius temperature as *y*. However, outside the classroom, students might see the formula solved for either variable.

Question 22b The most accurate equations relating the distance traveled with the fare involve a step function, but the steps here are so short that we have ignored them.

12. The graph at the right shows the linear relationship between Fahrenheit and Celsius temperatures. The freezing point of water is 32°F and 0°C. The boiling point of water is 212°F and 100°C.

   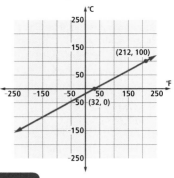

   a. Find an equation that relates Celsius temperatures *C* and Fahrenheit temperatures *F*. $C = \frac{5}{9}F - \frac{160}{9}$

   b. When it is 155°F, what is the temperature in degrees Celsius? $68\frac{1}{3}°C$

   c. When it is −10°C, what is the temperature in degrees Fahrenheit? 14°F

REVIEW

13. A cab company charges a base rate of $2.50 plus $1.60 per mile. A 15-mile cab ride costs $26.50.

   a. Write an equation relating the number of miles driven to the cost of the cab ride. $y = 1.60x + 2.5$

   b. Make up a question about this cab company that you can answer using your equation from Part a. (**Lesson 6-5**)

   13b. Answers vary. Sample answer: If the charge for a ride was $39.30, how long was that ride? 23 mi

14. What is an equation for the line through the point (5, 5) with slope $-\frac{3}{5}$? (**Lesson 6-5**) $y - 5 = -\frac{3}{5}(x - 5)$

15. Graph $y = 3x + 9$ by using its slope and *y*-intercept. (**Lesson 6-4**) See margin.

16. The points (3, *b*) and (−2, 4) are on a line with slope $\frac{1}{2}$. Find *b*. (**Lesson 6-2**) $b = 6.5$

17. Interstate 70 leads from Denver, Colorado into the mountains. There are signs that post the elevation. (**Lesson 6-1**)

Miles from Denver	Elevation (ft)
0	5,260
33	7,524
45	8,512
47	9,100
72	9,042

Source: Colorado Tourism Office

A hiker at Alpine Ridge Trail's summit in Rocky Mountain National Park in Colorado.

   a. Between which two signs is the rate of change of elevation negative? between the 47-mi and the 72-mi signs

   b. Calculate the rate of change of elevation for the entire distance listed in the table. about 52.5 ft per mi

366 Slopes and Lines

Additional Answers

15.

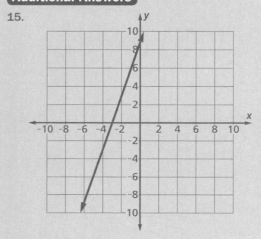

18. Simplify $\frac{3a^2b}{c^2} \div \frac{12a}{c^4}$. (Lesson 5-2) $\frac{abc^2}{4}$

19. A rectangle is 3 cm longer than twice its width w. Its perimeter is 42 cm. (Lesson 3-4, Previous Course)

w

ℓ

    a. Write an expression for the length ℓ in terms of w. $\ell = 2w + 3$

    b. Find its width and length. 6 cm and 15 cm

    c. What is its area? 90 cm²

In 20–22, simplify the expression. (Lessons 2-2, 2-1)

20. $4(-7x) - 9(x - 1)$ $-37x + 9$

21. $\frac{3}{4}(16g - h) + 4(2h)$ $12g + 7.25h$

22. $-4p - 3(p - 2.5)$ $-7p + 7.5$

EXPLORATION

23. In many places, a taxi ride costs a fixed number of dollars plus a constant charge per mile.

    a. Find a rate for taxi rides in your community or in a nearby place.

    b. Find an equation relating distance traveled and the cost of a ride.

23a. Answers vary. Sample answer: A taxi service charges a flat fee of $1.50 plus an additional 20 cents for each $\frac{1}{6}$ of a mile.

23b. For this taxi service; $c = 1.5 + 1.2d$; where c is the cost in dollars and d is the distance traveled in miles.

QY ANSWER

Does $68 = \frac{1}{4} \cdot 124 + 37$?

$68 = 31 + 37$?

Yes, it checks.

Equations for Lines through Two Points   **367**

---

4   Wrap-Up

Ongoing Assessment

Ask students to explain how to find the slope of a line containing two given points. When students correctly answer the question, ask them how to find the equation of the line now that they know the slope. Ask them if they can choose either point to use with the known slope to find the equation of the line.

Project Update

Project 4, Slopes of Perpendicular Lines, on page 388 relates to the content of this lesson.

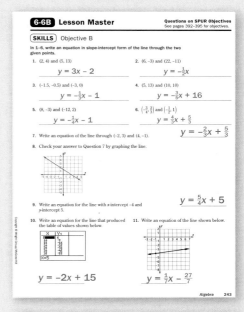

Lesson 6-7

GOAL

Find an equation of a line that fits a set of points.

SPUR Objective

G Given data whose graph is approximately linear, find a linear equation to fit the graph and make predictions about data values.

Materials/Resources

· Lesson Masters 6-7A and 6-7B
· Resource Masters 1, 2, 4, 92, and 93
· Graphing calculator

HOMEWORK

Suggestions for Assignment
• Questions 1–22
• Question 23 (extra credit)
• Reading Lesson 6-8
• Covering the Ideas 6-8

Local Standards

1 Warm-Up

Graph the three points (1, 5), (2, 9), and (4, 12).

1. Eyeball two points on a line that is close to these points and find its equation. **Answers vary. Sample answer: $y = 2.25x + 3$.**

Lesson 6-7 — Fitting a Line to Data

Vocabulary

line of best fit
linear regression
least squares line

▶ **BIG IDEA** When points lie nearly on a line, it is useful to determine an equation for a line that lies on or comes close to the points.

If data points are not all on one line but are close to being linear, you can often use an equation for a line to describe trends in the data. For example, the table and graph below show the life expectancy of people in the United States at birth in ten-year intervals from 1930 to 2000. Notice that the life expectancy has been increasing each decade.

It is natural to wonder what the life expectancy will be in 2010, 2020, or 2050. Of course no one knows, but we can make educated guesses by using algebra.

Notice that the change in life expectancy each decade is not constant. So the points do not lie on the same line. Still, the points seem to be reasonably close to a line. There are different ways of estimating a line that comes close to the data. This is called *fitting a line to the data*.

Year	Life Expectancy (yr)
1930	59.7
1940	62.9
1950	68.2
1960	69.7
1970	70.8
1980	73.7
1990	75.4
2000	77.0

Source: National Center for Health Statistics

Mental Math

Give the conversion factor for converting

a. $\frac{\text{inches}}{\text{year}}$ to $\frac{\text{inches}}{\text{month}}$.

b. $\frac{\text{meters}}{\text{pound}}$ to $\frac{\text{millimeters}}{\text{pound}}$.

c. $\frac{\text{feet}}{\text{second}}$ to $\frac{\text{inches}}{\text{minute}}$.

a. $\frac{1}{12} \frac{\text{year}}{\text{months}}$

b. $1{,}000 \frac{\text{millimeters}}{\text{pound}}$

c. $12 \frac{\text{inches}}{\text{foot}} \cdot 60 \frac{\text{seconds}}{\text{minute}}$

Eyeballing a Line of Fit

Activity 1

Step 1 After carefully graphing the data from the table, take a ruler and draw a line that seems close to all the points. This is called "fitting a line by eye" or "eyeballing." One such line is graphed at the right.

Step 2 Find two points on the line. The line we drew happens to not pass through any of the original data points. Our line contains (1930, 61) and (1990, 76).

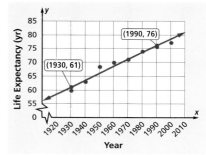

Background

The purpose of this lesson is for students to understand the idea of *approximating* data using an equation when no line contains all the points.

Lines are the simplest descriptors for trends in data arising in science, medicine, politics, psychology, economics, quality control, business, and so on. Many students don't study situations in which data fail to lie in a perfect line until later courses. Fitting a line to data, however, is a technique that is accessible to algebra students who have the

appropriate technology, and it introduces a rich source of applications of algebra.

Line-fitting is the simplest form of curve-fitting. In Lesson 7-2, we fit an exponential function to data. In *Advanced Algebra*, students study other types of graphs and discuss fitting a curve to data in situations of variation. Curve-fitting to exponential, logarithmic, and trigonometric functions is discussed in *Functions, Statistics and Trigonometry*.

(continued on next page)

Step 3 Find an equation for the line through the two points. We follow the algorithm in Lesson 6-6 for finding an equation of a line given two points. First we use these two points to find the slope of the line.

$$\text{slope} = \frac{76 - 61}{1990 - 1930} = \frac{15}{60} = 0.25$$

Now substitute the slope and the coordinates of one of the points into $y = mx + b$ and solve. We use $(1930, 61)$.

$$61 = 0.25 \cdot 1930 + b$$

$$61 = 482.5 + b$$

$$-421.5 = b$$

An equation for the line is $y = 0.25x - 421.5$.

With this method, an estimate for the life expectancy for someone born in 2020 is $0.25 \cdot 2020 - 421.5$, or about 83.5 years.

Eyeballing is a simple method but it has a weakness in that two different people will likely eyeball two different lines.

Linear Regression

Most graphing calculators have a feature that will give you what is known as the **line of best fit.** The method they use is called **linear regression.** This is the most common way of finding a line to fit data. In Activity 2, we show only how to use a calculator to find an equation for this line.

Activity 2

Step 1 Enter the eight ordered pairs for the data into two lists, one for the x-coordinate and the other for the corresponding y-coordinate. On some calculators, these lists are called L1 and L2.

Step 2 Have the calculator automatically calculate the line of best fit. One calculator showed the screen at the right. The letter a indicates slope.

Step 3 Round a and b to reasonable accuracy. Here we need four decimal places for a because the x values for the years are so large. Substitute the rounded values for a and b into the equation $y = ax + b$. So, by this method, a line of best fit is $y = 0.2395x - 400.9893$.

Using linear regression, an estimate for the life expectancy for someone born in 2020 is $0.2395 \cdot 2020 - 400.9893$, or about 82.8 years. This is a little lower than what was predicted by eyeballing.

Notes on the Lesson

You may wish to do this lesson as an in-class activity. Questions 2 and 3 provide data similar to those on page 368. Questions 5–7 provide other sets of data.

It is instructive to compare an eyeballed line with one that has been calculated by the regression line process.

Students may naturally wonder how to determine whether a line is a line of good fit. Because we are using the line to predict values, the critical idea is how well the line fits the data points at a vertical distance from the line. A line of good fit should have about as many data points above it as below, and the distances from the points to the line should balance.

Be sure to instruct students to clear data in the lists they will use to find a line of fit. They can usually do this by using the up arrow to highlight the list name (like L1 or L2) and then pressing the CLEAR button followed by the ENTER button. Ask them to test this method with their calculators. Point out that it will be difficult to spot errors in the equation for the line of fit if the errors are due to 1) using lists that are not empty at the start, 2) typing in lists with different lengths (usually due to errors in typing), or 3) actual errors in the lists. The third error can be avoided if points are checked carefully before finding the line of fit.

The lesson is centered around one set of data: the change in life expectancy over the past 70 years. Two methods are given for estimating these data with a line: eyeballing and finding the *regression line* (also known as the *line of best fit* and the *least squares line*). For both methods, calculators are useful. For eyeballing, students are likely to obtain different slopes and intercepts as answers. But the other two methods provide one line. Most graphing utilities will show the line of best fit.

Linear regression. We show the criterion by which the least squares line is the line of best fit, and this shows how "least squares" gets its name. An eyeballed line may actually be closer to the data points than the least squares line, geometrically speaking. That is, the distances from the data points to the eyeballed line measured *along the perpendiculars* from the points to the line may be less, but the interest in a line of fit is to predict y-values from x-values, and so the deviations in lines of best fit are measured *vertically* from a data point to a line.

6-7

Additional Example

Example The table below shows the number of U.S. cell phone subscribers in millions from 2000 to 2006.

Year	Year since 2000	Subscribers (millions)
2000	0	97.0
2001	1	118.4
2002	2	134.6
2003	3	148.1
2004	4	169.5
2005	5	194.5
2006	6	219.4

a. Using a graphing calculator, create a scatterplot of the points (Year since 2000, Total Subscribers).

b. Use a calculator to find an equation for the line of best fit. Graph the line in the same window as the scatterplot. $y = 19.8x + 95.1$

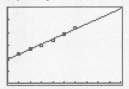

c. In this situation what is the meaning of $x = -4$ and $x = 10$? 1996; 2010

d. Use the equation of the line to predict the number of cell phone subscribers in 1996. The actual number was 38.2 million. Did the line of best fit over or under predict the number of 1990 subscribers? 15.9 million; under predict

e. Use the equation to predict the number of subscribers in 2010. Do you expect the equation to over predict or under predict the number of 2010 subscribers? Explain why. 293.1 million; Answers vary. Sample answer: over predict; Recent cell phone growth has been about 15 million subscribers per year but the model predicts 18.8 million per year.

Both an eyeballed line and the line of best fit can be considered as models of life expectancy in the United States from 1930 to 2000. Recall that the difference between the actual amount and the amount predicted by a model is called the deviation.

The table below shows the actual life expectancy, the expectancies predicted by these models, and the deviations for each model. It also shows the predicted life expectancies for 2010 and 2020.

Year	Life Expectancy	Eyeball a Line of Fit $(y = 0.25x - 421.5)$	Line of Best Fit $(y = 0.2395x - 400.9893)$	Eyeball Deviation	Best Fit Deviation
1930	59.7	61.0	61.2	1.3	1.5
1940	62.9	63.5	63.6	0.6	0.7
1950	68.2	66.0	66.0	-2.2	-2.2
1960	69.7	68.5	68.4	-1.2	-1.3
1970	70.8	71.0	70.8	0.2	0
1980	73.7	73.5	73.2	-0.2	-0.5
1990	75.4	76.0	75.6	0.6	0.2
2000	77.0	78.5	78.0	1.5	1.0
2010		81.0	80.4		
2020		83.5	82.8		

The line of best fit has the following property: The sum of the squares of the deviations of its values from the actual values is the least of all lines. For this reason, it is called the **least squares line.**

GUIDED

Example

Show that the sum of the squares of the eyeball line deviations for the life expectancies is greater than the sum of the squares of the best fit deviations.

Solution For the eyeball line, the sum of the squares of the deviations is
$1.3^2 + 0.6^2 + (-2.2)^2 + (-1.2)^2 + 0.2^2 + (-0.2)^2 + 0.6^2 + 1.5^2 = $ __?__. 11.02

For the least squares line, the sum of the squares of the deviations is __?__. 10.56

Questions

COVERING THE IDEAS

1. If three people were to use the indicated method for fitting a line to a particular set of data, would their answers necessarily be the same? (Assume they made no errors in calculations.)

   a. eyeballing no   **b.** linear regression yes

Accommodating the Learner ⬆

The table on the following page shows the progress at several points in time of the women's world record in the 100-meter dash during the past century.

Have students enter the data in their calculators using the STAT and EDIT commands with the years entered in L1 and the time entered in L2. Setting an appropriate window, have the students use the STAT PLOT and GRAPH commands to graph the data. Now have students find and graph the line of best fit using the following sequence of commands. Go to the Y= command and set Y1 = according to the following instructions. Use the VARS command followed by the Statistics command followed by the EQ command followed by the RegEQ command followed by the GRAPH command. Students should recognize that the line of best fit does not contain each of the data points. They should observe that some of the points lie above the line and some lie below.

(continued on next page)

In 2 and 3, use the table at the right of life expectancies for people in the United States. **2a–e. Answers vary. Sample answers are given.**

2. a. Construct a scatterplot of the ordered pairs (year, female life expectancy). **See margin.**

   b. Eyeball a line to fit the data and find its equation.

   c. What female life expectancies does your equation predict for the years 1930–2000?

   d. Calculate the sum of the squares of the deviations of the predicted values in Part c from the actual values. **35.8**

   e. Use your equation to predict the female life expectancy in the U.S. in the year 2020. **85 yr**

3. Follow the directions for Question 2, but use linear regression. **See margin.**

4. Why is the line found using linear regression called the *least squares* line? **See margin.**

Year	All	Females	Males
1930	59.7	61.6	58.1
1940	62.9	65.2	60.8
1950	68.2	71.1	65.6
1960	69.7	73.1	66.6
1970	70.8	74.7	67.1
1980	73.7	77.4	70.0
1990	75.4	78.8	71.8
2000	77.0	79.7	74.3

Source: U.S. Census Bureau

2b. $y = 0.25x - 420$; See margin for graph.

2c. 62.5, 65, 67.5, 70, 72.5, 75, 77.5, and 80 yr

APPLYING THE MATHEMATICS

In 5 and 6, the table shows women's 800-meter freestyle swimming long course (50-meter pool) world records between 1971 and 1978.

Person and Country	Year	Time (min)
Shane Gould, Australia	1971	8.97
Keena Rothhammer, USA	1972	8.88
Novella Calligaris, Italy	1973	8.87
Jo Ann Harshbarger, USA	1974	8.79
Jennifer Turrall, Australia	1975	8.72
Petra Thumer, East Germany	1976	8.67
Petra Thumer, East Germany	1977	8.58
Tracey Wickham, Australia	1978	8.40

Source: USA Swimming

5a. See margin.

5. a. Construct a scatterplot of the ordered pairs (year, time).

   b. Use linear regression to predict the world record in 1989. **about 7.67 min**

   c. In 1989, Janet Evans set the most recent world record in the long course women's 800-meter. Her time was 8 minutes, 16.22 seconds, or about 8.27 minutes. Calculate the deviation from the linear regression prediction. **0.6 min**

   d. The first women's 800-meter freestyle world record was in 1919. The record was set by Gertrude Ederle in a time of 13.32 minutes. This time deviates from the linear regression equation's predicted time by how much? **0.51 min**

   e. Is the linear regression line a good model for predicting world record times in the women's 800-meter freestyle before or after the 1970s? Explain why or why not.

In her 11-year career, Evans won 25 of 27 major international races at the 400-meter freestyle and 22 of 23 at the 800-meter freestyle.

Source: United States Olympic Committee

5e. Answers vary. Sample answer: No, since a half-minute deviation is very large in an 8-min race.

Fitting a Line to Data **371**

---

3 **Assignment**

Recommended Assignment

• Questions 1–22
• Question 23 (extra credit)
• Reading Lesson 6-8
• Covering the Ideas 6-8

Notes on the Questions

We recommend going through the questions in order.

Question 2 Life expectancy depends on more than just one's gender. For example, life expectancy is about 8 years higher for someone living in Hawaii (80 years) than for someone living in Washington, D.C. (72 years).

Questions 2 and 3 If two data sets are reasonably close to fitting a line, then their difference will also be close to fitting a line. So you could take the difference between the female and male life expectancies and subject it to the same analysis as in Questions 2 and 3.

Additional Answers

2a., 3a.

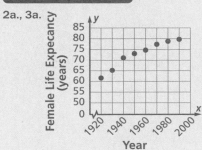

2b, 3b–e, 4, and 5a. See page 372 for answers.

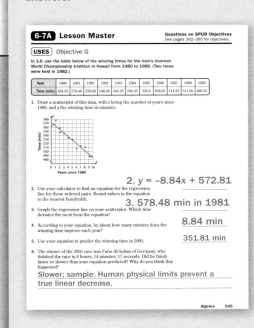

6-7A Lesson Master

Questions on SPUR Objectives
See pages 392–395 for objectives.

(USES) Objective G

In 1–6, use the table below of the winning times for the men's Ironman World Championship triathlon in Hawaii from 1980 to 1989. (Two races were held in 1982.)

Year	1980	1981	1982	1982	1983	1984	1985	1986	1987	1988	1989
Time (min)	564.55	578.48	559.68	548.38	545.95	534.33	530.9	508.62	514.22	511.00	489.25

1. Draw a scatterplot of this data, with x being the number of years since 1980, and y the winning time in minutes.

2. Use your calculator to find an equation for the regression line for these ordered pairs. Round values in the equation to the nearest hundredth.

   2. $y = -8.84x + 572.81$

3. Graph the regression line on your scatterplot. Which time deviates the most from the equation?

   3. 578.48 min in 1981

4. According to your equation, by about how many minutes does the winning time improve each year?

   8.84 min

5. Use your equation to predict the winning time in 2005.

   351.81 min

6. The winner of the 2005 race was Faris Al-Sultan of Germany, who finished the race in 8 hours, 14 minutes, 17 seconds. Did he finish faster or slower than your equation predicted? Why do you think this happened?

   Slower; sample: Human physical limits prevent a true linear decrease.

Algebra **245**

Time (seconds)	Person	Date
12.8	Mary Lines (GBR)	August 20, 1922
12.2	Leni Junker (GER)	August 29, 1926
11.9	Hilda Strike (CAN)	August 2, 1932
11.5	Helen Stephens (USA)	June 1, 1935
11.5	Marjorie Jackson (AUS)	July 22, 1952
11.3	Wilma Rudolph (USA)	July 19, 1961
11.0	Wyomia Tyus (USA)	October 15, 1968
10.88	Marlies Oelsner (GDR)	July 1, 1977
10.49	Florence Griffith Joyner (USA)	July 16, 1988

Notes on the Questions

Questions 8–11 These questions are important conceptually to demonstrate that not all sets of points are best fitted by a line. For Question 9, a curve might be appropriate. For Question 11, there seems to be no particular pattern.

Additional Answers

2b.

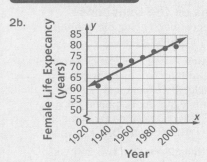

Year

3b. Answers vary. Sample answer:

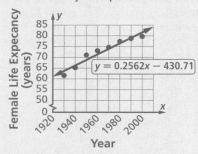

$y = 0.2562x - 430.71$

Year

3c. approximately 63.8, 66.3, 68.9, 71.4, 74.0, 76.6, 79.1, and 81.7 yr

3d. ≈ 19

3e. 86.67 yr

4. The sum of the squares of the deviations of its values from the actual values used to find it is the least of all lines.

5a.

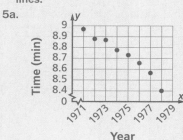

Year

7a.

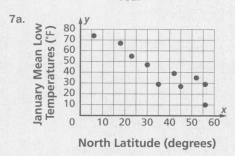

North Latitude (degrees)

---

6. Add the 1919 and 1989 world record times from Question 5 to the table. How does the linear regression equation change? Do you think it is more or less accurate for predicting world records in the women's 800-meter freestyle?

7. Refer to the data below.

City	Latitude (°North)	January Mean Low Temperature (°F)
Lagos, Nigeria	6	74
San Juan, Puerto Rico	18	70
Calcutta, India	23	55
Cairo, Egypt	30	47
Tokyo, Japan	35	31
Rome, Italy	42	39
Belgrade, Serbia	45	28
London, England	52	35
Copenhagen, Denmark	56	29
Moscow, Russia	56	9

Source: infoplease.com

a. Make a scatterplot showing a point for each city. See margin.

b. Use linear regression to find an equation.

c. **Fill in the Blank** As you go one degree north, the January low temperature tends to ___?___. decrease by about one degree Fahrenheit

d. Which city's January mean low temperature deviates most from that predicted by the equation? Tokyo, Japan

e. Predict the January mean low temperature for the North Pole.

f. The January mean low temperature for Acapulco, Mexico, which is at 17° north latitude, deviates from the equation by +8.3°F. Find the actual January mean low temperature in Acapulco. about 71°F

In 8–11, tell whether fitting a line to the data points would be appropriate.

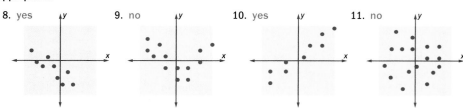

8. yes   9. no   10. yes   11. no

---

6. It changes from $y \approx -0.073x + 153.53$ to $y \approx -0.078x + 163.20$. Answers vary. Sample answer: No. It is still over a half minute off in predicting Janet Evans's record.

7b. $y \approx -1.086x + 81.139$

7e. about –16°F

The domes and minarets of the Sultan Hassan Madrasa stand on the eastern edge of Cairo.

Accommodating the Learner ⬇

Have students graph the two sets of data below on separate coordinate systems.

Set 1: (–1, 7), (0, 5), (1, 3), (2, 2), (5, 3)

Set 2: (8, 1), (6, –1), (0, –4), (–1, –6), (–2, –5), (–3, –7)

Ask what they can tell about the slope of the line of best fit. Enter each set of data into a graphing calculator and calculate the line of best fit for each.

ENGLISH LEARNERS
Vocabulary Development

The expressions "fitting a line by eye" or "eyeballing" will be new to most students. They may think they should just look at the data points and pick out the "correct" ones to compute the equation. However, the choice of points is subjective. Students should pick two points such that when they plot the points and draw the line passing through these points, about half of the remaining points should be above the line while approximately half should be below.

REVIEW

12. Find an equation for the line with y-intercept -2 and x-intercept 4. (**Lesson 6-6**) $y = \frac{1}{2}x - 2$

13. a. Find an equation for the line through (6, 4) with a slope of $\frac{5}{3}$.
b. Give the coordinates of one other point on this line. (**Lesson 6-5**)

14. a. Give the slope and y-intercept of the line $4x - 9y = 3$.
b. Graph the line. (**Lesson 6-4**) See margin.

In **15** and **16**, find the slope and y-intercept of the line. (**Lesson 6-4**)

15. $y = -\frac{x}{6}$ $-\frac{1}{6}$; 0

16. $y = 4$ 0; 4

17. a. Draw a line that has no y-intercept. See margin.
b. What is the slope of your line? (**Lesson 6-4**) not defined

18. The Tigers scored 15 points in the first 8 minutes of a basketball game. At that rate, how many points would the team score in a 48-minute game? (**Lesson 5-8**) 90 points

19. In a game of chess, each player begins the game with 8 pawns, 2 knights, 2 bishops, 2 rooks, 1 queen, and 1 king. What is the ratio of bishops to the total number of pieces? (**Lesson 5-5**) $\frac{1}{8}$

20. Solve for y. (**Lesson 4-4**)
a. $y - 3 = 6y + 2$ $y = -1$
b. $y - a = by + c$ $y = \frac{-c - a}{b - 1}$

21. Describe all solutions to the following sentences. (**Lesson 2-8**)
a. Six times a number is zero. 0
b. Zero times a number is zero. all numbers
c. Zero times a number is six. no solutions

22. If a is the cost of an adult's ticket to an amusement park and c is the cost of a child's ticket, what is the cost of tickets for 2 adults and 5 children? (**Lesson 1-2**) $2a + 5c$

EXPLORATION

23. The method of least squares was independently discovered by two mathematicians, the German Carl Friedrich Gauss and the Frenchman Adrien-Marie Legendre, in the years 1795–1809. Research to find the problem that led Gauss to this discovery. Answers vary. See students' work.

13a. $y - 4 = \frac{5}{3}(x - 6)$
13b. Answers vary.
    Sample answer:
    (0, –6)

14a. slope $= \frac{4}{9}$;
    y-intercept $= -\frac{1}{3}$

Prior to the founding of the World Chess Federation in 1924, chess had existed as a sport played at a competitive level for centuries.

Source: World Chess Federation

Fitting a Line to Data **373**

4 Wrap-Up

Ongoing Assessment
Ask students to explain the process of "eyeballing" a line that represents the data points. Students should point out in their explanations that no equation will contain all of the data points. They should also point out that different students will pick different points to create the equation of the line.

Project Update
Project 2, Paper Towels: Price vs. Absorbency, on page 387, relates to the content of this lesson.

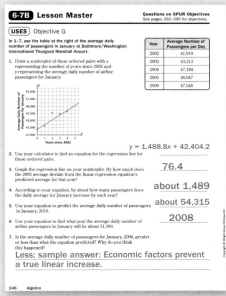

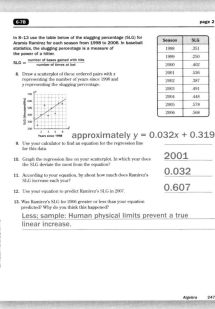

Additional Answers

14b.
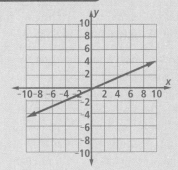

17a. Answers vary. Sample answer:
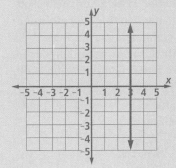

Lesson

6-8

Lesson

6-8

Standard Form of the Equation of a Line

GOAL

Write an equation for a line in standard form.

SPUR Objectives

C Write an equation for a line in standard form or slope-intercept form, and from either form, find its slope and *y*-intercept.

F Use equations for lines to describe real situations.

H Graph a line given its equation, or given a point and its slope.

Materials/Resources

· Lesson Master 6-8A or 6-8B
· Resource Masters 1, 2, 94, and 95

HOMEWORK

Suggestions for Assignment

• Questions 1–21
• Questions 22–23 (extra credit)
• Reading Lesson 6-9
• Covering the Ideas 6-9

Local Standards

---

1 ▶ Warm-Up

Examine the neon ball and necklace situation in the lesson, where Lourdes spent $24 on 30 neon bouncing balls and 12 glow-in-the-dark necklaces.

1. If a neon ball cost $0.30, then how much did a necklace cost? **$1.25**
2. What is the most a necklace could have cost? **$2** What is the cost of one neon ball? **It is free.**
3. What is the most a neon ball could have cost? **$0.80**

Vocabulary

linear combination

standard form of an equation for a line

oblique

▶ **BIG IDEA**   Every line has an equation of the form $Ax + By = C$.

In this chapter, lines have been used to describe situations involving a constant increase or decrease. Lines have also been used to model data in a scatterplot. The slope-intercept form $y = mx + b$ arises naturally from these applications. However, other situations can also lead to linear relations.

Linear Combination Situations

Lourdes had ordered party favors from an online store. When the 30 neon bouncing balls and the 12 glow-in-the-dark necklaces came, however, she had forgotten the price of each item. The bill said that the total cost was $24. What was the cost of one neon ball? What was the cost of one glow-in-the-dark necklace?

We can describe this situation as "The cost of the neon balls plus the cost of the necklaces is $24." Let x = the cost of one neon ball and y = the cost of one glow-in-the-dark necklace. Then $30x + 12y = 24$.

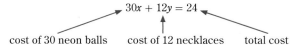

$$30x + 12y = 24$$

cost of 30 neon balls   cost of 12 necklaces   total cost

This equation can be quickly graphed by finding its *x*- and *y*-intercepts.

To find the *x*-intercept, find *x* when $y = 0$.	To find the *y*-intercept, find *y* when $x = 0$.
$30x + 12 \cdot 0 = 24$	$30 \cdot 0 + 12y = 24$
$30x = 24$	$12y = 24$
$x = 0.80$	$y = 2$
The point is $(0.80, 0)$.	The point is $(0, 2)$.

Plot the two intercepts and draw the line. Negative numbers do not make sense for *x* or *y*, so we ignore the part of the line in Quadrants II or IV.

Mental Math

Find the average speed of a car going

a. 300 miles in 6 hours.

b. 50 mph for an hour, then 70 mph for an hour.

c. 55 mph for 2 hours, 45 mph for an hour, then 60 mph for 2 hours.

a. 50 mph

b. 60 mph

c. 55 mph

Background

Linear combination situations. The lesson begins with a situation that leads to this form. Linear combination situations typically combine rate-factor multiplications with putting-together addition or take-away subtraction. This can be seen by including units. For example, for the necklace and neon ball situation in the lesson:

$$30 \text{ neon balls} \cdot \frac{x \text{ dollars}}{\text{neon ball}} +$$

$$12 \text{ necklaces} \cdot \frac{y \text{ dollars}}{\text{necklace}} = 24 \text{ dollars}$$

The unit arithmetic works. The unit for each side of the equation is dollars.

The standard form of an equation for a line. One reason for studying the standard form $Ax + By = C$ is that linear combination situations naturally lead to equations of lines in this form. A second reason for studying the standard form is that it works for all lines, whereas vertical lines do not have equations in slope-intercept form.

(continued on next page)

Each pair of possible prices (cost of one ball, cost of one necklace) corresponds to a point. As shown at the right, the point (0.50, 0.75) lies on the graph. If a ball costs $0.50 and a necklace costs $0.75, then 30 balls and 12 necklaces cost $24. Other possible (x, y) pairs can be found algebraically by first changing the equation of the line into slope-intercept form.

$$30x + 12y = 24$$
$$12y = -30x + 24$$
$$y = -2.5x + 2$$

This is a formula that gives y, the cost of a necklace, in terms of x, the cost of a neon ball. Suppose a neon ball costs $0.20. Then the cost of a necklace could be found by $y = -2.5(0.20) + 2 = -0.50 + 2 = \$1.50$.

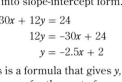 **QY1**

An expression of the form $Ax + By$, where A and B are fixed numbers, is called a **linear combination** of x and y. The name *linear combination* is appropriate because when $Ax + By$ has a constant value, the graph of all ordered pairs (x, y) lies on a line.

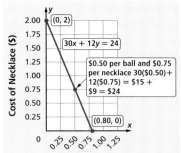

Cost of Neon Ball ($)

▶ QY1

Use $y = -2.5x + 2$ to find another possible pair of costs for the neon balls and necklaces that Lourdes ordered.

The Standard Form of an Equation for a Line

The equation $3x - 4y = 24$ has the form $Ax + By = C$, where $A = 3$, $B = -4$, and $C = 24$. The variables x and y are on one side of the equation and the constant term C is on the other. The equation $Ax + By = C$, where A, B, and C are constants, is the **standard form of an equation for a line.** Linear combination situations naturally lead to equations of lines in standard form.

To graph a line whose equation is in standard form, you do not need to rewrite the equation in slope-intercept form. Instead, you can find the intercepts and draw the line that contains the intercepts.

Example 1
Graph $3x - 4y = 24$.

Solution

Find the x-intercept. Let $y = 0$.	Find the y-intercept. Let $x = 0$.
$3x - 4(0) = 24$	$3(0) - 4y = 24$
$x = 8$	$y = -6$
The x-intercept is 8, so the point (8, 0) is on the line.	The y-intercept is -6, so the point (0, -6) is on the line.

(continued on next page)

Standard Form of the Equation of a Line **375**

2 Teaching

Notes on the Lesson

You might wish to read this lesson in class, and then as you read, you might consider parallel situations in which the numbers are different. For example, with Lourdes' situation, you could ask what the equation would be if she spent $42.

Example 1 This example is important because it shows students an "easy" way of graphing lines in standard form. When $x = 0$, you get the y-intercept -6. When $y = 0$, you get the x-intercept 8. This is a particularly effective way to graph an equation $Ax + By = C$ when A and B are factors of C, that is, when the intercepts are integers.

Additional Example
Example 1 Graph $5x + 2y = 10$.

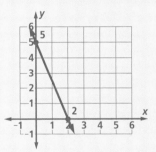

Rewriting equations in slope-intercept and standard form. The second half of the lesson discusses the conversion of equations of lines into standard form and slope-intercept form. Being able to convert equations into different forms is important when one has graphing or CAS technology.

This idea has applications beyond the study of lines: there are standard and square forms for quadratics, standard form and factored form for polynomials, and traditional forms for virtually every other type of equation. It is common to prefer that the coefficients in $Ax + By = C$ be integers and that A be positive, but you should not be overly rigid. The context of the problem should determine the kinds of numbers used. Percent problems might best use decimals, and a problem about a recipe might use values that are fractions. If the situation involves first a loss and then a gain, an appropriate value of A might be negative.

Notes on the Lesson

Example 2 Emphasize that the equations in the final form are equivalent to the equations in the form that was given. You can do this by checking that points that satisfy one of the equations satisfy the other. They are equivalent formulas for lines, as discussed in Lesson 4-6. For example, in Example 2, the point $\left(7, 5\frac{2}{7}\right)$ satisfies both the given equation and the final equation. You might ask students to check each one of these examples.

Examples 2 and 3 apply the notions of clearing fractions and decimals first discussed in Chapter 3.

Additional Example

Example 2 Rewrite $y = -\frac{3}{5}x - \frac{1}{5}$ in standard form with integer coefficients. Tell the values of A, B, and C.

$3x + 5y = 1$, $A = 3$; $B = 5$; $C = 1$

Plot $(8, 0)$ and $(0, -6)$ and draw the line through them, as shown.

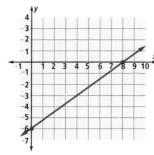

Check Find a point satisfying the equation, and check that it is on the graph of the line. The point $(4, -3)$ is on the graph so it satisfies $3x - 4y = 24$.

STOP QY2

Rewriting Equations in Slope-Intercept and Standard Form

The idea of equivalent equations is useful in dealing with lines. In Example 1, the standard form equation $3x - 4y = 24$ is convenient to use to find the intercepts. But the slope-intercept equation is useful if you are graphing with a calculator, or if you need to know the slope. You should be able to quickly change an equation of a line into either of these forms. In standard form, the equation is usually written with A, B, and C as integers.

> **Example 2**
> Rewrite $y = \frac{4}{7}x + \frac{9}{7}$ in standard form with integer coefficients. Find the values of A, B, and C.
>
> **Solution**
>
> $7y = 7 \cdot \frac{4}{7}x + 7 \cdot \frac{9}{7}$ Multiply each side of the given equation by 7 to clear the fractions.
>
> $7y = 4x + 9$ Simplify.
>
> $-4x + 7y = 9$ Add $-4x$ to both sides so the x and y terms are both on the left side of the equation. Write the x term first.
>
> This is written in standard form with $A = -4$, $B = 7$, and $C = 9$. Some people prefer that A be positive. Then multiply both sides of the equation by -1 to obtain $4x - 7y = -9$.

> **▶ QY2**
>
> Give the equation in standard form that fits the following situation and draw a graph. A fruit grower ships peaches and berries to grocery stores. A carton of peaches weighs 5 pounds and a carton of berries weighs 4 pounds. The shipment to one store weighed 90 pounds. Let $x =$ the number of cartons of peaches and $y =$ the number of cartons of berries.

Accommodating the Learner ⬇

Write the following equations on the board. Tell students that some of them are equivalent. Instruct students to find the equivalent equations. Ask students to explain how they know the equations are equivalent.

$y = \frac{2}{3}x + \frac{1}{3}$ $3y + x = 2$ $\frac{1}{3}y - x = 2$

$2y + \frac{1}{3}x = 1$ $2x - 3y = -1$

$y = \frac{2}{3}x + \frac{1}{3}$ and $2x - 3y = 1$ are equivalent; Multiply by 3 to clear fractions and write in standard form.

Example 3

Rewrite $y = -0.75x$ in standard form with integer values of A, B, and C.

Solution

$y = -0.75x$

$100y = -75x$ — Multiply each side by 100 to clear the decimal.

$75x + 100y = 0$ — Add $-75x$ to both sides so the x and y are both on the left side. Write the x term first.

Here $A = 75$, $B = 100$, and $C = 0$.

In the Activity below, you will practice changing the form of equations. An equivalent form of the equation of a line describes the same set of points.

Activity

Five equations are given below. Fill in the table so that each equation is written in both slope-intercept form and in standard form.

	Equation	Slope-Intercept Form	Standard Form
1.	$20x - 5y = 35$	?	?
2.	$y - 5 = 8(x - 1)$	?	?
3.	$2x + 4(y + x) = 5y + 15$	?	?
4.	$y = \frac{2}{3}x + 11$	?	?
5.	$14x + 4y = 20$	?	?

The lines graphed so far in this lesson are **oblique,** meaning they are neither horizontal nor vertical. In Lesson 4-2, you saw very short equations for horizontal and vertical lines. If a line is vertical, then its equation has the form $x = h$. If a line is horizontal, it has an equation $y = k$. These short equations are in standard form, but only one variable shows because one coefficient is zero. For example, $x = 4$ is equivalent to $x + 0y = 4$, where $A = 1$, $B = 0$, $C = 4$. The equation $y = -3$ is equivalent to $0x + y = -3$, where $A = 0$, $B = 1$, $C = -3$.

Thus, *every line* has an equation in the standard form $Ax + By = C$.

Questions

COVERING THE IDEAS

1. What is the form $Ax + By = C$ called?

Additional Example

Example 3 Rewrite $y = -0.8x$ in standard form with integer values of A, B, and C. $8x + 10y = 0$

Notes on the Activity

Students need to understand when to use the slope-intercept form of an equation and when to use the standard form of an equation. Have them give reasons why they would choose to put an equation in slope-intercept form. Have them give reasons why they would choose to put an equation in standard form. Ask them to explain what advantages each form of an equation offers when it comes to graphing the line.

Note-Taking Tips

Check students' notebooks to see that they have the following concepts. Examples should accompany each concept.

Slope: $m = \frac{y_2 - y_1}{x_2 - x_1}$

Slope-Intercept Form: $y = mx + b$

Point-Slope Form: $y - y_1 = m(x - x_1)$

Standard Form: $Ax + By = C$; A and B not both zero

Vertical Line: $x = a$

Horizontal Line: $y = b$

Activity
1. $y = 4x - 7$; $4x - y = 7$
2. $y = 8x - 3$; $8x - y = 3$
3. $y = 6x - 15$; $6x - y = 15$
4. $y = \frac{2}{3}x + 11$; $2x - 3y = -33$
5. $y = -3.5x + 5$; $7x + 2y = 10$

1. standard form for an equation of a line

Accommodating the Learner

Using the equation $Ax + By = C$, ask students to find the x- and y-intercepts in terms of A, B, and C. Repeat the process for the equation $y = mx + b$, this time finding the intercepts in terms of m and b. Ask students to identify the intercepts for the equation $y = a$ and the equation $x = b$. In each case, students should justify their answers by showing their work.

x-intercept: $\left(\frac{C}{A}, 0\right)$; y-intercept: $\left(0, \frac{C}{B}\right)$

x-intercept: $\left(\frac{b}{m}, 0\right)$; y-intercept: $(0, b)$

x-intercept: $(b, 0)$; y-intercept: $(0, a)$

6-8

Additional Answers

5b.

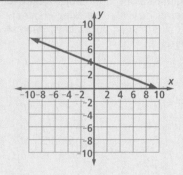

2. Refer to the following situation. The Hawkins family bought 3 sandwiches and 4 salads. They spent $36. Let x = the cost of each sandwich and y = the cost of each salad.

   a. Write an equation to describe the possible combinations of costs for the sandwiches and salads. $3x + 4y = 36$

   b. Graph the equation from Part a.

   c. If the salads cost $6.30 each, how much did each sandwich cost? $3.60

   d. Give the coordinates of the point on the graph corresponding to your answer to Part c. $(3.6, 6.3)$

   e. Give another pair of possible costs for the sandwich and salad.

In 3 and 4, the equation is in standard form. Give the values of A, B, and C. 3. $A = 5$; $B = -3$; $C = 9$

   3. $5x - 3y = 9$ 4. $8x + y = 2.4$

In 5 and 6, an equation for a line is given. 5b., 6b. See margin.

   a. Find the x- and y-intercepts of the graph of the line.
   b. Graph the line.

   5. $2x + 5y = 20$ 6. $3x - 2y = 12$

APPLYING THE MATHEMATICS

   7. Refer to the following situation. Cheryl scored a total of 27 points in her basketball game last night. None of the points came from free throws. All of her points came from 2- or 3-point shots.

   a. Find three different combinations of 2- and 3-point shots that Cheryl may have had last night.

   b. Write an equation in standard form to describe all the different possible combinations of 2-point shots and 3-point shots Cheryl may have made.

   c. What is the greatest number of 3-point shots she may have made? 9

   d. What is the greatest number of 2-point shots she may have made? 12

   e. Graph the solutions to the equation in Part b. See margin.

In 8–10, an equation in slope-intercept form is given.

   a. Find an equivalent equation in standard form with integer coefficients.
   b. Give the values of A, B, and C.

   8. $y = -\frac{4}{5}x + 10$ 9. $y = \frac{9}{8}x$ 10. $y = -x - 12$

   8a. $4x + 5y = 50$ 8b. $A = 4$; $B = 5$; $C = 50$
   9a. $9x - 8y = 0$ 9b. $A = 9$; $B = -8$; $C = 0$
   10a. $x + y = -12$ 10b. $A = 1$; $B = 1$; $C = -12$

378   Slopes and Lines

2b.

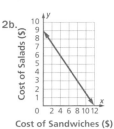

Cost of Salads ($)
Cost of Sandwiches ($)

2e. Answers vary.
   Sample answer:
   $x = \$4.00$;
   $y = \$6.00$

4. $A = 8$; $B = 1$;
   $C = 2.4$

5a. x-intercept $= 10$;
   y-intercept $= 4$

6a. x-intercept $= 4$;
   y-intercept $= -6$

7a. Answers vary.
   Sample answer:
   $(0, 9)$; $(3, 7)$; $(6, 5)$

7b. $2x + 3y = 27$,
   where x are the 2-point shots
   and y are the 3-point shots

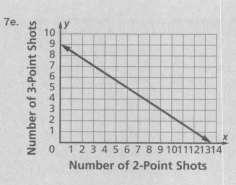

Basketball is the most popular high school sport for girls with 452,929 participants in 2006.

Source: National Federation of State High School Associations

6b.

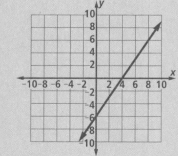

7e.

Number of 3-Point Shots
Number of 2-Point Shots

In 11 and 12, an equation in standard form is given. Find the equivalent equation in slope-intercept form.

11. $4x - 7y = 308$ $y = \frac{4}{7}x - 44$ **12.** $x + y = 0$ $y = -1x + 0$

13. On many multiple-choice tests, 1 point is given for each correct answer and 0.25 point is taken away for every wrong answer. (This is to discourage guessing.) Answers that are left blank do not affect the score. Gloria scored 62 on a test with 100 questions. Let C be the number of questions Gloria correctly answered and let W be the number of wrong answers she had.
   a. Give three possible pairs of values of C and W.
   b. Write an equation that describes all possible solutions.
   c. Graph all possible solutions. **See margin.**

14. Suppose $Ax + By = C$, with $B \neq 0$.
   a. Solve this equation for y. $y = -\frac{A}{B}x + \frac{C}{B}$
   b. Identify the slope and the y-intercept of this line.
      slope $= -\frac{A}{B}$, y-intercept $= \frac{C}{B}$

REVIEW

15. The time of the winning runner in the men's 100-meter race has decreased since the first Olympics in 1896. The scatterplot below shows the time of the winning race in seconds in each Olympic race from 1900 through 2004. **(Lesson 6-7)**
   15a–c. See margin.

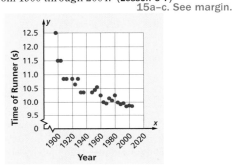

Source: International Olympic Committee

   a. Trace the graph and fit a line to the data.
   b. Find an equation for the line in Part a by approximating the coordinates of two points it goes through.
   c. Use your equation to predict the time of the winning runner in the year 2012. Why might this prediction be incorrect?

16. Find an equation for the line through the points $(-3, 4)$ and $(6, 1)$. **(Lesson 6-6)** $y - 1 = -\frac{1}{3}(x - 6)$

13a. Answers vary.
   Sample answer:
   $C = 62$, $W = 0$;
   $C = 65$, $W = 12$;
   $C = 68$, $W = 24$

13b. $C - \frac{1}{4}W = 62$

Standard Form of the Equation of a Line   **379**

Notes on the Questions

Question 13 This type of formula has been used on the SAT of the College Board and in national mathematics contests sponsored by the Mathematical Association of America and other organizations. If there are 5 choices to each question, a person who randomly guesses on a test graded with this formula will neither gain nor lose points.

Question 15 Ask students why there is no data for 1916 (World War I) and 1940 and 1944 (World War II). Some students may know that the United States did not participate in the 1980 Moscow Olympics, and the Soviet Union did not participate in the 1984 Los Angeles Olympics. Had all nations participated, the 100-meter dash might have produced new records that would have followed the linear trend represented by most of the data. Here is a situation in which politics may have affected the data.

Additional Answers

13c.
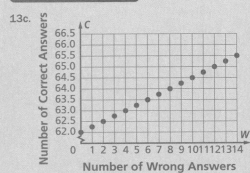

15a. Answers vary. Sample answer:
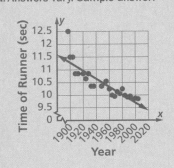

Additional Answers

15b. Answers vary. Sample answer: (1946, 10.4), (1984, 9.9); $T = -\frac{1}{76}x + \frac{6,841}{190}$

15c. Answers vary. Sample answer: 9.5 seconds; the line is only an approximation of the data.

Chapter 6

Notes on the Questions

Questions 20 and 21 These questions prepare students for Lesson 6-9, Graphing Linear Inequalities.

Question 23 The general result here is that, for fixed values of A and B, the graphs of all equations of the form $Ax + By = C$ are parallel. The reason is that the equation $Ax + By = C$ is equivalent to $y = -\frac{A}{B}x + \frac{C}{B}$, and so this line has slope $-\frac{A}{B}$, a value that does not depend on C. This property should be discussed.

4 Wrap-Up

Ongoing Assessment

Put students in groups of three. Ask each student to write an equation in standard form on a piece of paper. Pass the papers clockwise. Instruct students to write down the y-intercept of the line without using any aids. Pass the papers clockwise. Ask the students to write down the x-intercept of the line. Pass the paper back to the original owner. Have the students check to see if the intercepts are correct.

---

17. The water in a 6-foot-deep pool is 8 inches deep. A hose is being used to fill the pool at the rate of 4 inches per hour. Let x be the number of hours passed and y be the depth (in inches) of the water in the pool. (Lessons 6-5, 6-2)

    a. Write an equation for a line which relates x and y.
    b. Give the slope of the line. **4**
    c. Use your answer to Part a to find how long it will take to fill the 6-foot pool. **16 hr**

18. A robot is moving along a floor that has a coordinate grid. The robot starts at the point $(10, -4)$ and moves along a line with slope 3. Does the robot pass through the given point? Justify your answer. (Lessons 6-5, 6-2)

    a. $(12, 0)$ b. $(17, 17)$

19. What is the probability that you will randomly select a letter that is *not* U in the word ALBUQUERQUE? (Lesson 5-6) $\frac{8}{11}$

In 20 and 21, tell whether $(0, 0)$ is a solution to the sentence. (Lesson 3-7)

20. $x - 2y < 3$ yes   21. $5x > 4 + \frac{2}{3}y$ no

EXPLORATION

22. Explain why an equation for the line with x-intercept a and y-intercept b is $\frac{x}{a} + \frac{y}{b} = 1$. (This is called the *intercept form* of the equation for a line.)

23. a. On a graphing calculator, graph the lines with the following equations. **See margin.**

    $3x - 2y = 6$
    $3x - 2y = 12$
    $3x - 2y = 18$

    b. What happens to the graph of $3x - 2y = C$ as C gets larger?
    c. Try values of C that are smaller, including 0 and negative values. What can you say about the graphs of $3x - 2y = C$ in these cases? **The line shifts up.**

17a. $y = 4x + 8$; with $y \le 72$
18. The line the robot moves along has equation $y = 3x - 34$.
18a. No. The point does not lie on the line.
18b. Yes. The point lies on the line.
22. A line with x-intercept a and y-intercept b is determined by the two points; $(0, b)$ and $(a, 0)$; thus its slope is $\frac{-b}{a}$. An equation of this line is $y = \frac{-b}{a}x + b$; by dividing both sides by b and then adding $\frac{-1}{a}x$ to both sides, one arrives at the equation $\frac{x}{a} + \frac{y}{b} = 1$.
23b. The line shifts down.

QY ANSWERS

1. Answers vary. Sample answer: cost of a neon ball = $0.30, cost of a necklace = $1.25. $30(0.30) + 12(1.25) = 24$.

2. $5x + 4y = 90$

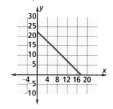

380   Slopes and Lines

Additional Answers

23a.

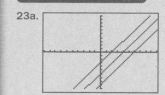

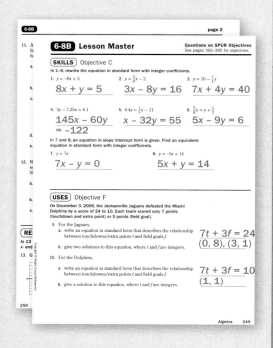

| 6-8B | page 2 |

6-8B Lesson Master Questions on SPUR Objectives
See pages 392–395 for objectives.

(SKILLS) Objective C

In 1–6, rewrite the equation in standard form with integer coefficients.

1. $y = -8x + 5$ 2. $y = \frac{3}{8}x - 2$ 3. $y = 10 - \frac{7}{4}x$

$8x + y = 5$ $3x - 8y = 16$ $7x + 4y = 40$

4. $3y - 7.25x = 6.1$ 5. $6.4y = \frac{1}{5}x - 11$ 6. $\frac{5}{6}x = y + \frac{2}{3}$

$145x - 60y = -122$ $x - 32y = 55$ $5x - 9y = 6$

In 7 and 8, an equation in slope intercept form is given. Find an equivalent equation in standard form with integer coefficients.

7. $y = 7x$ 8. $y = -5x + 14$

$7x - y = 0$ $5x + y = 14$

(USES) Objective F

On December 3, 2006, the Jacksonville Jaguars defeated the Miami Dolphins by a score of 24 to 10. Each team scored only 7 points (touchdown and extra point) or 3 points (field goal).

9. For the Jaguars,
   a. write an equation in standard form that describes the relationship between touchdowns/extra points t and field goals f. $7t + 3f = 24$
   b. give two solutions to this equation, where t and f are integers. $(0, 8), (3, 1)$

10. For the Dolphins,
    a. write an equation in standard form that describes the relationship between touchdowns/extra points t and field goals f. $7t + 3f = 10$
    b. give a solution to this equation, where t and f are integers. $(1, 1)$

Algebra   249

Lesson 6-9

Graphing Linear Inequalities

Vocabulary

boundary line

half-planes

linear inequalities

▶ **BIG IDEA** The two sides (half-planes) of the line with equation $Ax + By = C$ can be described by the inequalities $Ax + By < C$ and $Ax + By > C$.

In Chapter 3, you graphed solutions to inequalities on a number line. Recall that to graph an inequality such as $x < 2$ you first find the point where $x = 2$. Next, decide which part of the line contains the solution to the inequality. The sentence $x < 2$ states that we want values less than 2, so we shade the points to the left of 2. An open circle is placed on the boundary point 2, because 2 is not a solution to $x < 2$ (2 is not less than 2).

These ideas can be extended to graphs of inequalities in two dimensions. In this case, the boundary is a line instead of a point. We call this line the **boundary line.**

Inequalities Involving Horizontal or Vertical Lines

Example 1

Graph $y < 4$ on the coordinate plane.

Solution Graph the line $y = 4$. This horizontal line is the boundary line of the solution. The line is *dashed* to show that the points having a y-coordinate of 4 are not part of the solution set. The solution set consists of all points that have a y-coordinate less than 4. This is the region below the boundary line, so this region is shaded purple.

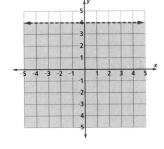

Check Pick a point in the purple shaded region. We choose (1, 1). Do the coordinates of this point satisfy the inequality $y < 4$? Yes, the y-coordinate is 1 and $1 < 4$.

The regions on either side of a line in a plane are called **half-planes.** The boundary line is the edge of the half-plane. In Example 1, the line $y = 4$ is the edge of the half-plane $y < 4$. If you were asked to graph $y \leq 4$, then the boundary line $y = 4$ would be included and shown as a solid line.

Graphing Linear Inequalities **381**

Mental Math

Find a single rule that describes each sequence. Then use your rule to find the next term in the sequence.

a. 2, 5, 8, 11, ...

b. 1, 2, 4, 8, 16, ...

c. 101, 103, 105, 107, 109, ...

a. $a_n = 3n - 1$; 14

b. $a_n = 2^{(n-1)}$; 32

c. $a_n = 2n + 99$; 111

Lesson 6-9

GOAL

Graph two-dimensional inequalities of the forms $x < h$, $y < k$, $y < mx + b$, and $Ax + By < C$, where the $<$ sign may be replaced by $\leq$, $>$, or $\geq$.

SPUR Objective

I Graph linear inequalities.

Materials/Resources

· Lesson Master 6-9A or 6-9B

· Resource Masters 1, 2, 96, and 97

HOMEWORK

Suggestions for Assignment

• Questions 1–21

• Question 22 (extra credit)

• Reading Lesson 7-1

• Covering the Ideas 7-1

Local Standards

1 Warm-Up

Consider the three sentences below.

a. $7x - 3y > 10$

b. $7x - 3y = 10$

c. $7x - 3y < 10$ Which sentence does each of these points satisfy?

1. (1, 1) c

2. (0, 0) c

3. (5, 4) a

4. (−3, −7) c

5. (−2, −8) b

6. (200, 100) a

7. (−200, −100) c

8. (40.328, 6.897) a

(Point out that these decisions are often easy to make if one has the graph of b.)

Background

Linear inequalities help with the understanding of lines. A student cannot fully understand what it means for a point to be on a line without understanding which points are not on the line.

The mathematics of this lesson is based on the Trichotomy Principle: Of two real numbers a and b, $a < b$, $a = b$, or $a > b$. If a and b are graphed on a horizontal number line, this means that a is to the left of b, a and b are the same point, or a is graphed to the right of b. In the plane, when a and b

are linear expressions, this means that a point is on one side of a line, on the line, or on the other side of the line.

Geometrically, linear inequalities allow one to easily describe half-planes. Graphing linear inequalities is important in business applications, and is the foundation of the process of linear programming.

Most graphing calculators can graph half-planes. Check your students' graphing utilities for this capability.

(continued on next page)

6-9

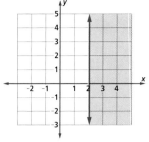

2 Teaching

Notes on the Lesson

Example 1 Note that $y < 4$ could be graphed on a number line as a ray without its endpoint. But in Example 1, the graph is a half-plane. These sets can be distinguished by using set-builder notation: $\{y: y < 4\}$ is the set of real numbers less than 4, while $\{(x, y): y < 4\}$ is the set of ordered pairs of real numbers with second coordinates less than 4. There is no way to tell which graph is meant without a context that indicates whether the graph is to be in one dimension or two. This is why in Example 1 the direction indicates "coordinate plane." Ask students what the graph would be if they were given $y \leq 4$.

Inequalities involving oblique lines. As you go through examples and questions, you might alter the inequality symbol in a sentence and ask students how that affects the graph. For instance, with Example 3, consider $2x - 3y \geq 12$, or $2x - 3y < 12$, or $2x - 3y \leq 12$, or $2x - 3y = 12$. Once a student has graphed one of these sentences, graphing any of the others should be relatively easy.

Emphasize the sentence preceding Example 3 and the paragraphs preceding and following Example 4.

Additional Examples

Example 1 Graph $x \leq -2$ on the coordinate plane.

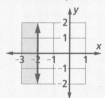

Example 2 Write an inequality that describes the set of points in the shaded region. $y > -1$

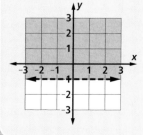

Example 2

Write an inequality that describes the set of points in the shaded region.

> **Solution** The boundary line is solid, which indicates that the edge $x = 2$ should be included. All points to the right of the line $x = 2$ are shaded purple, meaning every point in the half-plane has an x-coordinate greater than 2. So the sentence describing the region is $x \geq 2$. This region is the union of a half-plane and its edge.

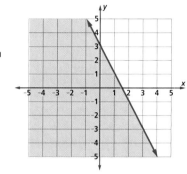

To distinguish $x > 2$ in the coordinate plane from $x > 2$ on a number line, we use set-builder notation. $\{(x, y): x \geq 2\}$ denotes a set of ordered pairs, so its graph is on the coordinate plane. $\{x: x \geq 2\}$ is a set of numbers, so its graph is on a number line.

Inequalities Involving Oblique Lines

Every line with an equation of the form $y = mx + b$ is the boundary line of the two half-planes described by $y < mx + b$ and $y > mx + b$.

Example 3

Draw the graph of $y \leq -2x + 3$.

> **Solution** Begin by graphing the boundary line $y = -2x + 3$. The $\leq$ sign indicates the points on the line should be included in the solutions, so make the line solid. We want the points whose y-coordinates are less than or equal to the y values that satisfy $y = -2x + 3$. Since y values decrease as x increases, shade the region below the line.

> **Check** Pick a point in the shaded region. We choose $(0, 0)$. Does it satisfy the inequality $y \leq -2x + 3$? Is $0 \leq 2(0) + 3$? Yes, 0 is less than 3, so the correct side of the line has been shaded.

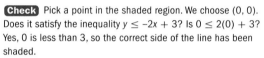

If an inequality is of the form $y < mx + b$, then you shade below the line, and if the sentence is of the form $y > mx + b$, then you shade above the line. But when an inequality is in standard form $Ax + By < C$, you cannot use the inequality sign to determine which side of the line to shade. For this type of inequality, the method of testing a point is usually used. The point $(0, 0)$ can be chosen if it is not on the boundary line. If $(0, 0)$ is a solution to the inequality, then the half-plane that contains $(0, 0)$ is shaded. If $(0, 0)$ does not satisfy the inequality, shade the half-plane on the other side of the boundary line.

If an inequality is in slope-intercept form, it is easy to decide which half-plane to shade. If $y > mx + b$, then the y-coordinates of points shaded should be bigger than the y-coordinates of corresponding points on the line $y = mx + b$. So you shade the upper half-plane. If $y < mx + b$, shade the lower half-plane. (Example 3 could be said to illustrate this idea.) This seems logical, but the concept is a new one to students, so encourage your students to check points by substituting. Inequalities in standard form are a little trickier to graph, and students should definitely check using the idea in Example 4 that is summarized in the algorithm for graphing linear inequalities.

Example 5 shows some of the utility of being able to graph linear inequalities, and is an important precursor to the linear programming students should encounter in their second course in algebra.

Example 4

Graph $2x - 3y > 12$.

Solution First graph the boundary line $2x - 3y = 12$. The line is dashed to show that the boundary line is not part of the solution. To determine which side of the line to shade, substitute $(0, 0)$ into the original inequality. Is $2(0) - 3(0) > 12$? No, $0 \not> 12$. Since $(0, 0)$ is in the upper half-plane and is *not* a solution, we shade the half plane that does not contain $(0, 0)$.

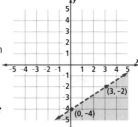

Sentences equivalent to $Ax + By < C$ or $Ax + By \leq C$ are called **linear inequalities.** The preceding examples show that there are two steps to graphing linear inequalities.

Graphing Linear Inequalities

Step 1 Graph the corresponding linear equation. Make this boundary line dashed (for < or >) or solid (for ≤ or ≥).

Step 2 Shade the half-plane that makes the inequality true. (You may have to test a point. If possible, use $(0, 0)$.)

Sometimes the graph of all solutions is not an entire half plane.

Example 5

An elevator has a capacity of 2,500 pounds. If an average adult weighs 150 pounds and an average child weighs 80 pounds, how many adults and children can the elevator hold?

Solution Let $A =$ the number of adults on the elevator. Let $C =$ the number of children on the elevator. Then the total weight of the adults and children is $150 \cdot A + 80 \cdot C$ pounds. So the elevator can hold A adults and C children as long as $150A + 80C \leq 2,500$.

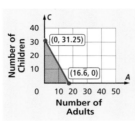

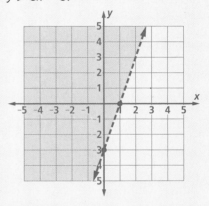

In 1852, Elisha Graves Otis invented the first safety brake for elevators.

Source: www.ideafinder.com

We can make either variable be first. We choose A to be the horizontal coordinate and C to be the vertical coordinate. Notice that the domain of both A and C is the set of nonnegative integers. So the graph will have no points in Quadrants II, III, or IV. To graph the boundary line $150A + 80C = 2,500$, we find its intercepts.

When $A = 0$, $C = \frac{2,500}{80} = 31.25$.

When $C = 0$, $A = \frac{2,500}{150} = 16.\overline{6}$.

(continued on next page)

Graphing Linear Inequalities **383**

Notes on the Lesson

Example 5 All points on the graph lie on or inside the triangle formed by the lines and axes. But only the lattice points (those with integer coordinates) make sense in the problem. Still, it is customary to shade the entire region because it is easier to do so than to draw the large number of individual points.

Additional Examples

Example 3 Draw the graph of $y > 3x - 3$.

Example 4 Graph $-3x + 5y < -15$.

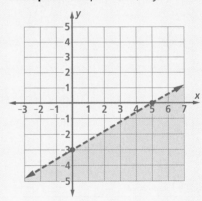

Example 5 You have $20 to spend on party decorations. Ribbon costs $1.50 a roll and balloons cost $2.00 per package. How many rolls of ribbon and packages of balloons can you buy? Let r be the number of rolls of ribbon purchased and b be the number of packages of balloons purchased. The solution is the set of points on or below the line $1.5r + 2b = 20$ in which both coordinates are nonnegative integers.

6-9

3 Assignment

Recommended Assignment
- Questions 1–21
- Question 22 (extra credit)
- Reading Lesson 7-1
- Covering the Ideas 7-1

1b.
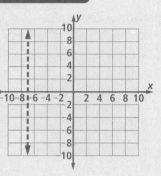

2b.
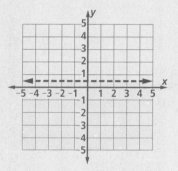

Because the elevator can hold 0 adults and 0 children, (0, 0) is a solution. So the points will be those on or below the line $150A + 80C = 2,500$ in which both coordinates are nonnegative integers. Although the graph is shaded for all rational numbers in the region, integers are the only possible values for A and C.

STOP QY

▶ **QY**

If no children are on the elevator in Example 5, use the graph to find the maximum number of adults it can hold.

Questions

COVERING THE IDEAS

1. **a.** Graph $\{x: x > -7\}$
   b. Graph $\{(x, y): x > -7\}$
   See margin.

2. **a.** Graph $\{y: y < 0.5\}$
   b. Graph $\{(x, y): y < 0.5\}$
   See margin.

1a.

2a.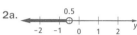

In 3 and 4, write an inequality describing the graph.

3.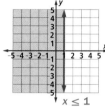
$x \le 1$

4.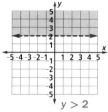
$y > 2$

5. **a. Fill in the Blank** A line separates a plane into two distinct regions called ___?___. half-planes
   b. Fill in the Blank The line in Part a is called a ___?___ line.
   boundary

6. Match the inequality with its graph.

a. iv 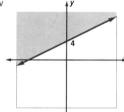   **b. iii** 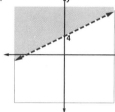   **c. i**

i. $y < \frac{1}{2}x + 4$ ii. $y \le \frac{1}{2}x + 4$

iii. $y > \frac{1}{2}x + 4$ iv. $y \ge \frac{1}{2}x + 4$

7. What is the difference between the graphs of $y < -2x + 6$ and $y \le -2x + 6$?

8. **True or False** The ordered pair (1, 3) is a solution to $y < -2x + 6$.
   true

7. The first is the graph of the half-plane under $y = -2x + 6$ *excluding* the line $y = -2x + 6$; the second is the same half-plane *including* the line.

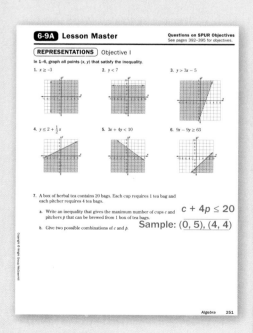
Accommodating the Learner

Ask students to graph the linear inequality $3x - 2y \le 12$ by first graphing the line $3x - 2y = 12$. Instruct them to identify on which side of the line each lies: (4, –4), (0, 0), (0, –8), (–2, 5). Students should test each point to determine whether it satisfies the inequality. Once a point is tested, have students shade the appropriate side of the line. In most cases the students are not given the points to test but must pick them. Ask students to name a point that might not be a good test point. Have them explain their reason for choosing the point.

In 9 and 10, graph all points (x, y) that satisfy the inequality.

9–10. See margin.

9. $x + y < 3$ 10. $y \geq 2x - 5$

11. A person in another country read Example 5 and felt the weights should be in kilograms rather than pounds. So here is a similar situation, but using kilograms. An elevator has a capacity of 1,100 kg. If an average adult weighs 65 kg and an average child weighs 35 kg, how many adults and children can the elevator hold? Answer this question with an appropriate graph. **See margin.**

APPLYING THE MATHEMATICS

12. The Strikers volleyball team is selling spirit items to raise money. Pom pons (p) cost $7 each and "Go Team!" buttons (b) cost $2.50 each. The team needs to make at least $400. Graph the set of points (p, b) that satisfies these conditions. **See margin.**

13. The scatterplot at the right shows data from the 75 top-ranked players in NCAA Division I men's basketball in 2006. Each point shows the number of field goals a player attempted and the number that the player actually made. **a, c. See margin.**

Source: NCAA

a. Explain why there are no points above the line $y = x$.

b. Write an inequality that represents the half-plane bounded by the line $y = x$ and contains the data points. $y \leq x$

c. Suppose a similar scatterplot of pairs (field goals attempted, field goals actually made) is made for a group of 8-year-old players. How would you expect the graph to look compared to the graph for the Division I players?

14. Suppose a person has less than $4.00 in nickels and dimes. Let n = the number of nickels and d = the number of dimes.

a. Write an inequality to describe this situation. $5n + 10d < 400$

b. Give one example of a combination of nickels and dimes that satisfies the inequality.

c. Graph the number of possible combinations of nickels and dimes. **See margin.**

14b. Answers vary. Sample answer: one nickel and one dime

15. Find a point that satisfies $y \leq x - 6$ but does not satisfy $y < x - 6$. Answers vary. Sample answer: (6, 0)

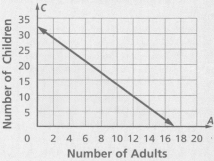

Approximately 14,578 high schools in the U.S. participate in girls' volleyball.

Source: National Federation of State High School Associations

Notes on the Questions

Questions 11 and 12 In both these situations, lattice points in the first quadrant are the only possible solutions.

Question 11 You might ask students if these are appropriate weights for adults and children. Do they remember that 1 pound ≈ 2.2 kilograms?

Question 22 You might try to graph the equation and the inequality using a graphing utility. Students may be surprised at how easily the utilities can deal with these sentences.

Additional Answers

11. The points in the shaded area with integer coordinates are solutions.

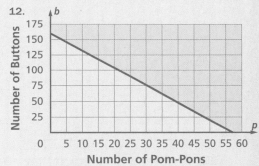

12.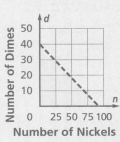

The points of the shaded area with integer coordinates are solutions.

13a. It would imply that someone made more field goals than he attempted!

13c. Answers vary. Sample answer: The points would lie farther away from the x-axis.

14c. The points of the shaded region with integer coordinates are solutions.

Additional Answers

9.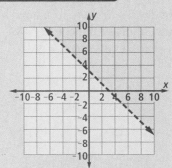

10.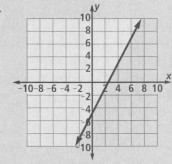

4 Wrap-Up

Ongoing Assessment

Ask students to write down a linear inequality that requires the shading to be above the line but does not include the line. Instruct them to graph their inequalities. Repeat by asking students to write down and graph an inequality that requires the shading to be below the line and does include the line. Check their work.

Project Update

Project 1, Marriage Age, on page 387, relates to the content of this lesson.

Additional Answers

22.

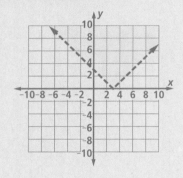

16. Refer to the graph at the right.
    a. Find an equation of the boundary line. $y = -1.5x + 0.5$
    b. Determine the inequality that is graphed. $y \geq -1.5x + 0.5$

REVIEW

17. Anna and Dion are selling cakes for a bake sale. Some cost $8 and some cost $12. They forgot to keep track of the number of each type of cake they sold, but when the bake sale was over they had collected $288. Let x = the number of $8 cakes, and y = the number of $12 cakes. (**Lessons 6-8, 6-6**)
    a. Write an equation in standard form describing the relationship between x and y. $8x + 12y = 288$
    b. Find the number of $12 cakes sold if only $12 cakes were sold. **24**
    c. Find the number of $12 cakes sold if fifteen $8 cakes were sold. **14**

18. a. Rewrite $5x - 36 = 3y$ in standard form. $5x + -3y = 36$
    b. Give the values of A, B, and C from the standard form of an equation. (**Lesson 6-8**) $A = 5, B = -3, C = 36$

19. The weight of an object on the moon is one-sixth its weight on Earth. (**Lesson 3-4**)
    a. Write an equation relating an object's weight y on the moon to its weight x on Earth. $y = \frac{1}{6}x$
    b. How much will a 171-pound man carrying a 9-pound camera weigh on the moon? **30 lb**
    c. If a backpack weighs 6.2 lb on the moon, how much does it weigh on Earth? **37.2 lb**

20. Evaluate each of the following. (**Lesson 1-1**)
    a. 3^4 **81**
    b. $(-4)^3$ **-64**
    c. $(-2)^8$ **256**

21. Rewrite each expression in decimal form. (**Previous Course**)
    a. $1 \cdot 10^{-2}$ **0.01**
    b. $6 \cdot 10^{-3}$ **0.006**
    c. $3 \cdot 4 \cdot 10^{-6}$ **0.000012**

EXPLORATION

22. In previous lessons you graphed equations like $y = |x - 3|$ using tables. Graph $y = |x - 3|$; then shade the appropriate region to represent the inequality $y > |x - 3|$. Check a point to verify that your shading is correct. **See margin for graph. Answers vary. Sample answer: (10, 0); 0 $\not>$ |10 − 3|**

QY ANSWER

16 adults

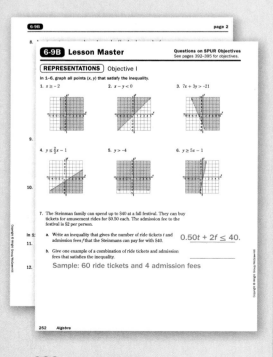

Extension

Students can use their graphing calculators to graph linear inequalities. Suppose students are asked to graph $y \leq -2x + 3$. Using the Y= command, set Y1 = $-2x + 3$. Next, position the cursor over the \ icon to the left of Y1. Have students press the ENTER command slowly but repeatedly. The icon will switch from one character to another until it returns to \. To shade above the line, the icon must be set to ▜.

To shade below the line, the icon must be set to ▙. Have students choose the less-than icon and graph the inequality.

Chapter 6 Projects

1 Marriage Age

Below are some data on the ages at which men and women first married in the second half of the 20th century.

Median Age at First Marriage		
Year	Men	Women
1950	22.8	20.3
1960	22.8	20.3
1970	23.2	20.8
1980	24.7	22.0
1990	26.1	23.9
2000	26.8	25.1

Source: U.S. Census Bureau

a. Plot all the data on one graph. What seems to be the trend shown by these data?

b. Calculate the lines of best fit (one for men and one for women). What do these lines predict about the ages at first marriage for the year 2050? For the year 3000? For the year 1800?

c. Look up the data for the years 1900–1940 at 10-year intervals. Plot these data on a new graph and make two more lines of best fit. What is your prediction for the year 2050? Which of the two sets of lines of best fit do you think will better predict the correct ages for 2050, and why?

2 Paper Towels: Price vs. Absorbency

Are expensive paper towels more absorbent than less expensive ones? Get samples of about six different kinds of paper towels, record their prices, and calculate the price paid per towel. Perform the following experiment to measure absorbency. Fold one piece of towel in half vertically, and then in half again horizontally.

Fill an eyedropper with a fixed amount of water and drop it on the corner with the folds.

Open the towel and measure and record the diameter of the circular area that is wet.

Repeat for each type of towel you have, making sure you use the same amount of water each time.

a. Plot your data with unit price on the horizontal axis and diameter on the vertical axis. Is the relation linear? If so, find a line to describe your data.

b. Plot your data with unit price on the horizontal axis and the area of the wet region on the vertical axis. If the relation is linear, describe it with a line.

c. What advice would you give someone shopping for paper towels?

Project Rubric

Advanced	Student correctly provides all of the details asked for in the project as well as additional correct independent conclusions.
Proficient	Student correctly provides all of the details asked for in the project.
Partially proficient	Student correctly provides some of the details asked for in the project or provides all details with some inaccuracies.
Not proficient	Student correctly provides few of the details asked for in the project or provides all details with many inaccuracies.
No attempt	Student makes little or no attempt to complete the project.

Chapter 6

The projects relate to the content of the lessons of this chapter as follows:

Project	Lesson(s)
1	6-9
2	6-7
3	6-5
4	6-6

1 Marriage Age

Not only should students look at the data, calculate the lines of best fit, and make their predictions, but they should also try to explain the trend. Why is it that from 1950 to 1970 both men's and women's average age for marriage rose only 0.5 years? Why did both of them begin to rise more quickly in the 1980s? Why do they appear to continue to be rising? Are there any reasons students can think of that might change this trend?

2 Paper Towels: Price vs. Absorbency

Consider asking students to expand upon this project to include a paragraph or two on which paper towel is the best value. Size and absorbency may not be the overriding factors in determining which towel to buy. At some point the increase in diameter and absorbency may not be worth the increase in cost per towel. Included in these paragraphs should be several reasons for buying paper towels in the first place and how these purposes relate to their choice of towel to purchase. Although students may not get too excited about paper towels, it is worth the time to get students to begin to understand that many factors need to be considered before making a purchase.

3 The Diagonal Game

It would help students if they actually modeled this game on a coordinate grid. The grid needs to be big enough that students can clearly graph and label everything. Suggest they make their coordinate system the size of a full sheet of paper. Neatness is critical in this activity. Working in groups might be a good idea for this activity.

4 Slopes of Perpendicular Lines

Suggest to students that they should carefully organize their data in this activity. Building a table for each set of data would be a good idea. Not only should each table include the ordered pairs, but it also should include the slope of the line containing successive points and the slope of the perpendicular line. You may have to explain the best way to organize the data.

3 The Diagonal Game

Choose a point (x, y), where both x and y are integers. The goal of the diagonal game is to start at the point $(0, 0)$ and end at the point (x, y), while following these two rules.

Rule 1 You may travel only along lines whose slope is 1 or –1.

Rule 2 At any point (m, n) where both m and n are integers, you may leave the line you were traveling along for a different line (with slope 1 or –1) that passes through that point. For example, suppose $(x, y) = (3, 1)$. You could travel along the line $y = -x$ until you hit the point $(1, -1)$, and then follow the line $y = x - 2$ until you hit the point $(3, 1)$.

a. Play the diagonal game in order to reach the points $(1, 3)$, $(4, -2)$, and $(-5, -1)$. Describe the lines you traveled along and the points at which you switched. At the point or points (m, n) where you switched, calculate $m + n$.

b. How many different lines did you have to travel along to reach each point? Could it have been done with fewer lines?

c. Some points cannot be reached by playing the diagonal game. One such point is $(0, 1)$. Explain why this point cannot be reached. (*Hint:* What do all the numbers $m + n$ that you calculated in Part a have in common?)

d. Suppose that Rule 1 of the game changed to say that you could travel along lines whose slope is 1, –1, or a. Give an example of a value of a that will allow you to reach the point $(1, 0)$

4 Slopes of Perpendicular Lines

a. For each row of the table below, find an equation for a line with the indicated slope. Then, by experimenting on a graph, find an equation for a line that is perpendicular to the line you have found. Finally, give the slope of the perpendicular line. Record your information in a table like the one shown below.

Slope m	Equation of Line	Equation of Line Perpendicular to Line with Slope m	Slope of Line Perpendicular to Line with Slope m
2			
5			
$\frac{1}{4}$			
–3			
$-\frac{2}{3}$			

b. If a line ℓ has a positive slope, what sign is the slope of a line that is perpendicular to ℓ? If a line ℓ has a negative slope, what sign is the slope of a line that is perpendicular to ℓ?

c. Find a formula relating the slope of a line you started with to the slope of a line perpendicular to it. That is, find a relationship between the numbers in the far left and far right columns of the table.

d. Use the relationship you have found in Part c to determine an equation for the line that is perpendicular to the line with equation $y = -4x + 5$ and containing the point $(1, 3)$.

Notes

Chapter 6 Summary and Vocabulary

○ The rate of change between two points (x_1, y_1) and (x_2, y_2) is $\frac{y_2 - y_1}{x_2 - x_1}$.

○ When points all lie on the same line, the rate of change between them is constant and is called the slope of the line. The slope tells how much the line rises or falls for every move of one unit to the right. When the slope is positive, the line goes up and to the right. When the slope is negative, the line goes down and to the right. When the slope is 0, the line is horizontal. The slope of vertical lines is undefined.

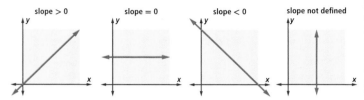

○ Constant-increase or constant-decrease situations lead naturally to linear equations of the form $y = mx + b$. The graph of the set of points (x, y) satisfying this equation is a line with slope m and y-intercept b. Linear-combination situations lead naturally to linear equations in the standard form $Ax + By = C$. When the $=$ sign in equations of either form is replaced by $<$ or $>$, the graph of the resulting linear inequality is a half-plane, the set of points on one side of a line. If the inequality is $\leq$ or $\geq$, the boundary line is included in the graph.

○ A line is determined by any point on it and its slope or by two points on the line. Its equation can be found from this information. If data are roughly linear, they can be modeled by lines. One model, the line of best fit or least-squares line, is easily found using a calculator or computer.

Theorems and Properties

Slope-Intercept Equation of a Line (p. 350)
Point-Slope Equation of a Line (p. 357)

Vocabulary

6-1
rate of change
rate unit

6-2
slope

6-4
y-intercept
slope-intercept form
direct variation

6-5
point-slope form
x-intercept

6-7
line of best fit
linear regression
least squares line

6-8
linear combination
standard form of an
    equation for a line
oblique

6-9
boundary line
half-planes
linear inequalities

Summary and Vocabulary

The Summary gives an overview of the entire chapter and provides an opportunity for students to consider the material as a whole. Thus, the Summary can be used to help students relate and unify the concepts presented in the chapter.

Terms and symbols are listed by lesson to provide a checklist of concepts that students must know. Emphasize to students that they should read the vocabulary list carefully before starting the Self-Test on the next page. If students do not understand the meaning of a term, they should refer back to the indicated lesson.

Theorems and Properties covered in the chapter are listed below the Summary, with page references included to lead students back to the location in the chapter where the theorem or property is stated.

Self-Test

For the development of mathematical competence, feedback and correction, along with the opportunity for practice, are necessary. The Self-Test provides the opportunity for feedback and correction; the Chapter Review provides additional opportunities for practice. We cannot overemphasize the importance of these end-of-chapter materials. It is at this point that the material gels for many students, allowing them to solidify skills and understanding. In general, student performance should improve after they complete these pages.

Assign the Self-Test as a one-night assignment. Worked-out solutions for all questions are in the Selected Answers section of the student book. Encourage students to take the Self-Test honestly, grade themselves, and then be prepared to discuss the test in class.

Advise students to pay special attention to those Chapter Review questions (pages 392–395) that correspond to the questions they missed on the Self-Test.

Additional Answers

2. No, because the slope between $(8, 2)$ and $(18, -6)$ is $\frac{2 - (-6)}{8 - 18} = \frac{8}{-10} = -\frac{4}{5}$, while the slope between $(18, -6)$ and $(12, -1)$ is $\frac{-1 - (-6)}{12 - 18} = \frac{5}{-6} = -\frac{5}{6}$. All points on a line have the same slope between them.

8. $y = \frac{1}{2}x + -\frac{1}{4}$; slope $= \frac{1}{2}$, y-intercept $= -\frac{1}{4}$

9b. The values are points with integer coordinates in the shaded area.

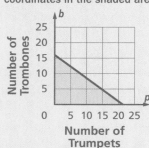

11. $\frac{103{,}111 - 96{,}500}{2004 - 1999} = 1{,}322.2$ people per year

---

Chapter 6 Self-Test

Take this test as you would take a test in class. You will need a calculator. Then use the Selected Answers section in the back of the book to check your work.

1. Refer to the line graphed below.

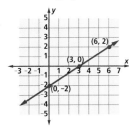

   a. Find its y-intercept. −2
   b. Find its x-intercept. 3
   c. Find its slope. $\frac{-2 - 0}{0 - 3} = \frac{-2}{-3} = \frac{2}{3}$

2. Do the points $(8, 2)$, $(18, -6)$, and $(12, -1)$ lie on the same line? Justify your answer. See margin.

3. Find an equation of the line with slope $\frac{8}{9}$ and y-intercept −12. $y = \frac{8}{9}x - 12$

4. The temperature at 8 A.M. is 58°F and is expected to rise 3°F each hour until 4 P.M. Write an equation in slope-intercept form to find the temperature T for each hour h from 8 A.M. to 4 P.M.
   $T = 3h + 58$, where h is hours after 8 A.M.

5. Describe the slope of every vertical line.
   The slope of a vertical line is undefined.

6. Rewrite the equation $8 - 3x = y$ in standard form $Ax + By = C$ and give the values of A, B, and C. $3x + y = 8$; $A = 3$, $B = 1$, and $C = 8$

7. If the slope of a line is $-\frac{1}{2}$, how does the y-coordinate change as you go one unit to the right? It will go down $\frac{1}{2}$ of a unit.

8. Find the slope and y-intercept of the line with equation $4x - 8y = 2$. See margin.

9. Lenny has $6,400 to spend at a music store buying trumpets and trombones for a jazz band. Suppose the cost of each trumpet p is $300 and the cost of each trombone b is $400.
   a. Write an inequality that describes all possible values of p and b.
   $6{,}400 \geq 300p + 400b$
   b. Graph these values. See margin.

In 10 and 11, use the following data of average yearly attendance at Pennsylvania State University football games.

Year	Average Attendance
1999	96,500
2000	95,543
2001	107,576
2002	107,239
2003	105,629
2004	103,111

Source: NCAA

10. Between which two consecutive years was there the greatest decrease in average yearly attendance? 2003 and 2004

11. What is the rate of change in average yearly attendance from 1999 to 2004? See margin.

In 12 and 13, graph the sentence.

12. $y = \frac{3}{8}x - \frac{5}{8}$ 13. $y \leq 6 - 4x$

12–13. See margin.

14. After driving for 22 miles, the gas tank in Masao's car had 14 gallons of gas. After 132 miles, the gas tank had 9 gallons of gas. Find a linear equation relating the amount of gas y in Masao's gas tank to the miles he has driven x. See margin.

Additional Answers

12.

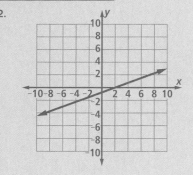

13.

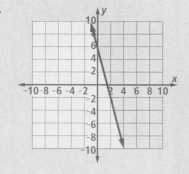

15. Find another point on the line through the point $(-4, 0)$ with slope $\frac{5}{4}$. **See margin.**

In 16 and 17, consider the data table and scatterplot that show the annual salary of employees of a company and the number of years they have worked for the company.

Years of Employment	Average Annual Salary (in thousands)
2	$35
3	$40
4	$39
5	$45
6	$60
7	$55
8	$62
9	$64
10	$68
12	$63
13	$75
15	$78
16	$80
17	$88
19	$82

16. **a.** Find the coordinates of two points on a line that you estimate would fit these data.

   b. Write an equation for your line in slope-intercept form. **See margin.**

16a. Answers vary. Sample answer: (2, 35) and (15, 78)

c. Use the equation from Part b to estimate the annual salary of an employee who has worked at the company for 25 years. **See margin.**

17. Find an equation for the line of best fit for the data. $y = 2.98x + 33.28$

In 18 and 19, use the graph of lines *a*, *b*, *c*, and *d* below.

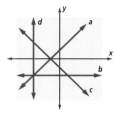

18. **a.** Name the line that has a negative slope. *c*
   b. Name the line that has a slope of 0. *b*

19. **a.** Which line could represent money in an account over time where money is added to the account at a constant rate? *a*
   b. Name the line that has an *x*-intercept but does not have a *y*-intercept. *d*

20. Felipe has only *x* ten-dollar bills and *y* five-dollar bills in his wallet. Graph all possible values of *x* and *y* if the total amount of money in his wallet is less than $100. **See margin.**

21. Patrick left his apartment and headed down the building stairs. He descended at a constant rate of 3 flights per minute. After 4 minutes, he was on the 10th floor.

   a. Write an equation in point-slope form relating the floor Patrick was on, *y*, to the number of minutes, *x*, it has been since he left. $y - 10 = -3(x - 4)$

   b. Use your equation to find the floor of Patrick's apartment. **See margin.**

Chapter **6** Review

Assessment

Evaluation The *Assessment Resources* provide five forms of the Chapter 6 Test. Forms A and B present parallel versions of a short-answer format. Form C consists of four to six short-response questions that cover the SPUR objectives from Chapter 6. Form D offers performance assessment that covers a subset (or even just one) of the SPUR objectives for the chapter. The fifth type of test is a Chapter 6 Test, Cumulative Form. About 50% of this test covers Chapter 6, and the remaining 50% covers the previous 5 chapters evenly.

Feedback After students have taken the test for Chapter 6 and you have scored the results, return the tests to students for discussion. Class discussion on the questions that caused trouble for most students can be very effective in identifying and clarifying misunderstandings. You might want to have them note the items they missed and work either in groups or at home to correct them. It is important for students to receive feedback on every chapter test, and we recommend that students see and correct their mistakes before proceeding too far into the next chapter.

Additional Answers

20. $10x + 5y < 100$; the points with integer coordinates in the shaded area are solutions.

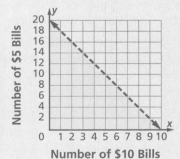

21b. Let $x = 0$. Then $y - 10 = -3(0 - 4)$ so $y - 10 = 12$, so $y = 22$. Patrick lives on the 22nd floor.

Additional Answers

14. The points (22, 14) and (132, 9) imply $m = \frac{14 - 9}{22 - 132} = -\frac{5}{110} = -\frac{1}{22}$. So, $y = -\frac{1}{22}x + b$. Substituting (22, 14), $14 = -\frac{1}{22}(22) + b$, so $b = 15$, and $y = -\frac{1}{22}x + 15$.

15. Answers vary. Sample answer: $y = \frac{5}{4}x + b$; $0 = \frac{5}{4}(-4)$, $0 = -5 + b$, $b = 5$; An equation of the line is $y = \frac{5}{4}x + 5$, so another point on the line is (0, 5).

16b. $m = \frac{78 - 35}{15 - 2} = \frac{43}{13} \approx 3.31$; Substitute (2, 35), so $35 = 3.31(2) + b$, $35 = 6.62 + b$, so $b = 28.38$; $y = 3.31x + 28.38$

16c. $y = 331(25) + 28.38 = 111.13$; $111,130

Chapter Review

The main objectives for the chapter are organized in the Chapter Review under the four types of understanding this book promotes—Skills, Properties, Uses, and Representations.

Whereas end-of-chapter material may be considered optional in some texts, in *UCSMP Algebra* we have selected these objectives and questions with the expectation that they will be covered. Students should be able to answer these questions with about 85% accuracy after studying the chapter.

You may assign these questions over a single night to help students prepare for a test the next day, or you may assign the questions over a two-day period. If you work the questions over two days, then we recommend assigning the *evens* for homework the first night so that students get feedback in class the next day, and then assigning the *odds* the night before the test because the answers are provided to the odd-numbered questions in the Selected Answers at the back of the book.

It is effective to ask students which questions they still do not understand and use the day as a total class discussion of the material that the class finds most difficult.

Resources

• Assessment Resources: Chapter 6 Test, Forms A–D; Chapter 6 Test, Cumulative Form; Comprehensive Test, Chapters 1–6

Additional Answers

4. Answers vary. Sample answer:
   Using C and E: $\frac{4-2}{3-0} = \frac{2}{3}$, using D and
   C: $\frac{2-0}{0-(-3)} = \frac{2}{3}$

17. Answers vary. Sample answer:
   $x + -2y = -14$, $A = 1$, $B = -2$,
   $C = -14$

18. Answers vary. Sample answer:
   $-\frac{7}{16}x + y = 14$, $A = -\frac{7}{16}$, $B = 1$,
   $C = 14$

Chapter **6** Chapter Review

SKILLS   Procedures used to get answers

OBJECTIVE A Find the slope of the line through two given points. (Lesson 6-2)

1. Calculate the slope of the line containing (2, 9) and (7, 15). $\frac{6}{5}$

2. Calculate the slope of the line through (−5, 1) and (−8, −8). 3

3. Find the slope of line ℓ below. $-\frac{5}{2}$

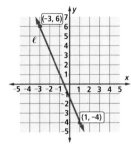

4. Using two different pairs of points, show that the slope of line m below is $\frac{2}{3}$. See margin.

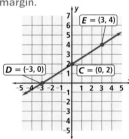

5. The points (3, −1) and (5, y) are on a line with slope 2. What is y? $y = 3$

6. The points (x, −6) and (2, 12) are on a line with slope $-\frac{3}{4}$. What is x? $x = 26$

OBJECTIVE B Find an equation for a line given either its slope and any point or two points on it. (Lessons 6-4, 6-5, 6-6)

7. Give an equation for the line with slope $2\frac{3}{5}$ and y-intercept 7. $y = 2.6x + 7$

8. What is an equation for the line with slope s and y-intercept t? $y = sx + t$

In 9–11, find an equation for the line through the given point with slope m.

9. (−5, 20), $m = -0.5$ $y - 20 = -0.5(x + 5)$

10. (18, −16), $m = 0$ $y = -16$

11. (30, 0.25), $m = 3$ $y - 0.25 = 3(x - 30)$

12. What is an equation for the line through (19, −11) with undefined slope? $x = 19$

In 13–16, find an equation for the line through the two given points. 13. $y - 4 = \frac{3}{2}(x - 3)$ 14. $y = \frac{9}{8}x$

13. (3, 4), (1, 1)   14. (−16, −18), (0, 0)

15. (−3, −8), (−3, 8)   16. (1, 1), (2, 1)
    $x = -3$ $y = 1$

OBJECTIVE C Write an equation for a line in standard form or slope-intercept form, and using either form find its slope and y-intercept. (Lessons 6-4, 6-8)
17–18. See margin.
In 17 and 18, write the equation in the form $Ax + By = C$. Then give the values of A, B, and C.

17. $x + 14 = 2y$ 18. $y = \frac{7}{16}x + 14$

In 19 and 20, rewrite the equation in slope-intercept form.

19. $8x + 4y = 10$ 20. $30x - 90y = 270$
    $y = -2x + \frac{5}{2}$ $y = \frac{1}{3}x - 3$

Additional Answers

21. slope = 12, y-intercept = −6.2

22. slope = $\frac{1}{2}$, y-intercept = $-\frac{1}{3}$

23. slope = −1, y-intercept = 0

24. slope = $\frac{1}{3}$, y-intercept = $-166\frac{2}{3}$

31. Any two points on a line can be used to determine the slope of the line. Choosing any two of the points must yield the same slope as any other two points. Therefore, if the slope between any two of the three points is different from the slope of the third point and either of the two points used, the points are not collinear.

---

34. 42.6 subscribers per year

35. 27.4 subscribers per year

40. slope = $0.49/mi, y-intercept = $29.95

41. slope = −$100/day,
    y-intercept = $1,000

48a.
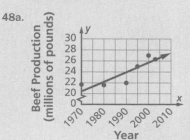

In 21–24, find the slope and *y*-intercept of the line.

21. $y = 12x - 6.2$

22. $3x - 6y = 2$

23. $x + y = 0$

24. $x = 3y + 500$
21–24. See margin.

PROPERTIES The principles behind the mathematics

OBJECTIVE D Use the definition and properties of slope. (Lessons 6-2, 6-3)

25. **Fill in the Blanks** The slope determined by two points is the change in the __?__ coordinates divided by the __?__ in the *x*-coordinates. *y*-, change

26. **Fill in the Blanks** Slope is the amount of change in the __?__ of the graph for every change of one unit to the __?__. *y*-coordinate, right

In 27 and 28, five lines are shown below, including the *x*-axis and *y*-axis.

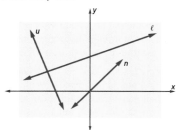

27. Which line or lines have negative slope? *u*

28. Which line or lines have positive slope? *n*, *ℓ*

29. What is the slope of the line with equation $y = 5$? 0

30. What is true about the slope of the line with equation $x = 2$? The slope is undefined.

31. How can you use slope to show that three points do not all lie on the same line?
See margin.

USES Applications of mathematics in real-world situations

OBJECTIVE E Calculate rates of change from real data and describe their real-world meanings. (Lessons 6-1, 6-3)

32. Consider the following ordered pairs of hours worked and pay received: (12, $93.60), (15, $117.00), (17, $132.60).

a. Calculate the slope of the line through these points. $\frac{39}{7.8}$

b. What does the slope represent in this situation? It is the hourly wage.

33. The picture below represents a ski slope. What is the slope of this ski slope? $-\frac{1}{5}$

200 m

1,000 m

In 34–36, use the table below that shows the number of subscribers to a magazine. 34–35. See margin.

Year	Subscribers
1985	1,145
1990	1,358
1995	1,601
2000	1,886
2005	2,023

34. Find the rate of change of the number of subscribers from 1985 to 1990.

35. Find the rate of change of the number of subscribers from 2000 to 2005.

36. a. According to these data, in which ten-year period did the number of subscribers increase the fastest? 1990 to 2000

b. What is this rate of change? 52.8 subscribers per year

50.

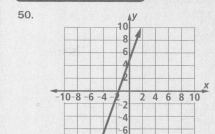

51.

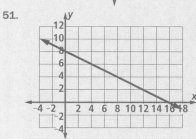

52.

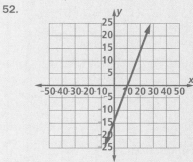

53.

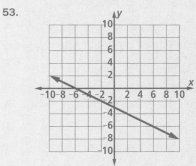

48b. Answers vary. Sample answer:
$y = 180x - 334,234$

48c. Answers vary. Sample answer:
27,566 million lb

48d. $y = 178.646x - 331,234$; 27,832.4 million lb

49a. Answers vary. Sample answer:

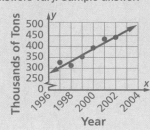

49b. Answers vary. Sample answer: 25

49c. It indicates how many additional tons of fish, crustaceans, and mollusks are being caught in the Philippines each year.

49d. Answers vary. Sample answer:
$T = 25y - 49,600$, where *T* is the thousands of tons and *y* is the year

49e. $T = 28.2y - 56,008$

49f. Answers vary. Sample answer: The equation in (d) predicts a value 24 thousand tons less (650) than the regression line (674).

Additional Answers

40, 41, 48–53. See answers on pages 392 and 393.

54.
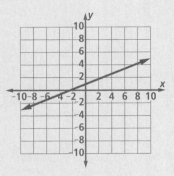

55.
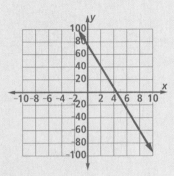

56.
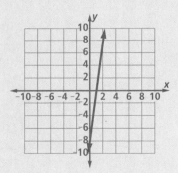

57.
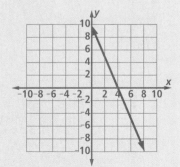

In 37–39, use the table below of mean Fahrenheit temperatures each month in Fairbanks, Alaska, based on records from 1971–2000.

Month	Month Number	Mean (°F)
Jan.	1	−10
Feb.	2	−4
Mar.	3	11
Apr.	4	32
May	5	49
Jun.	6	60
Jul.	7	62
Aug.	8	56
Sept.	9	45
Oct.	10	24
Nov.	11	2
Dec.	12	−6

Source: National Climatic Data Center

37. Find the average rate of change of temperature per month from July to December. −13.6 °F/month

38. Between which two months is the rate of change of temperature per month the greatest? **March and April**

39. Between which two months is the rate of change of temperature per month the least (it will be negative)? **October and November**

OBJECTIVE F Use equations for lines to describe real situations. (Lessons 6-4, 6-5, 6-6, 6-8)

In 40 and 41, each situation can be represented by a straight line. Give the slope and y-intercept of the line describing this situation. 40–41. See margin.

40. Julie rents a truck. She pays an initial fee of $29.95 and then $0.49 per mile driven. Let y be the cost of driving x miles.

41. Nestor is given $1,000 to spend on a vacation. He decides to spend at most $100 a day. Let y be the minimal amount Nestor has left after x days.

42. The 28th Summer Olympic games were in 2004. The 27th summer Olympic games were 4 years earlier. Let y be the year of the nth summer Olympic games. Give a linear equation which relates n and y. $y = 4n + 1892$

In 43 and 44, each situation leads to an equation of the form $y = mx + b$. Find that equation.

43. A stack of 25 small paper cups is 8 in. high. Each additional cup adds $\frac{1}{4}$ inch to the stack. Let y be the height of the stack when there are x cups. $y = 0.25x + 1.75$

44. A plane loses altitude at the rate of 5 m/sec. It begins at an altitude of 8,000 m. Let y be its altitude after x seconds. $y = -5x + 8,000$

45. Each month, about 50 new people move into a town. After 5 months, the town has 25,600 people. Write an equation relating the number of months m to the number of people p in the town. $p = 50m + 25,350$

46. On March 2, 1962, Wilt Chamberlain scored 100 points in a professional basketball game. At this time, only free throws worth one point and baskets worth two points were possible. (There were no 3-point shots.) Let F be the number of free throws and B be the number of baskets a team might make to score a total of 100 points. What equation do F and B satisfy? $100 = 2B + F$

47. Roberto baby-sat for $7 an hour and worked in a store for $8 an hour. He earned a total of $820. Write an equation that describes the possible hours B of baby-sitting and hours S of store work that he could have worked at those jobs. $820 = 8S + 7B$

Additional Answers

59. The possible values are points (n, q) with integer coordinates in the shaded area.

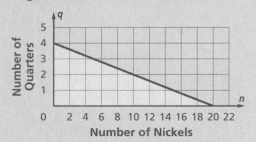

60.
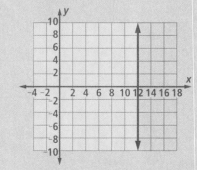

OBJECTIVE G Given data whose graph is approximately linear, find a linear equation to fit the graph and make predictions about data values. (Lesson 6-7)

48. Beef production in the United States has tended to increase since 1970. Here is the production in selected years.

Year	Beef Production (millions of pounds)
1970	21,684
1980	21,643
1990	22,743
1995	25,525
2000	27,338
2003	26,339

Source: U.S. Dept. of Agriculture

48a–d. See margin.

a. Graph the data and draw a line of fit.

b. Find an equation for your line.

c. Use the equation to predict the amount of U.S. beef production in 2010.

d. Calculate the line of best fit for these data. Use that line to predict the amount of U.S. beef production in 2010.

49. The table below shows the number of fish, crustaceans, and mollusks caught in the Philippines from 1997 to 2002.

Year	Weight (thousands of tons)
1997	327
1998	313
1999	353
2000	394
2001	435
2002	443

Source: Food and Agricultural Organization of the United Nations

49a–f. See margin.

a. Graph the data and eyeball a line to fit the data.

b. Find the slope of the fitted line.

c. Explain what the slope tells you about the trend in the data.

d. Find an equation for the eyeballed line.

e. Find an equation for the line of best fit for these data.

f. By how much do your line and the line of best fit differ in their predictions for the number of tons that would be caught in 2010?

REPRESENTATIONS Pictures, graphs, or objects that illustrate concepts

OBJECTIVE H Graph a line given its equation, or given a point and its slope. (Lessons 6-3, 6-4, 6-8)

In 50–53, graph the line with the given equation.

50. $y = 3x + 5$

51. $y = -\frac{1}{2}x + 8$

52. $7x - 5y = 70$

53. $x + 2y = -6$

50–53. See margin.

In 54–57, graph the line satisfying the given condition. 54–57. See margin.

54. passes through $(0, 1)$ with a slope of 0.4

55. passes through $(4, 7)$ with a slope of -17

56. slope 8 and y-intercept -8

57. slope $-2\frac{1}{2}$ and y-intercept 10

OBJECTIVE I Graph linear inequalities. (Lesson 6-9)

58. Choose the correct words. The graph of a linear inequality with a $<$ sign is a (line, plane, half-plane) that (does, does not) contain its boundary line.
half-plane, does not

59. If you have only n nickels and q quarters and a total of less than \$1.00, graph all possible values of n and q. See margin.

In 60–65, graph the inequality on the coordinate plane.

60. $x \leq 12$

61. $y \geq 4.5$

62. $y \geq 2x + 1$

63. $y < -x + 5$

64. $2x - 5y < 10$

65. $x + 4y \geq 0$

60–65. See margin.

63.

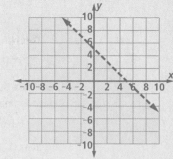

64.

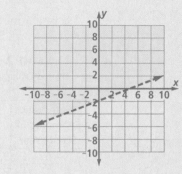

65.

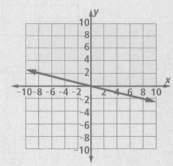

61.

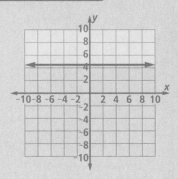

62.

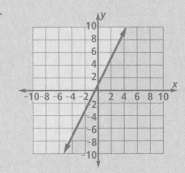

Selected Answers

Chapter 1

Lesson 1-1 (pp. 6–12)

Guided Example 2: $\left(\frac{6.8 - w}{n + w}\right)^3$; $\left(\frac{6.8 - 0.5}{21 + 0.5}\right)^3$;

$((6.8 - 0.5)/(21 + 0.5))\char`^3$; 0.025

Questions: 1. 24 **3.** 81 **5.** –105 **7. a.** 32 **b.** –16 **9. a.** 500
b. 2,500 **11.** 6 **13.** false, $-13 \neq -9$ **15. a.** $\frac{63}{225} = \frac{28}{100}$

b. yes, by the Transitive Property of Equality **17.** $\frac{1}{-9} \cdot 4$
19. $\frac{6}{55}$ **21.** –$5 **23.** 70 **25.** $617.50 **27.** 22 **29.** 15.08

Lesson 1-2 (pp. 13–19)

Guided Example 1:

a.

Months Since Beginning of School Year	Calculation	Pattern	Magazines in Library
0	3,600	3,600 + 22(0)	3,600
1	3,600 + 22	3,600 + 22(1)	3,622
2	3,600 + 22 + 22	3,600 + 22(2)	3,644
3	3,600 + 22 + 22 + 22	3,600 + 22(3)	3,666

b. Let $m =$ the number of months since the beginning of
the school year; $3,600 + 22m$

Questions: 1. Answers vary. Sample answer: $7 - 7 = 0$
and $2 - 2 = 0$ **3.** Answers vary. Sample answer: $5 \cdot 5 = 5^2$ and $6 \cdot 6 = 6^2$ **5.** $(3 + x) - 2 = 1 + x$ **7. a.** $1,155;
$1,110; $1,065 **b.** $1,200 - 45w$ dollars **9.** C
11. a.

Istu's Age	Christine's Age
9	4
16	11
25	20
89	84

b. $i - 5$ **c.** $(i - 5) + 3$
or $i - 2$ **13. a.** For 1
cut there are 2 pieces;
for 2 there are 4; for
3 there are 6; for 4
there are 8; and for 5
there are 10.
b. Let c be the number of cuts and p be the number of
pieces. Then, $p = 2c$. **15. a.** 0 **b.** No; $xy = yx$ by the
Commutative Property of Multiplication. **17.** –309
19. a. –15 **b.** 420 **21.** $7

Lesson 1-3 (pp. 20–26)

Guided Example 1:

Alf	
n	$(n + 1) + 3 + (n + 1)$
1	7
2	9
3	11
10	25
20	45
35	75

Beth	
n	$5 + 2n$
1	7
2	9
3	11
10	25
20	45
35	75

Questions: 1. a. For $n = 1$, $3n - 2 = 1$; for $n = 2$,
$3n - 2 = 4$; and for $n = 3$, $3n - 2 = 7$ **b.** 298 tiles

3.

x	$3x - 17$
10	13
9	10
8	7
7	4
6	1
5	–2

x	$x - 6 - (11 - 2x)$
10	13
9	10
8	7
7	4
6	1
5	–2

Because the tables have the same values, the two
expressions seem to be equivalent. **5. a.** Answers vary.
Sample answer:

x	$25 + (x - 5)(x + 5)$	x^2
0	0	0
2	4	4
3	9	9
–1	1	1

b. Yes, they appear equivalent. **7. a.** Answers vary.
Sample answer:

x	$x^2 - 4x - 3$	$(x - 3)(x + 1)$
0	–3	–3
2	–7	–3
3	–6	0
–1	2	0

b. No, they are different. **9.** Answers vary. Let $a = 0$
and $b = 1$. Then $(a - 5) + b = -4$ and $a - (5 + b) =$
-6. **11.** $x^2 - x = x(x - 1)$ **13. a.** Answers vary. Sample
answer: $2^2 \cdot 2 = 2^3$ and $(-1)^2 \cdot (-1) = (-1)^3$ **b.** Answers
vary. Sample answer: $3(-1) - (-1) - (-1) = -1$ and
$3(0) - 0 - 0 = 0$ **c.** Answers vary. Sample answer:
$3(3 + 8) = 3(3) + 8(3)$ and $45(3 + 8) = 45(3) + 8(45)$

15. >   **17.** =   **19.** $37.89

Lesson 1-4 (pp. 27–32)

Questions:

1. a.

n	n(n + 2)
1	3
2	8
3	15
4	24
5	35

b.

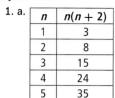

3.

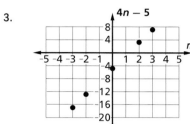

n	4n − 5
−3	−17
−2	−13
0	−5
2	3
3	7

5.

x	Value of Expression
−3	4
0	−2
2	−6
−1	0
−4	6
1	−4

7. a. 5 **b.** 3 and 5
9. Answers vary.
Sample answer:
{x : x is an integer
and x < −8}   **11.**
Scatterplot corresponds
to b.; Connected graph
corresponds to a.

13. d   **15.**

n	2(n − 3)
−5	−16
−3	−12
1	−4
2	−2
5	4

n	2n − 3
−5	−13
−3	−9
1	−1
2	1
5	7

The expressions are not equivalent, since for given
values of n, the expressions give different values.
17. a. For t = 0, t − 2t + 3t = and 2t = 0; for t = 1,
t − 2t + 3t = 2 and 2t = 2; and for t = −2, t − 2t +
3t = −4 and 2t = −4.   **b.** The pattern holds for all real
numbers because the expressions are equivalent.
19. 150.28 cm³   **21.** 18 students

Lesson 1-5 (pp. 33–41)

Questions: 1. −7 ≤ x ≤ 6 and −10 ≤ y ≤ 20

3.

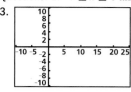

5.

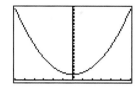 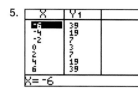

7. a.

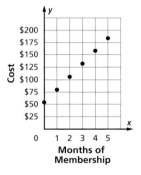

b. Xmin: −4, Xmax: 10,
Ymin: −80, Ymax: 10

9. a.

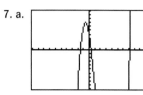

b. Answers vary. Sample
answer: (2, 2), (0, −4),
(−1, −7)   **11.** Answers vary.
Sample answer: −10 ≤ x ≤
10 and −40 ≤ y ≤ 10   **13.**
The expressions are not
equivalent because the
graphs do not overlap
entirely.

15. a. 54 + 26m dollars **b.** Answers vary. Sample answer:

m	54 + 26m
0	$54
1	$80
2	$106
3	$132
4	$158
5	$184

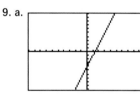

17. d   **19. a.** 9.2 **b.** 8.5 **c.** The air conditioner in Part a
is more efficient because it has a higher EER.   **21.** 0
23. −4   **25.** −19

Lesson 1-6 (pp. 42–46)

Questions: **1. a.** 2,833 ft **b.** −2,907 ft **c.** 2,907 ft
3. a. 75 **b.** 75 **c.** 5 **d.** 75   **5.** 1   **7.** 1
9. Answers vary. Sample answer: $t = -3$
11. a.   **b.**

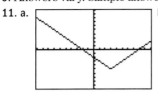   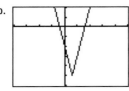

c. Xmin: −15, Xmax: 0, Ymin: −6, Ymax: 10   **13.** 5   **15.** $\frac{1}{2}$
17. a.   **b.** $(1, 0)$ **19.** {5, 6, 7, 8, 9,
10}   **21. a.** 12 **b.** 1

Lesson 1-7 (pp. 47–54)

Questions: **1.** about 2.46 runs

3.

Score	Mean	Deviation	|Absolute Deviation|
21	22	−1	1
15	22	−7	7
25	22	3	3
22	22	0	0
27	22	5	5

m.a.d. = 3.2   **5.** mean = 3, m.a.d. = 1   **7. a**   **9. c**
11. a. For Presidents, the mean is about 5.0 years with a
m.a.d. of about 2.1 years and range of 12, while for the
English rulers, the mean is about 21.9 years with a m.a.d.
of about 12.8 years and range of 63.   **b.** Answers vary.
Sample answer: Presidents have set term-lengths and a
limit to the total amount of terms, whereas rulers, who
may be very old or very young when crowned, typically
reign until death.   **13.** Answers vary. Sample answer:
3, 4, 7, 9, 10, 11, 12   **15.** San Diego   **17.** x-min = −120;
x-max = 60; y-min = −1.5; y-max = 0.5

19.

n	$n^2 - n$
−3	12
−2	6
0	0
2	2
3	6

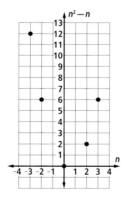

21. a.

Term Number	Number of Toothpicks
1	3
2	5
3	7
4	9
5	11

b. $2n + 1$ **c.** 201

Self-Test (pp. 58–59)

1. a. $9 \cdot 4 + 9 \cdot 6 = 9 \cdot 10; 9 \cdot 4 + 9 \cdot 7 = 9 \cdot 11; 9 \cdot 4 + 9$
$\cdot 8 = 9 \cdot 12$ **b.** Generally, for any x, $9 \cdot 4 + 9 \cdot x = 9 \cdot (x + 4)$.   **2.** Answers vary. Sample answer: $3 \cdot 17 = 17 \cdot 3$
3. $3x \div 7y = 3x \cdot \frac{1}{7y}$ **4.** The total cost for the jerseys is
the cost of a single jersey times the number of jerseys plus
the cost of a single T-shirt times the number of T-shirts,
so Total Cost = $179j + 24t$ dollars.
5. a.

n	$\frac{6n - 12}{3}$	$-4 + 2n$
−5	−14	−14
−3	−10	−10
0	−4	−4
2	0	0

b. Yes. For all values on this table, the two expressions are equal.   **6. a.** $10 + 7 + 7 + 7 = 31$ tiles

b.

n	1	2	3	4	5	6
Tiles	10	17	24	31	38	45

c. The original design has 10 tiles, and each nth design
has an additional $(n - 1) \cdot 7$ tiles, so the nth design has
$10 + (n - 1) \cdot 7$, which simplifies to $3 + 7n$.
6. d.

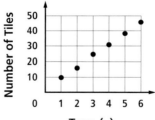

Term (n)

7. a. Answers vary. Sample answer: $m = 0$,
since $\frac{m}{2} + \frac{3}{2} = \frac{0}{2} + \frac{3}{2} = 0 + \frac{3}{2} = \frac{3}{2}$ but $\frac{3 + m}{4} = \frac{3 + 0}{4} = \frac{3}{4}$
b. Answers vary. Sample answer: By the Distributive
Property of Multiplication, we can factor out a $\frac{1}{2}$, and the
definition of division gives the expression $\frac{m + 3}{2}$.
8. a. They appear to be equivalent. **b.** No. For instance,
the value $x = 1$ gives 3.01 for the first expression and 3 for
the second.

9. a. 3 **b.**

x	0	1	2	3	4	5
y	3	2	1	2	3	4

c. B. **10.** Answers vary. Sample answer: x-min $= -2$; x-max $= 20$; y-min $= -20$; y-max $= 2$ **11.** skewed left; The tail is to the left.

12. μ
$$= \frac{6 + 7 + 9 + 8 + 10 + 2 + 7 + 10 + 10 + 9 + 8 + 8 + 9 + 9 + 10}{15},$$
$$\mu = \frac{1(2) + 1(6) + 2(7) + 3(8) + 4(9) + 4(10)}{15} \approx 8.1$$

m.a.d. $=$
$$\frac{|2 - \mu| + |6 - \mu| + |27 - \mu| + |38 - \mu| + |49 - \mu| + |410 - \mu|}{15},$$

m.a.d. $= \dfrac{6.1 + 2.1 + 2(1.1) + 3(0.1) + 4(0.9) + 4(1.9)}{15} \approx 1.5$

13. The m.a.d. is what determines the spread, and since we have a lower m.a.d. in the original data set, there is less spread in the original set.

14. a. 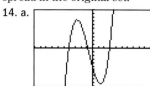 **b.** Answers vary. Sample answer: Xmin $= -4$, Xmax $= -1$, Ymin $= 3$, Ymax $= 8$

The chart below keys the **Self-Test** questions to the objectives in the **Chapter Review** on pages 60–63 or to the **Vocabulary (Voc)** on page 57. This will enable you to locate those **Chapter Review** questions that correspond to questions missed on the **Self-Test.** The lesson where the material is covered is also indicated on the chart.

Question	1	2	3	4	5	6	7	8	9	10
Objective(s)	B	G	F	H	A, C	B	C	L	D, J, K	M
Lesson(s)	1-2, 1-3	1-1, 1-2	1-1	1-2	1-1, 1-3	1-4	1-3	1-4, 1-5, 1-6	1-4, 1-5, 1-6	1-5

Question	11	12	13	14
Objective(s)	I	E, I	I	M
Lesson(s)	1-7	1-7	1-7	1-5

Chapter Review (pp. 60–63)

1. 0.8 **3.** 2.15 **5.** 676 **7.** $-\frac{251}{14}$, or about -17.93 **9.** 43.6 **11.** $4x + 3x = 7x$ **13. a.** 25 dots **b.** Answers vary. Sample answer: There is one central dot and four "spokes," each with one with one less dot than the term number. **c.** Answers vary. Sample answer: $4n - 3$ **15.** They appear not to be equivalent. **17.** 5 **19.** -10 **21.** 2 **23.** $r = 2.25$, m.a.d. $= 0.89$ **25.** $r = 28$ points, m.a.d. $=$ about 9.42 points **27.** $-8 + -y + -32$ **29.** true **31.** $6.21 \cdot \frac{1}{3.14}$ **33.** Commutative Property of Multiplication **35.** Transitive Property of Equality **37.** $1{,}225a + 1{,}405b$ dollars

39. a.

Week (w)	Total (t)
0	50
1	70
2	90
3	110
4	130

b.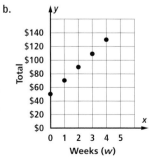

41. a.

n	2n + (n + 2)
1	5
2	8
3	11
4	14
5	17

b.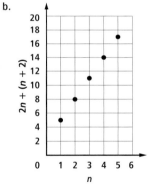

c. 35

43. They are not equivalent.

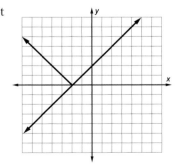

45. They are not equivalent.

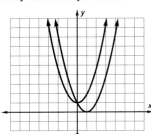

47.

x	y
0	−5
2	3
3	4
6	−5

Chapter 2

Lesson 2-1 (pp. 66–71)

Guided Example 3: $2x(5x − 3) = 2x \cdot 5x − 2x \cdot 3 = 10x^2 − 6x$

Questions: 1. a. $nk + nw$ **b.** $gd − ge$ **c.** $\frac{n}{r} + \frac{p}{r}$
3. Answers vary. Sample answer: $45(1.00 + 0.03) =$
$45 + 1.35 = \$46.35$ **5.** $5m + 20$ **7.** $12k − 2$ **9.** $18v −$
$48w + 54z^3$ **11.** $0.12 \cdot (17 + 6); 0.12 \cdot 17 + 0.12 \cdot 6 =$
$\$2.76$ **13.** $k; m$ **15.** Answers vary. Sample answer: $9 \cdot$
$\left(13\frac{1}{2}\right) = 9 \cdot \left(13 + \frac{1}{2}\right) = 9 \cdot 13 + 9 \cdot \frac{1}{2} = 117 + 4.5 = 121.5$
minutes. **17. a.** 40.3 films **b.** 9.3 films; On average, they
have been within 9.3 films of their mean of 40.3.
19. 99 **21.** $1,442 **23.** −2, 5, 8

Lesson 2-2 (pp. 72–78)

Guided Example 2: $4f^2 + f + 9 + 120f − 10f^3 − 30 \ (4f^2 +$
$−10f^2) + (f + 120f) + (9 + −30) = −6f^2 + 121f + −29$

Guided Example 4: $m; 2p$

Questions: 1. c and d are like terms. **3.** $12x$
5. $8x + 3y$ **7.** $\frac{x + 5}{3m}$ **9.** $26f + 3h$ **11.** $a^2; 4b$
13. $8p^2 + p$ **15.** $5(3ab + 8c − 2)$ **17.** $9f$ **19.** Answers
vary. Sample answer: let $x = 0; 2 \neq 1$ **21.** Answers vary.
Sample answer: Timothy, you did not distribute −4 over all
the terms **23.** Answers vary. Sample answer:
$8(40 − 0.05) = 320 − 0.40 = \$319.60$ **25. a.** $JM = x$ cm;
$JI = x + 5$ cm; $IM = 2x − 7$ cm **b.** $4x − 2$ cm **27.** b
29. a **31. a.** $6,200 **b.** $27,900 **c.** $41,850 **d.** $9,300y$
e. $775m$ **33.** about $60.77

Lesson 2-3 (pp. 79–84)

Guided Example 1: Answers vary. Sample answer: 17; 18;
36; 108; 104; 109; 7 **Guided Example 3:** $n − 4; 8n − 32;$
$8n − 32 + 8n; 16n − 32; \frac{16n − 32}{16}; n − 2; n − 2 + 8;$
$n + 6; n + 6 − n; 6$

Questions: 1. Answers vary. Sample answer: Variables
are used to see how the puzzle works for *any* number.
3. The result is 97. **5.** The result is 192.
7. The result is 7. **9. a.** 7; −1; 6; 36; 41; 45; 15; 1
b. −2.9; −10.9; −3.9; −23.4; −18.4; −14.4; −4.8; 1 **c.** $n; n − 8;$
$n − 1; 6n − 6; 6n − 1; 6n + 3; 2n + 1; 1$ **11.** Answers

vary. Sample answer: 1. Pick a number. 2. Subtract 11.
Multiply by 3. 4. Add 5 times your original number. 5. Add
1. 6. Divide by 8. 7. Add 4. 8. Your answer should be the
number you picked. **13. a.** yes **b.** 39 **c.** Answers vary.
Sample answer: yes, suppose the numbers in a certain
row, column, or diagonal are x, y, and z, which add to 15.
Their new sum is $(x + k) + (y + k) + (z + k) =$
$x + y + z + 3k$. This will be the sum in every row, column,
and diagonal. **15.** Answers vary. Sample answer:

Spectator's Choice	Number of Cards in Small Pile
10	$10 − 1 = 9$
11	$11 − 2 = 9$
12	$12 − 3 = 9$
13	$13 − 4 = 9$
14	$14 − 5 = 9$

17. unlike
19. unlike
21. a. $\frac{29}{15}$
b. $\frac{11x}{14}$ **c.** $\frac{6}{5y}$

23. $33n^2 − 132n; 33(5)^2 − 132(5) = 165;$
$5(11(3(5 − 4))) = 165$ **25. a.** Eddie has $100 − 4w$ dollars
b. Liseta owes $−350 + 5w$ dollars **27.** 45 **29.** 78

Lesson 2-4 (pp. 85–90)

Guided Example 2: $−7; −14x + 21; −13x + 27$

Questions: 1. a. $48 − f − n$ ounces and $48 − (f + n)$ ounces
b. $48 − 12 − 5 = 31$ ounces and $48 − (12 + 5) = 31$ ounces
3. $2n$ **5.** $2a^2 − 28a + 15$ **7.** C **9.** $−x − 15$ **11.** −2
13. $−4k^4 + 13$ **15.** $2b − 2c$
17. a.

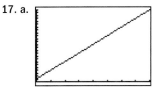

Yes, the expressions appear to be equivalent.
b. $4n − (n − 1) = 4n − n + 1 = 3n + 1 = 2n + n + 1$
19. a. True, they are both equal to −125. **b.** False. $(−5)^4$
is positive, $−5^4$ is negative. **c.** True, they are both equal to
−625. **21.** Answers vary. Sample answer: We can think
of "number of about-faces" as n and "facing direction" as
$(−1)^n$, where a positive result is forward and a negative
result is reverse. **23. a.** $\frac{1}{3}$ **b.** $−\frac{1}{4}$ **c.** $\frac{1}{5}$ **d.** $−\frac{1}{10}$ **25.** 16
27. $\frac{17}{3y}$ **29.** $6(15g − 12) = 90g − 72$ dollars
31. a. Answers vary. Sample answer: 13 and 56. **b.**
Answers vary. Sample answer: −1.3 and −56. **c.** Answers
vary. Sample answer: 1.3 and 5.6

Lesson 2-5 (pp. 91-97)

Guided Example 2: Answers vary. Sample answer:
$x = 1$ gives $4x - x = 4(1) - 1 = 4 - 1 = 3 \neq 4$

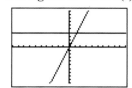

The graphs are not identical;

Guided Example 3: $-(6)^2 = -36$;
$(-6)^2 = (-6)(-6) = 36$;
-36 and 36 **Questions: 1. a.** 21 **b.**

Design Number	$1 + 3n + 2n$	$6n - (n - 1)$
4	21	21
5	26	26
6	31	31

c.

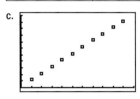

d. Dion's expression is
$1 + 3n + 2n = 5n + 1$.
Ellis's expression is $6n - (n - 1) = 6n - n + 1 = 5n + 1$.
They are equivalent.   **3.** They are not equivalent:
$3x^2 + 6x(x + 2) = 3x^2 + 6x^2 + 12x \neq 3x^2 + 6x^2 + 2$
5. Answers vary. Sample answer: $x = 2$
7. $2x + 3 + 2x + 3 + 2x + 3 + 2x + 3 = 8x + 12 = 4(2x + 3)$ **9. a.** Answers vary. Sample answer:

x	$20(3x) - 2(8x)$	$20x + 4x + 20x$
0	0	0
1	44	44
2	88	88
3	132	132
4	176	176

b. $20(3x) - 2(8x) = 60x - 16x = 44x = 20x + 4x + 20x$,
which shows the expressions are equivalent. **c.** 220 units
squared   **11.** $0.8v + 5.6$ **13. a.** yes **b.** no **c.** no **d.** yes
15. a. p^3 **b.** $3p$ **c.** $8p^3$ **d.** $6p$ **17.** Answers vary. Sample
answer: $m = 1, 6 + 1 = 7, 2(1) - 3(1 - 2) = 5$

Lesson 2-6 (pp. 98-104)

Questions: 1. $35x^2 - 45xy$ **3.** Answers vary. Sample
answer: The CAS recognized that $5t$ and $-5t$ are additive
inverses and applied the Additive Inverse Property.
5. Answers vary. Sample answer: $3k(3k - 1)$;
$10k^2 - 3k - k^2; 9k\left(k - \frac{1}{3}\right)$ **7.** Answers vary. Sample
answer: $-2 \cdot 3 \cdot 4y; 0 - 24y; 6 + 6y - 3(10y + 2); \frac{-120y^2}{5y}$

9. Answers vary. Sample answer: First, add $-3y$ and $3y$
to get $5x - 7y - 3y + 3y$. Then regroup terms to get
$(5x - 10y) + 3y$. Finally, factor 5 out of the first part of the
expression.
11. Answers vary. Sample answer:

n	$3n - 15$	$3(n - 4) - 3$
-2	-21	-21
0	-15	-15
1	-12	-12
5	0	0
10	15	15

$3(n - 4) - 3 = 3n - 12 - 3 = 3n - 15$
They are equivalent.   **13. a.**
Multiplying any
real number by -1 gives the opposite of that number.
b. Answers vary. Sample answer: $-5 \cdot -1 = 5$ **15. a.** 3
folds has a paper thickness of 8, and 4 folds has a paper
thickness of 16.   **b.** 64 times the original thickness
c. 2^n **17.** $5\frac{1}{2}L$ **19.** 33%

Lesson 2-7 (pp. 105-111)

Questions: 1. $0.23 + 0.44 = 0.67, 0.44 + 0.23 = 0.67$,
$0.67 - 0.44 = 0.23, 0.67 - 0.23 = 0.44$ **3.** $-\frac{1}{8} = -4 + 3\frac{7}{8}$,
$-\frac{1}{8} = 3\frac{7}{8} + -4$, and $-\frac{1}{8} - (-4) = 3\frac{7}{8}$

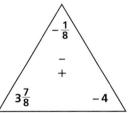

5. a. $y = 14 - (-6) = 20$ **b.** $y - 6 = 14$,
so $y = y - 6 + 6 = 14 + 6 = 20$ **7.** -10
9. Answers vary. Sample answer: 629 and -629   **11.** x
13. Answers vary. Sample answers:

a.   **b.**

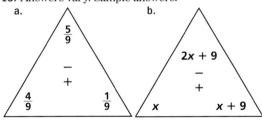

15. a.

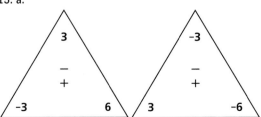

15a. (*continued*)

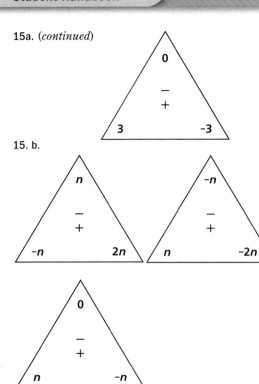

15. b.

17. 19°F   **19.** Answers vary. Sample answer: $350 \cdot 200 -$
$W - C \, \text{yd}^3$ **21.** $p - 8$ **23.** $6m + 15$ **25. a.** $-\frac{376}{3}$ **b.** 5

Lesson 2-8 (pp. 112–120)
Guided Example 3: $0.64; \frac{1}{\frac{1}{4}} = 1 \cdot \frac{15}{4}; \frac{1}{-34}$
$\frac{1}{\frac{15}{15}}$

Questions: 1. $-14 \cdot -2 = 28, -2 \cdot -14 = 28, \frac{28}{-14} = -2,$ and
$\frac{28}{-2} = -14.$ **3.** $cb = a, \frac{a}{b} = c$ and $\frac{a}{c} = b.$ **5.** $6b$ **7.** $-\frac{1}{6}$ **9.** 1
11. Answers vary. Sample answer: Division by 0 is not
defined.   **13.** $x = 0$ **15.** Any number is a solution.
17. Multiplicative Property of Zero

19.

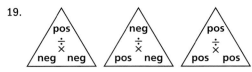

The product of two negative numbers or two positive
numbers is positive. The product of a negative number
and a positive number is negative.   **21.** 6   **23. a.** Yes, it
is possible.   **b.** The width of the rectangle is $\frac{1}{50}$ cm.
25. a. $d = tr, r = \frac{d}{t},$ and $t = \frac{d}{r}$ **b.** about 3.81 hr
27.

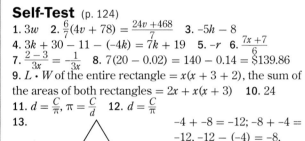

$P - 2a = 2b; P - 2b = 2a;$
$P = 2b + 2a$ **29.** They
are equivalent when $p = 6,$
because $18p^2 + p = 18(6^2)$
$+ 6 = 654$ and $p^3 + 9p^2 +$
$19 = 9(6)^2 + (6)^3 +$
$19(6) = 654.$ **31.** never
positive   **33.** always
positive   **35.** about 1,588 bricks

Self-Test (p. 124)
1. $3w$ **2.** $\frac{6}{7}(4v + 78) = \frac{24v + 468}{7}$ **3.** $-5h - 8$
4. $3k + 30 - 11 - (-4k) = 7k + 19$ **5.** $-r$ **6.** $\frac{7x + 7}{6}$
7. $\frac{2 - 3}{3x} = -\frac{1}{3x}$ **8.** $7(20 - 0.02) = 140 - 0.14 = \$139.86$
9. $L \cdot W$ of the entire rectangle $= x(x + 3 + 2)$, the sum of
the areas of both rectangles $= 2x + x(x + 3)$ **10.** 24
11. $d = \frac{C}{\pi}, \pi = \frac{C}{d}$ **12.** $d = \frac{C}{\pi}$
13.

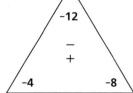

$-4 + -8 = -12; -8 + -4 =$
$-12, -12 - (-4) = -8,$
$-12 - (-8) = -4$
14. $3p$ **15.** $-b - 2$
16. $\frac{1}{-2.50} = -\frac{2}{5}$ **17.** $\frac{1}{\frac{4}{11d}}$
$= \frac{11d}{4}$ **18.** False;
A negative number to an
odd power is negative. $(-2)^5 = -32$ and $2^5 = 32$
19. (1) n; (2) $10n$; (3) $10n + 30$;

The chart below keys the **Self-Test** questions to the objectives in the **Chapter Review** on pages 125–127 or to the **Vocabulary (Voc)** on page 123. This will enable you to locate those **Chapter Review** questions that correspond to questions missed on the **Self-Test.** The lesson where the material is covered is also indicated on the chart.

Question	1	2	3	4	5	6	7	8	9	10
Objective(s)	B	A	A	B	A	F	A	D	C	C
Lesson(s)	2-4	2-1, 2-2	2-1, 2-2	2-4	2-1, 2-2	2-1	2-1, 2-2	2-4, 2-8	2-7, 2-8	2-7, 2-8
Question	11	12	13	14	15	16	17	18	19	20
Objective(s)	C	E	E	D	D	B	H	G	G	J
Lesson(s)	2-7, 2-8	2-7	2-7	2-4, 2-8	2-4, 2-8	2-4	2-1, 2-2	2-3	2-3	2-5, 2-6
Question	21	22	23							
Objective(s)	I	H	I							
Lesson(s)	2-5	2-1, 2-2	2-5							

(4) $2n + 6$; (5) $n + 6$; (6) $n + 7$; (7) n **20.** No, they do not seem to be equivalent.   **21.** They are not equivalent. $w + (2w - 1) + 3(w + 6) = 3w - 1 + 3w + 18 = 6w + 17 \neq 6w - 5$ **22.** Let t be the amount of time Darryl worked. Then, Carol worked $2t$, Beryl worked $3t$, Errol worked $4t$. We solve $t + 2t + 3t + 4t = \$150$. So, $t = 150$ dollars. Darryl got $150, Carol got $300, Beryl got $450, and Errol got $600.   **23.** Answers vary. Sample answer:

x	$2x + 1$	$|-2x - 1|$
-2	-3	3
-1	-1	1
0	1	1
1	3	3
2	5	5

Chapter Review (pp. 125-127)

1. $3x + 12$ **3.** $4x - 31$ **5.** $4y - 52$ **7.** $18x$ **9.** $\frac{22x - 3}{8}$
11. $\frac{n}{3} + 2$ **13.** $-7a - 4$ **15.** z **17.** $\frac{3}{4} + y$ **19.** -8
21. a. 81 **b.** -81 **c.** -243 **d.** -243 **23.** negative; Of the two factors one is negative, yielding a negative product.
25. There are no solutions.   **27.** all real numbers
29. $\frac{1}{2} = \frac{1}{3} + \frac{1}{6}$, $\frac{1}{6} = \frac{1}{2} - \frac{1}{3}$ and $\frac{1}{3} = \frac{1}{2} - \frac{1}{6}$ **31.** $317.23 = 317.23 \cdot 1$, $\frac{317.23}{1} = 317.23$ and $1 = \frac{317.23}{317.23}$ **33.** $x = 70$
35. $-\frac{1}{5}$ **37.** $8x$ **39.** Subtraction Property of Equality
41. 0 **43.** 6 **45.** 0 **47.** 7.536 **49.** $-x$ **51.** Distributive Property of Multiplication over Addition   **53.** First, find 36 times 100. Then, add 36 times 3 to get 3,708.   **55.** $\$3.50(10 + 1) = \$3.50(10) + \$3.50(1) = \$38.50$ **57.** After Step 2, you have $4n$. After Step 3, you have $4n + 10$. After Step 4, you have $4n + 12$. After Step 5, you have $n + 3$. After Step 6, you have n.   **59.** $\$29,000$ **61.** $\frac{2F}{5}$ **63.** Answers vary. Sample answer: For $x = 1$, $x^2 = 1$ but $2x = 2$
65. They are not equivalent.   **67.** They are not equivalent.

Chapter 3

Lesson 3-1 (pp. 130-134)

Questions:

1. a.

Time x	Height y
0	18
1	15
2	12
3	9
4	6

b. 2 hr **c.** 9 in. **d.** 6 hr   **3. a.** 102.5 ft **b.** 145 ft **c.** C

d.

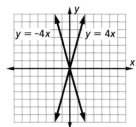

e. 570 ft

5. a–b.

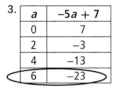

c. $(0, 0)$ **d.** Answers vary. Sample answer: They are reflections of each other over the y-axis.   **7.** linear
9. linear   **11.** $\frac{9}{11}h$ **13.** 0
15. $\frac{1}{6}$ mi or about 0.17 mi
17. giraffe   **19. a.** 36 **b.** -36
c. 36 **d.** -216 **e.** -216 **f.** $-1,296$

Lesson 3-2 (pp. 135-138)

Questions: **1. a.** no **b.** yes **c.** yes

3.

a	$-5a + 7$
0	7
2	-3
4	-13
6	-23

5.

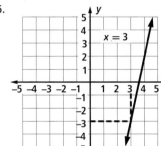

7. Let p be the price of a piece of pizza. Then, $20 - 5p = 7.65$.   **9.** Let y be the number of years they save. Then, $5,275 + 950y = 20,000$.

11.

h	Savings
0	250
10	360
20	470
21	481

13. a.

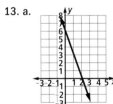

b. about 0.74.   **15.** $2(3x - 6) + 2x + 1 = 97$; $x = 13.5$ **17.** It is not a line.

19. a.

Years	Height
0	28
1	31.5
2	35
3	38.5

b.

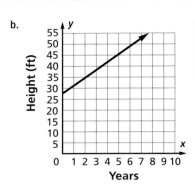

Years

c. 101.5 ft d. 66 yr **21. a.** –8.3 **b.** $\frac{1}{8.3}$ ≈ 0.12 **23.** $\frac{142}{3}$ or about 47.33

Lesson 3-3 (pp. 139-143)

Questions: 1. All three equations have the same solution, 3. **3. a.** add 27; divide by 5. **b.** $x = 8$ **5.** added 11 **7.** multiplied by $\frac{5}{3}$ **9.** Answers vary. Sample answer: Add 100. **11. a.** $y + \frac{-14}{3} = \frac{-98}{3}$ **b.** Answers vary. Sample answer: No, subtracting 14 would have avoided fractions. **13. a.** $x = \frac{c - 5y}{3}$ **b.** Answers vary. Sample answer: Let $y = 2$, $c = 3$. $3x + 5(2) = 3$; $x = -\frac{7}{3}$ and $x = 3 - \frac{5(2)}{3} = -\frac{7}{3}$ **15. a.** Let c be the number of cards in a pack. $200 + c + c + c + c + c + 2c = 284$ or $200 + 7c = 284$ **b.** 12 cards

17.a.

Time of day	Temperature (°F)
9:00 A.M.	85
10:00 A.M.	92
11:00 A.M.	99
12:00 P.M.	106
1:00 P.M.	113
2:00 P.M.	120
3:00 P.M.	127
4:00 P.M.	134

b.

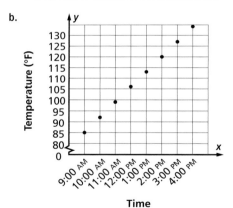

Time

19. a. symmetric **b.** The mean is about 19.73 mosquitoes, and the m.a.d. is 1.52 mosquitoes.

Lesson 3-4 (pp. 144-148)

Guided Example 1: 53; 53; 53; 60; $-\frac{2}{3}$; $-\frac{2}{3}$; –40
Guided Example 3: 4; 3; 4; $(n + 10)$; $4n + 40$; 4; 52; 4; 52; –52; –52; $\frac{1}{4}$; $4n$; $\frac{1}{4}$; 42; 10.5
Questions: 1. a. 57; multiply; $\frac{1}{7}$ **b.** $t = 22$; $7(22) - 57 = 154 - 57 = 97$ **3.** $a = 73$; $b = -432$; $c = 1,101$ **5.** A **7.** $A = 5$; $11(5) - 24 = 55 - 24 = 31$ **9.** $B = \frac{2}{5}$; $16 + 5(\frac{2}{5}) = 16 + 2 = 18$ **11.** $n = 2$; $2.4(2) - 2.4 = 4.8 - 24 = 2.4$ **13.** $m = -56$; $4 - \frac{7}{2}(-56) = 4 + 196 = 200$ **15. a.** Let g be the number of gallons the driver bought. Then, $1.50 + 2.39g = 31.15$. **b.** g is about 12.4 gal **17. a.** Let r be the number of seats in a row. Then, $3 + 7r = 80$. **b.** $r = 11$ seats **19.** $x = \frac{1,889}{121} ≈ 15.61$; $\frac{11}{17}(\frac{1,889}{121}) + \frac{17}{11} = \frac{1,889}{187} + \frac{17}{11} = 11\frac{11}{17}$ **21.** $a = 3$; $\frac{4}{3}(3 - \frac{1}{2}) = \frac{4}{3}(\frac{5}{2}) = 3\frac{1}{3}$ **23. a.** $7x + 1 = 15$ **b.** Remove 1 ounce from each side. Leave one seventh of the weight on each side. **c.** 2 oz

25. a.

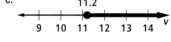

b. $a = \frac{10}{7} ≈ 1.43$
c. $m + 1$ **27.** $a + 3b$
29. $y = 128$

Lesson 3-5 (pp. 149-154)

Guided Example 5: $6k + 8 - 9k + 7$; –3; –3; Subtract 15 from each side.; –3; –9; $\frac{-3k}{-3} = \frac{-9}{-3}$; 3; 3; 3

Questions: 1. 2 **3.** $\frac{8}{3}$ **5.** $\frac{3}{2}$ **7.** –7 **9.** 31 **11. a.** Answers vary. Sample answer: $15,000 + 4E + \frac{1}{2}E = 150,000$ **b.** $E = \$30,000$ and the head mechanic received $15,000. **13. a.** 36 in^2 **b.** 8 in. **c.** 16 in. **15.** 23 cm **17.** $40,000 in the CD, $60,000 in the savings account **19.** –2.81; 3.4 + $-(-2.81) = 3.4 + 2.81 = 6.21$ **21. a.** 8 in. **b.** 6:40 A.M. **23.** 6:15 P.M. **25.** $\frac{2}{7}$

Lesson 3-6 (pp. 155-161)

Guided Example 2: a. $≥$; $≥$; $≤$

b.

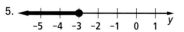

c. Step 1: 20; 5; Yes **Step 2:** 20; 0; 20; 0; $x ≤ 5$
Questions: 1. a. $v ≥ 11.2$ **b.** 11.2

c.

11.2

3.

120 122 124 126 128 130 w

5.

–5 –4 –3 –2 –1 0 1 y

7. $x > \frac{1}{3}$; $15\left(\frac{1}{3}\right) = 5$; Pick $x = 1$. $15(1) = 15 > 5$ **9.** $y \le 25$; $\frac{4}{5}(25) = 20$; Pick $y = 0$. $\frac{4}{5}(0) = 0 \le 20$ **11.** $a \ge 2$; $-3(2) = -6$; Pick $a = 3$. $-3(4) = -12 \le -6$ **13. a.** $\frac{1}{2} > \frac{1}{3} > \frac{1}{4} > \frac{1}{5} > \frac{1}{6}$ **b.** $-4 < -\frac{8}{3} < -2 < -\frac{8}{5} < -\frac{4}{3}$ **c.** Yes, because we multiplied by a negative number.   **15.** 30; 31   **17. a.** Let r be the number of rows. Then, $80r \ge 2{,}200$.   **b.** $r \ge 27.5$ rows   **19.** $x = -\frac{13}{6}$ **21. a.** Let p be the number of bottles of soda Grafton buys. Then, $1.99p + 2.99(2p) + 0.15 = 40$.   **b.** 5 bottles of soda, 10 bags of chips   **23.** $5(x + 1) + (2 - x) = 31$, $(2 - x) + 5(x + 1) = 31$, $31 - 5(x + 1) = 2 - x$, and $31 - (2 - x) = 5(x + 1)$; $x = 6$ **25.** 198.25 mi

Lesson 3-7 (pp. 162–166)

Questions: 1. For real numbers a, b, and c, if $a > b$, then $a + c > b + c$.   **3.** $x < 5$

(number line from 2 to 8 with open circle at 5, shaded to the left)

5. $n \le 20$

(number line from 18 to 24 with closed circle at 20, shaded to the left)

7. 39 shirts

9. $y \le 0.1$ **11.** $d > -108$ **13.** $q > -22$ **15. a.** $x = 7$ **b.** Answers vary. Sample answer: $x = 3$ **c.** Answers vary. Sample answer: $x = 11$ **d.** $x < 7$ **17.** 11 mo or fewer   **19.** Except for 2, which is a solution to both, every real number is a solution to exactly one of these inequalities.   **21. a.** $800 > -200$ **b.** $-40 < 10$ **c.** $4 > -1$ **d.** No inequality results.   **23.** $j > \frac{17}{5}$ **25.** $x \le \frac{72}{5}$ **27.** 1,480 mi

Lesson 3-8 (pp. 167–173)

Guided Example 2: 12; 12; 12; 12; 12; 12; 3; 96; 3; 98; $\frac{98}{3}$
Questions: 1. a. $3w + 10 = 130$ **b.** $w = 40$ **c.** $\frac{3}{5}(40) + 2 = 26$; $24 + 2 = 26$ **3. a.** 1,000; 10; and 100   **b.** $15.2 = 30m - 43$; $m = 1.94$ **c.** $\frac{152}{1{,}000} = \frac{3}{10}m - \frac{43}{100}$; $m = 1.94$ **d.** Converting decimals to fractions does not change the solution.
5. a. $10a + 3a \ge 315$ **b.** $a \ge \frac{315}{13}$

c.

(number line from 23 to 27 with closed circle at $\frac{315}{13}$, shaded to the right)

d. $\frac{2}{3}\left(\frac{315}{13}\right) + \frac{\left(\frac{315}{13}\right)}{5} = \frac{210}{13} + \frac{63}{13} = 21$; Pick $a = 30$. $\frac{2}{3}(30) + \frac{30}{5} = 20 + 6 = 26 \ge 21$

7. $y = \frac{64}{9}$, $\frac{3}{4}\left(\frac{64}{9}\right) - \frac{1}{3} = \frac{16}{3} - \frac{1}{3} = 5$ **9.** $c = 49$; $138{,}000 - 2{,}000(49) = 40{,}000$ **11.** $n \le 18$; $1 - \frac{18}{10} = \frac{-4}{5}$; Pick $n = 0$. $1 - \frac{0}{10} = 1 \ge -\frac{4}{5}$ **13.** $m \ge \frac{305}{286}$; $\frac{\left(\frac{305}{286}\right)}{5} - \frac{1}{3} = \frac{61}{286} - \frac{1}{3} = \frac{3}{22}$; Pick $m = 5$. $\frac{5}{5} - \frac{1}{13} = \frac{12}{13} \ge \frac{3}{22}$ **15.** Yes because it simplifies the equation.   **17.** $x = \frac{269}{3}$ **19.** $t > -6$ **21.** $y > 13$ **23.** $w = 9$ **25.** $\frac{31}{7t}$ **27.** $\frac{x^2}{18}$

Self-Test (p. 177)

1. $t = 4.5$. First, add 5 to both sides. Then divide by 4.   **2.** $t = -4$. First, distribute to get $10 + 5t = -10$. Then subtract 10 from both side and divide by 5.   **3.** $f = \frac{109}{7}$. First, distribute and combine like terms to get $101 = 13f - 8 - 6f = 7f - 8$. Then add 8 to both sides and divide by 7.   **4.** $x \ge 8$ **5.** $x < -8$ **6.** $x < 8$ **7. a.** Question 6   **b.** Question 4   **c.** Question 5   **8.** $2n - n = 24$, so $n = 24$ **9.** Let $2x$ be the value of the grand prize. Then, $x + x + x + 2x = 3{,}500$. Combining like terms gives $5x = 3{,}500$, and dividing by 5 gives $x = 700$, so the grand prize is \$1,400.   **10.** Subtract 7 from both sides and then divide both sides by -2. $x = \frac{-15 - 7}{-2} = 11$ Answers vary. Sample answer: $-15 = -2(11) + 7$; $-15 = -15$

11.

Months	Money in Account
0	\$350
1	\$330
2	\$310
3	\$290
8	\$190

12.

13. after 8 months

14.

x	$2x - 6$
12	18
14	22
16	26
18	30
20	34

So, $30 < 2x - 6$ when $x > 18$.   **15.** Subtract 5, then divide by -3. The solution is $x < -4$.   **16.** Let w be the number of weekends Toni collects. Toni has enough leaves when $9 + 7w \ge 37$. Subtracting 9 and dividing by 7 gives $w \ge 4$. So, she must collect for at least 4 weeks.   **17. a.** $P = 0.39 + 0.24(w - 1)$ **b.** Let $P = 3.27$. Then solve $3.27 = 0.39 + 0.24(w - 1)$ by subtracting 0.39 from both sides, which implies $2.88 = 0.24(w - 1)$. Then divide by 0.24, which implies $w - 1 = 12$. So $w = 13$ oz.

The chart below keys the **Self-Test** questions to the objectives in the **Chapter Review** on pages 178–179 or to the **Vocabulary (Voc)** on page 176. This will enable you to locate those **Chapter Review** questions that correspond to questions missed on the **Self-Test**. The lesson where the material is covered is also indicated on the chart.

Question	1	2	3	4	5	6	7	8	9	10
Objective(s)	A	A	A	B	B	B	F	C	D	C
Lesson(s)	3-4, 3-5	3-4, 3-5	3-4, 3-5	3-7, 3-8	3-7, 3-8	3-7, 3-8	3-6, 3-7	3-3, 3-6, 3-8	3-2, 3-4, 3-5, 3-7, 3-8	3-3, 3-6, 3-8

Question	11	12	13	14	15	16	17
Objective(s)	E	E	E	B	C	D	D
Lesson(s)	3-1, 3-2	3-1, 3-2	3-1, 3-2	3-7, 3-8	3-3, 3-6, 3-8	3-2, 3-4, 3-5, 3-7, 3-8	3-2, 3-4, 3-5, 3-7, 3-8

Chapter Review (pp. 178–179)

Guided Example 4: P; $0.15P$; $1P$; $0.15P$; $0.85P$; 0.85; 320; 272;
1. $t = 3$ **3.** $n = 7$ **5.** $y = 46.15$ **7.** $W = 5$ **9.** $z = -15$
11. $w = 2.6$ **13.** $x < 94$ **15.** $y \leq 13$ **17.** 17 was added to each side.   **19.** Sample answer: You could enter $(2x - 3 = 7) + 3$. The result would be $2x = 10$.   **21.** Yes. The student multiplied both sides by -1, which changes the sense of the inequality.   **23.** more than $26°C$
25. 32 hr   **27.** approximately 1,015 billion barrels
29. a.

Years	Radius (cm)
0	12
1	12.5
2	13
3	13.5
x	$12 + 0.5x$

b.

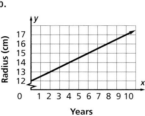

c. 6 yr **d.** 16 cm

31. a. $b = 55 + 20w$
b.

Weeks	Balance
0	$55
1	$75
2	$95
3	$115

c.

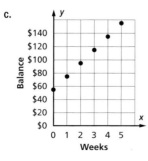

d. Answers vary. Sample answer: After 6 weeks find $175 on the y-axis and draw a horizontal line to the graph, then a vertical line down to the x-axis to find when Darnell has $175.

33.

35.

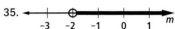

Chapter 4

Lesson 4-1 (pp. 182–187)

Questions: **1.** 959.4   **3.** 20%   **5. a.** 90% **b.** $21.15   **7.** $0.6T$
9. $16.84   **11.** 7.25%   **13.** 59,670,000 U.S. citizens
15. about 51.5%   **17. a.** $148.13 **b.** The regular price is not 120% of the sale price. The sale price is 80% of the regular price.   **19.** $k = -59.5$ **21.** $a = -13$ **23.** $322.23
25. a. 13 cubes **b.** Answers vary. Sample answer: $4n - 3$
c. 9   **27.** 0

Lesson 4-2 (pp. 188–195)

Questions: **1. a.** Answers vary. Sample answer: $(0, 4)$, $(-3, 4)$, and $(-0.6, 4)$
b.

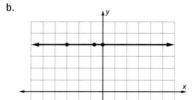

c. $y = 4$ **3.** $x = -4$ **5.** x
7. a.

7.b.

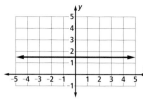

9. a. $S = 98.5$
b. 1997 **11. a.** 2000 and 2001 **b.** Answers vary. Sample answer: Bad news; snow depths below normal could affect snow tourism and also result in lower water supply from runoff.

13. $x = -6$ **15.** $x; y$ **17.** $(7, 5)$ **19.** 10 A.M.
21. a. $y = 35 + 70x$

b.

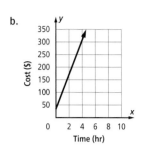

c.

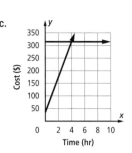

d. 4 hours **e.** Solving $35 + 70x \leq 315$ yields $x \leq 4$ hours.
23. $16,037.74 **25. a.** $18,550 > \frac{1}{4}I$ **b.** $I < 74,200$
27.

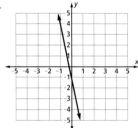

Lesson 4-3 (pp. 196–201)

Guided Example: Solution 1:

1.

Number of Copies x	Acme's Price $250 + 0.01x$	Best's Price $70 + 0.03x$
0	250	70
2,000	270	130
4,000	290	190
6,000	310	250
8,000	330	310
10,000	350	370
12,000	370	430
14,000	390	490
16,000	410	550
18,000	430	610
20,000	450	670

2. 10,000; 8,000

3. The break-even point is between 8,000 and 10,000 copies.

4.

Number of Copies x	Acme's Price $250 + 0.01x$	Best's Price $70 + 0.03x$
8,000	330	310
8,500	335	325
9,000	340	340
9,500	345	355
10,000	350	370

5. 9,000; $340 **6. a.** 9,000 **b.** $340 **Solution 2:**
2. 9,000; 340 **3.** 9,000; both companies charge the same amount for 9,000 copies. 340; the companies both charge $340 at the break-even point.
Questions: 1. a. 4 or more copies **b.** 1 or 2 copies

c.

The graph of Shop A is higher for 2 copies. The graph of Shop B is higher for 7 copies, assuming the patterns hold. **d.** (3, 1.80)

3. a. Answers vary. Sample answer: around (70, 40)
b. number of miles driven for which the two costs are equal; cost of the rental **c.** Rhodes is less expensive when 80 miles are driven because at $x = 80$, the Rhodes' line is below the Extra Value line.
5. a. $30 + 6w$ **b.** $150 - 5w$ **c.** after about 11 wk

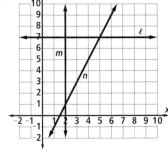

7. $x = 1$ **9.**

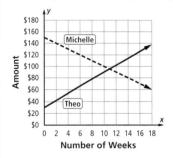

a. (2, 7)
b. (5, 7)
c. 9 units squared
11. 15
13. 372 coins
15. a. They are equivalent.
b. Answers vary. Sample answer: Distributing the left-hand side of both equations

yields $-18x - 18 + 6x$, which simplifies to $-12x - 18$, in the first equation and $-12x - 18$ in the second equation. These expressions are identical.

Lesson 4-4 (pp. 202–209)

Guided Example 3: 1. $-x - 5; 4x + 44$ **2.** $2; 5x + 44; -42;$ $5x; -8.4$ **3.** $-8.4; -8.4; -3.4; 2.6$

Questions: 1. $a = 9.3; b = -4; c = 2; d = 11$ **3. a.** $-4t$ or $-10t$
b. $t = \frac{1}{3}$ **5.** $n = 9{,}000$ **7.** $k = 11; 4(11) + 39 = 83, 7(11) + 6 = 83$ **9.** $y = -1; 14(-1) + 5 = -9, 8(-1) - 1 = -9$

11. $m = \frac{1}{2}; 7 - \frac{1}{2} = \frac{13}{2}, 8 - 3\left(\frac{1}{2}\right) = \frac{13}{2}$ **13.** $d = -\frac{1}{2}; 3\left(-\frac{1}{2}\right) + 4\left(-\frac{1}{2}\right) + 5 = \frac{3}{2}, 6\left(-\frac{1}{2}\right) + 7\left(-\frac{1}{2}\right) + 8 = \frac{3}{2}$ **15.** about 8.15 years after 2000 (late February 2008) **17. a.** $4W + 6 = 2W + 10$ **b.** First, remove 6 ounces from each side. Then, remove $2W$ from both sides. Then, remove half the weight on each side. **c.** $W = 2$ oz
d. because you cannot have a negative number of boxes on the balance scale **19. a.** $53.84 - 0.32x$ **b.** $48.17 - 0.18x$
c. about 40 yrs

21. a.

Hours	Chris's Distance (mi)	Lance's Distance (mi)
0	24	0
1	33	13
2	42	26
3	51	39
4	60	52
5	69	65
6	78	78

b 6 hr
c. $13x = 9x + 24; x = 6;$ 6 hr
23. $y = d$
25. $c > 6$
27. $-5\frac{5}{6}$
29. 3

Lesson 4-5 (pp. 210–215)

Guided Example 2: Solution 1. $11x; 11x; 11x; 12; 12; 12; \frac{-5}{15};$ $\frac{15x}{15};$ divide; $\frac{-1}{3}$. **Solution 2.** $4x; 4x; 4x; 7; 7; 7; \le;$ reverse; $\le$
Check. $\frac{-1}{3}; \frac{-1}{3}; \frac{-1}{3}; \frac{-1}{3}$; Sample answer: $-1; -1$
Questions: 1. a. Answers vary. Sample answer: 2, 4, and 9.
b. $t < 10$. **c.** $t > 10$. **3. a.** $m < -\frac{10}{3}$ **b.** $m < -\frac{10}{3}$ **c.** Yes, the solutions are the same regardless of how the sentence is solved. **d.** In Part a, the second step is subtract 14 from both sides, and the third step is to divide both sides by 3. In Part b, the second step is to subtract 4 from both sides, and the third step is to divide both sides by -3.
5. a. $x \ge -9$ **b.** Step 1: Is $-53 + 15 \cdot -9 = -8 + 20 \cdot -9$? Yes, $-188 = -188$. Step 2: Answers vary. Sample answer: for $x = 0$, is $-53 + 15 \cdot 0 < -8 + 20 \cdot 0$? Yes, $-53 < -8$.
7. a. $n < -\frac{3}{2}$ **b.** Step 1: Is $14 - 4 \cdot -\frac{3}{2} = 29 + 6 \cdot -\frac{3}{2}$? Yes, $20 = 20$. Step 2: Answers vary. Sample answer: For $n = -2$, is $14 - 4 \cdot -2 > 29 + 6 \cdot -2$? Yes, $22 > 17$. **9.** $x > \frac{1}{14}$
11. It determines what side of the inequality x is on and could result in a negative coefficient of x, which affects the sense of the inequality. **13.** Let h be the number of hits.

Then, Elevator Tunes' ads are more profitable when $5.00 + 0.06h > 3.50 + 0.10h$. This occurs when there are 37 hits or fewer. **15.** $z = -\frac{280}{39}$ **17.** $r = \frac{619}{380}$

19. a.

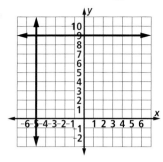

b. $(-5, 9)$ **21.** B

Lesson 4-6 (pp. 216-220)

Guided Example 2: $42k - 42k < 42k + 6 - 42k$; Simplify; $42k < 80k + 6 - 38k$

Questions: 1. a. Answers vary. Sample answer:

Year	Hamburger Heaven	Video King
0	6.90	7.50
1	7.90	8.50
2	8.90	9.50
3	9.90	10.50
4	10.90	11.50
5	11.90	12.50
6	12.90	13.50

b. Let y be the number of years worked at either place. $6.90 + 1y < 7.50 + 1y$ **c.** never

3. a. $40 = 40$ **b.** Any real number is a solution to the equation.

c.

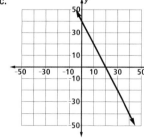

5. no solutions **7.** Any real number is a solution.
9. a. $40{,}000 + 800y$
b. $200{,}000 + 800y$
c. never **11.** Answers vary. Sample answer: $x + 7 = x + 9$ **13.** $p < -2$
15. Brokefast is cheaper, because $4.75 + 16(0.10) < 3.50 + 16(0.25)$.
17. about 16%

Lesson 4-7 (pp. 221-226)

Guided Example 1: $F - 32 = \frac{9}{5}C + 32 - 32; \frac{5}{9}(F - 32) = \frac{5}{9}$ $\left(\frac{9}{5}C\right); \frac{5}{9}F - \frac{160}{9} = C; 212 = 1.8 \cdot 100 + 32; 212 = 180 + 32;$ $212 = 212; 100 = \frac{5}{9}(212 - 32); 100 = \frac{5}{9}(180); 100 = 100$
Guided Example 2: Multiply each side by 3.; Divide each side by π.; Divide each side by r^2.
Questions: 1. $1.8(-40) + 32 = -72 + 32 = -40$ and $\frac{5}{9}(-40 - 32) = \frac{5}{9}(-72) = -40$ **3. a.** $\ell = \frac{p}{2} - w$

4. b. ℓ; p; w **c.** Answers vary. Sample answer: let $\ell = 1$, $w = 2$, and $p = 6$. $6 = 2(1) + 2(2)$, which checks with $\ell = \frac{p}{2} - w = \frac{6}{2} - 2 = 3 - 2 = 1$ **5.** $y = \frac{1}{2}x + 5$
7. $n = \frac{S}{180} + 2$ **9.** $h = \frac{2A}{b_1 + b_2}$ **11.** Both students are correct, and their expressions are equivalent.
13. a. $\pi = \frac{C}{d}$ **b.** Measure a circle's circumference and divide it by the diameter. **c.** Answers vary. Sample answer: A circle with circumference of 22 cm has a diameter of about 7 cm, meaning $\pi \approx \frac{22}{7} \approx 3.143$ **15.** They are parallel. **17.** no solutions **19. a.** $y = -3$ **b.** $x = 5$
21. a. $x = 2$ **b.** It would have sides of negative length.
23. $4x - 6 + 2x + 10 = 40$; $40 - 4x + 6 = 2x + 10$;
$40 - 2x - 10 = 4x - 6$; $x = 6$

Lesson 4-8 (pp. 227-233)
Guided Example 4: left column: 2; –84; –7. right column: 0; –9; >; 3
Questions: 1. and **3.** a **5.** b **7.** Let i be the size of the incision. $1 \le i \le 2$

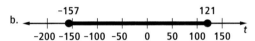

9. a. Let t be the temperatures that astronauts can endure. $-157°C \le t \le 121°C$
b.

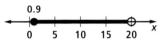

11. $0.9 \le x < 20$

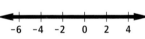

13. all real numbers

15. 6.5 ± 20.5

17.

x	–5	–4	–3	–2	–1	0	1	2	3	4	5
y	18	16	14	12	10	8	6	4	2	0	–2

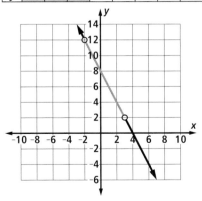

19. a. $r = \frac{d}{t}$ **b.** 61.25 mph **21.** all real numbers
23. the second store

Lesson 4-9 (pp. 234-239)
Guided Example 1: Solution 1. (–6, 18); (12, 18); –6; 12; –6; 12
Solution 2. 18; –18; 18; –18; –12; 24; –6; 12
Guided Example 2: –64; 16; –8; 2

x	$\lvert 8x + 24 \rvert$
–10	56
–8	40
–6	24
–4	8
–2	8
0	24
2	40
4	56
6	72

Questions: 1. C **3.** $A = 6$ or $A = -6$ **5.** $C = 0$ **7.**
a. $x = -2$ or $x = 5$ **b.** $-2 < x < 5$
c. $x < -2$ or $x > 5$ **9.** C **11.** $a = 2$ or $a = -22$
13. $-1 < c < 17$ **15.** $g \ge -\frac{2}{5}$ or $g \le -2$ **17. a.** $x = -1$ or $x = 8$
b. $x = 3.5$ **c.** no solutions **d.** $x < 1$ or $x > 6$
19. a.

$23\frac{7}{8}$

b. Let x be the amount in the box. $\lvert x - 24.4375 \rvert \le 0.5625$
21. $\lvert x - 15.6 \rvert > 3.8$ **23. a.** Let t be the time her commute takes. $12 \le t \le 20$ **b.** 16 ± 4 **25.** $m \le -2$ or $m > \frac{37}{4}$

27. horizontal: $y = \frac{9}{11}$
vertical: $x = -4.25$

Self-Test (pp. 243-244)
1. The dress is cheaper online, because it costs $262 + \$262(0.09) = \$285.58$ and $\$285.58 > \$285$, which is the price of the dress online. **2.** Answers vary. Sample answer: $8t$, since it would isolate the variable on one side **3.** Answers vary. Sample answer: 40
4. $-5m + 21 + 5m = 6m - 56 + 5m$; $21 + 56 = 11m - 56 + 56$; $\frac{77}{11} = \frac{11}{11}m$; $m = 7$ **5.** $0.73v + 37.9 + v = 16 - v + v$; $1.73v + 37.9 - 37.9 = 16 - 37.9$; $\frac{1.73}{1.73}v = \frac{-21.9}{1.73}$; $v \approx -12.659$ **6.** $\frac{1}{4}x + \frac{3}{5} - \frac{1}{4}x = \frac{1}{2}x - \frac{1}{4}x$; $4\left(\frac{3}{5}\right) = 4\left(\frac{1}{4}x\right)$; $x = \frac{12}{5}$ **7.** $-6 + 2d > 6d - 9$; $-6 + 2d - 2d > 6d - 9 - 2d$; $-6 + 9 > 4d - 9 + 9$; $\frac{3}{4} > \frac{4}{4}d$; $d < \frac{3}{4}$ **8.** $-29 + 44 < 7.5p - 44 + 44 \le 28 + 44$; $\frac{15}{7.5} < \frac{7.5}{7.5}p \le \frac{72}{7.5}$; $2 < p \le 9.6$ **9.** $(2x - 3) = 21$ or $(2x - 3) = -21$; $2x - 3 + 3 = 21 + 3$ or $2x - 3 + 3 = -21 + 3$; $\frac{2}{2}x = \frac{24}{2}$ or $\frac{2}{2}x = -\frac{18}{2}$; $x = 12$ or $x = -9$
10. $32 - 16n = -16n + 16$; $32 - 16n + 16n = -16n + 16 + 16n$; $32 = 16$; no solutions **11. a.** $x \approx 5$ **b.** $x \ge 5$
12. a. Using the formula $30{,}000 + 0.05s$ for TurboTV and $25{,}000 + 0.08s$ for Sparkle Cable, where s is her sales, we construct the following table:

Sales ($)	Total Salary from TurboTV	Total Salary from Sparkle Cable
$25,000	$31,250	$27,000
$50,000	$32,500	$29,000
$75,000	$33,750	$31,000
$100,000	$35,000	$33,000
$125,000	$36,250	$35,000
$150,000	$37,500	$37,000
$175,000	$38,750	$39,000

b. $s \geq \$175,000$. **c.** TurboTV, because she would earn more there

13.

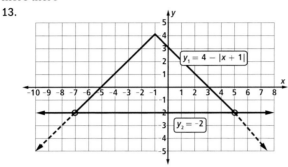

14. **a.** $y = 3$ **b.** $x = -2$

---

15. $-6x + 7y + 6x = -84 + 6x$; $7y + 84 = -84 + 6x + 84$; $x = \frac{7}{6}y + 14$

16. There is no solution, since the lines are parallel, but not the same. **17a.** 1990 **b.** 1996, which tells us that the deviation was smallest that year. **c.** Answers vary. Sample answers: bad, since they would rather produce more ice cream

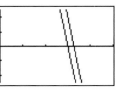

18. **a.** Let e be the number of strokes Elena took. $\frac{9}{10}e - 9 = e - 18$; $\frac{9}{10}e - 9 - \frac{9}{10}e = e - 18 - \frac{9}{10}e$; $-9 + 18 = \frac{1}{10}e - 18 + 18$; $10(9) = 10\left(\frac{1}{10}e\right)$; $e = 90$ **b.** $\frac{9}{10}(90) = 81$ strokes **c.** $90 - 18 = 72$ strokes **19. a.** Let n be the number of CDs produced. $452.54 + 5.25n$ **b.** $17.99n$ **c.** $17.99n > 452.54 + 5.25n$; $12.74n > 452.54$; $n > 35.52$; 36 CDs or more **20.** $0.3 \cdot x = 7$, so $x = \frac{7}{0.3} = 23\frac{1}{3}$

Chapter Review (pp. 245–249)

1. $A = -6$ **3.** $n = -1$ **5.** $f = \frac{7}{8}$ **7.** $a = -\frac{3}{8}$ **9.** $w \leq 129$
11. $n > -\frac{7}{3}$

(number line showing open circle at $-\frac{7}{3}$, shaded to the right; marks at -4, -3, -2, -1, 0, labeled n)

13. $1 \leq p < 9$

(number line showing closed circle at 1, open circle at 9, shaded between; marks at 1–9)

The chart below keys the **Self-Test** questions to the objectives in the **Chapter Review** on pages 245–249 or to the **Vocabulary (Voc)** on page 242. This will enable you to locate those **Chapter Review** questions that correspond to questions missed on the **Self-Test**. The lesson where the material is covered is also indicated on the chart.

Question	1	2	3	4	5	6	7	8	9	10
Objective(s)	J	F	F	A	A	A	B	B	E	G
Lesson(s)	4-1	4-4, 4-5	4-4, 4-5	4-4	4-4	4-4	4-5, 4-8	4-5, 4-8	4-9	4-6

Question	11	12	13	14	15	16	17	18	19	20
Objective(s)	L	J	N	K	C	M	I	H	H	D
Lesson(s)	4-3	4-1	4-9	4-2	4-7	4-6	4-1	4-4, 4-5	4-4, 4-5	4-1

---

15. $-2 < x < -4$

(number line showing open circles at -2 and 4, shaded between; marks at -2, -1, 0, 1, 2, 3, 4)

17. $p = \frac{2A}{a}$ **19.** $h = \frac{S}{2\pi r} - r$ **21.** $y = 7 - 2x$
23. $2.40 **25.** 43%   **27.** 200   **29.** $x = 12$ or $x = 16$
31. no solutions
33. Let t be the temperatures at which Lisel's dog will go outside. $|t - 60| < 15$

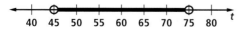

(number line showing open circles at 45 and 75, shaded between; marks at 40, 45, 50, 55, 60, 65, 70, 75, 80, labeled t)

35. a. $x = -5$ **b.** $x = -5$ **c.** They are the same.

---

37. a. Multiplication Property of Equality **b.** Distributive Property **c, d.** Addition Prperty of Equality **e.** Multiplication Property of Equality or Division Property of Equality   **39. a.** She subtracted $90n$ from the left side of the equation, but added $90n$ to the right side. **b.** $190n + 10 = 4$; $n = \frac{-3}{95}$ **41.** no solutions   **43.** If you subtract x from both sides, you get $5 > 6$, which is never true.   **45. a.** Calling Cabs **b.** It does not matter; they cost the same. **c.** 15 mi   **47.** 24 signs

49. a.

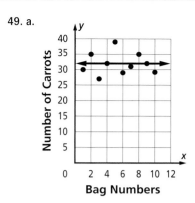

b. mean = 31.9 **c.** bags 4 and 9 **d.** bag 5
51. about 1,447,000 people **53.** $1,280

55.

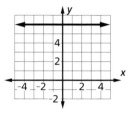

57. $x = 5$ **59. a.** $a = 35,000 - 1,750m$

59. b.

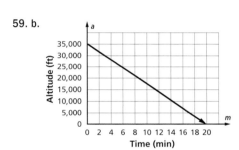

c. 20 min **61.** $x \leq 0$ **63. a.** $80 + 10n$ dollars
b. $65 + 10n$ dollars

c.

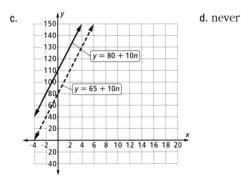

d. never

65. no solution

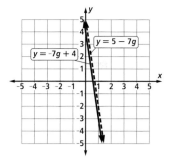

67. a. 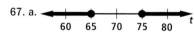 **b.** $t \leq 65$ or $t \geq 75$

Chapter 5

Lesson 5-1 (pp. 252–257)

Questions: **1.** For all real numbers a, b, c and d, with b and d not zero, $\frac{a}{b} \cdot \frac{c}{d} = \frac{ac}{bd}$. **3.** $\frac{ab}{14}$ **5.** always true **7.** D **9.** $\frac{-1}{6n}$
11. 1.44 **13.** $\frac{2}{9ab^2}$ **15. a.** One rectangle has one eighth as much area as the other. **b.** Answers vary. Sample answer:

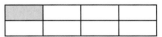

17. a. The Brocks' garden is half the area of the Peases' garden. **b.** Answers vary. Sample answers: The Peases have a 12-by-12 foot garden that has 144 ft² area; the Brocks' 8-by-9 foot garden has a 72 ft² area, which is half of 144 ft². **19.** 4 **21.** $\frac{1}{7}$ **23.** Answers vary.
Sample answers: $\frac{6a^3}{5}$ and $\frac{6}{ax}$ **25. a.** $\frac{L^3}{6}$ units³
b. $(12)(6)(4) = 288 = \frac{(12)^3}{6}$ **c.** 6, stack them 2 high and 3 deep **27.** $x = 40$ **29.** 3,025 ft²

Lesson 5-2 (pp. 258–262)

Guided Example 2: $\frac{6x}{5}$; $\frac{9x}{10}$; $\frac{9x}{10}$, $\frac{10}{9x}$; 4; 3; 24; 18; yes
Questions: **1.** $\frac{5}{3} \approx 1.67$, $\frac{7}{11} \approx 0.64$, $1.67 \div 0.64 \approx 2.61 \approx \frac{55}{21}$
3. a. n **b.** $\frac{1}{n}$ **5.** $\frac{24}{25}$ **7.** 3 **9.** $\frac{14m}{5n}$ **11.** $\frac{1}{10}$ **13.** $m = 92$
15. a. $200 \div \frac{1}{4}$ **b.** 800 **17.** b^2 **19.** $\frac{48}{n}$ **21.** $\frac{5d^3}{169}$
23. a. $V = 13,574.7$ **b.** 6%; $14,289.16; the car before taxes or discounts **25. a.** $3B + 2 = 10$ **b.** $\frac{8}{3}$ kg

Lesson 5-3 (pp. 263–268)

Guided Example 3: **a.** denominator; $x + 4$; –4; –4 **b.** numerator; x; 0
Questions: **1.** hundreds of thousands of people per year; $40 per ticket; $150 per ticket; $20 per hour; 50 dollars per hour to park; 230 miles per hour; 354 kilometers per hour; 2.5 miles per lap **3.** $\frac{6}{t}$ blocks per minute

5. about 7.77 books per person   **7. a.** $\frac{-5 \text{ degrees}}{8 \text{ hr}} = -\frac{5}{8}$ degrees per hour   **b.** $-\frac{5}{8}$ degrees per hour $\cdot$ 8 hours $= -5$ degrees   **9. a.** $w = 12$ **b.** $w = -5$

11. a. $y = -2$ **b.** none

13.

x	y
-3	$\frac{-2}{5}$
-2	$-\frac{1}{4}$
-1	0
0	$\frac{1}{2}$
1	2
2	undefined
3	-4

15. a. 1,000 people/mile^2 **b.** about 6.1 people/mile^2 **17. a.** \$0.10/min.   **b.** \$6/hr   **c.** $70 - 0.10m$ dollars   **19.** $\frac{4b^2}{21}$ **21.** $8n$ **23.** $\frac{5}{7}$ **25.** $\frac{2}{15}$ **27. a.** $y < -10$ **b.** $x > -2$ **c.** $A \geq -3.5$ **d.** $B \leq -0.25$

Lesson 5-4 (pp. 269–273)

Guided Example 2: feet; seconds; 60 min; 1 min; 5,280 ft; 5,280; sec; about 100 ft/sec

Questions: 1. a. 22 mi   **b.** $\frac{11m}{15}$ mi   **3.** $\frac{1,370 \text{ pages}}{1} \cdot \frac{1 \text{ day}}{12 \text{ pages}} \cdot \frac{1 \text{ mo}}{30 \text{ days}} \approx 3.8$ months   **5. a.** Answers vary. Sample answer: Those delicious tomatoes cost \$4/kg.   **b.** 0.25 kg/dollar   **c.** Answers vary. Sample answer: With one dollar you can buy 0.25 kg of those delicious tomatoes.   **7.** $\frac{36 \text{ in.}}{1 \text{ yd}}, \frac{1 \text{ yd}}{36 \text{ in.}}$.   **9.** 48 km/hr   **11.** Answers vary. Sample answer: Annie the ant crawls one foot per minute. How far does the ant go, in inches, in 16 minutes and 40 seconds?   **13. a.** $2k$ dishes per min   **b.** $\frac{1}{2k}$ min per dish   **15. a.** 25 mi per day   **b.** about 11.5 marathons   **17.** 3.1 mi per day   **19.** 27 boxes   **21.** 73 in.   **23.** B   **25.** B

Lesson 5-5 (pp. 274–279)

Questions: 1. a. $\frac{9}{4}$ **b.** 225%   **3.** $6\frac{2}{3}$ qt of fruit punch and $13\frac{1}{3}$ qt of ginger ale   **5. a.** 0.684   **b.** $\frac{11}{17 + n}$ **c.** 1   **7.** about 143 children   **9. a.** 20 min   **b.** 384 words   **11.** approximately 441 mi/hr   **13. a.** no   **b.** no   **c.** no   **d.** no   **15.** $0 < h < 432$ cm

Lesson 5-6 (pp. 280–288)

Questions: 1. the probability that event E occurs   **3. a.** 20%   **b.** 80%   **5. a.** $\frac{1}{36}$ **b.** 0   **c.** $\frac{1}{6}$ **7. a.** 11.1%   **b.** about 84.7%   **c.** about 15.3%   **d.** conditional   **9. a.** 5 to 7   **b.** 7 to 5   **11.** A diamond, spade, or club is chosen from a standard deck of playing cards.   **13. a.** $\frac{1}{52}$ **b.** $\frac{1}{13}$ **c.** $\frac{2}{13}$ **15.** $\frac{1}{3}$ **17. a.** $\frac{1}{200}$ **b.** $\frac{101}{200}$ **c.** 0   **19.** Answers vary. Sample answer: Complementary events do not necessarily have equal probabilities.   **21. a.** \$513   **b.** rate   **23.** $D = \frac{64}{3}$ **25.** \$149.50

Lesson 5-7 (pp. 289–295)

Guided Example 1: a. 198   **b.** 21   **c.** 95; 198; 0.48   **d.** 70; about 35%

Questions: 1. The event did not occur in any trial.   **3.** The event will never happen.   **5. a.** $\frac{5}{26}$ **b.** 12 vowels; 24 consonants   **c.** $\frac{1}{3}$ **d.** Answers vary. Sample answer: because most words have a vowel in them   **7.** 46% of tests were given this or a lower score.   **9.** 82 in. About 80.3% of the NBA players in the sample answer are 82 in. tall or shorter.   **11.** $a = 28$ and $b = 37$ **13.** A   **15.** about 37%   **17. a.** $\frac{3}{19}$ **b.** $\frac{1}{578}$ **c.** twice   **19.** 8.13 in.   **21.** $x = -3$ or $x = 7$

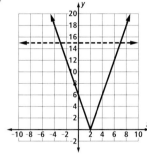

Lesson 5-8 (pp. 296–300)

Questions: 1. a. 0.49π ft^2 **b.** 5.29 ft^2 **c.** 29%   **d.** 71%   **3. a.** $\frac{1}{6}$ **b.** $\frac{1}{12}$ **c.** $\frac{1}{3}$ **5.** approximately 60.5%   **7.** $\frac{5}{9}$ **9. a.** approximately 29.2%   **b.** approximately 70.8%   **11.** Answers vary. Sample answer:

13. $\frac{9\pi}{160}$ **15.** 9.8 ft and 4.2 ft   **17. a.** 0   **b.** The Zero Product Property   **19.** $\frac{7}{9}$

Lesson 5-9 (pp. 301–307)

Questions: 1. 54   **3.** a statement that two ratios are equal   **5. a.** $p = -48$ **b.** $\frac{64}{-48} = \frac{-4}{3}, \frac{-28}{21} = \frac{-4}{3}$ **7. a.** about 1.85 million people   **b.** about 150,000   **9.** 280 wolves   **11.** $m = 16$ **13.** $c = \frac{3b}{2}$ **15.** $a = \frac{bx}{y}$ **17.** 570 min   **19. a.** 114 bpm   **b.** no   **21.** 56 earned runs   **23. a.** $\frac{4}{29}$ **b.** $\frac{17}{29}$ **c.** $\frac{21}{29}$ **25. a.** $n = \frac{S}{180} + 2$ **b.** 9 sides   **27. a.** your seven-digit phone number   **b.** If we let x be the first three digits of your phone number and y be the last four, then your phone number can be written as $10,000x + y$. We can also write the result of the puzzle as an algebraic expression involving x and y: $\frac{(80x+1) \cdot 250 + y + y - 250}{2} = 10,000x + y$, which is the same as the expression for your phone number.

Lesson 5-10 (pp. 308–314)

Guided Example 2: $\overline{LM}$; $\overline{BC}$; $\overline{KL}$, $\overline{LM}$; $\overline{BC}$; $\overline{KL}$;
12.6; 3; 4.8, 4.8; 3; 12.6, 7.875; 4.8

Questions: **1.** Corresponding angles have the same measure.
Ratios of lengths of corresponding sides are equal.
3. a. $\overline{XZ}$ **b.** $\overline{YZ}$ **c.** $\overline{XY}$ **5. a.** 7.5 **b.** 19.5 **7. a.** 1.5 in.
b. $\frac{1}{24}$ **c.** 1 in. **d.** 24 in. **9.** $\frac{40}{3}$ **11. a.** $x = 21$ **b.** 96
13. a.

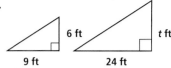

b. $\frac{6}{9} = \frac{t}{24}$ **c.** 16 ft
15. $x = 48$ **17.** 75% **19.** about 69.3 g **21. a.** 3 **b.** $\frac{1}{12}$
c. There are 6 ways to achieve a sum of 7, and each other
sum has fewer than 6 ways in which it can be obtained.
23. 3,705,386 mi^2

Self-Test (pp. 318–319)

1. $\frac{75c}{8p} \cdot \frac{2}{15c} = \frac{5}{4p} \cdot \frac{1}{1} = \frac{5}{4p}$ **2.** $\frac{5}{a} \div \frac{9}{3a^2} = \frac{5}{a} \cdot \frac{3a^2}{9} = \frac{5}{1} \cdot \frac{a}{3} = \frac{5a}{3}$
3. $\frac{2x}{5} \div \frac{x}{5} = \frac{2x}{5} \cdot \frac{5}{x} = \frac{2}{1} \cdot \frac{1}{1} = 2$ **4.** B **5.** $h = \frac{6}{101} \cdot 17 = \frac{102}{101}$
6. $4u = \frac{9}{5} \cdot 3$; $u = \frac{27}{5} \cdot \frac{1}{4} = \frac{27}{20}$ **7.** $24\left(\frac{x}{8}\right) = 24\left(\frac{2x-3}{24}\right)$;
$3x = 2x - 3$; $x = -3$ **8. a.** $8x = 105$ **b.** $x = \frac{105}{8} = 13.125$
9. $\left(6 \text{ boxes} \cdot \frac{10 \text{ pencils}}{\text{box}}\right) \div 4 \text{ children} = 60 \text{ pencils} \div$
$4 \text{ children} = 15 \frac{\text{pencils}}{\text{child}}$ **10.** $\frac{221}{1,563} \approx 0.141 = 14.1\%$
11. $\frac{7.5 \text{ min}}{1 \text{ mi}} \cdot \frac{1 \text{ mi}}{1.6 \text{ km}} \cdot \frac{60 \text{ sec}}{1 \text{ min}} = 281.25 \frac{\text{sec}}{\text{km}}$; 281.25 sec
12. $\frac{x}{x-5} = \frac{12}{4}$; $4x = 12(x-5)$; $4x = 12x - 60$; $60 = x$;
$x = \frac{60}{8} = 7.5$ **13.** The sector between 3 and 4
represents $\frac{1}{12}$ of the clock, so the probability is $\frac{1}{12}$.
14. The discount is \$4.50 off \$22.50, so \$4.50/\$22.50 = 0.2,
or 20%. **15. a.** $50 \text{ km}/\left(1\frac{47}{60}\text{hr}\right) \approx 28 \text{ km/hr}$ **b.** about 0.036
hr/km **16.** 18%, because $7 + 2 = 9$ people out of 50.
17. 50%, because $50 - 7 - 16 - 2 = 25$ people out of
50. **18.** 46%, because $7 + 16 = 23$ people out of 50.
19. k cannot be 2, because then the denominator would be
0, and division by zero is undefined. **20.** $\frac{c}{f+s+c+d}$ **21.**
Let m be the number of miles. Then $\frac{350}{20} = \frac{m}{35}$; $20m =$
12,250; $m = 612.5$ mi. **22.** Area of rectangle $= 4 \text{ ft} \cdot 7 \text{ ft} =$
28 ft^2. Area of circle $= \pi \cdot \left(21 \text{ in.}/ 12 \frac{\text{in.}}{\text{ft}}\right)^2 \approx 9.62 \text{ feet}^2$.
So the probability is about $\frac{9.62}{28} \approx 34\%$. **23.** $\frac{1,210}{x} = \frac{4}{6}$;
$x = 1,815$ ft **24.** 24; The 75th percentile implies
25% performed better. $\frac{6}{x} = \frac{1}{4}$; $x = 24$

The chart below keys the **Self-Test** questions to the objectives in the **Chapter Review** on pages 320–323 or to the **Vocabulary (Voc)** on page 317. This will enable you to locate those **Chapter Review** questions that correspond to questions missed on the **Self-Test**. The lesson where the material is covered is also indicated on the chart.

Question	1	2	3	4	5	6	7	8	9	10
Objective(s)	A	B	B	A	C	C	C	D	E	H
Lesson(s)	5-1	5-2, 5-3	5-2, 5-3	5-1	5-9	5-9	5-9	5-9	5-3	5-6, 5-7

Question	11	12	13	14	15	16	17	18	19	20
Objective(s)	F	L	I	E	F	H	H	H	B	G
Lesson(s)	5-4	5-10	5-8	5-3	5-4	5-6, 5-7	5-6, 5-7	5-6, 5-7	5-2, 5-3	5-5

Question	21	22	23	24
Objective(s)	J	I	J	K
Lesson(s)	5-9, 5-10	5-8	5-9, 5-10	5-7

Chapter Review (pp. 320–323)

1. $\frac{14a}{5}$ **3.** $\frac{12}{p}$ **5.** $11b$ **7.** $\frac{c}{27}$ **9.** $\frac{-3}{25}$ **11.** -8
13. $k = -\frac{5}{6}$ **15.** $t = -1$ **17.** 486 **19.** $\frac{15}{6}$ **21.** $\frac{u}{m}$
23. a. \$0.075 per oz **b.** \$0.05625 per oz **c.** the 32-oz box
25. $4w$ words in $6m$ min, since $\frac{4w}{6m} = \frac{2w}{3m} > \frac{w}{2m}$

27. Answers vary. Sample answer: 1.5 ft per year **29. a.**
161,280 breaths **b.** The cat breathes at a faster rate, since
humans take $16 \cdot 60 = 960$ breaths per hour **31. a.** $2n$
envelopes **b.** $\frac{1}{2n}$ min **33.** D **35.** 8 **37.** 12.5 gal of blue
paint, 7.5 gal of yellow paint **39.** 5 hits **41.** $\frac{1}{3}$

43. 69%   **45.** $\frac{11}{36}$ **47. a.** $\frac{\pi}{64}$ **b.** $\frac{\pi}{8}$ **49.** $1,176   **51.** 40 moose   **53.** 25th   **55. a.** 3 **b.** 6 **c.** 16   **57. a.** Answers vary. Sample answer: $\frac{x}{6}, \frac{y}{4}$ **b.** $y = \frac{128}{9}$ **c.** $x = \frac{27}{16}$ **59.** 93.75 units^2

Chapter 6

Lesson 6-1 (pp. 326–332)

Questions: 1. dollars; hours   **3. a.** 1920s **b.** 1910–1930 **c.** 1970s **d.** (B10 − B9)/(A10 − A9)   **5.** increase **7.** decrease   **9.** $-\frac{2}{3}$ **11. a.** $\frac{7}{60} \frac{m}{hr}$ **b.** negative

13. −$131 per day   **15.** True; $\frac{9}{15} = \frac{\frac{3}{5}}{1}$ **17.** 850 + 48x coins

Lesson 6-2 (pp. 333–340)

Guided Example 3: 3; −2; $-\frac{1}{2}$; 3; 2; $-\frac{1}{2}$; $\frac{9-5}{-10--2}$; $-\frac{1}{2}$; $-\frac{1}{2}$; $-\frac{1}{2}$

Questions: 1. line   **3. a.** Answers vary. Sample answer: (6, 3.9) and (8, 3.3) **b.** Answers vary. Sample answer: $\frac{5.4-5.7}{1-0} = -0.3$ **c.** 0.3 cm of the candle burns every second.   **5.** 5   **7. a.** $\frac{10}{3}$ **b.** $\frac{29}{9}$ **c.** No, because the line connecting the first two points has a different slope than the line connecting the next two.   **9.** 2   **11. a.** Answers vary. Sample answer: (0, −6) and (5, 0)   **b.** $\frac{6}{5}$ **c.**

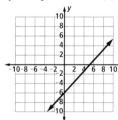

13. a. $-\frac{1}{5}$ **b.** Water is removed from the bathtub at a rate of one gallon every five seconds.   **15. a.** degrees per hour **b.** The rate of change describes the variations in temperature over time.   **17.** y = 11   **19. a.** 3 toothpicks per term **b.** Answers vary. Sample answer: Note that (0, 1) and (1, 4) lie on the line and $\frac{4-1}{1-0} = 3$ **c.** It is the rate at which the number of toothpicks increases from one term to the next.   **21.** no solution   **23.** 2b

Lesson 6-3 (pp. 341–347)

Questions: 1. a.

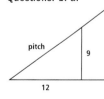

b. No, because $\frac{9}{12} > \frac{8}{12}$, and $\frac{8}{12}$ is considered the limit for the pitch of a safe roof. **c.** 0.75   **3.** Not possible because $\frac{12}{0}$ is undefined.   **5.** 1

7. a.

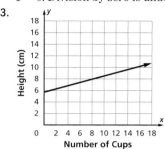

b. Answers vary. Sample answer: (3, 6) **c.** $\frac{6-2}{3-2} = \frac{4}{1} = 4$ **9.** Answers vary. Sample answer: (0, −5)   **11.** Answers vary. Sample answer: A vertical line is one that passes through points with the same x-coordinate, such as (1, 4) and (1, 2). If we calculate the slope of the line using the formula $\frac{y_2 - y_1}{x_2 - x_1}$, the denominator is 1 − 1 = 0. Division by zero is undefined.

13.

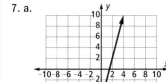

15.

x	y
2	0
3	−4
4	−8
5	−12

17. 37 ft

19.

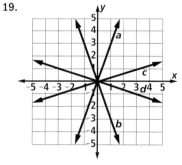

a. Lines a and c **b.** Lines b and d **c.** The lines with positive slope are slanted up to the right; the lines with negative slope are slanted down to the right. **d.** lines a and b **e.** Answers vary. Sample answer: 4

21. 1.5   **23. a.** 2001 and 2002 **b.** 2001 and 2002

25. $b = -13.75$

Lesson 6-4 (pp. 348-355)

Questions: **1.** $m; b$ **3. a.** 2 **b.** 3

c.

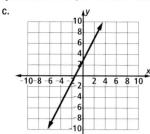

5. a. $y = -1.3x + 5.6$
b. -1.3 **c.** 5.6 **7. a.** $h = 2t + 3$

b.

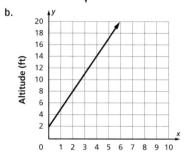

c. $m = 2$;
$b = 3$ **d.** 123 ft
9. $y = 4x + 3$
11. $y = 2x - 5$
13. c; i **15.** b; ii

17. a.

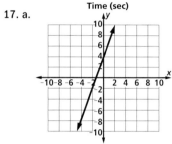

b.

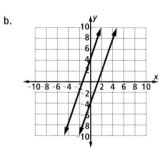

c. $y = 3x - 4$ **d.** They
have the same slope.
19. $\frac{10}{27} \approx 0.37$
21. $x = \frac{3}{2}$ **23.** -3 and -2

Lesson 6-5 (pp. 356-360)

Guided Example 2: $k; h; 0; -5; 22$

Questions: **1. a.** $y = 9,700x + 143,560$ **b.** $289,060$ people
c. 2027 **3.** $y - 6 = -2(x + 8)$ **5.** $y = -\frac{1}{2}$ **7.** $y - 15 = -2(x - 20)$ **9.** $y + 3 = -4.3(x - 6.8)$ **11. a.** $y = 1.5x + 2$
b. 74 cm **13. a.** $m = 0.3; x = 5; y = 12$ **b.** $y - 12 = 0.3(x - 5)$ **c.** 14.1 lb **15.** $y = 4x + 3$ **17. a.** $m = 1.75; (15, 29.25)$
b. $y - 29.25 = 1.75(x - 15)$

19.

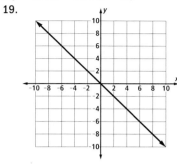

21. $\$2.31$ per bushel;
the price of each
bushel **23. a.** $\frac{6}{5}$
b. $\frac{6}{5}$ **c.** $\frac{z}{y}$

Lesson 6-6 (pp. 361-367)

Guided Example 3:
$(10, 2.23)$ and $(20, 4.12)$; slope; $\frac{4.12 - 2.23}{20 - 10}$; 2.23; 10 (or 4.12; 20); $b = 0.34$; 0.189; 0.34; 0; cost per minute; y; x; about 130
Questions: **1. a.** $y = \frac{25}{54}x + \frac{1,015}{27}$ **b.** about $79°$F
3. $y = -1.5x + 7$ **5.** $y - 11 = -(x - 4)$ **7.** $y - 27 = 0.5 \cdot (x - 30)$ **9. a.** $y = -\frac{389}{60}x + \frac{757,027}{60}$ where x is the year and
y is the price **b.** about $-\$70.77$ **c.** Answers vary. Sample
answer: No, since the price of penicillin should never be
negative. **11. a.** $(2.1, 59.24)$ and $(3.7, 70.08)$ **b.** 6.775
c. The slope represents how much longer you will have to
wait for the next eruption for every minute of an eruption.
d. $y = 6.775x + 45.0125$ **e.** 7.23 min **13.** $y = 1.60x + 2.5$

15.

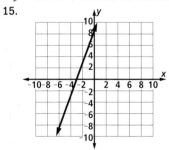

17. a. between the 47-mi
and the 72-mi signs
b. about 52.5 ft per mi
19. a. $l = 2w + 3$
b. 6cm and 15cm
c. 90cm^2
21. $12g + 7.25h$

Lesson 6-7 (pp. 368–373)

Guided Example: 11.02; 10.56

Questions: **1. a.** no **b.** yes

3. a.

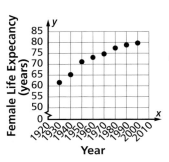

b. Answers vary. Sample answer:

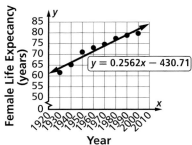

$y = 0.2562x - 430.71$

c. approximately 63.8, 66.3, 68.9, 71.4, 74.0, 76.6, 79.1, and 81.7 yr **d.** about 18.82 **e.** 86.67 yr

5. a.

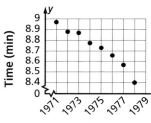

b. about 7.67 min
c. 0.6 min **d.** 0.51 min
e. Answers vary.
Sample answer: No, since a half-minute deviation is very large in an 8-min race.

7. a.

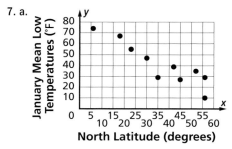

b. $y \approx -1.086x + 81.139$ **c.** decrease by about one degree Fahrenheit **d.** Tokyo, Japan **e.** about –16°F **f.** about 71°F
9. no   **11.** no   **13. a.** $y - 4 = \frac{5}{3}(x - 6)$ **b.** Answers vary.
Sample answer: (0, –6)   **15.** $-\frac{1}{6}$; 0

17. a. Answers vary. Sample answer:

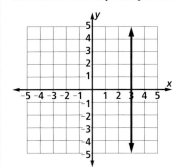

b. not defined
19. $\frac{1}{8}$ **21. a.** 0
b. all numbers **c.** no solutions

Lesson 6-8 (pp. 374–380)

Questions: **1.** standard form for an equation of a line
3. $A = 5$; $B = -3$; $C = 9$ **5. a.** x-intercept $= 10$;
y-intercept $= 4$ **b.**

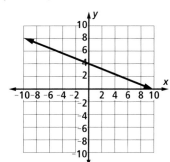

7. a. Sample answer:
(0, 9); (3, 7); (6, 5)
b. $2x + 3y = 27$, where x are the 2-point shots and y are the 3-point shots **c.** 9 **d.** 12

e.

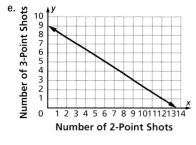

9. a. $9x - 8y = 0$
b. $A = 9$; $B = -8$; $C = 0$ **11.** $y = \frac{4}{7}x - 44$ **13. a.** Answers vary. Sample answer: $C = 62$, $W = 0$; $C = 65$, $W = 12$; $C = 68$, $W = 24$ **b.** $C - \frac{1}{4}W = 62$

c.

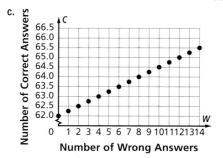

15. a. Answers vary. Sample answer:

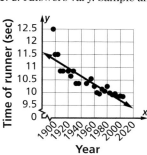

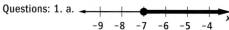
Year

b. Answers vary. Sample answer:
(1946, 10.4),
(1984, 9.9);
$T = -\frac{1}{76}x + \frac{6,841}{190}$
c. Answers vary. Sample answer:
9.5 seconds; the line is only an approximation of the data.

17. a. $y = 4x + 8$; with $y \le 72$ **b.** 4 **c.** 16 hr **19.** $\frac{8}{11}$

21. no

Lesson 6-9 (pp. 381–386)

Questions: 1. a.

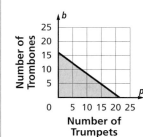

b.

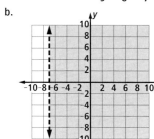

3. $x \le 1$ **5. a.** half-planes **b.** boundary **7.** The first is the graph of the half-plane under $y = -2x + 6$ *excluding* the line $y = -2x + 6$; the second is the same half-plane *including* the line.

9.

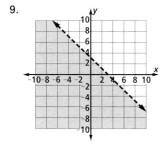

11. The points in the shaded area with integer coordinates are solutions.

13. a. It would imply that someone made more field goals than he attempted! **b.** $y \le x$ **c.** Answers vary. Sample answer: The points would lie farther away from the *x*-axis. **15.** Answers vary. Sample answer: (6, 0) **17. a.** $8x + 12y = 288$ **b.** 24 **c.** 14 **19. a.** $y = \frac{1}{6}x$ **b.** 30 lb **c.** 37.2 lb **21. a.** 0.01 **b.** 0.006 **c.** 0.000012

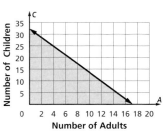

Number of Adults

Self-Test (pp. 390–391)

1. a. –2 **b.** 3 **c.** $\frac{-2 - 0}{0 - 3} = \frac{-2}{-3} = \frac{2}{3}$ **2.** No, because the slope between (8, 2) and (18, –6) is $\frac{2 - (-6)}{8 - 18} = \frac{8}{-10} = -\frac{4}{5}$, while the slope between (18, –6) and (12, –1) is $\frac{-1 - (-6)}{12 - 18} = \frac{5}{-6} = -\frac{5}{6}$. All points on a line have the same slope between them.

3. $y = \frac{8}{9}x - 12$ **4.** $T = 3h + 58$, where h is hours after 8 A.M. **5.** The slope of a vertical line is undefined.

6. $3x + y = 8$; $A = 3$, $B = 1$, and $C = 8$ **7.** It will go down $\frac{1}{2}$ of a unit. **8.** $y = \frac{1}{2}x + -\frac{1}{4}$; slope $= \frac{1}{2}$, *y*-intercept $= -\frac{1}{4}$ **9. a.** $6,400 \ge 300p + 400b$ **b.** The values are points with integer coordinates in the shaded area.

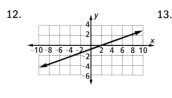

Number of Trumpets

10. 2003 and 2004

11. $\frac{103,111 - 96,500}{2004 - 1999} = 1,322.2$ people per year

12.

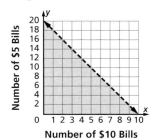

13.

14. The points (22, 14) and (132, 9) imply $m = \frac{14 - 9}{22 - 132} = \frac{-5}{110} = -\frac{1}{22}$. So, $y = -\frac{1}{22}x + b$. Substituting (22, 14), $14 = -\frac{1}{22}(22) + b$, so $b = 15$, and $y = -\frac{1}{22}x + 15$. **15.** Answers vary. Sample answer: $y = \frac{5}{4}x + b$, $0 = \frac{5}{4}(-4)$, $0 = -5 + b$, $b = 5$; an equation of the line is $y = \frac{5}{4}x + 5$, so another point on the line is (0, 5). **16. a.** Answers vary. Sample answer: (2, 35), (15, 78) **b.** $m = \frac{78 - 35}{15 - 2} = \frac{43}{13} \approx 3.31$; Substitute (2, 35), so $35 = 3.31(2) + b$, $35 = 6.62 + b$, so $b = 28.38$; $y = 3.31x + 28.38$ **c.** $y = 3.31(25) + 28.38 = 111.13$; $111,130 **17.** $y = 2.98x + 33.28$ **18. a.** c **b.** b **19. a.** a **b.** d **20.** $10x + 5y < 100$; the points with integer coordinates in the shaded area are solutions.

21. a. $y - 10 = -3(x - 4)$ **b.** Let $x = 0$. Then $y - 10 = -3(0 - 4)$ so $y - 10 = 12$, so $y = 22$. Patrick lives on the 22nd floor

Number of $10 Bills

The chart below keys the **Self-Test** questions to the objectives in the **Chapter Review** on pages 392–395 or to the **Vocabulary (Voc)** on page 389. This will enable you to locate those **Chapter Review** questions that correspond to questions missed on the **Self-Test**. The lesson where the material is covered is also indicated on the chart.

Question	1	2	3	4	5	6	7	8	9	10
Objective(s)	A	A	C	F	D	C	D	C	I	E
Lesson(s)	6-2	6-2	6-4, 6-8	6-4, 6-5, 6-6, 6-8	6-2, 6-3	6-4, 6-8	6-2, 6-3	6-4, 6-8	6-9	6-1, 6-3

Question	11	12	13	14	15	16	17	18	19	20
Objective(s)	E	H	I	F	B	G	G	D	D	I
Lesson(s)	6-1, 6-3	6-3, 6-4, 6-8	6-9	6-4, 6-5, 6-6, 6-8	6-4, 6-5, 6-6	6-7	6-7	6-2, 6-3	6-2, 6-3	6-9

Question	21
Objective(s)	F
Lesson(s)	6-4, 6-5, 6-6

Chapter Review (pp. 392-395)

1. $\frac{6}{5}$ 3. $-\frac{5}{2}$ 5. $y = 3$ 7. $y = 2.6x + 7$
9. $y - 20 = -0.5(x + 5)$ 11. $y - 0.25 = 3(x - 30)$
13. $y - 4 = \frac{3}{2}(x - 3)$ 15. $x = -3$ 17. Answers vary.
Sample answer: $x + -2y = -14, A = 1, B = -2, C = -14$
19. $y = -2x + \frac{5}{2}$ 21. slope = 12, y-intercept = -6.2
23. slope = -1, y-intercept = 0 25. y, change 27. u
29. 0 31. Any two points on a line can be used to
determine the slope of the line. Choosing any two of the
points must yield the same slope as any other two points.
Therefore, if the slope between any two of the three points
is different from the slope of the third point and either
of the two points used, the points are not collinear.
33. $-\frac{1}{5}$ 35. 27.4 subscribers per year 37. $-13.6°F$/month
39. October and November 41. slope = $-\$100$/day,
y-intercept = $\$1,000$ 43. $y = 0.25x + 1.75$
45. $p = 50m + 25,350$ 47. $820 = 8S + 7B$
49. a. Answers vary. Sample answer:

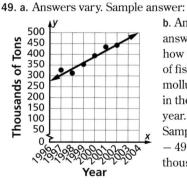

b. Answers vary. Sample
answer: 25 c. It indicates
how many additional tons
of fish, crustaceans, and
mollusks are being caught
in the Philippines each
year. d. Answers vary.
Sample answer: $T = 25y$
$- 49,600$, where T is the
thousands of tons and y
is the year e. $T = 28.2y - 56,008$ f. Answers vary. Sample
answer: The equation in Part d predicts a value 24
thousand tons less (650) than the regression line (674).

51.

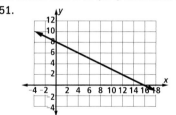

53.

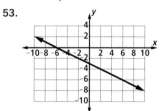

55.

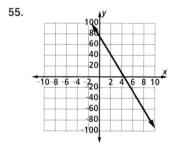

57.

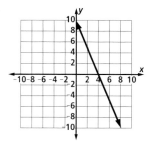

59. The possible values are points (n, q) with integer coordinates in the shaded area.

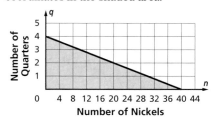

61.

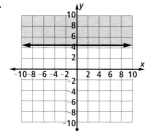

63.

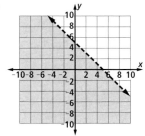

65.

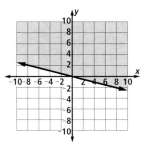

Glossary

A

absolute value (A) The distance a number x is from 0 written $|x|$. (B) $|x| = x$ if $x \geq c$; $|x| = -x$ if $x < c$. (43)

addition method for solving a system Given two equations in a system, applying the Addition Property if $a = b$ and $c = d$, then $a + c = b + d$, to obtain another equation that is satisfied by the solution to the system. (602)

Addition Property of Equality For all real numbers a, b, and c, if $a = b$, then $a + c = b + c$. (106)

Addition Property of Inequality For all real numbers a, b, and c, if $a < b$, then $a + c < b + c$.

Additive Identity Property For any real number a, $a + 0 = 0 + a = a$. (108)

Additive Inverse Property For any real number a, $a + -a = -a + a = 0$. (109)

additive inverses Two numbers whose sum is zero; also called opposites. (85)

Algebraic Definition of Division For all real numbers a and b with $b \neq 0$, $a \div b = \frac{a}{b} = a \cdot \frac{1}{b}$. (7)

Algebraic Definition of Subtraction For all real numbers a and b, $a - b = a + -b$. (7)

algebraic expression An expression that includes one or more variables. (6)

algebraic fraction A fraction with a variable in the numerator, in the denominator, or in both. (252)

annual yield The percent of interest that money on deposit earns per year. (398)

antecedent The clause following *if* in an if-then statement. (778)

Arrangements Theorem If there are n ways to select each object in a sequence of length L, then n^L different sequences are possible. (459)

Associative Property of Addition For any real numbers a, b, and c, $(a + b) + c = a + (b + c)$. (10)

Associative Property of Multiplication For any real numbers a, b, and c, $(ab)c = a(bc)$. (9)

axis of symmetry Given a figure, a line over which the reflection image of the figure is the figure itself. (526)

B

base The number x in the power x^n. (398)

binomial A polynomial that has two terms. (663)

boundary line A line that separates two sets, e.g., solutions from nonsolutions in the graph of a linear inequality. (381)

boundary A point or number that separates solutions from nonsolutions on a number line. (155)

C

capture-recapture method The use of proportions to estimate the total number of objects in a set (e.g., the number of deer in a forest or the number of fish in a pond). (303)

Celsius scale The temperature scale of the metric system, developed by Anders Celsius, in which the freezing point of water is $0°$ and the boiling point of water is $100°$; also known as the *centigrade scale*. (221)

centigrade scale See *Celsius scale*. (221)

chi-square statistic A member calculated from data to determine whether the difference in two frequency distributions is greater than that expected by chance. (698)

circular permutation An ordering of objects around a circle. (695)

clearing fractions Multiplying each side of an equation or inequality by a constant to get an equivalent equation without fractions as coefficients. (170)

closed under an operation A set is closed under an operation if the result of the operation always lies within the particular set. (802)

coefficient A number that is a factor in a term containing a variable. (73)

coefficient matrix In the matrix equation $\begin{bmatrix} a & b \\ c & d \end{bmatrix} \cdot \begin{bmatrix} x \\ y \end{bmatrix} = \begin{bmatrix} e \\ f \end{bmatrix}$, the coefficient matrix is $\begin{bmatrix} a & b \\ c & d \end{bmatrix}$. (622)

coincident Two or more lines or other sets of points that are identical. (618)

collinear points Points that all lie on the same line. (130)

Commutative Property of Addition For all real numbers a and b, $a + b = b + a$. (16)

Commutative Property of Multiplication For all real numbers a and b, $ab = ba$. (**16**)

complementary events Two events that have no elements in common, but together they contain all the possible outcomes. (**283**)

complete factorization The representation of a polynomial as a product of prime polynomials. (**676**)

completing the square Converting a quadratic equation in standard form to one in vertex form. (**724**)

complex fraction A fraction that has a fraction in the numerator or a fraction in the denominator, or both. (**259**)

compound interest The money a bank pays on the principal and earned interest in an account. (**399, 400**)

compound sentence A single sentence consisting of two or more sentences linked by the words *and* or *or*. (**227**)

conditional probability The probability that an event will occur given that another event has occurred. (**283**)

consequent The clause following *then* in an if-then statement. (**778**)

constant-decrease situation A quantity that decreases at a constant amount in a period of time. (**130**)

constant-increase situation A quantity that increases at a constant amount in a period of time. (**130**)

constant matrix In the matrix equation $\begin{bmatrix} a & b \\ c & d \end{bmatrix} \cdot \begin{bmatrix} x \\ y \end{bmatrix}$ $= \begin{bmatrix} e \\ f \end{bmatrix}$, the constant matrix is $\begin{bmatrix} e \\ f \end{bmatrix}$. (**622**)

constant term A term in a polynomial without a variable. (**736**)

converse An if-then statement in which the antecedent and the consequent of the statement have been switched. (**784**)

conversion rate A rate determined from an equality between two quantities with different units. (**269**)

coordinates The numbers x and y that locate a point (x, y) in the coordinate plane. (**27**)

counterexample An instance for which a general statement is not true. (**23**)

cube The third power of a number x, or x^3. (**493**)

Cube of the Cube Root Property For any nonnegative number x, $\sqrt[3]{x} \cdot \sqrt[3]{x} \cdot \sqrt[3]{x} = \sqrt[3]{x^3} = x$. (**493**)

cube root If $V = s^3$, then s is a cube root of V. (**493**)

cubic polynomial A polynomial of degree 3. (**756**)

D

deduction Using a proof to show that one if-then statement follows from another. (**789**)

define a variable The process of describing the quantity a variable represents. (**14**)

degree of a monomial The sum of the exponents of the variables in the monomial. (**664**)

degree of a polynomial The highest degree of any of the monomial terms of a polynomial. (**664**)

dependent variable A variable (y) whose value is determined by the value of at least one other variable in a given function. (**426**)

deviation (A) The difference between a member of a data set and the mean of that data set. (**42**) (B) The difference between an expected number and an actual observed number. (**697**)

difference of squares An expression of the form $x^2 - y^2$. For all real numbers x and y, $x^2 - y^2 = (x + y)(x - y)$. (**687–688**)

dimensions (of a matrix) The number of rows and columns in a matrix. (**622**)

direct variation A number y varies directly with a number x if y is a constant multiple of x. (**353**)

discount The amount by which the original price of an item is lowered. (**184**)

discount rate The ratio of the discount to the original price. (**275**)

discriminant The value of $b^2 - 4ac$ in the quadratic equation $ax^2 + bx + c = 0$. (**561**)

Discriminant Property Suppose $ax^2 + bx + c$ and a, b, and c are real numbers with $a \neq 0$. Let $D = b^2 - 4ac$. Then when $D > 0$, the equation has two real solutions. When $D = 0$, the equation has exactly one real solution. When $D < 0$, the equation has no real solutions. (**561**)

Discriminant Theorem When a, b, and c are integers, with $a \neq 0$, either all three of the following conditions are true or none are true. **1.** $b^2 - 4ac$ is a perfect square. **2.** $ax^2 + bx + c$ is factorable over the set of polynomials with integer coefficients. **3.** The solutions to $ax^2 + bx + c = 0$ are rational numbers. **(749)**

Distance between Two Points in a Coordinate Plane The distance AB between the points $A = (x_1, y_1)$ and $B = (x_2, y_2)$ in a coordinate plane is $AB = \sqrt{(x_2 - x_1)^2 + (y_2 - y_1)^2}$. **(507)**

Distributive Property of Multiplication over Addition For all real numbers a, b, and c, $c(a + b) = ca + cb$. **(66)**

Distributive Property of Multiplication over Subtraction For all real numbers a, b, and c, $c(a - b) = ca - cb$. **(67)**

Dividing Fractions Property For all real numbers a, b, c, and d, with $b \neq 0$, $c \neq 0$, and $d \neq 0$, $\frac{a}{b} \div \frac{c}{d} = \frac{a}{b} \cdot \frac{d}{c}$. **(258)**

Division Property of Equality For all real numbers a, b, and all real nonzero numbers c, if $a = b$, then $\frac{a}{c} = \frac{b}{c}$. **(113)**

domain of a function The set of possible values of the first (independent) variable. **(426)**

domain of a variable All the values that may be meaningfully substituted for a variable. **(28)**

double inequality An inequality of the form $a < x < b$. (The $<$ may be replaced with $>$, $\leq$, or $\geq$.) **(156, 227)**

E

elements (of a matrix) The objects in a rectangular array. **(622)**

empty set A set that has no elements in it, written as $\{\}$ or $\varnothing$. **(584)**

endpoints (A) The points A and B in the segment $\overline{AB}$. (B) The coordinates of those points on a number line. **(156)**

Equal Fractions Property For all real numbers a, b, and k, if $b \neq 0$ and $k \neq 0$, then $\frac{a}{b} = \frac{ak}{bk}$. **(253)**

equivalent equations Equations with exactly the same solutions. **(139)**

equivalent expressions Expressions that have the same value for *every* number that can be substituted for the variable(s). **(22)**

equivalent formulas Two or more formulas in which every set of values that satisfies one of the formulas also satisfies the others. **(222)**

equivalent statements When an if-then statement and its converse are both true, then the antecedent and consequent are equivalent. **(784)**

equivalent systems Systems with exactly the same solutions. **(608)**

evaluating an expression The process of finding the numerical value of an expression. **(6)**

even integer (even number) An integer that can be written as $2n$, where n is an integer. **(802)**

event A set of possible outcomes. **(280)**

expected number The mean frequency of a given event that is predicted by a probability. **(697)**

exponent The number n in the power x^n. **(398)**

exponential decay A situation in which $y = bg^x$ and $0 < g < 1$. **(411)**

exponential growth A situation in which $y = bg^x$ and $g > 1$. **(404)**

exponential growth equation If the amount at the beginning of the growth period is b, the growth factor is g, and y is the amount after x time periods, then $y = b \cdot g^x$. **(405)**

exponential regression A method to determine an equation of the form $y = b \cdot g^x$ for modeling a set of ordered pairs. **(419)**

Extended Distributive Property To multiply two sums, multiply each term in the first sum by each term in the second sum, and then add the products. **(680)**

extremes The numbers a and d in the proportion $\frac{a}{b} = \frac{c}{d}$. **(301)**

F

factors (A) A number or expression that is multiplied. (B) If $ab = c$, then a and b are factors of c. **(15)**

factored form of a quadratic function A quadratic function $y = ax^2 + bx + c$ is in factored form when it is written as $y = a(x - r_1)(x - r_2)$. **(730)**

factoring The process of expressing a given number or expression as a product. **(75, 675)**

factorization The result of factoring a number or polynomial. **(676)**

Factor Theorem Let r be a real number and $P(x)$ be a polynomial in x. If $x - r$ is a factor of $P(x)$, then $P(r) = 0$; that is, r is an x-intercept of the graph of P. If $P(r) = 0$, then $x - r$ is a factor of $P(x)$. **(755)**

Factor Theorem for Quadratic Functions The x-intercepts of the graph of $y = a(x - r_1)(x - r_2)$ are r_1 and r_2. **(731)**

fact triangle A triangle in which any pair of numbers in the triangle can be added, subtracted, multiplied, or divided to produce the third number. **(105, 112)**

Fahrenheit scale A temperature scale, developed by Gabriel Fahrenheit, in which the freezing point of water is 32° and the boiling point of water is 212°. **(221)**

fair A situation in which each outcome has the same probability; also called *unbiased*. **(281)**

Fundamental Property of Similar Figures If two polygons are similar, then the ratios of corresponding lengths are equal. **(309)**

function A set of ordered pairs in which each first coordinate corresponds to *exactly one* second coordinate. **(426)**

function notation Notation to indicate a function, such as $f(x)$, and read "f of x." **(435)**

$f(x)$ notation Notation indicating the value of a function f at x. When a function f contains the ordered pair (x, y), then y is the value of the function at x, and we may write $y = f(x)$. **(435)**

G

general formula for the height of a projectile over time Let h be the height (in feet) of a projectile launched from Earth's surface with an initial upward velocity v feet per second and an initial height of s feet. Then, after t seconds, $h = -16t^2 + vt + s$. **(546)**

generalization An if-then statement in which there is a variable in the antecedent and in the consequent. **(778)**

Generalized Addition Property of Equality For all numbers or expressions a, b, c, and d: If $a = b$ and $c = d$, then $a + c = b + d$. **(601)**

general linear equation An equation of the form $ax + b = cx + d$, where $a \neq 0$. **(202)**

greatest common factor (GCF) For two or more integers, the greatest integer that is a common factor. For two or more monomials, the GCF is the product of the greatest common factor of the coefficients and the greatest common factor of the variables. **(675)**

growth factor In exponential growth or decay, the positive number which is repeatedly multiplied by the original amount. **(404)**

growth model for powering If a quantity is multiplied by a positive number g (the growth factor) in each of x time periods, then, after the x periods, the quantity will be multiplied by g^x. **(405)**

H

half-life The time it takes for one half the amount of an element to decay. **(414)**

half-plane In a plane, the region on either side of a line. **(381)**

horizontal line A line with the equation $y = k$, where k is a real number. **(189)**

I

if and only if A phrase used to connect equivalent if-then statements. **(785)**

if-then statement A statement that contains an antecedent and a consequent. **(778)**

independent variable A variable whose value does not rely on the values of other variables. **(426)**

inductive reasoning The process of arriving at a general conclusion (not necessarily true) from specific instances. **(776)**

inequality A mathematical sentence with one of the verbs < (is less than), > (is greater than), ≤ (is less than or equal to), ≥ (is greater than or equal to), or ≠ (is not equal to). **(155)**

initial height The starting height of a projectile. **(545)**

initial upward velocity The velocity of a projectile when it is first launched, assuming no gravity effects. **(545)**

input A number substituted for the independent variable in a function. **(221, 426)**

instance A special case of a general pattern. **(13)**

interest The amount that a bank or other financial institution pays on money in an account, based on a percentage of the principal. **(398)**

intersection of sets The set of elements in both set A and set B and written as $A \cap B$. **(227)**

interval The set of numbers between two numbers a and b, possibly containing a or b. **(156)**

inverse (of a matrix) For a matrix A, the matrix B such that AB and BA are the identity matrix. **(629)**

Irrationality of $\sqrt{n}$ Theorem If n is an integer that is not a perfect square, then $\sqrt{n}$ is irrational. **(819)**

irrational number A real number that is not a rational number. For example, the square roots of integers that are not perfect squares are irrational. **(817)**

J

justification A statement explaining why each step in a proof follows from preceding statements. **(787)**

L

least squares line The line whose squares of deviations from data set points are least. Also called the *line of best fit*. **(370)**

like terms Two or more terms in which the variables and corresponding exponents are the same. **(72)**

linear combination An expression of the form $Ax + By$, where A and B are fixed numbers. **(375)**

linear inequalities Inequalities of the form $Ax + By < C$ or $Ax + By \le C$, where A, B, and C are constants. ($>$ and $\ge$ can be substituted for $<$ and $\le$.) **(383)**

linear polynomial A polynomial of degree one. **(664)**

linear regression The fitting of a straight line through a given set of points according to specific criteria, such as least squares. **(369)**

linear term A term containing one variable with a power equal to 1. **(736)**

line of best fit A line whose equation is determined by the method of least squares and represents a linear relationship between data values. **(369)**

lowest terms (A) A fraction whose numerator and denominator have no common factors other than 1. **(761)** (B) A rational expression with no polynomial being a factor of both its numerator and denominator. **(762)**

M

markup A percent by which the original price of an item is raised. **(184)**

matrix (matrices) A rectangular array, such as $\begin{bmatrix} 3 & -4 \\ 15 & 0 \end{bmatrix}$. **(622)**

matrix form A way of expressing a system of equations using matrices. The matrix form for $\begin{cases} ax + by = e \\ cx + dy = f \end{cases}$ is $\begin{bmatrix} a & b \\ c & d \end{bmatrix} \cdot \begin{bmatrix} x \\ y \end{bmatrix} = \begin{bmatrix} e \\ f \end{bmatrix}$. The coefficient matrix is $\begin{bmatrix} a & b \\ c & d \end{bmatrix}$, the variable matrix is $\begin{bmatrix} x \\ y \end{bmatrix}$, and the constant matrix is $\begin{bmatrix} e \\ f \end{bmatrix}$. **(623)**

mean absolute deviation (m.a.d.) The average difference between individual measurements and the mean. **(48)**

means The numbers b and c in the proportion $\frac{a}{b} = \frac{c}{d}$. **(301)**

Means-Extremes Property For all real numbers a, b, c, and d (with $b \ne 0$ and $d \ne 0$), if $\frac{a}{b} = \frac{c}{d}$, then $ad = bc$. **(302)**

monomial A polynomial with 1 term. **(663)**

Multiplication Counting Principle If one choice can be made in m ways and a second choice can be made in n ways, then there are mn ways of making the first choice followed by the second choice. **(459)**

multiplication method for solving a system Given two equations in a system, applying the Multiplication Property of Equality to obtain another equation that is satisfied by the solution to the system. **(609)**

Multiplication Property of Zero For any real number a, $a \cdot 0 = 0 \cdot a = 0$. **(115)**

Multiplication Property of –1 For any real number a, $a \cdot -1 = -1 \cdot a = -a$. **(86)**

Multiplication Property of Equality For all real numbers a, b, and c, if $a = b$, then $ca = cb$. **(113)**

Multiplication Property of Inequality If $x < y$ and a is positive, then $ax < ay$. If $x < y$ and a is negative, then $ax > ay$. **(157)**

Multiplicative Identity Property of 1 For any real number a, $a \cdot 1 = 1 \cdot a = a$. **(116)**

Multiplicative Inverse Property For any real number a, where $a \ne 0$, $a \cdot \frac{1}{a} = \frac{1}{a} \cdot a = 1$. **(116)**

Multiplying Fractions Property For all real numbers a, b, c, and d, with $b \ne 0$ and $d \ne 0$, $\frac{a}{b} \cdot \frac{c}{d} = \frac{ac}{bd}$. **(252)**

N

n factorial (n!) The product of the integers from 1 to n. (693)

Negative Exponent Property For any nonzero b and all n, $b^{-n} = \frac{1}{b^n}$, the reciprocal of b^n. (474)

Negative Exponent Property for Fractions For any nonzero x and y and all n, $\left(\frac{x}{y}\right)^{-n} = \left(\frac{y}{x}\right)^n$. (475)

nonlinear system A system of equations or inequalities in which at least one of the equations or inequalities is nonlinear. (640)

nth power The number x^n is the nth power of x. (398)

null set See *empty set*. (584)

O

oblique A line that is neither horizontal nor vertical. (377)

odd integer (odd number) An integer that can be written as $2n + 1$, where n is an integer. (803)

odds of an event The ratio of the probability that an event will not occur to the probability that an event will occur. (284)

Opposite of a Difference Property For all real numbers a and b, $-(a - b) = -a + b$. (87)

Opposite of a Sum Property For all real numbers a and b, $-(a + b) = -a + -b = -a - b$. (86)

Opposite of Opposites Property For any real number a, $-(-a) = a$. (85)

opposites Two numbers that add to zero; also called additive inverses. (85)

order of operations The correct order of evaluating numerical expressions: perform operations within parentheses or other grouping symbols. Then evaluate powers from left to right. Next multiply or divide from left to right. Then add or subtract from left to right. (6)

origin The point $(0, 0)$ on a coordinate graph. (44)

outcomes A result of an experiment. (280)

output A number that is returned by a function after it is evaluated. (221, 426)

P

parabola The curve that is the graph of an equation of the form $y = ax^2 + bx + c$, where $a \neq 0$. (526)

Parabola Vertex Theorem The graph of all ordered pairs (x, y) satisfying the equation $y - k = a(x - h)^2$ is a parabola with vertex (h, k). (716)

pattern A general idea for which there are many instances. (13)

P(E) The probability of event E or "P of E." (280)

percent (%) A number times $\frac{1}{100}$ or "per 100." (182)

percentile The pth percentile of a data set is the smallest data value that is greater than or equal to p percent of the data values. (292)

perfect square trinomial A trinomial that is the square of a binomial. $a^2 + 2ab + b^2 = (a + b)^2$ and $a^2 - 2ab + b^2 = (a - b)^2$. (687)

period of a pendulum The time it takes a pendulum to complete one swing back and forth. On Earth, the formula $p = 2\pi \sqrt{\frac{L}{32}}$ gives the time p in seconds for one period in terms of the length L (in feet) of the pendulum. (501)

permutation An ordered arrangement of letters, names, or objects. (691)

± notation (A) $\pm x$ means (x or $-x$). (B)$a \pm b$ means ($a + b$ or $a - b$). (553)

point-slope form An equation of a line in the form $y - k = m(x - h)$, where m is the slope and (h, k) is a point on the line. (357)

polynomial An expression that is either a monomial or a sum of monomials. (663)

polynomial in x A sum of multiples of powers of x. (657)

population The set of individuals or objects to be studied. (302)

power An expression written in the form x^n. (398)

Power of a Power Property For all m and n, and all nonzero b, $(b^m)^n = b^{mn}$. (466)

Power of a Product Property For all nonzero a and b, and for all n, $(ab)^n = a^n b^n$. (481)

Power of a Quotient Property For all nonzero a and b, and for all n, $\left(\frac{a}{b}\right)^n = \frac{a^n}{b^n}$. (482)

prime polynomial A polynomial that cannot be factored into polynomials of lower degree. (676)

polynomial over the integers A polynomial with integer coefficients. (**738**)

principal Money deposited in an account. (**398**)

probability of an event A number from 0 to 1 that measures the likelihood that an event will occur. (**280**)

probability distribution The set of ordered pairs of outcomes and their probabilities. (**281**)

Probability Formula for Geometric Regions Suppose points are selected at random in a region and some of that region's points represent an event E of interest. The probability $P(E)$ of the event is given by $\frac{\text{measurement of region in event}}{\text{measure of entire region}}$. (**296**)

Product of Powers Property For all m and n, and all nonzero b, $b^m \cdot b^n = b^{m+n}$. (**465**)

Product of Square Roots Property For all nonnegative real numbers a and b, $\sqrt{a} \cdot \sqrt{b} = \sqrt{ab}$. (**498**)

proof argument A sequence of justified conclusions, starting with the antecedent and ending with the consequent. (**789**)

proportion A statement that two fractions are equal. (**301**)

Pythagorean Theorem In any right triangle with legs of lengths a and b and hypotenuse of length c, $a^2 + b^2 = c^2$. (**492**)

Q

quadratic equation An equation that can be written in the form $ax^2 + bx + c = 0$ with $a \neq 0$. (**552**)

Quadratic Formula If $ax^2 + bx + c = 0$ and $a \neq 0$, then $x = \frac{-b \pm \sqrt{b^2 - 4ac}}{2a}$. (**553**)

quadratic polynomial A polynomial of degree 2. (**664**)

Quotient of Powers Property For all m and n, and all nonzero b, $\frac{b^m}{b^n} = b^{m-n}$. (**469**)

Quotient of Square Roots Property For all positive real numbers a and c, $\frac{\sqrt{c}}{\sqrt{a}} = \sqrt{\frac{c}{a}}$. (**499**)

R

radical sign (A) ($\sqrt{}$) The symbol for square root. (**489**) (B) ($\sqrt[3]{}$) The symbol for cube root. (**493**)

radicand The quantity under the radical sign. (**499**)

randomly (chosen) Every member of a population has an equal chance of being chosen. (**302**)

range (A) The difference between the maximum value M and minimum value m of a data set. (**48**) (B) The set of possible values of the second (dependent) variable. (**426**)

rate The quotient of two quantities with different units. (**263**)

rate of change The difference of values of a quantity divided by the amount of time between the values. The rate of change between points (x_1, y_1) and (x_2, y_2) is $\frac{y_2 - y_1}{x_2 - x_1}$. (**328**)

rate unit The unit of a rate. (**328**)

ratio A quotient of two quantities with the same units. (**274, 275**)

rational expression A quotient of two polynomials. (**761**)

rational number A number that can be expressed as a simple fraction. (**816**)

ratio of similitude The ratio of the lengths of corresponding sides of two similar figures. (**309**)

reciprocal rates Two rates in which the quantities are compared in both orders. (**264**)

reflection-symmetric The property held by a figure that coincides with its image under a reflection over a line. (**526**)

Related Facts Property of Addition and Subtraction For all real numbers a, b, and c, if $a + b = c$, then $b + a = c$, $c - b = a$, and $c - a = b$. (**106–107**)

Related Facts Property of Multiplication and Division For all nonzero real numbers a, b, and c, if $ab = c$, then $ba = c$, $\frac{c}{b} = a$, and $\frac{c}{a} = b$. (**113–114**)

relation Any set of ordered pairs. (**428**)

relative frequency The ratio of the number of times an event occurs to the total number of possible occurrences. (**280, 289**)

Repeated Multiplication Property of Powers When n is a positive integer, $x^n = x \cdot x \cdot \ldots \cdot x$ for n factors. (**398**)

S

sample A subset taken from a set of people or things. (**302**)

scatterplot A two-dimensional coordinate graph of individual points. (**27**)

scientific notation A number represented as $x \cdot 10^n$, where n is an integer and $1 \leq x < 10$. (**460**)

semiperimeter Half the perimeter of a figure. (**807**)

sequence A collection of numbers or objects in a specific order. (**20**)

simple fraction A fraction with integers in its numerator and denominator. (**816**)

skewed left A distribution in which the lower half of the values extends much farther to the left than the upper half, leaving a tail on the left. (**51**)

skewed right A distribution in which the upper half of the values extends much farther to the right than the lower half, leaving a tail on the right. (**51**)

slope The rate of change between points on a line. The slope of the line through (x_1, y_1) and (x_2, y_2) is $\frac{y_2 - y_1}{x_2 - x_1}$. (**334**)

slope-intercept form An equation of a line in the form $y = mx + b$, where m is the slope and b is the y-intercept. (**350**)

Slopes and Parallel Lines Property If two lines have the same slope, then they are parallel. (**616**)

solution to an equation Any value of a variable that makes an equation true. (**135**)

solution to a system In a system of equations with two variables, the solution is all ordered pairs (x, y) that satisfy all equations in the system. (**582**)

square The second power of a number x, or x^2. (**488**)

Square of the Square Root Property For any nonnegative number x, $\sqrt{x} \cdot \sqrt{x} = \sqrt{x^2} = x$. (**490**)

square root If $A = s^2$, then s is a square root of A. (**489**)

square term The terms containing a variable with a power equal to 2. (**736**)

squaring function A function defined by $y = x^2$. (**426**)

standard form of an equation of a line An equation in the form $Ax + By = C$, where A, B, and C are constants. (**375**)

standard form for a polynomial A polynomial written with the terms in descending order of the exponents of its terms. (**658**)

standard form of a quadratic equation An equation of the form $ax^2 + bx + c = 0$, where $a \neq 0$. (**555**)

standard window The common view on a graphing calculator. (**34**)

Subtraction Property of Equality For all real numbers a, b, and c, if $a = b$, then $a - c = b - c$. (**106**)

symmetric distribution Data that are centered around one point and in which the values on the left and right sides are roughly mirror images. (**51**)

system A set of equations or inequalities separated by the word *and* that together describe a single situation. (**582**)

T

tax rate The ratio of the tax to the amount being taxed. (**275**)

term A number, variable, or product of numbers and variables. (**15, 20, 663**)

Transitive Property of Equality For any real numbers a, b, and c, if $a = b$ and $b = c$, then $a = c$. (**10**)

trinomial A polynomial that has three terms. (**663**)

trivial factors In every expression, the factors 1 and the expression itself. (**675**)

2 × 2 identity matrix The matrix $\begin{bmatrix} 1 & 0 \\ 0 & 1 \end{bmatrix}$. (**626**)

U

unbiased A situation in which each outcome has the same probability; also called *fair*. (**281**)

uniform distribution A distribution that has roughly the same quantity for all events. (**51**)

union of sets The set of elements in either set A or set B (or in both) and written as $A \cup B$. (**228**)

Unique Factorization Theorem for Polynomials Every polynomial can be represented as a product of prime polynomials in exactly one way, disregarding order and integer multiples. (**677**)

V

value of a function The output of a function obtained for a given first variable. (**426**)

variable A letter or other symbol that can be replaced by any number (or other object) from a set. **(6)**

variable matrix In the matrix equation $\begin{bmatrix} a & b \\ c & d \end{bmatrix} \cdot \begin{bmatrix} x \\ y \end{bmatrix}$ $= \begin{bmatrix} e \\ f \end{bmatrix}$, the variable matrix is $\begin{bmatrix} x \\ y \end{bmatrix}$. **(622)**

vertex The point of intersection of a parabola with its axis of symmetry. **(526)**

vertex form of an equation for a parabola An equation of the form $y - k = a(x - h)^2$, where (h, k) is the vertex. **(716)**

vertical line A line with the equation $x = h$, where h is a real number. **(189)**

W

window The part of a coordinate grid that is visible on a graphing calculator. **(33)**

X

x-intercept The x-coordinate of a point where a graph intersects the x-axis. **(357)**

Xmax The greatest x-value (right edge) displayed on the window screen of a graphing calculator. **(34)**

Xmin The least x-value (left edge) displayed on the window screen of a graphing calculator. **(34)**

Xscl The x-scale of a graphing calculator. **(34)**

Y

y-intercept The y-coordinate of a point where a graph intersects the y-axis. **(350)**

Ymax The greatest y-value (top edge) displayed on the window screen of a graphing calculator. **(34)**

Ymin The least y-value (bottom edge) displayed on the window screen of a graphing calculator. **(34)**

Yscl The y-scale of a graphing calculator. **(34)**

Z

Zero Exponent Propery If x is any nonzero real number, then $x^0 = 1$. **(405)**

Zero Product Property For any real numbers a and b, if $ab = 0$, then either $a = 0$, $b = 0$, or both a and b equal 0. **(115)**

Index

Z

Photo Credits

Volume 1 Chapters 1–6

Cover: ©Scott McDermott/Corbis, cover **front, back**.
©Bob Abraham/Pacific Stock, p. **306**; ©Aflo Foto Agency/Alamy, p. **28**; ©age fotostock/SuperStock, pp. **vii** *right*, **180-181**; ©Altrendo Images/Getty Images, p. **x** *left*; ©AP/Wide World Photos, pp. **169, 195, 207, 266, 305, 329, 371, 378**; ©Yann Arthus-Bertrand/Corbis, p. **274** *right*; ©Dave Bartruff, Inc./Corbis, p. **269**; ©Tom Bean/Stone/Getty Images, p. **277**; ©Gary Bell/zefa/Corbis, p. **358**; ©Bettmann/Corbis, p. **301**; ©Blend Images/Superstock, p. **218**; ©Brand X Pictures/Jupiterimages, p. **174** *left*; ©Brand X Pictures/PunchStock, p. **308**; ©S Burbridge/Alamy, p. **346** *bottom*; ©C Squared Studios/Getty Images, p. **18**; Courtesy Caerbont Automotive Instruments Ltd., p. **227**; ©Tom Carter/Painet Inc., p. **385**; ©Marita Collins, pp. **205, 219, 383**; ©Kit Cooper-Smith/Alamy, p. **201**; ©Thomas Michael Corcoran/PhotoEdit, p. **84**; ©Paul Costello/Stone/Getty Images, p. **373**; ©Bob Daemmrich/PhotoEdit, pp. **15, 166**; ©Mary Kate Denny/PhotoEdit, p. **136**; ©Digital Vision/Getty Images, pp. **25, 40, 121, 154, 172**; ©Digital Vision/PunchStock, pp. **120, 134**; ©DK Limited/Corbis, p. **274** *center*; ©Robert Dowling/Corbis, p. **346** *top*; ©Clive Druett; Papilio/Corbis, p. **229**; ©Duc Do/iStockphoto, p. **11**; ©Enigma/Alamy, p. **ix**; ©Rachel Epstein/PhotoEdit, p. **31**; ©ER Productions/Corbis, p. **326**; ©Don Farrall/Photodisc/Getty Images, pp. **vii** *left*, **128-129**; ©Myrleen Ferguson Cate/PhotoEdit, p. **78**; ©Casey Figlewicz/PhotoSpin, p. **67**; ©Rick Fischer/Masterfile, p. **283**; ©Natalie Fobes/Corbis, p. **303**; ©Tony Freeman/PhotoEdit, pp. **190, 275**; ©Jose Fuste Raga/Corbis, p. **372**; ©Jose Gil/Shutterstock, p. **271**; ©Robert W. Ginn/PhotoEdit, p. **164**; ©Todd Gipstein/National Geographic/Getty Images, p. **237**; ©Robert Glusic/Photodisc/Getty Images, p. **156**; ©Chet Gordon/The Image Works, p. **145**; ©William Gottlieb/Corbis, p. **163**; ©Klaus Hackenberg/zefa/Corbis, p. **214**; ©Gayle Harper, p. **174** *right*; ©Will Hart/PhotoEdit, p. **50**; ©Gavin Hellier/Robert Harding World Imagery, Getty Images, pp. **viii** *left*, **250-251**; ©Ross M Horowitz/Iconica/Getty Images, p. **55** *left*; ©Horticopia, Inc., p. **213**; ©Dave G. Houser/Post-Houserstock/Corbis, p. **355**; ©George H. H. Huey/Corbis, pp. **3, 45**; ©Richard Hutchings/PhotoEdit, p. **122**; ©Jupiterimages Corporation, pp. **153, 173**; ©Victor Kapas/iStockphotos, p. **221**; ©Breck P. Kent/Animals Animals-Earth Scenes, p. **362**; ©Tan Kian Khoon/Shutterstock, p. **152**; ©Art Kowalsky/Alamy, p. **xii**; ©Eric Lessing/Art Resource, NY, p. **xi** *right*; ©Larry Lilac/Alamy, p. **274** *left*; ©Nicholas K. Lim/Shutterstock, p. **312** *bottom*; ©The McGraw-Hill Companies, Inc./Ken Karp photographer, p. **26**; ©Ian Mckinnell/Getty Images, pp. **vi**, *right* **64-65**; ©Wally McNamee/Corbis, p. **52**; ©mdd/Shutterstock, p. **xi** *left*; ©Doug Menuez/Getty Images, p. **256**; ©Gail Mooney/Corbis, p. **261**; ©Gillian Mowbray/iStockphoto, p. **312** *top*; Courtesy NASA, pp. **159, 232**; ©Michael Newman/PhotoEdit, pp. **12, 32, 147, 270**; ©North Wind/North Wind Picture Archives, p. **144**; ©Jonathan Nourok/PhotoEdit, p. **210**; ©Richard T. Nowitz/Corbis, p. **366**; ©Owaki/Kulla/Corbis, p. **118**; ©Photodisc/Getty Images, pp. **90, 280**; ©Photodisc/Punchstock, p. **332**; ©Adam Pretty/Reportage/Getty Images, p. **x** *right*; ©Proframe/Painet Inc., p. **55** *right*; ©Punchstock, pp. **6, 42**; ©Reuters/Corbis, p. **240**; ©David Richard/SmallTown Stock, p. **110**; ©Mark Richards/PhotoEdit, p. **272**; ©John A. Rizzo/Getty Images, p. **88**; ©Deborah Roundtree/The Image Bank/Getty Images, p. **ix** *right*; ©Royalty-Free/Corbis, pp. **143, 185, 186, 226, 287, 299, 313, 314, 316**; ©Ross Setford/Getty Images News/Getty Images, p. **130**; ©W.A. Sharman/Milepost 92 1/2/Corbis, p. **133**; ©Joseph Sohm/VisionsofAmerica.com/Photodisc/Getty Images, pp. **viii** *right*, **279, 324-325**; ©Harry Spurling/Corbis, p. **138**; ©SSPL/The Image Works, p. **56**; ©Stockbyte/Stockbyte Platinum/Getty Images, p. **387**; ©StockTrek/Photodisc/Getty Images, p. **315**; ©Katsuyoshi Tanaka-Woodfin Camp/IPNstock, p. **70**; ©William Taufic/Corbis, p. **54**; Courtesy Texas Instruments, p. **8, 175**; ©ThinkStock/Jupiterimages, p. **76**; ©Tim Thompson/Corbis, p. **356**; ©Susan Van Etten/PhotoEdit, p. **282**; ©Ana Vasileva/Shutterstock, p. **309**; ©Bartosz Wardzinski/iStockphoto, p. **365**; ©Stuart Westmorland/Corbis, p. **353**; ©Dana White/PhotoEdit, p. **183**; ©Ralph White/Corbis, p. **262**; ©Jim Whitmer Photography, p. **71**; ©Alex Wilson/Digital Vision/Getty Images, p. **276**; ©Steve Woltmann, p. **165**; ©Ross Woodhall/Taxi/Getty Images, pp. **vi** *left*, **4-5**; ©David Young-Wolff/PhotoEdit, pp. **86, 340**. **Illustrations:** Ron Carboni

Acknowledgements: It is impossible for UCSMP to thank all the people who have helped create and test these books. We wish particularly to thank Carol Siegel, who coordinated the use of the test materials in the schools; Kathleen Anderson, Aisha Bradshaw, Paul Campbell, Jena Dropela, Meri Fohran, Lisa Hodges, Rachel Huddleston, Evan Jenkins, Nurit Kirshenbaum, Lindsay Knight, Nathaniel Loman, Matthew McCrea, Jadele McPherson, Erin Moore, Dylan Murphy, Gretchen Neidhardt, Jennifer Perton, Daniel Rosenthal, Luke I. Sandberg, Sean Schulte, Andrew L. Shu, Emily Small, John Stevenson, James Thatcher, Alex Tomasik, Erica Traut, Alex Yablon, and Melissa Yeung.

We wish to acknowledge the generous support of the Amoco Foundation and the Carnegie Corporation of New York in helping to make it possible for the first edition of these materials to be developed, tested, and distributed, and the additional support of the Amoco Foundation for the second edition.

We wish to acknowledge the contribution of the text *Algebra Through Applications with Probability and Statistics*, by Zalman Usiskin (NCTM, 1979), developed with funds from the National Science Foundation, to some of the conceptualizations and problems used in this book.

Symbols

$>$	is greater than
$<$	is less than
$\geq$	is greater than or equal to
$\leq$	is less than or equal to
$=$	is equal to
$\neq$	is not equal to
$\approx$	is approximately equal to
$\pm$	plus or minus
$+$	plus sign
$-$	minus sign
$\times, \cdot, *$	multiplication signs
$\div, /$	division signs
$\%$	percent
π	pi
$\lvert n \rvert$	absolute value of n
$\sqrt{}$	radical sign
$\sqrt[3]{}$	cube root
A'	image of point A
$(\ )$	parentheses
$[\ ]$	brackets
$\{\ \}$	braces
$\ldots$	continuing pattern

$0.\overline{a}$	repetend bar
$\{\ \}, \varnothing$	empty or null set
$:, \mid$	such that
$P(E)$	probability of an event E
$\cap$	intersection of sets
$\cup$	union of sets
$\overleftrightarrow{AB}$	line through A and B
$\overrightarrow{AB}$	ray with endpoint at A and containing B
$\overline{AB}$	segment with endpoints A and B
AB	length of segment from A to B; distance between A and B
$\angle ABC$	angle ABC
$m\angle ABC$	measure of angle ABC
$\triangle ABC$	triangle with vertices A, B, C
$\llcorner$	right angle symbol
n°	n degrees
(x, y)	ordered pair
$\dfrac{a}{b}$	a divided by b
$a^{b}, a^{\wedge}b$	a to the bth power
b_{1}	superscript variable ("b sub 1")
$f(x)$	function notation "f of x"
$-x$	opposite of x
$n!$	n factorial
Q_{1}, Q_{2}, Q_{3}	first, second, and third quartiles
μ	mean